Operator Theory
Advances and Applications
Vol. 81

Editor
I. Gohberg

Toeplitz Operators and Index Theory in Several Complex Variables

Harald Upmeier

Birkhäuser Verlag
Basel · Boston · Berlin

Author's address:
Harald Upmeier
Department of Mathematics
University of Marburg
D-35032 Marburg
Germany

A CIP catalogue record for this book is available from the Library of Congress, Washington D.C., USA

Deutsche Bibliothek Cataloging-in-Publication Data
Upmeier, Harald:
Toeplitz operators and index theory in several complex variables / Harald Upmeier. – Basel ; Boston ; Berlin : Birkhäuser, 1996
(Operator theory ; Vol. 81)
ISBN 3-7643-5282-5 (Basel ...)
ISBN 0-8176-5282-5 (Boston)
NE: GT

Printed on acid-free paper produced from chlorine-free pulp. ∞ TCF
Cover design: Heinz Hiltbrunner, Basel
Printed in Germany
ISBN 3-7643-5282-5
ISBN 0-8176-5282-5

9 8 7 6 5 4 3 2 1

Table of Contents

Introduction

Toeplitz operators on the classical Hardy space (on the 1-torus) and the closely related Wiener-Hopf operators (on the half-line) form a central part of operator theory, with many applications e.g., to function theory on the unit disk and to the theory of integral equations. The aim of this book is to extend the theory of Toeplitz operators, in particular the spectral behavior and index theory, to the higher dimensional setting involving holomorphic functions in several complex variables on various classes of domains in $\mathbb{C}^n$. These "multi-variable" Toeplitz operators are important for several reasons. First, they may serve as concrete models for n-tuples of Hilbert space operators and thus form a tool to apply the deep results of multi-variable complex analysis to the study of joint spectrum, joint hyponormality and other properties of operator n-tuples.

Conversely, the properties of multi-variable Toeplitz operators and their associated C^*-algebras reflect the geometry and analytic structure of the underlying domain. Thus Toeplitz operators may lead to new and unexpected operator-theoretic methods to study problems in several complex variables, e.g., by providing new geometric invariants to characterize biholomorphic equivalence (this is a deep unsolved problem for domains in $\mathbb{C}^n$, if $n > 1$). A third motivation to study multi-variable Toeplitz and Wiener-Hopf operators lies in applications to elliptic boundary value problems on manifolds with non-smooth "singular" boundary and to multi-dimensional diffraction problems over convex cones in $\mathbb{R}^n$. Finally, the study of multi-variable Toeplitz operators is a core part of the so-called "quantization" of symplectic manifolds (more precisely: Berezin type quantization of Kähler manifolds), a currently very active area of modern analysis [BLU, C3].

For certain domains, e.g., the bidisk, the hyperball and more general strongly pseudo-convex domains, multi-variable Toeplitz operators have already been studied extensively in the literature. In this book, we develop a more general theory which applies to large classes of domains, not necessarily with smooth boundary or of product type. Among these domains are the so-called symmetric domains studied by the author, and the more general K-circular domains. An important feature is the non-smoothness of the boundary which accounts for the fact that multi-variable Toeplitz operators are in general not essentially normal and thus have a more complicated spectral behavior and index theory. It turns out that the description of Toeplitz C^*-algebras over non-smooth domains involves the concept of "solvable" C^*-algebra, introduced by A. Dynin in the context of pseudo-differential operators as a natural framework for a hierarchy of spectral and Fredholm properties. Our spectral results and topological index formulas for multi-variable Toeplitz operators will be formulated in the context of solvable C^*-algebras. The classical results for the unit disk and for strongly pseudo-convex domains arise as special cases, namely for solvable C^*-algebras of length 1.

We will now describe the contents of the book in more detail. The behavior of multi-variable Toeplitz operators depends in a crucial way on the holomorphic structure of the underlying domain and on the geometry of its boundary. The basic facts concerning the analytic geometry of domains in $\mathbb{C}^n$, which is considerably more complicated than in the 1-dimensional case, are therefore described in Chapter 1. After discussing holomorphic functions of several variables in general, we introduce geometric properties of multi-variable domains. Of primary importance is the notion of pseudo-convexity, a geometric condition characterizing domains of holomorphy, and the idea of boundary component, which is analogous to the concept of face in convexity theory. The so-called Shilov boundary, consisting of the one-point boundary components ("holomorphically" extreme points) will play an important role. For the open unit disk the Shilov boundary coincides with the 1-torus whereas the bidisk has holomorphic faces of complex dimension 1 or 0. The first important class of domains in $\mathbb{C}^n$ (and in many ways the most elementary) are the so-called strongly pseudo-convex domains with smooth boundary (and the more general smooth domains of "finite type"). These domains, with the n-dimensional Hilbert ball as the basic example, have been studied extensively in connection with the generalized Cauchy-Riemann equations ($\bar{\partial}$-Neumann problem). We give an outline of this theory, developed by J. J. Kohn, E. M. Stein and others. Domains with non-smooth boundary are somewhat more typical of the general situation and methods of partial differential equations are less powerful here. Instead, we consider domains invariant under holomorphic group actions, namely the polycircular (or Reinhardt) domains and the K-circular domains which comprise as an important subclass the so-called symmetric domains, also called classical or Cartan domains.

The symmetric domains are of particular interest, also to other parts of mathematics (automorphic functions, group representations) and lead to a rich theory of Toeplitz operators. The geometric and holomorphic structure of these domains is described in full detail using certain non-associative algebraic objects, the so-called Jordan algebras and Jordan triple systems. We also give the generalization of this approach to the larger class of K-circular domains. The basic idea in all these cases is to "stratify" the boundary into "partial Shilov boundaries", using the holomorphic faces of the domain. A similar decomposition is valid for certain unbounded domains of holomorphy (tube domains and Siegel domains) which are related to multi-variable Wiener-Hopf operators.

Chapter 2 treats the theory of Hilbert spaces of holomorphic functions (Bergman space and Hardy space) over domains in $\mathbb{C}^n$. The main topics are the description of the orthogonal projections in terms of kernel functions (Bergman and Szegö kernel) and orthogonal decompositions of the Hilbert space into irreducible components. (Unlike the 1-dimensional situation it is rarely possible to determine an orthogonal basis explicitly.) After discussing general facts about Bergman and Hardy spaces, we turn to a more detailed description for the basic classes of domains (strongly pseudo-convex domains, polycircular domains, symmetric and K-circular domains). For symmetric domains, the Bergman and Szegö kernel functions can be described in terms of the underlying Jordan theoretic structure, leading to a generalized Cauchy integral formula. One main result is the explicit Peter-Weyl decomposition of the Hardy space over the Shilov boundary, with respect to the canonical group action. This theorem is the substitute for the (discrete) Fourier analysis on the 1-torus, which has no straightforward generalization to the higher-dimensional case. A similar decomposition theorem is also proved for the "partial Shilov boundaries" which will be useful in the proof of the index theorem. For the unbounded tube domains and Siegel domains the methods of (continuous) Fourier analysis still apply, and are used for Bochner's generalization of the classical Paley-Wiener Theorem.

Chapters 3 and 4 study the fine structure of multi-variable Toeplitz operators on Bergman and Hardy spaces, defined in terms of the Bergman and Szegö projection, respectively. Due to the complicated geometric setting in higher dimensions, we consider mainly Toeplitz operators with continuous symbol functions, although the L^∞-theory plays an important role in the classical case and discontinuous symbols have also been studied in the multi-variable setting (by Berger, Coburn, Zhu and others). Since it is in general not possible to give an explicit matrix representation of a Toeplitz operator in terms of the Fourier coefficients of its symbol, the structural analysis of Toeplitz operators uses more advanced methods depending on the nature of the underlying domain. For strongly pseudo-convex domains (and domains of finite type), Toeplitz operators are still essentially normal and their theory closely resembles the classical case. The main technical tool for the study of Toeplitz operators on these domains with smooth boundary is the $\bar{\partial}$-Neumann problem, a multi-variable generalization of the Cauchy-Riemann equations. Toeplitz operators on poly-circular domains can be represented quite explicitly as weighted shift operators, using the canonical orthonormal basis of the

Hilbert space. On the other hand, for symmetric (and K-circular) domains such an explicit matrix representation is no longer possible, and the fine structure of Toeplitz operators applies deep results about the geometry and harmonic analysis of Jordan algebras. There is a corresponding theory for Wiener-Hopf operators on half-spaces where the methods of (continuous) Fourier analysis are still applicable.

Chapter 4 constitutes the core of the book and is devoted to a systematic study of the C^*-algebras generated by multi-variable Toeplitz operators. Our aim is to show that the structure of these C^*-algebras reflects deep geometric and holomorphic properties of the underlying domain and its boundary. The main results describe irreducible representations of the Toeplitz C^*-algebra associated with holomorphic faces and prove for the most important classes of domains that these "geometric" representations exhaust the full spectrum of the Toeplitz C^*-algebra and thus determine its ideal structure completely. In the strongly pseudo-convex case, the holomorphic faces are just the extreme points, and we obtain the classical result (I. Raeburn, K. Yabuta, J. Janas) that the Toeplitz C^*-algebra is essentially commutative with spectrum determined by the boundary points. This implies the fundamental spectral inclusion theorem, even for L^∞-symbols. For polycircular and tube domains, the Toeplitz C^*-algebras can be analyzed via groupoid-theoretic methods. For bounded symmetric domains, such a groupoid theoretic description of the Toeplitz C^*-algebra has not yet been found but an application of non-commutative C^*-duality (Hopf C^*-algebras, co-actions) gives a complete analysis of the ideal structure culminating in the fundamental result that this C^*-algebra is solvable of length r, where r denotes the geometric rank of the underlying domain. In particular, each irreducible representation has a geometric realization on a holomorphic face. For domains of rank ≤ 2, we obtain as special cases the well-known results of Berger, Coburn and Korányi. We also sketch the extension of this theory to the more general case of K-circular domains (leading to non-type I C^*-algebras) and obtain a similar structure theory for Wiener-Hopf C^*-algebras, studied extensively by Dynin and Curto, Muhly and Renault.

Whereas Chapter 4 describes the "set-theoretic" topology (i.e., ideal structure) of the C^*-algebra generated by Toeplitz operators, Chapter 5 is devoted to their "algebraic topology" which in the operator-theoretic context means index theory. After recalling the basic facts of Fredholm theory and K-theory, we introduce a general notion of analytic Fredholm index for domains with stratified boundary. For the holomorphic faces of maximal dimension this is the classical Fredholm index, but for the faces of lower dimension we obtain Fredholm family indices which take values in groups of (virtual) vector bundles. (These generalized indices are also of importance in modern applications to elliptic boundary value problems on manifolds with singular boundary.) In the subsequent sections, we derive topological index formulas for these analytical Fredholm indices. Section 5.2 is devoted to the classical index formulas for essentially normal Toeplitz operators, due to Gohberg (for the unit disk), Boutet de Monvel (for strictly pseudo-convex domains) and Baum-Douglas-Taylor (for domains of finite type). For non-smooth domains these results do not apply directly but it is shown that the stratified geometry of the boundary gives rise to strictly pseudo-convex singular domains, and our new index formulas describing the analytic Fredholm indices in terms of the boundary geometry follow from the general theory of C^*-algebra extensions and the harmonic analysis on the Hardy space. The special case of symmetric domains of rank ≤ 2 gives the previously known index theorems of Venugopalkrishna and Berger-Coburn-Korányi. In Section 5.6 we obtain similar index formulas for Wiener-Hopf operators on half-spaces and Siegel domains, and establish a striking relationship to the Atiyah-Singer index formula on "facial" manifolds. The final Section 5.7 studies a non-type I index problem associated with polycircular domains.

The prerequisites for studying this book are a basic knowledge of operator theory on Hilbert space and of the elementary theory of C^*-algebras. The reader should also have some familiarity with complex analysis, although the necessary background from the theory of several complex variables is described in detail in Chapter 1. The approach towards the important class of symmetric domains uses Jordan algebras whose theory is carefully reviewed. The use of fundamental examples (Hilbert ball, hyperbolic matrix ball, Lie ball, etc.) throughout the text should help in understanding the general theory. The last chapter on the index theory uses some algebraic topology and K-theory (reviewed in Section 5.1) and the basic properties of C^*-algebra extensions.

Multi-variable Toeplitz operators have been studied for many years, notably by U. Venugopalkrishna, L. Coburn, J. Janas, I. Raeburn, K. Yabuta, C. Berger, A. Korányi, R. Douglas, P. Baum, M. Taylor, R. Howe, L. Boutet de Monvel, P. Muhly, N. Salinas, A. Dynin, R. Curto, K. Zhu, A. Sheu, J. Renault and others. The present author's contributions lie in the class of symmetric domains for which our knowledge of multi-variable Toeplitz operators is currently the most complete. In this book we try to put all these results into perspective by developing a general framework to study Toeplitz operators in relationship to the geometry of the underlying domain. It is hoped that this general approach leads to further progress in the theory and applications of multi-variable Toeplitz operators.

The author gratefully acknowledges NSF-support during the period of writing this book.

1. Multi-variable Complex Analysis and Domains of Holomorphy

1.0. Introduction

Unlike the 1-dimensional situation, the complex-analytic geometry of domains in complex n-space $\mathbb{C}^n$ is very complicated and exhibits many different phenomena, even among simply-connected domains of holomorphy. Therefore this chapter is devoted to a detailed description of the various geometric situations arising in the context of Toeplitz operators. A common theme is the emphasis on suitable Lie group actions on the domains, in particular the so-called polar decomposition, which will be crucial in later chapters.

As a background, Section 1.1 recalls the basic facts concerning functions in several complex variables. The first type of domains studied are the *(strictly) pseudoconvex domains* introduced in Section 1.2. These domains are the domains of holomorphy and we describe the interplay between internal convexity (Cartan-Thullen theorem) and external convexity (Levi convexity), in particular for the strictly pseudoconvex case.

The first class of domains with a significant group action are the *tubular domains* introduced in Section 1.3. These domains are multi-dimensional analogues of the (right) half-plane and their geometry is essentially described by a convex cone in euclidean space. While one can consider tubular domains in full generality, the richest theory emerges for certain types of cones, namely the homogeneous cones and its subclass of symmetric cones. We will concentrate on the symmetric case which is algebraically described in terms of certain non-associative algebras called *Jordan algebras*. This concept is illustrated by several examples. The most important concept related to Jordan algebras is the "determinant" function which will be used to describe the kernel functions (Szegö kernel, Bergman kernel). At the end of Section 1.3 we mention briefly an important generalization of tubular domains, the so-called *Siegel domains* giving rise to generalized Heisenberg groups.

The *polycircular* (or *Reinhardt*) *domains* introduced in Section 1.4 admit an action of the r-torus which leads to very interesting foliations describing the boundary geometry of the underlying domain. These foliations will be shown later to determine the operator theoretic behavior of Toeplitz operators. For the class of Reinhardt domains, the most interesting phenomena occur already in the (complex) 2-dimensional case, and we will often restrict our attention to this situation which can still be visualized neatly in the absolute quarter-plane.

Section 1.5 is devoted to the so-called *symmetric domains* which play a fundamental role in differential geometry, Lie group representations and automorphic functions in several complex variables. It is for this class of domains that our knowledge of Toeplitz operators and C^*-algebras is currently the most complete. The basic geometric feature of symmetric domains is a stratification of the boundary which gives rise to various types of "boundary components". Generalizing the concept of Jordan algebra (Section 1.3), we introduce the so-called *Jordan triples* which characterize symmetric domains in algebraic terms. As with Jordan algebras, we illustrate this concept by many examples.

Section 1.6 introduces a new class of "K-*circular*" *domains* (K a compact Lie group) which simultaneously generalizes the polycircular domains (K = r-torus) and the symmetric domains. It is shown that these domains admit boundary foliations or fibrations analogous to these special cases which enable us to carry out much of the theory of Toeplitz operators in this very general setting. In the case that $K = S \times S$ is a two-fold copy of a Lie group S, one obtains domains with special features (S-*bicircular domains*) treated in Section 1.7.

1.1. Holomorphic Functions in Several Complex Variables

Throughout this book, we will be concerned with geometric and operator-theoretic properties of domains in complex n-space $\mathbb{C}^n$. It is sometimes preferable to think of $\mathbb{C}^n$ as an abstract finite-dimensional complex vector space, usually denoted by Z, with no set of basis vectors distinguished. By a *domain* in Z we understand an *open connected* subset of Z, with regard to the unique Hausdorff topology making the linear operations continuous. Given a domain Ω in Z, we denote its closure by $\bar{\Omega}$ and its boundary by $\partial\Omega$.

The basic analytic object associated with domains in $\mathbb{C}^n$ are Hilbert spaces of holomorphic functions. Therefore we need to recall the basic facts about holomorphic mappings in several complex variables [N1, N2, R2].

Let Z and W be complex vector spaces of finite dimension. For any integer $j \geq 0$, let

$$\mathcal{L}^j(Z,W) := \{q : Z^j \to W : \ q \text{ j-linear}\}$$

be the complex vector space of all multi-linear mappings q from $Z \times \cdots \times Z$ (j times) into W. Multi-linearity means that for each m with $1 \leq m \leq j$, the mapping

$$z_m \to q(z_1, \ldots, z_m, \ldots, z_j)$$

is linear for each choice of vectors $z_1, \ldots, z_{m-1}, z_{m+1}, \ldots, z_j \in Z$. We are interested in the subspace

$$\mathcal{L}^j_{sym}(Z,W) := \{q \in \mathcal{L}^j(Z,W) : q \text{ symmetric}\}$$

of all symmetric j-linear mappings q, characterized by the condition

$$q(z_{\pi(1)}, z_{\pi(2)}, \ldots, z_{\pi(j)}) = q(z_1, \ldots, z_j)$$

for any permutation π of $\{1, \ldots, j\}$. A mapping $p: Z \to W$ is called a j-*homogeneous polynomial* if there exists a (unique) symmetric j-linear mapping $\hat{p} \in \mathcal{L}^j_{sym}(Z,W)$ such that $p(z) = \hat{p}(z, \ldots, z)$ for all $z \in Z$. The set

$$\mathcal{P}^j(Z,W) := \{p : Z \to W : p \text{ homogeneous polynomial}\}$$

is a closed linear subspace of the space $C(Z,W)$ of all continuous linear mappings from Z to W. The same is true of the direct sum

$$\mathcal{P}(Z,W) := \sum_{j \in \mathbb{N}} \mathcal{P}^j(Z,W)$$

consisting of all *polynomials* from Z to W. In the most important case $W = \mathbb{C}$, i.e., scalar valued functions, we write

(1.1.1) $$\mathcal{P}^j(Z) := \mathcal{P}^j(Z,\mathbb{C}) = \{\text{j-homogeneous polynomials} : Z \to \mathbb{C}\}$$

and

(1.1.2) $$\mathcal{P}(Z) = \sum_{j \geq 0} \mathcal{P}^j(Z) = \{\text{polynomials} : Z \to \mathbb{C}\}.$$

Note that $\mathcal{P}(Z)$ is a complex algebra under pointwise multiplication.

1.1.3 EXAMPLE. Suppose Z has a distinguished basis, inducing an identification $Z \approx \mathbb{C}^n$. Consider the set

$$\mathbb{N}^n := \{(k_1, \ldots, k_n) : k_j \in \mathbb{N} \text{ for all } j\}$$

of all *multi-indices* $k = (k_1, \ldots, k_n)$ of non-negative integers. For any $k \in \mathbb{N}^n$ and each fixed vector $a \in W$, the "monomial"

$$a\, z^k := a\, z_1^{k_1} z_2^{k_2} \cdots z_n^{k_n}$$

is a homogeneous polynomial from $\mathbb{C}^n$ to W, of degree $|k| = k_1 + \cdots + k_n$. Conversely, every j-homogeneous polynomial $p : \mathbb{C}^n \to W$ has a unique representation

$$p(z) = \sum_{\substack{k \in \mathbb{N}^n \\ |k| = j}} a_k\, z^k, \tag{1.1.4}$$

where the "coefficients" a_k belong to W.

Using the notion of homogeneous polynomials, we can introduce holomorphic mappings in the following way:

1.1.5 DEFINITION. Let Ω be a domain in Z and let f be a mapping from Ω to W. Then f is called *holomorphic* (or complex-analytic) if, for every point $o \in \Omega$, there exists an expansion

$$f(o + z) = \sum_{j=0}^{\infty} P_j(z) \tag{1.1.6}$$

into a series of j-homogeneous continuous polynomials $P_j : Z \to W$, which converges uniformly in a neighborhood of $0 \in Z$.

By uniform convergence, the limit mapping f is continuous in a neighborhood of $o \in \Omega$. Since o is arbitrary, it follows that every holomorphic mapping is continuous. A similar argument shows that f is even (infinitely often) complex-differentiable, and the polynomials P_j can be identified with the j-th derivative

$$P_j(z) = \frac{1}{j!} f^{(j)}(o)(z, \ldots, z)$$

of f at $o \in \Omega$. Here $f^{(j)}(o) \in \mathcal{L}^j_{sym}(Z,W)$ by the symmetry of higher-order partial derivatives. In particular, P_j is uniquely determined by f and o. Identifying $Z = \mathbb{C}^n$, we can use (1.1.6) and (1.1.4) to obtain the usual power series expansion

(1.1.7) $$f(o + z) = \sum_{k \in \mathbb{N}^n} a_k \, z^k$$

which also converges uniformly in a neighborhood of $0 \in \mathbb{C}^n$, and whose coefficients $a_k \in W$ are determined by $a_k = f^{(k)}(o) \,/\, k!$ where $k! = k_1! \cdots k_n!$ and

$$f^{(k)}(o) = \frac{\partial^{(k)} f}{\partial z_1^{k_1} \cdots \partial z_n^{k_n}} (o).$$

1.2. Pseudoconvex Domains

It is well-known that every domain Ω in $\mathbb{C}$ is a *domain of holomorphy*, i.e., the proper domain of existence of a holomorphic function f which cannot be extended analytically in a neighborhood of any boundary point. For domains in $\mathbb{C}^n$, $n \geq 2$, the situation is different. For example, the Hartog's domain

$$\Omega := \{(z_1, z_2) \in \mathbb{B}^2 : |z_1| \geq \tfrac{1}{2} \Rightarrow |z_2| > \tfrac{1}{2}\}$$

has the property that every holomorphic function f on Ω has a (unique) analytic continuation to the bidisk

$$\mathbb{B}^2 = \{(z_1, z_2) \in \mathbb{C}^2 : |z_1| < 1, |z_2| < 1\}$$

itself. This follows easily by expanding f into a double Laurent series (cf. [N2]):

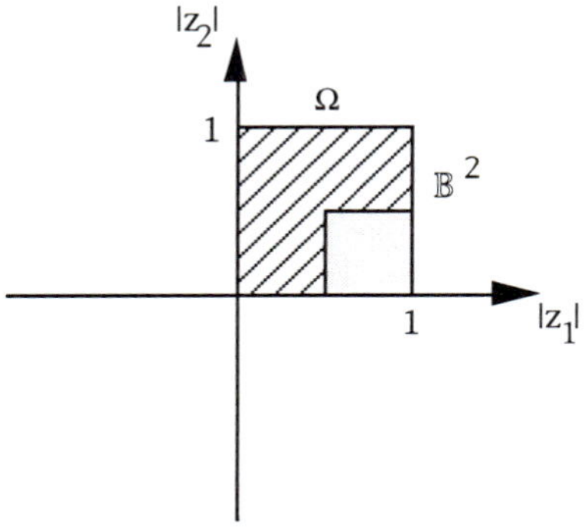

Those domains Ω in $\mathbb{C}^n$ which are the proper domain of existence of an analytic function (for a precise formulation, cf. [N1]) are called *domains of holomorphy.* The fundamental Cartan-Thullen theorem [N1] characterizes domains of holomorphy by a convexity property with respect to holomorphic functions:

1.2.1. DEFINITION. A domain Ω in $\mathbb{C}^n$ is called *holomorphically convex* or *pseudoconvex* if for every compact subset $K \subset \Omega$ its "holomorphically convex hull"

$$\hat{K}_\Omega := \{z \in \Omega : |f(z)| \leq \sup |f(K)| \text{ for every holomorphic function } f : \Omega \to \mathbb{C}\}$$

is again compact.

1.2.2. PROPOSITION. *Every convex domain* Ω *in* $\mathbb{C}^n$ *is pseudoconvex.*

Proof. Let K be a compact subset of Ω. Then the closed convex hull $\overline{co}(K)$ is again a compact subset of Ω. By a separation theorem, we can write

$$(1.2.3) \qquad \overline{co}(K) = \{z \in \Omega : \operatorname{Re} \lambda(z) \leq \sup \operatorname{Re} \lambda(K) \text{ for every linear function } \lambda : \mathbb{C}^n \to \mathbb{C}\}.$$

Since every linear function $\lambda : \mathbb{C}^n \to \mathbb{C}$ defines a holomorphic function $f(z) := e^{\lambda(z)}$ satisfying $|f(z)| = e^{\operatorname{Re}\lambda(z)}$, it follows from (1.2.3) that $\hat{K}_\Omega \subset \overline{co}(K)$. Therefore $\hat{K}_\Omega$ (which is always closed in the relative topology of Ω) is again compact. Hence Ω is pseudoconvex. Q.E.D.

1.2.4. EXAMPLE. Let $Z = \mathbb{C}^n$ be endowed with the usual scalar product

$$(1.2.5) \qquad z \cdot \overline{w} := \sum_{i=1}^{n} z_i \overline{w}_i$$

for all $z = (z_1, \ldots, z_n)$, $w = (w_1, \ldots, w_n) \in \mathbb{C}^n$. Then

$$(1.2.6) \qquad \mathbb{B}_n := \{z \in \mathbb{C}^n : z \cdot \overline{z} < 1\}$$

is a domain in $\mathbb{C}^n$ called the *Hilbert ball* (being the unit ball of $\mathbb{C}^n$ with respect to the Hilbert space norm $\|z\|_2 := (z \cdot \overline{z})^{1/2}$). Its boundary

(1.2.7) $$\partial\mathbb{B}_n = \mathbb{S}^{2n-1}$$

is the (2n - 1)-dimensional sphere which is a smooth hypersurface in $\mathbb{C}^n \approx \mathbb{R}^{2n}$. For $n = 1$, we get the unit disc

(1.2.8) $$\mathbb{B} = \mathbb{B}_1 = \{z \in \mathbb{C} : |z| < 1\}$$

with boundary $\partial\mathbb{B} = \mathbb{S}^1 = \mathbb{T}$ (the 1-torus). By Proposition 1.2.2, the domains (1.2.6) are pseudoconvex.

1.2.9. EXAMPLE. Let $Z = \mathbb{C}^n$ be endowed with the "maximum norm"

$$\|z\|_\infty := \max_{1 \le i \le n} |z_i|$$

for all $z = (z_1, \ldots, z_n) \in \mathbb{C}^n$. Then

(1.2.10) $$\mathbb{B}^n := \{z \in \mathbb{C}^n : \|z\|_\infty < 1\}$$

is a domain in $\mathbb{C}^n$ called the (unit) *polydisk* since it coincides with the n-fold cartesian product of the unit disc (1.2.8). The boundary $\partial\mathbb{B}^n$ can be identified with the union

$$\partial\mathbb{B}^n = \bigcup_{j=1}^{n} \bar{\mathbb{B}} \times \cdots \times \bar{\mathbb{B}} \times \mathbb{T} \times \bar{\mathbb{B}} \times \cdots \times \bar{\mathbb{B}}$$

(with $\mathbb{T}$ in the j-th place). Note that $\partial\mathbb{B}^n$ is not a smooth hypersurface unless $n = 1$. By Proposition 1.2.2 the domains (1.2.10) are pseudoconvex.

1.2.11. EXAMPLE. The domains (1.2.6) and (1.2.10) are special cases of the more general *open unit balls*

(1.2.12) $$\Omega := \{z \in \mathbb{C}^n : \|z\|_p < 1\}$$

in $\mathbb{C}^n$, with respect to the p-norm

$$\|z\|_p := \left(\sum_{i=1}^{n} |z_i|^p\right)^{1/p}$$

for all $z = (z_1, ..., z_n) \in \mathbb{C}^n$. Here $1 \leq p \leq \infty$. By convexity, Ω is a domain of holomorphy.

The definition of pseudoconvexity uses only the "internal" structure of Ω (independent of an embedding Ω in $\mathbb{C}^n$) but is quite difficult to verify in general. It turns out that for domains $\Omega \subset \mathbb{C}^n$ whose topological boundary $\partial\Omega$ is smooth (of class C^∞) there exists an equivalent condition in terms of the differential geometry of the manifold $\partial\Omega$ which is easier to verify. Suppose there exists a C^∞-function $\rho : \mathbb{C}^n \to \mathbb{R}$ with the following two properties

(1.2.13) $$\Omega = \{z \in \mathbb{C}^n : \rho(z) < 0\}$$

and

(1.2.14) $$\rho(z) = 0 \Rightarrow d\rho(z) \neq 0.$$

Here $d\rho(z) : \mathbb{C}^n \to \mathbb{R}$ is the derivative of ρ at z, regarded as a real-linear form. Then the boundary

$$\partial\Omega = \{z \in \mathbb{C}^n : \rho(z) = 0\}$$

is a smooth real submanifold of $\mathbb{C}^n \approx \mathbb{R}^{2n}$ whose (real) tangent space at $z \in \partial\Omega$ can be identified with the real subspace

$$T_z^{\mathbb{R}}(\partial\Omega) = \{u \in \mathbb{C}^n : d\rho(z)u = 0\}$$

of $\mathbb{C}^n$ (this follows from the fact that ρ is a "submersion" in a neighborhood of $\partial\Omega$, cf. [L3]). The real-linear map $d\rho(z)$ can be written as $d\rho(z) = \partial\rho(z) + \bar{\partial}\rho(z)$ where

$$\partial\rho(z)u := \frac{1}{2}\,(d\rho(z)u - i\, d\rho(z)(iu)),$$
$$\bar{\partial}\rho(z)u := \frac{1}{2}\,(d\rho(z)u + i\, d\rho(z)(iu))$$

are complex-linear (resp. conjugate-linear) mappings

$$\partial\rho(z) : \mathbb{C}^n \to \mathbb{C}\,,\ \bar{\partial}\rho(z) : \mathbb{C}^n \to \mathbb{C}.$$

The complex subspace

$$T_z(\partial\Omega) := \{u \in \mathbb{C}^n : \partial\rho(z)u = 0\} = T_z^{\mathbb{R}}(\partial\Omega) \cap iT_z^{\mathbb{R}}(\partial\Omega)$$

is called the *holomorphic tangent space* at $z \in \partial\Omega$. It is the largest complex subspace contained in $T_z^{\mathbb{R}}(\partial\Omega)$. In terms of coordinates $z_1, \ldots, z_n$ we have

$$\partial\rho(z)u = \sum_{i=1}^{n} \frac{\partial\rho}{\partial z_i}(z)u_i,$$

$$\bar{\partial}\rho(z)u = \sum_{i=1}^{n} \frac{\partial\rho}{\partial \bar{z}_i}(z)\bar{u}_i$$

for every vector $u = (u_1, \ldots, u_n) \in \mathbb{C}^n$. Here

$$\frac{\partial\rho}{\partial z_i} = \frac{1}{2}\left(\frac{\partial\rho}{\partial x_i} - i\frac{\partial\rho}{\partial y_i}\right), \quad \frac{\partial\rho}{\partial \bar{z}_i} = \frac{1}{2}\left(\frac{\partial\rho}{\partial x_i} + i\frac{\partial\rho}{\partial y_i}\right)$$

are the usual Wirtinger derivatives. Now consider, for every $z \in \partial\Omega$, the sesqui-linear form

$$(u|v)_z := \partial\bar{\partial}\rho(z)(u,v) = \sum_{1\le i,j\le n} \frac{\partial^2\rho}{\partial z_i\,\partial\bar{z}_j}(z)\, u_i\, \bar{v}_j \tag{1.2.15}$$

defined for $u,v \in \mathbb{C}^n$. Since ρ is real-valued, we have $\overline{(u|v)_z} = (v|u)_z$, i.e., (1.2.15) is a hermitian form called the *Levi form* associated with Ω (and ρ). A fundamental result of E. E. Levi [K7, R2] says that for smooth domains pseudoconvexity can be characterized in terms of the Levi form:

1.2.16. THEOREM. *A smooth domain Ω with defining function ρ is pseudoconvex if and only if at every boundary point $z \in \partial\Omega$ the Levi form $(u|v)_z$ is positive (semi-definite) when restricted to the holomorphic tangent space* $T_z(\partial\Omega)$, i.e.

$$u \in T_z(\partial\Omega) \Rightarrow (u|u)_z \ge 0. \tag{1.2.17}$$

Note that the condition (1.2.17) is satisfied in the 1-dimensional case since $T_z(\partial\Omega) = \{0\}$ at every boundary point.

1.2.18. DEFINITION. A smooth domain Ω with defining function ρ is called *strictly pseudoconvex* if and only if at every boundary point $z \in \partial\Omega$ the Levi form $(u|v)_z$ is strictly positive (definite) on $T_z(\partial\Omega)$, i.e.

$$u \in T_z(\partial\Omega),\ u \neq 0 \Rightarrow (u|u)_z > 0. \tag{1.2.19}$$

For example, the unit ball (1.2.6) is strictly pseudoconvex since $\rho(z) := z \cdot \bar{z} - 1$ is a smooth defining function with $\partial\bar{\partial}\rho(z)(u,v) = u \cdot \bar{v}$ for all u and v. On the other hand, the polydisk (1.2.10) is pseudoconvex but not strictly pseudoconvex (not even smooth) if $n > 1$.

The boundary $\partial\Omega$ of a pseudoconvex domain Ω need not be a smooth manifold, and even if $\partial\Omega$ is smooth it may decompose into holomorphic strata of different kinds much like the faces of a compact convex set. The general concept defining these strata is the notion of a boundary component. For any subset E of $Z \approx \mathbb{C}^n$, a *holomorphic arc* in E is a holomorphic mapping $\gamma : C_\gamma \to Z$ defined on a convex open neighborhood C_γ of the unit interval $[0,1]$ in $\mathbb{C}$ which satisfies $\gamma(C_\gamma) \subset E$. Two points $z,w \in E$ are called (holomorphically) equivalent, denoted by

$$z \underset{E}{\sim} w, \tag{1.2.20}$$

if and only if there exist finitely many holomorphic arcs

$$\gamma_j : C_j \to E, \quad 1 \leq j \leq k$$

satisfying $z \in \gamma_1(C_1)$, $w \in \gamma_k(C_k)$ and $\gamma_j(C_j) \cap \gamma_{j+1}(C_{j+1}) \neq \emptyset$ for $1 \leq j < k$ ("overlapping arcs"). Clearly, (1.2.20) is an equivalence relation on E whose equivalence classes are the *holomorphic arc components* of E. If E is an open set, the holomorphic arc components of E coincide with the (path) components of E. More interesting is the case where $E = \bar{\Omega}$ is the closure of a domain Ω. In this case the holomorphic arc components of $\partial\Omega$ are called the *boundary components* of Ω.

1.2.21. EXAMPLE. Let Ω be a strongly pseudoconvex domain in Z. Then every point in $\partial\Omega$ is a boundary component, i.e. all boundary components of Ω are singletons ("holomorphic extreme points").

1.2.22. EXAMPLE. The bidisc $\Omega = \mathbb{B}^2$ has the boundary components $\{z_1\} \times \mathbb{B}$ and $\mathbb{B} \times \{z_2\}$ ($|z_1| < 1$, $|z_2| < 1$) of complex dimension 1, and the 0-dimensional components $\{(z_1,z_2)\}$, where $|z_1| = |z_2| = 1$.

1.3. Tubular Domains

The symmetric tube domains introduced in this section are the natural generalization of the half-plane in one complex variable. They play a fundamental role in the theory of group representations and automorphic functions. In the following let $X \approx \mathbb{R}^n$ be a n-dimensional real vector space and let

$$Z := X \otimes \mathbb{C} = X \oplus iX \tag{1.3.1}$$

be the complexification of X. Let

$$z = x + iy \mapsto z^* := x - iy \qquad (x,y \in X) \tag{1.3.2}$$

be the canonical "involution" of Z, and put

$$\mathrm{Re}(z) := \frac{z + z^*}{2}$$

for all $z \in Z$.

1.3.3. DEFINITION. A domain $\Pi \subset Z$ is called *tubular* (or a tube domain) if it is invariant under imaginary translations $z \in \Pi \Rightarrow z + ib \in \Pi$ for all $b \in X$.

Every tubular domain can be written in the form

$$\Pi = \Lambda \oplus iX = \{z \in Z : \mathrm{Re}(z) \in \Lambda\} \tag{1.3.5}$$

where $\Lambda = \mathrm{Re}(\Pi)$ is a domain in X called the *base* of Π. A tubular domain Π is called *convex* if $\Lambda = \mathrm{Re}(\Pi)$ is a convex open set, and *conical* if Λ is even a convex open cone, i.e., satisfies

$$x \in \Lambda, t > 0 \Rightarrow tx \in \Lambda$$

and

$$x,y \in \Lambda \Rightarrow x + y \in \Lambda.$$

Then it is known [N2, H3]:

1.3.6. THEOREM. *A tubular domain* Π *is pseudoconvex (i.e., a domain of holomorphy) if and only if* Π *is convex.*

Let $GL(X)$ be the group of invertible linear transformations of X. For a convex open cone $\Lambda \subset X$ consider the subgroup

(1.3.7) $$GL(\Lambda) := \{g \in GL(X) : g \cdot \Lambda = \Lambda\}.$$

The cone Λ is called *homogeneous* if $GL(\Lambda)$ acts transitively on Λ, i.e.

$$\forall x,y \in \Lambda \ \exists \ g \in GL(\Lambda) : g \cdot x = y.$$

Let $X^{\#} = \mathcal{L}(X,\mathbb{R})$ be the dual space of X. The closed convex cone

(1.3.8) $$\Lambda^{\#} := \{\xi \in X^{\#} : \forall x \in \Lambda : \xi(x) \leq 0\}$$

in $X^{\#}$ is called the *polar cone* of Λ. After choosing an inner product $(x|y)$ on X, we may identify $X^{\#} = X$ and $\Lambda^{\#}$ becomes a closed cone in X.

1.3.9. DEFINITION. A convex open cone $\Lambda \subset X$ is called *symmetric* if Λ is homogeneous and there exists an inner product on X such that $\Lambda^{\#} = -\bar{\Lambda}$. A tubular domain Π is called symmetric if and only if its base Λ is a symmetric cone.

The reason for this terminology is that every symmetric cone Λ becomes a Riemannian symmetric space [FK2] in a natural way. The associated tubular domain Π is a hermitian (complex) symmetric space. As is well-known [BK, FK2] there exists an algebraic characterization of symmetric cones and their associated tubular domains in terms of *Jordan algebras*. Let $\Lambda \subset X$ be a symmetric cone with linear automorphism group $GL(\Lambda)$. Consider the Lie algebra

(1.3.10) $$\mathfrak{gl}(\Lambda) := \{A \in \mathfrak{gl}(X) : \ \exp(tA) \in GL(\Lambda) \ \forall t \in \mathbb{R}\}$$

of $GL(\Lambda)$. Here $\mathfrak{gl}(X)$ is the set of all linear endomorphisms of X, with commutator

$$[A,B]x := ABx - BAx.$$

Now let $(x|y)$ be an inner product on X satisfying $\Lambda^{\#} = -\bar{\Lambda}$. Then for any $g \in GL(\Lambda)$, the transpose g^T belongs to $GL(\Lambda)$. Similarly, $A^T \in \mathfrak{gl}(\Lambda)$ whenever $A \in \mathfrak{gl}(\Lambda)$. Now fix a base point $-e \in \Lambda$ and consider the stabilizer subgroup

(1.3.11) $$L = \{g \in GL(\Lambda) : g \cdot e = e\}$$

and its Lie algebra

$$\mathfrak{l} = \{A \in \mathfrak{gl}(\Lambda) : A \cdot e = 0\}.$$

Since L may be realized as a closed subgroup of the orthogonal group [FK2], it is compact and we may assume that

$$L = U(\Lambda) := \{g \in GL(\Lambda) : \ g^{-1} = g^T\}$$

and, similarly

$$\mathfrak{l} = \mathfrak{u}(\Lambda) := \{A \in \mathfrak{gl}(\Lambda) : A^T + A = 0\}.$$

Then $\mathfrak{gl}(\Lambda)$ has a Cartan decomposition

(1.3.12) $$\mathfrak{gl}(\Lambda) = \mathfrak{l} \oplus \mathfrak{m}$$

where

$$\mathfrak{m} = \{M \in \mathfrak{gl}(\Lambda) : M^T = M\}.$$

Moreover, the evaluation mapping $\mathfrak{m} \ni M \mapsto Me \in X$ is bijective. We write $M = M_x$ if $M \in \mathfrak{m}$ satisfies $Me = x$ and call M_x the *multiplication operator* associated with x. Let

(1.3.13) $$x \circ y := M_x y$$

be the corresponding commutative product on X. It is known [BK] that (1.3.13) defines a (non-associative) *real Jordan algebra* on X, such that

(1.3.14) $$-\overline{\Lambda} = \{x^2 : x \in X\}$$

is precisely the set of squares in X. The point e becomes the *unit element* of X. The real Jordan algebra X associated with the symmetric cone Λ gives rise to two important classes of transformations of Λ. For any $x \in \Lambda$, the mapping

(1.3.15) $$P_x := 2M_x^2 - M_{x^2}$$

belongs to $GL(\Lambda)$ and satisfies $P_x e = x^2$. These transformations are called the *quadratic representation* of X. On the other hand,

(1.3.16) $$S(x) := x^{-1}$$

is a non-linear diffeomorphism of Λ called the *symmetry* of Λ about -e. For other points $y \in \Lambda$ write $y = -x^2$ for a (unique) $x \in \Lambda$. Then

$$S_y := P_x \circ S \circ P_x^{-1}$$

is the symmetry of Λ about y. As a densely defined rational map on X, the inversion (1.3.16) has a unique reduced representation [S5]

(1.3.17) $$x^{-1} := \frac{\operatorname{grad} \Delta(x)}{\Delta(x)}$$

where

(1.3.18) $$\Delta : X \to \mathbb{R}$$

is a polynomial satisfying $\Delta(e) = 1$, and $\operatorname{grad} \Delta(x)$ is an X-valued polynomial which coincides with the gradient of Δ with respect to the euclidean structure. The polynomial Δ is called the *Jordan algebra determinant* associated with Λ.

1.3.19. EXAMPLE. The *half-line*

$$\mathbb{R}_< := \{x \in \mathbb{R} : x < 0\}$$

is a symmetric cone in $X = \mathbb{R}$, with base point $-e = -1 \in \mathbb{R}$, and symmetry

$$S(x) = \frac{1}{x}$$

for all $x \in \mathbb{R}_<$. The associated Jordan product on $\mathbb{R}$ is the ordinary multiplication and (1.3.17) implies $\Delta(x) = x$ for all x. Taking direct products, we obtain the r-*orthant*

$$\mathbb{R}^r_< := \{x \in \mathbb{R}^r : x_i < 0 \text{ for all } 1 \le i \le r\}$$

as a symmetric cone in $X = \mathbb{R}^r$. The associated Jordan product is componentwise multiplication in $\mathbb{R}^r$, and $\Delta(x_1, ..., x_r) = x_1 \cdots x_r$.

1.3.20. EXAMPLE. Let $\mathbb{K}$ be one of the real division algebras $\mathbb{K} = \mathbb{R}$ (real numbers), $\mathbb{K} = \mathbb{C}$ (complex numbers), or $\mathbb{K} = \mathbb{H}$ (quaternions). Let

$$X_{\mathbb{K}} = \mathcal{H}_r(\mathbb{K}) = \{x \in \mathbb{K}^{r \times r} : x^* = x\} \tag{1.3.21}$$

be the real vector space of all self-adjoint (r×r)-matrices x with entries in $\mathbb{K}$. Then $X_{\mathbb{K}}$ becomes a real Jordan algebra under the anti-commutator product

$$x \circ y := \frac{xy + yx}{2}. \tag{1.3.22}$$

We call (1.3.21) the *matrix Jordan algebra* of rank r over $\mathbb{K}$. The unit matrix

$$e := \begin{pmatrix} 1 & & 0 \\ & \ddots & \\ 0 & & 1 \end{pmatrix}$$

of size $r \times r$ is the unit element of $X_{\mathbb{K}}$. By (1.3.14) the associated symmetric cone

$$\Lambda_{\mathbb{K}} = \mathcal{H}^<_r(\mathbb{K}) = \{x \in \mathcal{H}_r(\mathbb{K}) : x < 0\} \tag{1.3.23}$$

consists of all negative definite matrices over $\mathbb{K}$. The symmetry

$$S(x) = x^{-1}$$

is the usual matrix inverse, and the quadratic representation operators (1.3.15) are given by

$$P_x y = xyx \tag{1.3.24}$$

for all $x, y \in X_{\mathbb{K}}$. More generally, write

$$P_g x := gxg^* \tag{1.3.25}$$

whenever $g \in GL_r(\mathbb{K})$ and $x \in X_{\mathbb{K}}$. Then

$$GL(\Lambda_{\mathbb{K}}) = \{P_g : g \in GL_r(\mathbb{K})\}, \tag{1.3.26}$$

$$U(\Lambda_{\mathbb{K}}) = \{P_g : g \in U_r(\mathbb{K})\}.$$

By (1.3.17) we have

$$\Delta(x) = \mathrm{Det}(x)$$

in case $\mathbb{K} = \mathbb{R}$ or $\mathbb{K} = \mathbb{C}$. In case $\mathbb{K} = \mathbb{H}$, Δ is related to the "Pfaffian".

1.3.27. EXAMPLE. Let X be a real Hilbert space of finite dimension $n \geq 3$. Fix a unit vector $e \in X$ and consider the orthogonal decomposition

$$X = \mathbb{R}e \oplus Y$$

where $Y = e^{\perp} = \{y \in X : e \cdot y = 0\}$. Here $x \cdot y$ denotes the inner product. (We use the notation $x \cdot y$ since the so-called "canonical" inner product $(x|y)$ on X differs by a constant factor.) Now let C be a bounded convex open set in Y containing 0. Then

$$\Lambda_C := \{te + y : t < 0, y/t \in C\}$$

is a sharp convex open cone in X. As a special case let

$$C = \{y \in Y : y \cdot y < 1\}$$

be the open unit ball. Then we obtain the (solid) *backward light cone*

$$\Lambda_n = \{te + y : t < -(y \cdot y)^{1/2}\} \tag{1.3.28}$$

of dimension n. One can show that Λ_n is a symmetric cone, with associated Jordan product

(1.3.29) $$(t_1 e + y_1) \circ (t_2 e + y_2) := (t_1 t_2 + y_1 \cdot y_2)e + (t_1 y_2 + t_2 y_1)$$

for all $t_1, t_2 \in \mathbb{R}$ and $y_1, y_2 \in Y$. This Jordan algebra is called a *real spin factor* because of its connection to spin systems in quantum mechanics [T3]. Its unit element is the vector e. The symmetry about -e has the form

(1.3.30) $$S(te + y) = (te + y)^{-1} = \frac{te - y}{t^2 - y \cdot y}.$$

This implies

(1.3.31) $$\Delta(te + y) = t^2 - y \cdot y.$$

One can show [BK] that, up to an "exceptional" cone of dimension 27, the matrix cones $\Lambda_{\mathbb{K}}$ (cf. Example 1.3.20) and the light cones Λ_n (cf. Example 1.3.27) constitute all "irreducible" symmetric cones. A general symmetric cone Λ is the direct product

$$\Lambda = \prod_i \Lambda_i$$

of irreducible symmetric cones Λ_i.

1.3.32. EXAMPLE. An example of a homogeneous cone which is not symmetric [G1, P2] is the 5-dimensional cone

$$\Lambda = \{x \in \mathcal{H}_3^{<}(\mathbb{R}) : x_{13} = 0\}$$

of symmetric real 3×3-matrices, consisting of matrices of the form

$$x = \begin{pmatrix} x_{11} & x_{12} & 0 \\ x_{12} & x_{22} & x_{23} \\ 0 & x_{23} & x_{33} \end{pmatrix}.$$

Non-symmetric homogeneous cones will not be discussed in detail in this book.

The *boundary structure* of a symmetric cone Λ is best described in terms of the underlying real Jordan algebra X. An element $p \in X$ is called an *idempotent* if

$$p^2 = p \circ p = p.$$

Putting

(1.3.33) $$X_\alpha(p) := \{x \in X : p \circ x = \alpha x\}$$

we have the *Peirce decomposition*

(1.3.34) $$X = X_1(p) \oplus X_{1/2}(p) \oplus X_0(p)$$

associated with p. Then we have [BK, FK2]:

1.3.35. THEOREM. *Let Λ be a symmetric cone in a real Jordan algebra X. Then for every idempotent $p \in X$ the set*

(1.3.36) $$\bar{\Lambda}_p := \bar{\Lambda} \cap X_0(p)$$

is a face of $\bar{\Lambda}$, and every face of $\bar{\Lambda}$ arises this way.

Recall that a *face* $F \subset \bar{\Lambda}$ is a closed convex cone satisfying the "extremality" condition

$$x \in \bar{\Lambda}, y \in F, y - x \in \bar{\Lambda} \Rightarrow x \in F.$$

The trivial faces $F = \bar{\Lambda}$ and $F = \{0\}$ correspond to the trivial idempotents $p = 0$ and $p = e$, respectively. One can show that the "open faces"

(1.3.37) $$\Lambda_p := \bar{\Lambda}_p^0 \quad \text{(relative to } X_0(p))$$

are pairwise disjoint and thus form a partition

(1.3.38) $$\partial\Lambda = \bigcup_{1 \le k \le r} \bigcup_{p \in P_k} \Lambda_p$$

of the boundary $\partial\Lambda$. Here r is the "rank" of X, and P_k is the compact real-analytic manifold consisting of all idempotents $p \in X$ of rank k. The "cone bundle"

$$\partial_k\Lambda := \bigcup_{p \in P_k} \Lambda_p \tag{1.3.39}$$

with base P_k is called the k-th *partial boundary* of Λ. It is a real-analytic manifold which is not closed in X if $k < r$. For $k = 1$, $\partial_1\Lambda$ consists of all *maximal* (open) faces whereas $\partial_r\Lambda = \{0\}$ is the vertex of Λ. Note that Λ has a smooth boundary if and only if $r = 1$, i.e., Λ is the half-line.

1.3.40. EXAMPLE. Consider the matrix Jordan algebras $X = \mathcal{H}_r(\mathbb{K})$ for $\mathbb{K} \in \{\mathbb{R},\mathbb{C},\mathbb{H}\}$. For $1 \le k \le r$, consider the idempotent

$$p := \begin{pmatrix} 1 & & & & 0 \\ & \ddots & & & \\ & & 1 & & \\ & & & 0 & \\ & & & & \ddots & \\ 0 & & & & & 0 \end{pmatrix} \quad \text{(k ones)}.$$

Then the Peirce spaces $X_\alpha(p)$ can be described in terms of block matrices

$$\begin{matrix} & k & r\text{-}k \\ k & \multicolumn{2}{c}{\multirow{2}{*}{}} \end{matrix} \quad \begin{array}{c} \\ k \\ r-k \end{array}\!\!\begin{array}{c|c} k & r-k \\ \hline a & b \\ \hline b^* & d \end{array}.$$

More precisely, we have

$$X_1(p) = \{\begin{pmatrix} a & 0 \\ 0 & 0 \end{pmatrix} : a \in \mathcal{H}_k(\mathbb{K})\},$$

$$X_{1/2}(p) = \{\begin{pmatrix} 0 & b \\ b^* & 0 \end{pmatrix} : b \in \mathbb{K}^{k\times(r-k)}\},$$

$$X_0(p) = \{\begin{pmatrix} 0 & 0 \\ 0 & d \end{pmatrix} : d \in \mathcal{H}_{r-k}(\mathbb{K})\}.$$

The space P_1 of minimal projections in X coincides with the *projective space* $\mathbb{P}(\mathbb{K}^r)$ of all $\mathbb{K}$-lines in $\mathbb{K}^r$ and is a compact symmetric space of rank 1 [L7].

1.3.41. EXAMPLE. Let $X = \mathbb{R}e \oplus Y$ be a real spin factor. By definition, an element $p = te + y$ is an idempotent if $p = p^2 = (t^2 + y \cdot y)e + 2ty$, i.e.,

$$t^2 + y \cdot y = t \quad \text{and} \quad 2ty = y. \tag{1.3.42}$$

We now distinguish two cases (for $p \neq 0$).

<u>Case 1</u> $y \neq 0$. Then (1.3.42) yields $t = \frac{1}{2}, y \cdot y = \frac{1}{4}$. The Peirce decomposition of X associated with $p = \frac{e}{2} + y$ is then

$$X_1(p) = \mathbb{R}p, \quad X_0(p) = \mathbb{R}(e - p) = \mathbb{R} \cdot (\frac{e}{2} - y),$$

$$X_{1/2}(p) = \mathbb{R}\langle p, e - p\rangle^{\perp} = \{x \in Y : x \cdot y = 0\}.$$

Thus the space P_1 of all minimal idempotents can be identified with the sphere $\mathbb{S}^{n-1}$ in Y.

<u>Case 2</u> $y = 0$. Then (1.3.42) yields $t = 1$ (since $p \neq 0$ by assumption) and hence $p = e$. We have $X_1(e) = X$, $X_{1/2}(e) = X_0(e) = \{0\}$.

The most interesting Jordan algebras (like the matrix Jordan algebras and the real spin factors) are *irreducible*: they cannot be written as the direct sum of algebras of lower dimension. Let X be an irreducible formally real Jordan algebra. Two idempotents $c, e \in X$ are called *orthogonal* if $c \circ e = 0$. An idempotent $c \neq 0$ is called *primitive* if it is not the sum of two non-zero orthogonal idempotents. A maximal family $e_1, \ldots, e_r$ of orthogonal primitive idempotents is called a *frame* of X. Its cardinality r coincides with the rank of X. Putting

$$X_{ij} := \{x \in X : e_k \circ x = \frac{\delta_{ik} + \delta_{jk}}{2} x \ \forall\ 1 \leq k \leq r\}, \tag{1.3.43}$$

we have the *joint Peirce decomposition* [BK, FK2]

(1.3.44)
$$X = \overset{\oplus}{\sum_{1 \le i \le j \le r}} X_{ij}.$$

We have

(1.3.45)
$$X_{ii} = \mathbb{R}e_i \qquad (1 \le i \le r)$$

and the number

(1.3.46)
$$a := \dim X_{ij} \qquad (1 \le i < j \le r)$$

which depends only on X is called the *characteristic multiplicity* of X. By (1.3.44), the dimension n of X is given by

(1.3.47)
$$n = r + \frac{a}{2}\, r(r - 1).$$

For any irreducible cone Λ, the positive definite inner product

(1.3.48)
$$(x|y) := \frac{r}{n} \operatorname{trace} M_{x \circ y}$$

on X is called the *euclidean structure* underlying the Jordan algebra X.

1.3.49. EXAMPLE. For the matrix algebras $X = \mathcal{H}_r(\mathbb{K})$ over $\mathbb{K} \in \{\mathbb{R}, \mathbb{C}, \mathbb{H}\}$, the canonical frame $e_1, \ldots, e_r$ is given by

$$e_i = \begin{pmatrix} 0 & & & & & 0 \\ & \ddots & & & & \\ & & 0 & & & \\ & & & 1 & & \\ & & & & 0 & \\ & & & & & \ddots \\ 0 & & & & & 0 \end{pmatrix}$$

with 1 at the (i,i)-th place. It follows that the rank of X equals r. For $1 \le i < j \le r$, X_{ij} consists of all matrices of the form

$$x = \begin{array}{cc} & \begin{array}{cc} i & j \end{array} \\ \begin{array}{c} \\ i \\ j \\ \\ \end{array} & \begin{pmatrix} \ddots & & & \\ & 0 & a & \\ & a^* & 0 & \\ & & & \ddots \end{pmatrix} \end{array}$$

with non-zero entries in $\mathbb{K}$ at the (i,j)-th place. It follows that the characteristic multiplicity

$$a = \dim_{\mathbb{R}} \mathbb{K} \tag{1.3.50}$$

has the values 1, 2 or 4. The so-called *exceptional Jordan algebra*

$$X = \mathcal{H}_3(\mathbb{O}),$$

consisting of all self-adjoint 3×3-matrices over the octonions $\mathbb{O}$, has rank $r = 3$ and characteristic multiplicity

$$a = \dim_{\mathbb{R}} \mathbb{O} = 8.$$

1.3.51. EXAMPLE. Let $X = \mathbb{R}e \oplus Y$ be a real spin factor of dimension $n \geq 3$. Take a unit vector $b \in Y$ and consider the idempotents

$$e_1 := \frac{e + b}{2}, \quad e_2 := \frac{e - b}{2}.$$

These idempotents form a frame so that rank $X = 2$. The joint Peirce decomposition is

$$X_{ii} = \mathbb{R} \cdot e_i \qquad (i = 1,2)$$

and

$$X_{12} = \{y \in Y : y \cdot b = 0\}.$$

Therefore $a = n - 2$ in this case. Unlike the previous case, a can become arbitrarily large for the spin factors. Up to isomorphism, we put $X = \mathbb{R} \times i\mathbb{R}^{n-1}$ and choose e_1 and e_2 as follows:

$$e_1 = (\tfrac{1}{2}, \tfrac{i}{2}, 0, ..., 0), \; e_2 = (\tfrac{1}{2}, -\tfrac{i}{2}, 0, ..., 0) = \bar{e}_1 \tag{1.3.52}$$

$$e = e_1 + e_2 = (1, 0, ..., 0). \tag{1.3.53}$$

In this case we have $X_{12} = \{(0, 0, ix_3, ..., ix_n)\} \cong i\mathbb{R}^a$.

The following table summarizes the basic geometric invariants of every irreducible Jordan algebra X.

algebra	rank	multiplicity a	dimension
$\mathcal{H}_r(\mathbb{R})$	r	1	$\frac{r(r+1)}{2}$
$\mathcal{H}_r(\mathbb{C})$	r	2	r^2
$\mathcal{H}_r(\mathbb{H})$	r	4	$r(2r-1)$
spin factor $\mathbb{R}^n$	2	n - 2	n
exceptional $\mathcal{H}_3(\mathbb{O})$	3	8	27

The complexification

$$Z = X \oplus iX$$

of a real Jordan algebra X becomes a complex Jordan *-algebra with the product $z \circ w$ and the involution (1.3.2). The corresponding multiplication operators are denoted by M_z. Assume now that X is irreducible. The positive definite inner product

(1.3.54) $$(z|w) := \frac{r}{n} \operatorname{trace} M_{z \circ w^*}$$

is called the *hermitian structure* underlying the complex Jordan *-algebra Z. By complexifying the determinant (1.3.18), we obtain a complex polynomial

(1.3.55) $$\Delta : Z \to \mathbb{C}$$

called the *Jordan algebra determinant* associated with the tubular domain Π.

1.3.56. EXAMPLE. The matrix Jordan algebras $X = \mathcal{H}_r(\mathbb{K})$ over $\mathbb{K} \in \{\mathbb{R},\mathbb{C},\mathbb{H}\}$ have the following complexification: For $\mathbb{K} = \mathbb{C}$ we have

(1.3.57) $$\mathcal{H}_r(\mathbb{C}) \otimes \mathbb{C} = \mathbb{C}^{r \times r}$$

via the mapping $x \oplus iy \mapsto x + iy$ for all $x,y \in \mathcal{H}_r(\mathbb{C})$. Now let z^T be the transpose of a complex matrix z. Then

(1.3.58) $$\mathcal{H}_r(\mathbb{R}) \otimes \mathbb{C} = \{z \in \mathbb{C}^{r \times r} : z^T = z\}.$$

In both cases, the complex Jordan product is the anti-commutator (1.3.22) and the unit element e is the $r \times r$ unit matrix.

For $\mathbb{K} = \mathbb{H}$, consider the embedding $\mathcal{H}_r(\mathbb{H}) \to \mathbb{C}^{2r\times 2r}$ given by

(1.3.59) $$u + vj \mapsto \begin{pmatrix} v & u \\ -\bar{u} & \bar{v} \end{pmatrix},$$

where $u = u^*$ and $v = -v^T$ are complex $(r \times r)$-matrices. Via this embedding we obtain

(1.3.60) $$\mathcal{H}_r(\mathbb{H}) \otimes \mathbb{C} \approx \{z \in \mathbb{C}^{2r\times 2r} : z^T = -z\}.$$

Note that the right hand side of (1.3.60) is not an algebra under the usual anticommutator (1.3.22) but only under the "triple product"

$$z \circ w := \frac{1}{2}(ze^*w + we^*z)$$

where

$$e = \begin{pmatrix} 0 & 1 \\ -1 & 0 \end{pmatrix}$$

is the "unit element".

The joint Peirce decomposition gives rise to a *spectral decomposition* of a symmetric cone Λ.

1.3.61. PROPOSITION. *Let $\Lambda \subset X$ be an irreducible symmetric cone of rank r. For any frame $e_1, \ldots, e_r$ of X there exists a continuous mapping*

$$x \mapsto \sigma(x) = (x_1, x_2, \ldots, x_r)$$

from Λ onto $\vec{\mathbb{R}}^r_< = \{(x_1,\ldots,x_r) \in \mathbb{R}^r : 0 > x_1 \geq x_2 \geq \cdots \geq x_r\}$ such that every point $x \in \Lambda$ has the form

(1.3.62) $$x = \ell \cdot \sum_{j=1}^{r} x_j e_j$$

where $(x_1, \ldots, x_r) \in \vec{\mathbb{R}}^r_<$ is unique and $\ell \in L$ (not necessarily unique). Here L is given by (1.3.11).

Proof. By the spectral theorem for real Jordan algebras [BK] every $x \in X$ can be written as

$$x = x_1 c_1 + \cdots + x_r c_r$$

where $\{c_1, \ldots, c_r\}$ is a frame of X and $x_1 \geq \cdots \geq x_r$. The "eigenvalues" x_j are uniquely determined by x and $x \mapsto \sigma(x) := (x_1, \ldots, x_r)$ defines a continuous open mapping from X onto

$$\vec{\mathbb{R}}^r := \{(x_1, \ldots, x_r) \in \mathbb{R}^r : x_1 \geq \cdots \geq x_r\}.$$

We have $\Lambda = \{x \in X : x_1 < 0\} = \{x \in X : \sigma(x) \in \vec{\mathbb{R}}^r_< \}$. Since X is irreducible, the group L acts transitively on the set of all frames. This proves (1.3.62). Q.E.D.

1.3.63. PROPOSITION. *Let* Π *be an irreducible symmetric tubular domain. Let* $dV(z)$ *be the Lebesgue measure. Then we have for every integrable function* f *on* Π:

$$\int_\Pi f(z) dV(z)$$

$$= \text{const.} \int_{\mathbb{R}^r_<} \int_L \int_X f(\ell \cdot \sum_{j=1}^r x_j e_j + i\xi) \, d\xi d\ell \prod_{i<j} |x_i - x_j|^a \, dx_1 \cdots dx_r$$

where a *is the characteristic multiplicity of* Λ. *Similarly we have*

$$\int_\Lambda f(x) \, dx = \text{const.} \int_{\mathbb{R}^r_<} \int_L f(\ell \cdot \sum_{j=1}^r x_j e_j) \, d\ell \prod_{i<j} |x_i - x_j|^a \, dx_1 \cdots dx_r .$$

Proof. Since $dV(z)$ is invariant under imaginary translations we may assume $f(x + i\xi) = f(x)$ for all $\xi \in X$. Then f becomes an integrable function for the Lebesgue measure $dV(x)$ on Λ. The continuous mappings

$$\Pi \xrightarrow{\text{Re}} \Lambda \xrightarrow{\sigma} \vec{\mathbb{R}}^r_< \tag{1.3.64}$$

$$z \mapsto x = \frac{z + z^*}{2} \mapsto (x_1, \ldots, x_r)$$

(cf. Proposition 1.3.61) give rise to the image measure $d(\text{Re } V)(x) = dV(x)$ and

$$d(\sigma \circ \text{Re } V)(x_1, \ldots, x_r) = \text{const.} \prod_{i<j} |x_i - x_j|^a \, dx_1 \cdots dx_r$$

as follows from the root decomposition [FK2] of the pair $(\mathfrak{gl}(\Lambda), \mathfrak{u}(\Lambda))$. Since $dV(x)$ is L-invariant, we may assume that f is L-invariant. Then f factorizes via the mappings (1.3.64) and the assertion follows. Q.E.D.

A natural generalization of tubular domains are the so-called *Siegel domains*. Let X be a (formally-real) Jordan algebra and consider the complexification

$$U = X \otimes \mathbb{C} = X \oplus iX, \tag{1.3.65}$$

endowed with the involution (1.3.2). Let V be another complex vector space and suppose

$$\Phi : V \times V \to U \tag{1.3.66}$$

is a sesqui-linear mapping (conjugate-linear in the second variable) satisfying $\Phi(v_1,v_2)^* = \Phi(v_2,v_1)$ and $-\Phi(v,v) \in \bar{\Lambda}\backslash\{0\}$ for all $v \neq 0$. Here Λ is the open convex cone associated with X. Put $Z := U \oplus V$.

1.3.67. DEFINITION. The open convex domain

$$\Pi := \{(u,v) \in Z : u + u^* + \Phi(v,v) \in \Lambda\} \tag{1.3.68}$$

is called the *Siegel domain* associated with Λ and Φ.

The convexity of Π follows from the calculation

$$\begin{aligned}(\lambda u_1 + \mu u_2) + (\lambda u_1 + \mu u_2)^* + \Phi(\lambda v_1 + \mu v_2, \lambda v_1 + \mu v_2) \\ = \lambda(u_1 + u_1^* + \Phi(v_1,v_1)) + \mu(u_2 + u_2^* + \Phi(v_2,v_2)) \\ - \lambda\mu\, \Phi(v_1 - v_2, v_1 - v_2) \in \Lambda + \Lambda + \bar{\Lambda} \subset \Lambda\end{aligned}$$

whenever $\lambda,\mu > 0$, $\lambda + \mu = 1$ and $(u_1,v_1), (u_2,v_2) \in \Pi$. The Siegel domains (1.3.68) play a fundamental role in complex analysis since, for example, every symmetric domain (cf. Section 1.5) is biholomorphically equivalent to a (symmetric) Siegel domain [P2] whereas only the domains of "tube type" correspond to the special class of tubular domains ($V = \{0\}$).

The subset

$$\Sigma := \{(u,v) \in Z : u + u^* + \Phi(v,v) = 0\} \tag{1.3.69}$$

of the boundary $\partial\Pi = \{(u,v) \in Z : u + u^* + \Phi(v,v) \in \partial\Lambda\}$ is called the *extreme boundary* of Π. For any pair $(a,b) \in iX \times V$, the *quasi-translation*

$$h_{a,b}(u,v) := (u + a - \Phi(v,b) - \frac{\Phi(b,b)}{2}, v + b) \tag{1.3.70}$$

leaves Π invariant. These transformations form a nilpotent group whose 0-orbit coincides with Σ:

$$\Sigma = \{(a - \frac{\Phi(b,b)}{2}, b) : a \in iX, b \in V\}. \tag{1.3.71}$$

1.3.72. EXAMPLE. Let $X = \mathbb{R}$ and $\Lambda = \mathbb{R}_<$. Put $V = \mathbb{C}^n$ and define $\Phi: V \times V \to \mathbb{C}$ by $\Phi(v_1,v_2) := (v_1|v_2)$ (Hilbert product), i.e.,

$$\Phi((v_1,\ldots,v_n), (w_1,\ldots,w_n)) := \sum_{j=1}^{n} v_j \overline{w}_j.$$

Then the corresponding Siegel domain (1.3.68) has the form

$$\Pi = \{(u,v) \in \mathbb{C} \times \mathbb{C}^n : u + \overline{u} < -(v|v)\}. \tag{1.3.73}$$

One can show that Π is biholomorphically equivalent to the (Hilbert) unit ball in $\mathbb{C}^{n+1}$ (cf. Example 1.2.4). Its extreme boundary

$$\Sigma = \{(u,v) \in \mathbb{C} \times \mathbb{C}^n : u + \overline{u} = -(v|v)\} \tag{1.3.74}$$

is the (2n+1)-dimensional Heisenberg group. More generally, consider the matrix spaces

$$U = \mathbb{C}^{r\times r}, V = \mathbb{C}^{r\times s}, Z = U \oplus V = \mathbb{C}^{r\times(r+s)} \tag{1.3.75}$$

and put $\Phi(v_1,v_2) = v_1 v_2^* \in U$ for all $v_1,v_2 \in V$. Then we obtain the Siegel domain

(1.3.76) $\Pi := \{(u,v) \in \mathbb{C}^{r\times(r+s)} : u + u^* + vv^* < 0$ (negative definite)$\}$.

Generalizing Theorem 1.3.35 we will now describe the boundary of a (symmetric) Siegel domain Π using the idempotents of the associated formally-real Jordan algebra X. Let $p \in X$ be an idempotent with Peirce decomposition

$$X = X_1(p) \oplus X_{1/2}(p) \oplus X_0(p). \tag{1.3.77}$$

Since p is also an idempotent in the complex Jordan *-algebra U, we have the complex Peirce decomposition

$$U = U_1(p) \oplus U_{1/2}(p) \oplus U_0(p). \tag{1.3.78}$$

Since, by assumption, Π is a symmetric Siegel domain one can show [KU] that the Jordan algebra product $u_1 \circ u_2$ on U (with unit element e) can be extended to a Jordan algebra product $z_1 \circ z_2$ on $Z = U \oplus V$ which is non-unital in case $V \neq \{0\}$. Since p is an idempotent in Z, we have a complex Peirce decomposition

$$Z = Z_1(p) \oplus Z_{1/2}(p) \oplus Z_0(p) \tag{1.3.79}$$

such that $Z_j(p) = \{z \in Z: p \circ z = jz\}$. Clearly, $U_j(p) = U \cap Z_j(p)$. We have $Z_1(p) = U_1(p) \subset U$ and put $V_1(p) := Z_{1/2}(p) \cap V$ and $V_0(p) := Z_0(p) \cap V$. Then $Z_0(p) = U_0(p) \oplus V_0(p)$.

1.3.80. EXAMPLE. For the matrix spaces (1.3.75) and the idempotent

$$p = \begin{pmatrix} 1 & & & & 0 \\ & \ddots & & & \\ & & 1 & & \\ & & & 0 & \\ & & & & \ddots \\ 0 & & & & 0 \end{pmatrix} \quad (k \text{ ones})$$

in $\mathbb{C}^{r\times r}$, we have the Peirce components

$$z = (u,v) = \begin{array}{c c} & \begin{array}{ccc} k & r\text{-}k & s \end{array} \\ \begin{array}{c} k \\ r\text{-}k \end{array} & \left(\begin{array}{c|cc} u_{11} & u_{12} & v_1 \\ \hline u_{21} & u_{22} & v_2 \end{array}\right) \end{array}$$

with $u_{11} \in U_1(p)$, $u_{12}, u_{21} \in U_{1/2}(p)$, $u_{22} \in U_0(p)$, $v_1 \in V_1(p)$ and $v_2 \in V_0(p)$.

Since $X_0(p)$ is a formally-real Jordan subalgebra of X (with unit element $e - p$), we may consider its open negative cone Λ_p and the corresponding Siegel domain

(1.3.81) $$\Pi_p := \{(u,v) \in Z_0(p) : u + u^* + \Phi(v,v) \in \Lambda_p\}$$

(one can show that $\Phi(v,v) \in X_0(p)$ for all $v \in V_0(p)$ [U4; p. 403]). By [U4; Proposition 1.1] we have

1.3.82. THEOREM. *The boundary components of* Π *are given by*

(1.3.83) $$h_{a,b}(\Pi_p)$$

where $p = p^2 \in X$ *is non-zero and* $h_{a,b}$ *is the quasi-translation (1.3.70), with*

$$ia \in X_1(p) \oplus X_{1/2}(p) = X_0(p)^\perp \qquad \text{(rel. } X)$$

and

$$b \in V_{1/2}(p) = V_0(p)^\perp \qquad \text{(rel. } V).$$

Thus the k-th partial boundary is

(1.3.84) $$\partial_k \Pi = \bigcup_{(p,a,b)\in \Sigma_k} h_{a,b}(\Pi_p),$$

where

(1.3.85) $$\Sigma_k = \bigcup_{p\in P_k} \{p\} \times iX_0(p)^\perp \times V_0(p)^\perp$$

is a vector bundle over the space P_k *of rank* k *idempotents in* X.

Note that, for $k = r$, we have $p = e$, $X_0(p) = \{0\}$ and $V_0(p) = \{0\}$. Thus

(1.3.86) $$\Sigma_r = iX \times V \approx \Sigma$$

is the extreme boundary (1.3.71).

1.4. Polycircular Domains

The polycircular domains (or Reinhardt domains) introduced in this section play an important role in complex analysis as the domains of convergence of multi-variable Taylor series (or Laurent series) [H3, N1].

Consider complex r-space $\mathbb{C}^r$ with coordinates $z = (z_1, ..., z_r)$. Put

(1.4.1) $$\bar{z} := (\bar{z}_1, ..., \bar{z}_r).$$

We multiply two r-vectors z and $w = (w_1, ..., w_r)$ in $\mathbb{C}^r$ componentwise, i.e.,

(1.4.2) $$zw := (z_1 w_1, ..., z_r w_r).$$

This has to be distinguished from the inner product

$$z \cdot w := \sum_{j=1}^{r} z_j w_j,$$

giving rise to the canonical scalar product

$$z \cdot \bar{w} = \sum_{j=1}^{r} z_j \bar{w}_j$$

on $\mathbb{C}^r$. Put $\mathbb{C}^\times := \mathbb{C}\backslash\{0\}$ and let $\mathbb{T}$ be the 1-torus (unit circle) in $\mathbb{C}$. Then the set

(1.4.3) $$(\mathbb{C}^\times)^r := \{z \in \mathbb{C}^r : z_1 \cdots z_r \neq 0\}$$

and the r-torus

(1.4.4) $$\mathbb{T}^r := \{s \in \mathbb{C}^r : |s_j| = 1 \text{ for all } j\}$$

are abelian groups under the multiplication (1.4.2). $(\mathbb{C}^\times)^r$ can be regarded as the *complexification* of $\mathbb{T}^r$. Now consider the action of $\mathbb{T}^r$ on the linear space $\mathbb{C}^r$ defined by the "polyrotations"

(1.4.5) $$z \mapsto zs = (z_1 s_1, \ldots, z_r s_r)$$

for $s = (s_1, \ldots, s_r) \in \mathbb{T}^r$.

1.4.6. DEFINITION. A domain $\Omega \subset \mathbb{C}^r$ is called *polycircular* (or a Reinhardt domain) if it is invariant under polyrotations:

$$z \in \Omega \rightarrow zs \in \Omega \text{ for all } s \in \mathbb{T}^r.$$

For any multi-index $k = (k_1, \ldots, k_r) \in \mathbb{Z}^r$ put

$$z^k := z_1^{k_1} \cdots z_r^{k_r}.$$

Note that some k_i may be negative in which case z^k is only holomorphic on the open dense set $z_i \neq 0$ in $\mathbb{C}^r$. For $k \in \mathbb{N}^r$, i.e., $k_i \geq 0$ for all i, we obtain the standard monomials. Let $\mathcal{P}(\mathbb{C}^r)$ denote the algebra of all *polynomials* on $\mathbb{C}^r$, i.e.,

$$\mathcal{P}(\mathbb{C}^r) = \mathbb{C}[z_1, \ldots, z_r].$$

The torus group $\mathbb{T}^r$ acts on $\mathcal{P}(\mathbb{C}^r)$ via

(1.4.7) $$f(z_1, \ldots, z_r) \mapsto f(z_1 s_1, \ldots, z_r s_r)$$

for fixed $(s_1, \ldots, s_r) \in \mathbb{T}^r$. Clearly,

$$\mathcal{P}(\mathbb{C}^r) = \sum_{k \in \mathbb{N}^r} \mathbb{C} \cdot z^k$$

gives the Peter-Weyl dcomposition of $\mathcal{P}(\mathbb{C}^r)$ into irreducible subspaces (of dimension 1) under the action (1.4.7).

1.4.8. PROPOSITION. *Let Ω be a polycircular domain. Then every holomorphic function* $f : \Omega \to \mathbb{C}$ *has a Laurent expansion*

$$f(z) = \sum_{k \in \mathbb{Z}^r_\Omega} a_k z^k$$

which converges compactly on Ω. Here

$$\mathbb{Z}^r_\Omega := \{k \in \mathbb{Z}^r : k_j \geq 0 \text{ } \textit{whenever} \text{ } \{z \in \Omega : z_j = 0\} \neq \emptyset\}.$$

In particular, $\mathbb{Z}^r_\Omega = \mathbb{N}^r$ *if* $0 \in \Omega$.

Proof. The mapping $\Omega \times \mathbb{T}^r \ni (z,s) \mapsto f(z_1 s_1, \ldots, z_r s_r)$ is continuous and holomorphic in the z-variables. It follows that for every $k \in \mathbb{Z}^r$

$$f_k(z) := \frac{1}{(2\pi i)^r} \int\limits_{|s_j| = 1} \cdots \int \frac{f(zs)}{s_1^{k_1+1} \cdots s_r^{k_r+1}} \, ds_1 \cdots ds_r \tag{1.4.9}$$

defines a holomorphic function on Ω. Now let $K \subset \Omega$ be compact. Then there exists $\rho > 1$ such that Ω contains the compact set $L := \{(z_1 s_1, \ldots, z_r s_r) : z \in K, \frac{1}{\rho} \leq |s_j| \leq \rho\}$. Given $k \in \mathbb{Z}^r$, put $\rho_j := \rho^{\operatorname{sgn}(k_j)}$. By Cauchy's homotopy theorem, we have for every $z \in K$

$$f_k(z) = \frac{1}{(2\pi i)^r} \int\limits_{|s_j| = \rho_j} \cdots \int \frac{f(z_1 s_1, \ldots, z_r s_r)}{s_1^{k_1+1} \cdots s_r^{k_r+1}} \, ds_1 \cdots ds_r.$$

Putting $M := \sup_L |f| < \infty$ and $|k| := |k_1| + \cdots + |k_r|$, we get

$$|f_k(z)| \leq M \cdot \prod_j \rho_j^{-k_j} = M \cdot \rho^{-|k|}.$$

Therefore Σf_k converges compactly on Ω towards a holomorphic function g on Ω. Now consider a polyannulus

$$U := \{w \in \mathbb{C}^r : \delta_j < |w_j| < \varepsilon_j \text{ for all } j\}$$

contained in Ω. Since f is holomorphic on U, it has a Laurent expansion

$$f(w) = \sum_{h \in \mathbb{Z}^r} a_h w^h$$

which we may assume to converge uniformly on U. Integrating term-by-term we obtain from (1.4.9) for all $z \in U$ (putting $w = zs$)

$$f_k(z) = \sum_{h \in \mathbb{Z}^r} \frac{a_h z^h}{(2\pi i)^r} \int \cdots \int_{|s_j| = 1} s_1^{h_1 - k_1 - 1} \cdots s_r^{h_r - k_r - 1} \, ds_1 \cdots ds_r = a_k z^k.$$

By analytic continuation it follows that $f_k(z) = a_k z^k$ on $\Omega^\times := \{z \in \Omega : z_1 \cdots z_r \neq 0\}$. Since z^k is not holomorphic on Ω if $k \notin \mathbb{Z}^r_\Omega$, we have $a_k = 0$ for those k. If $k \in \mathbb{Z}^r_\Omega$, we get $f_k(z) = a_k z^k$ on Ω and hence $f = g$.

Q.E.D.

Every polycircular domain has a "polar decomposition".

1.4.10. PROPOSITION. *Let* $\Omega \subset \mathbb{C}^r$ *be a polycircular domain. Then* $\Omega^\times := \{z \in \Omega : z_1 \cdots z_r \neq 0\}$ *is a dense subdomain, and there exist continuous open mappings*

$$\Omega \xrightarrow{|\cdot|} |\Omega| \subset \mathbb{R}^r_+ ,$$

$$\Omega^\times \xrightarrow{\log |\cdot|} \Lambda := \log |\Omega^\times| \subset \mathbb{R}^r$$

such that every point $z = (z_1, \ldots, z_r) \in \Omega$ *(resp.* $z \in \Omega^\times$*) has the form*

$$z = (y_1 s_1, \ldots, y_r s_r) \quad (\text{resp., } z = (e^{x_1} s_1, \ldots, e^{x_r} s_r))$$

where $(y_1, \ldots, y_r) \in |\Omega^\times|$ *and* $(x_1, \ldots, x_r) \in \Lambda$ *are uniquely determined, and* $(s_1, \ldots, s_r) \in \mathbb{T}^r$.

Proof. For $z \in \mathbb{C}^r$ put

$$(1.4.11) \qquad |z| := (|z_1|, \ldots, |z_r|) \in \mathbb{R}^r_+.$$

Then the mapping $z \mapsto |z|$ from $\mathbb{C}^r$ onto $\mathbb{R}^r_+$ is continuous and open. Therefore

(1.4.12) $$|\Omega| := \{|z| : z \in \Omega\}$$

is a domain in $\mathbb{R}^r_+$. Since Ω is polycircular we have $z \in \Omega \Leftrightarrow |z| \in |\Omega|$ and every $z \in \Omega$ has the form

(1.4.13) $$z = (|z_1|s_1, \ldots, |z_r|s_r)$$

for some $(s_1, \ldots, s_r) \in \mathbb{T}^r$ (not necessarily unique). For $z \in (\mathbb{C}\backslash\{0\})^r$ we have $|z_j| > 0$ for all j and

(1.4.14) $$\log |z| := (\log |z_1|, \ldots, \log |z_r|) \in \mathbb{R}^r$$

defines a continuous open mapping $z \mapsto \log |z|$ from $(\mathbb{C}\backslash\{0\})^r$ onto $\mathbb{R}^r$. The open subset

$$\Omega^x := \Omega \cap (\mathbb{C}\backslash\{0\})^r$$

is easily seen to be connected and dense. Therefore

(1.4.15) $$\Lambda := \log |\Omega^x| := \{\log |z| : z \in \Omega^x\}$$

is a domain in $\mathbb{R}^r$. For $z \in \Omega^x$, the decomposition (1.4.13) is unique. Writing $|z_j| = e^{x_j}$ for every j, we have $(x_1, \ldots, x_r) \in \Lambda$ and

$$z = (e^{x_1}s_1, \ldots, e^{x_r}s_r).$$

Q.E.D.

1.4.16. DEFINITION. Let $\Omega \subset \mathbb{C}^r$ be a polycircular domain. Then

$$|\Omega| := \{|z| : z \in \Omega\} \subset \mathbb{R}^r_+$$

is called the *absolute domain* of Ω, and

$$\Lambda := \log |\Omega^x| := \{\log |z| : z \in \Omega^x\} \subset \mathbb{R}^r$$

is called the *logarithmic base* of Ω^x. A polycircular domain Ω is called *log-convex* if $\Lambda = \log |\Omega^x|$ is a convex open set, and *log-conical* if Λ is a convex open cone. Analogously to Theorem 1.3.6, we have [H3, N1]:

1.4.17. THEOREM. *A polycircular domain* Ω *is pseudoconvex (i.e., a domain of holomorphy) if and only if* Ω *is log-convex.*

Note that a log-convex polycircular domain Ω is not necessarily convex.

1.4.18. EXAMPLE. Let $\mathbb{B} := \{z \in \mathbb{C} : |z| < 1\}$ be the open unit disk. The *poly-disk*

$$\Omega = \mathbb{B}^r := \{z \in \mathbb{C}^r : |z_j| < 1 \quad \text{for all } j\}$$

is a polycircular domain, for which $|\Omega|$ and $\log|\Omega|$ have the following form (if $r = 2$)

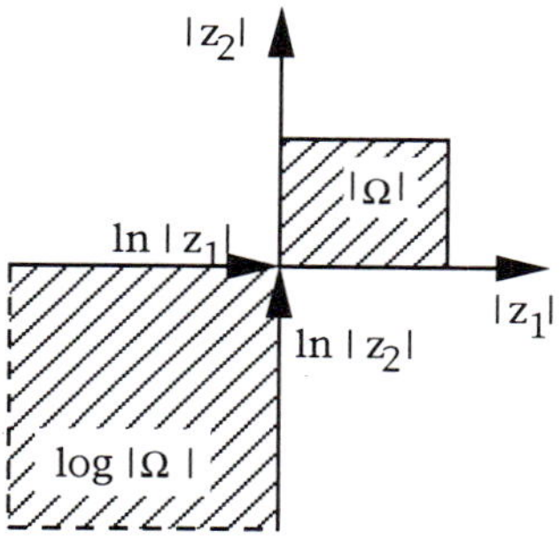

More generally, the open "poly-cylinder"

$$\Omega = P(\rho_1, \ldots, \rho_r) := \rho_1\mathbb{B} \times \cdots \times \rho_r\mathbb{B}$$

$$= \{z \in \mathbb{C}^r : |z_j| < \rho_j \quad \text{for all } j\}$$

centered at the origin is a polycircular domain whose absolute domain $|\Omega|$ is "rectangle-shaped". For $\rho_1 = \cdots = \rho_r = 1$, we have $P(1, \ldots, 1) = \mathbb{B}^r$. These domains are log-conical and hence pseudoconvex.

1.4.19. EXAMPLE. For any family Ω_α of polycircular domains containing the origin, the union $\Omega = \bigcup \Omega_\alpha$ is again a polycircular domain (since it is connected). In particular, the union of open polycylinders centered at the origin is again a polycircular domain. In case $r = 2$, we obtain the "L-shaped domains"

$$P_{\delta,\varepsilon} = P(1,\varepsilon) \cup P(\delta,1) \qquad (0 < \delta, \varepsilon < 1)$$

considered in [CM]. The corresponding domains $|P_{\delta,\varepsilon}|$ and $\log |P_{\delta,\varepsilon}|$ are sketched below

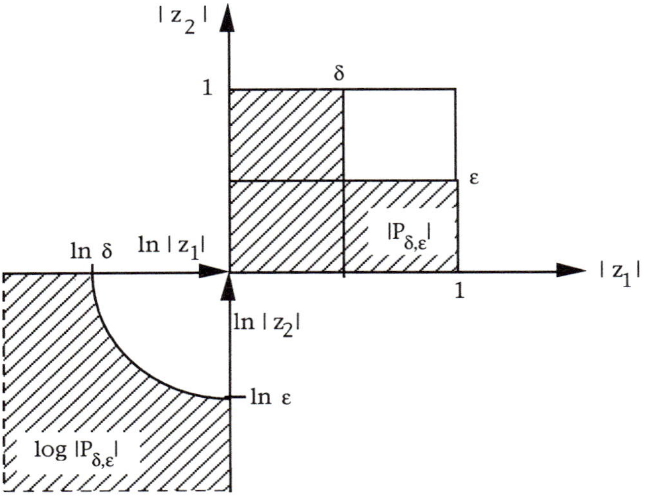

The L-shaped domain $P_{\delta,\varepsilon}$ is not pseudoconvex. Its "pseudoconvex hull"

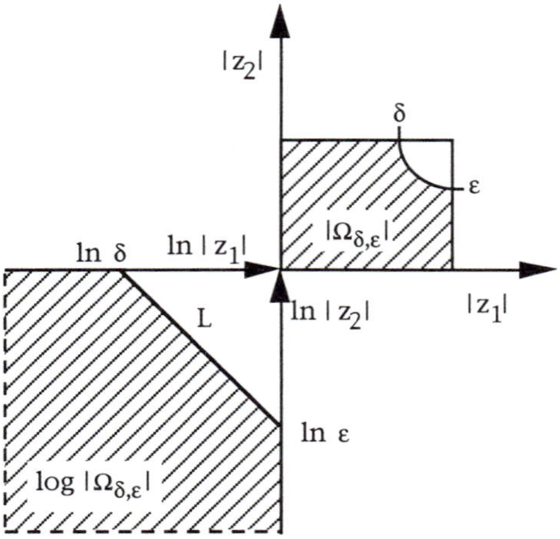

is given by

(1.4.20) $$\Omega_{\delta,\varepsilon} := \{z \in \mathbb{C}^2 : |z_1|^{(-1/\ln \delta)}|z_2|^{(-1/\ln \varepsilon)} < \frac{1}{e}\}.$$

We will often choose $\delta = \frac{1}{e}$ and $\varepsilon = e^{-1/\theta}$ for some real number $\theta > 0$. Then we obtain the domain

$$\Omega_\theta = \{z \in \mathbb{C}^2 : |z_1| \cdot |z_2|^\theta < \frac{1}{e}\} \tag{1.4.21}$$

whose supporting line L has the equation $x_1 + \theta x_2 = -1$ and the slope $-\frac{1}{\theta}$. In case θ is irrational, this line L will give rise to foliations of Kronecker type.

1.4.22. EXAMPLE. The basic example of a log-conical polycircular domain is *Hartogs' wedge* $\Omega = \Omega_{\alpha,\beta}$ in $\mathbb{B}^2$ given by the diagram

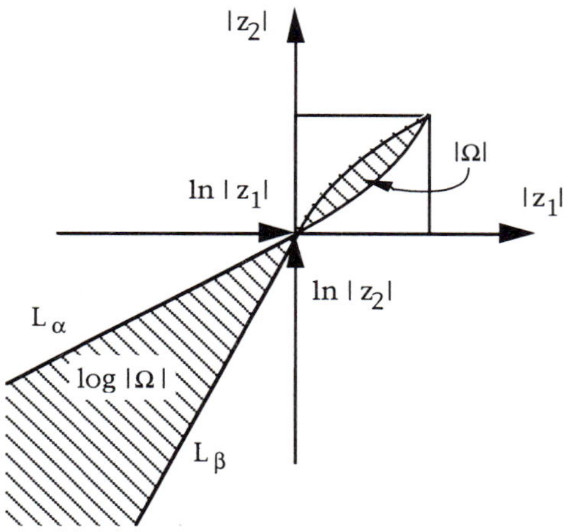

Here $0 \le \alpha < \beta \le +\infty$ are the slopes of the half-lines L_α and L_β forming the edges of the cone $\Lambda := \log |\Omega|$, i.e.

$$\Lambda = \{x \in \mathbb{R}^2 : x_1 < 0, \beta x_1 < x_2 < \alpha x_1\}. \tag{1.4.23}$$

In the extreme case $\alpha = 0$ and $\beta = +\infty$, we have $\Omega = \mathbb{B}^2$. As in Example 1.4.19, the most interesting case arises when α or β are irrational.

The next Proposition expresses integration in polar coordinates.

1.4.24. PROPOSITION. *Let* $\Omega \subset \mathbb{C}^r$ *be a polycircular domain. Let* $dV(z)$ *be the Lebesgue measure. Then we have for every integrable function* f *on* Ω :

$$\int_{\Omega} f(z)\ dV(z) = (2\pi)^r \int_{|\Omega|} \int_{\mathbb{T}^r} f(ys)\ y_1 \cdots y_r\ ds\ dy_1 \cdots dy_r$$

$$= (2\pi)^r \int_{\Lambda} \int_{\mathbb{T}^r} f(e^x s)\ e^{2x_1} \cdots e^{2x_r}\ ds\ dx_1 \cdots dx_r.$$

Proof. Since $dV(z)$ is invariant under $\mathbb{T}^r$ we may assume that $f(zs) = f(z)$ for all $z \in \Omega$ and $s \in \mathbb{T}^r$. Since Ω^x is a dense open subset of Ω is suffices to consider the integral over Ω^x. The continuous mappings

(1.4.25) $$\Omega^x \xrightarrow{|\cdot|} |\Omega^x| \xrightarrow{\log} \log |\Omega^x| =: \Lambda$$

$$(z_1, \ldots, z_r) \mapsto (|z_1|, \ldots, |z_r|) \mapsto (\log |z_1|, \ldots, (\log |z_r|)$$

give rise to the image measures

$$d|V|(y) = (2\pi)^r y_1 dy_1 \cdots y_r dy_r\ ,$$

$$d(\log|V|)(x) = (2\pi)^r e^{2x_1} dx_1 \cdots e^{2x_r} dx_r$$

(put $x_j = \log y_j$ so that $dx_j = dy_j/y_j$). Since f factorizes via the mappings (1.4.25), the assertion follows. Q.E.D.

The *boundary structure* of a log-convex polycircular domain Ω is best described in terms of its logarithmic base Λ. Since $\bar{\Lambda}$ is a closed convex subset of $\mathbb{R}^r$ we can consider the *faces* of $\bar{\Lambda}$. By definition, a non-empty closed convex subset $F \subset \bar{\Lambda}$ is called a face if it is extremal in the sense that every line segment $[a,b] \subset \bar{\Lambda}$ meeting F at an interior point is contained in F :

$$[a,b] \subset \bar{\Lambda},\ ]a,b[\ \cap F \neq \emptyset \Rightarrow [a,b] \subset F.$$

For example, the extreme points of $\bar{\Lambda}$ are precisely the singleton faces of $\bar{\Lambda}$. In case Λ is a cone, the faces F are also conical and the only extreme point of $\bar{\Lambda}$ is the vertex $\{0\}$.

1.4.26. DEFINITION. Let F be a face of the closed convex subset $\bar{\Lambda} \subset \mathbb{R}^r$, with tangent space $T(F)$, defined as the linear subspace parallel to F. Put

(1.4.27) $$L_F := \{(e^{i\xi_1}, \ldots, e^{i\xi_r}) : (\xi_1, \ldots, \xi_r) \in T(F)\}.$$

Then the translates $L_F \cdot s$, for $s \in \mathbb{T}^r$, form the *leaves of a foliation* of $\mathbb{T}^r$ denoted by $\mathcal{F}_F$.

1.4.28. EXAMPLE. In the case $r = 2$ and $\dim(F) = 1$, $T(F)$ is determined by its slope $1/\theta$:

$$T(F) = \{(\xi_1, \xi_2) : \xi_1 + \theta\xi_2 = 0\}.$$

In this case $\mathcal{F}_F$ is the well-known Kronecker foliation of $\mathbb{T}^2$, given by the slope $1/\theta$. It is well-known that in case θ is rational, the leaves (1.4.27) are closed whereas in case θ is irrational, the leaves are not closed but dense in $\mathbb{T}^2$.

1.4.29. THEOREM. *Let Ω be a log-convex polycircular domain. Let F be any face of its logarithmic base $\bar{\Lambda}$ and denote by F^0 its interior relative to the affine subspace $\mathrm{aff}(F) = F + T(F)$ spanned by F. Put*

(1.4.30) $$\Omega_F := \{(e^{x_1+i\xi_1}, \ldots, e^{x_r+i\xi_r}) : (x_1, \ldots, x_r) \in F^0, (\xi_1, \ldots, \xi_r) \in T(F)\}.$$

Then the translates $\Omega_F \cdot s$ for $s \in \mathbb{T}^r$, for all faces F, are the holomorphic arc components of $\bar{\Omega}^{\times}$.

Proof. Assume first that $z,w \in \bar{\Omega}^{\times}$ are holomorphically equivalent. We may assume that there exists a convex open neighborhood $C \subset \mathbb{C}$ of $[0,1]$

and a holomorphic mapping $f = (f_1, ..., f_r) : C \to \bar{\Omega}^x$ satisfying $f(0) = z$ and $f(1) = w$. We may further assume that, for each $1 \le k \le r$, $f_k(C) \subset \mathbb{C} \setminus \{0\}$ admits a holomorphic branch of the logarithm, denoted by

$$\ell_k : f_k(C) \to \mathbb{C}.$$

The interiors F^0, for all faces $F \subset \bar{\Lambda}$, form a partition of $\bar{\Lambda}$. It follows that there exists a unique face $F \subset \bar{\Lambda}$ such that

$$\log |z| := (\log |z_1|, ..., \log |z_r|) \in F^0.$$

For any linear functional

$$\xi(x) = \sum_{k=1}^{r} \xi_k x_k$$

on $\mathbb{R}^r$ and any convex subset $B \subset \mathbb{R}^r$ we write

$$B_\xi := \{x \in B : \xi(x) = \sup \xi(B)\}.$$

This is a convex set supporting B, which can be empty. Applying this concept to $\bar{\Lambda}$, there exists a linear form ξ satisfying $F \subset \bar{\Lambda}_\xi$. Put $c := \sup \xi(\bar{\Lambda}) < \infty$. The holomorphic function

$$g_\xi(\zeta) := \exp \sum_{k=1}^{r} \xi_k(\ell_k(f_k(\zeta)) - \ell_k(f_k(0)) \tag{1.4.31}$$

on C satisfies

$$|g_\xi(\zeta)| = \prod_k |f_k(\zeta)/f_k(0)|^{\xi_k} = \frac{1}{c} \prod_k |f_k(\zeta)|^{\xi_k} \le 1$$

since $\log |f(\zeta)| \in \bar{\Lambda}$ by assumption. Since $g_\xi(0) = 1$, g_ξ is constant by the maximum modulus principle. In particular, we have $\log |f(\zeta)| \in \bar{\Lambda}_\xi$ for all $\zeta \in C$. If $F \subsetneq \bar{\Lambda}_\xi$ there exists another linear form η on $\mathbb{R}^r$ such that

$$F \subset (\bar{\Lambda}_\xi)_\eta \subsetneqq \bar{\Lambda}_\xi.$$

Applying the previous argument to the holomorphic function g_η on C, defined as in (1.4.31), it follows that $\log |f(\zeta)| \in (\bar{\Lambda}_\xi)_\eta$ for all $\zeta \in C$. Continuing this way we show after a finite number of steps that $\log |f(\zeta)| \in F$ for all $\zeta \in C$. Suppose that $\log |f(\zeta_1)| \notin F^0$ for some $\zeta_1 \in C$. Then there exists a proper face $G \subsetneqq F$ of F containing $\log |f(\zeta_1)|$. The previous proof shows that $\log |f(\zeta)| \in G$ for all $\zeta \in C$, contradicting the fact that $\log |f(0)| \in F^0 \subset F \setminus G$. Thus we have shown

$$\log |f(\zeta)| \in F^0$$

for all $\zeta \in C$, in particular $\log |w| \in F^0$. In order to show that $w \in \Omega_F$, we may assume that $\text{aff}(F)$ is determined by the equations

$$t_i + \sum_{j \in J} \beta_{ij} t_j = \log(\eta_i) \tag{1.4.32}$$

for $i \in I$, where I and J form a partition of $\{1,...,r\}$. Here $\beta_{ij} \in \mathbb{R}$ and $\eta_i > 0$. For $i \in I$, consider the holomorphic function

$$h_i(\zeta) := \frac{f_i(\zeta)}{z_i} \exp \sum_{j \in J} \beta_{ij}(\ell_j(f_j(\zeta)) - \ell_j(z_j))$$

on C. Since $\log |f(\zeta)| \in F^0$ by the first part of the proof, we have $|h_i(\zeta)| = 1$ for all ζ. Hence $h_i(\zeta) = h_i(0) = 1$ is constant, showing that

$$1 = h_i(1) = \frac{w_i}{z_i} \exp \sum_j \beta_{ij}(\ell_j(w_j) - \ell_j(z_j)). \tag{1.4.33}$$

Putting $\ell_k(z_k) := \log |z_k| + 2\pi i \varphi_k$ and $\ell_k(w_k) := \log |w_k| + 2\pi i \psi_k$, (1.4.33) implies for all $i \in I$

$$1 = \exp 2\pi i(\psi_i - \varphi_i + \sum_j \beta_{ij}(\psi_j - \varphi_j)) .$$

For $t_k = \psi_k - \varphi_k$ this implies $(t_1,\ldots,t_r) \in T(F)$, and the assertion $w \in \Omega_F$ follows. Thus, equivalent points belong to some Ω_F. Conversely, suppose z and w belong to Ω_F for some face F. Then F^0 contains $\log |z|$ and $\log |w|$, and we have

$$z_k = |z_k| \exp 2\pi i\varphi_k, \quad w_k = |w_k| \exp 2\pi i(\varphi_k + t_k)$$

for all k, where $(t_1,\ldots,t_r) \in T(F)$. In order to show that z and w are holomorphically equivalent in $\bar{\Omega}^x$, we may assume that $|t_j|$ is small for all $j \in J$. Then there exists a branch ℓ_j of the logarithm about z_j and w_j with

$$\ell_j(w_j) - \ell_j(z_j) = \log |w_j| - \log |z_j| + 2\pi i t_j. \tag{1.4.34}$$

The entire function

$$f_j(\zeta) := \exp(\zeta \cdot \ell_j(w_j) + (1 - \zeta)\ell_j(z_j))$$

satisfies $f_j(0) = z_j$, $f_j(1) = w_j$ and

$$\log |f_j(t)| = t \log |w_j| + (1 - t) \log |z_j| \tag{1.4.35}$$

for $0 \le t \le 1$. Choose a convex open neighborhood C of $[0,1]$ in $\mathbb{C}$ such that ℓ_j is defined on $f_j(C)$ for all $j \in J$. Then

$$f_i(\zeta) := z_i \exp(-\sum_j \beta_{ij}(\ell_j(f_j(\zeta)) - \ell_j(z_j)))$$

is a holomorphic function on C for each $i \in I$, satisfying $f_i(0) = z_i$. By (1.4.34), we have

$$\begin{aligned} f_i(1) &= z_i \exp(-\sum_j \beta_{ij}(\ell_j(w_j) - \ell_j(z_j))) \\ &= |z_i| \prod_j |z_j/w_j|^{\beta_{ij}} \exp 2\pi i(\varphi_i - \sum_j \beta_{ij}t_j) \\ &= |w_i| \exp 2\pi i(\varphi_i - \sum_j \beta_{ij}t_j) = w_i. \end{aligned}$$

Put $f(\zeta) := (f_1(\zeta),...,f_r(\zeta))$. Since

$$(1.4.36) \qquad |f_i(\zeta)| \cdot \prod_j |f_j(\zeta)|^{\beta_{ij}} = |z_i| \prod_j |z_j|^{\beta_{ij}} = \eta_i$$

for all $i \in I$, we have $\log |f(\zeta)| \in \text{aff}(F)$ for all $\zeta \in C$. Further, (1.4.35) and (1.4.36) imply

$$\log |f_i(t)| = \log \eta_i - \sum_j \beta_{ij} \log |f_j(t)| = t \cdot \log |w_i| + (1 - t) \cdot \log |z_i|$$

for all $0 \leq t \leq 1$. Since F^0 is convex, it follows that $\log |f[0,1]| \subset F^0$. Thus $f : C \to \bar{\Omega}^x$ is holomorphic and satisfies $f(0) = z$, $f(1) = w$, showing that z and w are holomorphically equivalent. Q.E.D.

1.5. Symmetric Domains

The bounded symmetric domains introduced in this section [FK2, L9] are the natural generalization of the open unit disk in one complex variable. They play a fundamental role in the theory of group representations and automorphic functions [P2]. Via a Cayley transform they are also related to the symmetric tubular domains considered in Section 1.3. In the following let $Z \approx \mathbb{C}^n$ be a n-dimensional complex vector space and consider the open unit ball

$$(1.5.1) \qquad \Omega = \{z \in Z : ||z|| < 1\}$$

with respect to a suitable norm on Z. Every such domain Ω contains the origin $0 \in Z$ and is invariant under the circle group

$$(1.5.2) \qquad z \in \Omega \to e^{it}z \in \Omega$$

for all $t \in \mathbb{R}$. Domains with this property are called *circular*. Let $GL(Z)$ be the group of invertible complex-linear transformations of Z, and put

$$(1.5.3) \qquad K = GL(\Omega) := \{g \in GL(Z) : g(\Omega) = \Omega\}.$$

More generally, let

(1.5.4) $$\mathrm{Aut}(\Omega) = \{g : \Omega \to \Omega : \ g \text{ biholomorphic}\}$$

be the group of all *biholomorphic* mappings $g : \Omega \to \Omega$ (i.e., g and g^{-1} are holomorphic). Since Ω is circular one can show [N2]

(1.5.5) $$GL(\Omega) = \{g \in \mathrm{Aut}(\Omega) : g(0) = 0\}.$$

1.5.6. DEFINITION. An open unit ball $\Omega \subset Z$ is called *symmetric* if the group $\mathrm{Aut}(\Omega)$ acts transitively on Ω, i.e.,

$$\forall z,w \in \Omega \ \exists g \in \mathrm{Aut}(\Omega) : g(z) = w.$$

The reason for this terminology is that every symmetric ball Ω becomes a hermitian (complex) symmetric space of non-compact type [FK2, L9, U3]. Conversely, every such symmetric space can be realized as a bounded symmetric domain which is the open unit ball with respect to a suitable norm on Z. In general a norm on Z does not give rise to a symmetric ball. For example, the unit ball (1.2.12) for the p-norm on $\mathbb{C}^n$ is symmetric whenever $p = 2$ or $p = \infty$. As is well-known [L9, K3] there exists an algebraic characterization of bounded symmetric domains in terms of *Jordan triples*. Let $\Omega \subset Z$ be a symmetric ball. By a theorem of H. Cartan [N2] the group $\mathrm{Aut}(\Omega)$ is a finite-dimensional real Lie group whose Lie algebra $\mathrm{aut}(\Omega)$ consists of all completely integrable holomorphic vector fields

(1.5.7) $$A = h(z) \frac{\partial}{\partial z}$$

on Ω, with commutator

$$[h(z) \frac{\partial}{\partial z}, k(z) \frac{\partial}{\partial z}] := (k'(z)h(z) - h'(z)k(z)) \frac{\partial}{\partial z}.$$

Here $h : \Omega \to Z$ is a holomorphic mapping with complex derivative $h'(z) \in \mathcal{L}(Z)$ and the symbol $\partial/\partial z$ indicates the complex Wirtinger derivatives. The vector field (1.5.7) is called completely integrable if there is a continuous 1-parameter subgroup $g_t = \exp(tA) \in \mathrm{Aut}(\Omega)$ satisfying the ordinary differential equation

$$\frac{\partial g_t(z)}{\partial t} = h(g_t(z))$$

for all $(t,z) \in \mathbb{R} \times \Omega$. It is known [L9, U3] that the Lie algebra $aut(\Omega)$ has a Cartan decomposition $aut(\Omega) = \mathfrak{k} \oplus \mathfrak{p}$, where

$$\mathfrak{k} = \mathfrak{gl}(\Omega) = \{A \in \mathfrak{gl}(Z): \exp(tA)\Omega = \Omega \ \ \forall t \in \mathbb{R}\}$$

is the Lie algebra of $GL(\Omega)$, and

$$\mathfrak{p} = \{h(z) \frac{\partial}{\partial z} \in aut(\Omega) : h'(0) = 0\}.$$

Moreover, the evaluation mapping

$$\mathfrak{p} \ni h(z) \frac{\partial}{\partial z} \mapsto h(0) \in Z$$

is a real linear isomorphism, and the vector fields in $\mathfrak{p}$ have the form

(1.5.8) $$(a - \{za^*z\}) \frac{\partial}{\partial z}$$

for a unique $a \in Z$, where

(1.5.9) $$(z,a,w) \mapsto \{za^*w\}$$

is a mapping from $Z \times Z \times Z$ into Z which is symmetric bilinear in z and w, and conjugate-linear in a. The triple product (1.5.9) is called the *Jordan triple product* on Z associated with Ω, and Z endowed with this composition is called a *complex Jordan triple.* The domain Ω can be recovered from this algebraic structure as follows: For fixed $a,b \in Z$ consider the linear endomorphism

(1.5.10) $$w \mapsto (a \square b^*)w := \{ab^*w\}$$

on Z. Then $z \square z^*$ has positive real spectrum for each z and we have

$$\Omega = \{z \in Z : I - z \square z^* > 0\}$$

where I is the identity operator on Z, and > 0 means positive definite.

The complex Jordan triple Z associated with the symmetric ball Ω gives rise to two important classes of transformations of Ω. For each pair $(a,b) \in Z \times Z$ the linear endomorphism

(1.5.11) $$B(a,b)z := z - 2\{ab^*z\} + \{a\{bz^*b\}^*a\}$$

is called the *Bergman endomorphism* associated with (a,b). One can show that $B(z,\zeta) \in GL(Z)$ is invertible whenever $z,\zeta \in \Omega$. In this case

(1.5.12) $$z^\zeta := B(z,\zeta)^{-1}(z - \{z\zeta^*z\})$$

is called the *quasi-inverse* of z with respect to ζ. Now fix $\zeta \in \Omega$. One can show [L9] that

(1.5.13) $$g_\zeta(z) := -\zeta + B(\zeta,\zeta)^{1/2}z^\zeta$$

defines a biholomorphic transformation $g_\zeta \in \mathrm{Aut}(\Omega)$ called the *Moebius transformation* associated with ζ. Since

(1.5.14) $$g_\zeta(0) = -\zeta\ ,\ g_\zeta(\zeta) = 0$$

these transformations map the origin to any given point in Ω (but they don't form a group under composition). The Moebius transformations (1.5.13) give an explicit description of the *symmetries* $S_\zeta \in \mathrm{Aut}(\Omega)$ associated with any $\zeta \in \Omega$. In fact,

$$S_0(z) = -z$$

is the reflection about the origin $0 \in \Omega$, and for any other $\zeta \in \Omega$ we have

(1.5.15) $$S_\zeta = g_\zeta^{-1} \circ S_0 \circ g_\zeta .$$

As a densely defined sesqui-rational map on $Z \times Z$ the quasi-inverse (1.5.12) has a unique reduced representation

(1.5.16) $$z^\zeta = \frac{p(z,\zeta)}{\Delta(z,\zeta)}$$

where

(1.5.17) $$\Delta : Z \times Z \to \mathbb{C}$$

is a sesqui-polynomial satisfying $\Delta(0,0) = 1$, and $p(z,\zeta)$ is a Z-valued sesqui-polynomial which has no common factors with $\Delta(z,\zeta)$. The sesqui-polynomial (1.5.17) is called the *Jordan triple determinant* associated with Ω. It should not be confused with the function defined in (1.3.55) which is the *unbounded* analogon of (1.5.17).

1.5.18. DEFINITION. A symmetric ball $\Omega \subset Z$ is called of *tube type* if it is biholomorphically equivalent to a symmetric tubular domain $\Pi = \Lambda \oplus iX$ (cf. Definition 1.3.9).

The real Jordan algebra X associated with Π has the complexification $Z = X \oplus iX$, and the Jordan triple product on Z can be expressed as

$$\{uv^*w\} = (u \circ v^*) \circ w + (w \circ v^*) \circ u - (u \circ w) \circ v^* \tag{1.5.19}$$

for all $u, v, w \in Z$. Here $z \circ w$ is the complexified Jordan algebra product and $(x + iy)^* = x - iy$ is the involution of Z. In terms of the unit element e of X, we have

$$X = \{z \in Z: \{ez^*e\} = z\}, \tag{1.5.20}$$

$$x \circ y = \{xe^*y\}. \tag{1.5.21}$$

1.5.22. EXAMPLE. The open unit disk $\mathbb{B} = \{z \in \mathbb{C}: |z| < 1\}$ is a symmetric ball, since the Moebius transformations

$$g_\zeta(z) = \frac{z - \zeta}{1 - \bar{\zeta} z}$$

for $\zeta \in \mathbb{B}$ belong to $\mathrm{Aut}(\mathbb{B})$. By (1.5.15),

$$s_\zeta(z) = \frac{2\zeta - (1 + \bar{\zeta}\zeta)z}{(1 + \bar{\zeta}\zeta) - 2\bar{\zeta}z}$$

is the symmetry of $\mathbb{B}$ about ζ. Geometrically, s_ζ is the geodesic reflection for the (non-euclidean) hyperbolic metric on $\mathbb{B}$. The associated Jordan triple product is

$$\{za^*w\} = z\bar{a}w$$

for all $z,a,w \in \mathbb{C}$. Since the Bergman operators (1.5.11) are given by

$$B(a,b)z = (1 - z\bar{b})^2 z$$

it follows from (1.5.12) that

$$z^\zeta = \frac{z}{1 - z\bar{\zeta}}$$

is the quasi-inverse. Thus the Jordan triple determinant is given by

(1.5.23) $$\Delta(z,\zeta) := 1 - z\bar{\zeta}$$

for all $z,\zeta \in \mathbb{C}$. The unit disk is of tube type, being equivalent to a half-plane via a Cayley transformation. Taking direct products, we obtain the r-*polydisk*

$$\mathbb{B}^r = \{z \in \mathbb{C}^r : |z_i| < 1 \text{ for all } 1 \le i \le r\}$$

as a symmetric ball of tube type in $Z = \mathbb{C}^r$. The associated Jordan triple product is defined componentwise, and

$$\Delta(z,\zeta) = \prod_i (1 - z_i\bar{\zeta}_i).$$

1.5.24. EXAMPLE. Let $1 \le r \le R$ be integers and put

(1.5.25) $$Z = \mathbb{C}^{r\times R} = \{\text{complex } (r\times R)\text{-matrices}\}.$$

Then the unit ball of Z, with respect to the usual "operator norm" is given by

(1.5.26) $$\Omega_{r,R} := \{z \in \mathbb{C}^{r\times R} : I_r - zz^* > 0\}.$$

Here I_r is the $(r\times r)$-unit matrix. One can show that the block matrix group

$$SU_{r,R}(\mathbb{C}) = \left\{ \begin{pmatrix} a & b \\ c & d \end{pmatrix} \in SL_{r+R}(\mathbb{C}) : \begin{matrix} a^*a - c^*c = I_r \\ b^*b - d^*d = I_R \\ a^*b = c^*d \end{matrix} \right\}$$

acts transitively on $\Omega_{r,R}$ via generalized Moebius transformations

(1.5.27) $$\begin{bmatrix} a & b \\ c & d \end{bmatrix}(z) := (az + b)(cz + d)^{-1}$$

for all $z \in \Omega_{r,R}$. It follows that $\Omega_{r,R}$ becomes a symmetric ball called the (complex) *matrix ball* of size $r \times R$. The associated Jordan triple product on Z is the generalized anti-commutator product

$$\{za^*w\} := \frac{1}{2}(za^*w + wa^*z)$$

for $z,a,w \in Z$ which makes sense even for non-square matrices ($r \neq R$). The domain (1.5.26) is of tube type if and only if $r = R$. The matrix Jordan triple (1.5.25) has the Bergman operators

$$B(a,b)z = (I - ab^*)z(I - b^*a)$$

and the quasi-inverse

$$z^\zeta := (I - z\zeta^*)^{-1}z.$$

It follows that

(1.5.28) $$\Delta(z,\zeta) = \mathrm{Det}(I - z\zeta^*)$$

is the Jordan triple determinant. One can show that the identity components satisfy

$$\mathrm{Aut}(\Omega)^0 = \left\{ \begin{bmatrix} a & b \\ c & d \end{bmatrix} : \begin{pmatrix} a & b \\ c & d \end{pmatrix} \in SU_{r,R}(\mathbb{C}) \right\}$$

and

$$GL(\Omega)^0 = \left\{ \begin{bmatrix} a & 0 \\ 0 & d \end{bmatrix} : \begin{pmatrix} a & 0 \\ 0 & d \end{pmatrix} \in S(U_r(\mathbb{C}) \times U_R(\mathbb{C})) \right\}.$$

As important special cases of complex matrix balls we have the following: For $r = R$, we obtain the "square" matrix ball

(1.5.29) $$\Omega_{r,r} = \{z \in \mathbb{C}^{r \times r} : I_r - zz^* > 0\}$$
$$\cong SU_{r,r}(\mathbb{C})/S(U_r(\mathbb{C}) \times U_r(\mathbb{C})).$$

The simplest case $r = 1$ gives the *unit disk*

(1.5.30) $$\Omega_{1,1} = \{z \in \mathbb{C} : |z| < 1\} \cong SU_{1,1}(\mathbb{C})/U(\mathbb{C}).$$

Here $U(\mathbb{C}) \mapsto SU_{1,1}(\mathbb{C})$ via $u \mapsto \begin{pmatrix} u & 0 \\ 0 & \bar{u} \end{pmatrix}$. For $1 = r \leq R$, we obtain the *Hilbert ball*

(1.5.31) $$\Omega_{1,R} = \{z \in \mathbb{C}^R : z \cdot \bar{z} < 1\} \cong SU_{1,R}(\mathbb{C})/U_R(\mathbb{C}).$$

Here $U_R(\mathbb{C}) \mapsto SU_{1,R}(\mathbb{C})$ via $u \mapsto \begin{pmatrix} u & 0 \\ 0 & \overline{\mathrm{Det}(u)} \end{pmatrix}$.

1.5.32. EXAMPLE. For $r \geq 1$, let

(1.5.33) $$Z = \mathbb{C}_+^{r \times r} := \{z \in \mathbb{C}^{r \times r} : z^T = z\}$$

be the space of all *symmetric* matrices of degree r. Then the (operator norm) unit ball

(1.5.34) $$\Omega_r^+ := \Omega_{r,r} \cap Z = \{z \in Z : I_r - zz^* > 0\}$$

admits a transitive action of a group of "Moebius" transformations and is therefore a symmetric ball of tube type. The associated Jordan triple product on Z is given by (1.5.28). In a similar way, let $\varepsilon \in \{0,1\}$ and let

(1.5.35) $$Z = \mathbb{C}_-^{(2r+\varepsilon)\times(2r+\varepsilon)} := \{z \in \mathbb{C}^{(2r+\varepsilon)\times(2r+\varepsilon)} : z^T = -z\}$$

be the space of all *skew-symmetric* matrices of degree $2r + \varepsilon$. Thus Z consists of even or odd dimensional matrices if $\varepsilon = 0$ or $\varepsilon = 1$, respectively. The (operator norm) unit ball

(1.5.36) $$\Omega_{2r+\varepsilon}^- := \Omega_{2r+\varepsilon,2r+\varepsilon} \cap Z = \{z \in Z : I - zz^* > 0\}$$

admits a transitive action of a group of "Moebius" transformations and is therefore a symmetric ball. The associated Jordan triple product on Z is given by (1.5.28). The domain (1.5.36) is of tube type if and only if $\varepsilon = 0$.

1.5.37. EXAMPLE. Let Z be a complex Hilbert space of finite dimension $n \geq 3$, endowed with a conjugation $z \mapsto \bar{z}$. Let $z \cdot \bar{w}$ denote the inner product of Z. Then Z becomes a Jordan triple called a *complex spin factor* under the product

$$\{uv^*w\} := (u \cdot \bar{v})w + (w \cdot \bar{v})u - (u \cdot w)\bar{v} \tag{1.5.38}$$

for all $u,v,w \in Z$. One can show [L9, U3] that the unit ball of the complex spin factor is the *Lie ball*

$$\Omega_n := \{z \in Z : z \cdot \bar{z} < 1, \ 1 + (z \cdot \bar{z})^2 - 2|z \cdot z|^2 > 0. \tag{1.5.39}$$

The norm describing Ω has a quantum mechanical interpretation in terms of creation or annihilation operators on the anti-symmetric Fock space over Z [T3]. The Lie balls (1.5.39) are of tube type, One can show that

$$\Omega_n \cong SU_{2,n}(\mathbb{R}) \,/\, S(U_2(\mathbb{R}) \times U_n(\mathbb{R}))$$

where $SU_{2,n}(\mathbb{R})$ acts by "fractional-quadratic" transformations [L9]. The Jordan triple determinant has the form

$$\Delta(z,w) = 1 - 2z \cdot \bar{w} + (z \cdot z)(\bar{w} \cdot \bar{w}). \tag{1.5.40}$$

One can show that, up to two "exceptional" domains of dimension 16 and 27, the matrix balls $\Omega_{r,R}$, Ω_r^+, and $\Omega_{2r+\varepsilon}^-$ (cf. Examples 1.5.24 and 1.5.32) and the Lie balls Ω_n (cf. Example 1.5.37) constitute all "irreducible" symmetric balls. A general symmetric ball Ω is a direct product $\Omega = \Pi\Omega_i$ of irreducible symmetric balls Ω_i.

For any complex vector space $Z \approx \mathbb{C}^n$ let $\mathcal{P}(Z)$ be the unital algebra of all holomorphic *polynomials* $p : Z \to \mathbb{C}$. There is a natural graduation

$$\mathcal{P}(Z) = \sum_{j \in \mathbb{N}} \mathcal{P}^j(Z) \tag{1.5.41}$$

where $\mathcal{P}^j(Z)$ consists of all j-homogeneous polynomials. For an inner product $(z|w)$ on Z, one can show that $\mathcal{P}^j(Z)$ is spanned by powers $z \mapsto (z|a)^j$ where $a \in Z$ is arbitrary.

1.5.42. PROPOSITION. *Let $\Omega \subset Z$ be a symmetric ball (or, more generally, any circular domain containing the origin). Then every holomorphic function $f : \Omega \to \mathbb{C}$ has an expansion*

$$f(z) = \sum_{j \in \mathbb{N}} f_j(z) \tag{1.5.43}$$

into a series of j-homogeneous polynomials $f_j \in \mathcal{P}^j(Z)$, which converges compactly on Ω.

Proof. The mapping $U(\mathbb{C}) \times \Omega \ni (s,z) \mapsto f(sz)$ is continuous and holomorphic in the z-variable. It follows that for every $j \in \mathbb{N}$

$$f_j(z) := \frac{1}{2\pi i} \int_{|s|=1} \frac{f(sz)}{s^{j+1}} \, ds \tag{1.5.44}$$

defines a holomorphic function on Ω. Now let $K \subset \Omega$ be compact. Then there exists $\rho > 1$ such that Ω contains the compact set $L := \{sz : z \in K, 1 \leq |s| \leq \rho\}$. By Cauchy's homotopy theorem we have

$$f_j(z) = \frac{1}{2\pi i} \int_{|s|=\rho} \frac{f(sz)}{s^{j+1}} \, ds$$

for all $z \in K$. Since $M := \sup_L |f| < \infty$, we have

$$\sum_{j \geq 0} |f_j(z)| \leq M \sum_{j \geq 0} \rho^{-j} < \infty$$

uniformly on K. It follows that the series $\sum f_j$ converges compactly towards a holomorphic function g on Ω. Now consider the local expansion

$$f(z) = \sum_{m \in \mathbb{N}} p_m(z)$$

into a series of m-homogeneous polynomials $p_m \in \mathcal{P}^m(Z)$, converging uniformly in a circular neighborhood U of $0 \in \Omega$. Integrating term-by-term, we obtain from (1.5.44)

$$f_j(z) = \sum_{m\in\mathbb{N}} \frac{1}{2\pi i} \int_{|s|=1} \frac{p_m(sz)\, ds}{s^{j+1}}$$

$$= \sum_{m\in\mathbb{N}} \frac{p_m(z)}{2\pi i} \int_{|s|=1} s^{m-j-1}\, ds = p_j(z)$$

for every $z \in U$. By analytic continuation, we get $f_j = p_j|_\Omega$ and $f = g$.

Q.E.D.

The *boundary structure* of a symmetric ball Ω is best described in terms of the underlying complex Jordan triple Z. An element $c \in Z$ is called a *tripotent* if

$$\{cc^*c\} = c.$$

Putting

$$Z_\alpha(c) := \{z \in Z : \{cc^*z\} = \alpha z\}$$

we have the *Peirce decomposition*

(1.5.46) $$Z = Z_1(c) \oplus Z_{1/2}(c) \oplus Z_0(c)$$

associated with c. By [L9; Theorem 6.3], we have

1.5.47. THEOREM. *Let Ω be a symmetric ball in a complex Jordan triple Z. Then, for every tripotent $c \in Z$, the set*

$$c + (\bar{\Omega} \cap Z_0(c))$$

is a face of $\bar{\Omega}$, and every face of $\bar{\Omega}$ arises this way.

Since $\bar{\Omega}$ is a compact convex set, its faces are defined as those non-empty closed convex subsets $F \subset \bar{\Omega}$ satisfying the "extremality" condition

$$[a,b] \subset \bar{\Omega},\ ]a,b[\cap F \neq \emptyset \Rightarrow [a,b] \subset F.$$

Here $[a,b] = \{tb + (1 - t)a : 0 \leq t \leq 1\}$ is the segment spanned by $a,b \in Z$ and $]a,b[$ is the "open" segment. The trivial face $F = \bar{\Omega}$ corresponds to the trivial tripotent $c = 0$. Since $Z_0(c)$ is a Jordan subtriple of Z, its unit ball

(1.5.48) $$\Omega_c := \Omega \cap Z_0(c)$$

is again a symmetric ball (of lower dimension).

One can show that the "open faces"

(1.5.49) $$c + \Omega_c := c + \Omega \cap Z_0(c) \quad \text{(relative to } c + Z_0(c))$$

are pairwise disjoint and thus form a partition

$$\partial\Omega = \bigcup_{1 \leq k \leq r} \bigcup_{c \in S_k} c + \Omega_c$$

of the boundary $\partial\Omega$. Here r is the "rank" of Ω and S_k is the compact real-analytic manifold consisting of all tripotents $c \in Z$ of rank k. The "ball bundle"

(1.5.50) $$\partial_k\Omega := \bigcup_{c \in S_k} c + \Omega_c$$

with base S_k is called the *k-th partial boundary* of Ω. It is a real-analytic manifold which is not closed in Z if $k < r$. For $k = 1$, $\partial_1\Omega$ consists of all *maximal* (open) faces of Ω whereas

$$\partial_r\Omega = S_r = S$$

coincides with the *Shilov boundary*. Note that Ω has a smooth boundary if and only if $r = 1$, i.e., Ω is the Hilbert ball (1.5.31).

1.5.51. EXAMPLE. For the matrix Jordan triple $Z = \mathbb{C}^{r \times R}$ of rank r, a tripotent c is characterized by the property $cc^*c = c$. It is known [H1] that matrices of this kind are precisely the *partial isometries* (this holds even in the rectangular case). For $1 \le k \le r$, S_k consists of all partial isometries c whose rank (i.e., the rank of the projection cc^*) equals k. For example,

$$S_1 = \{\xi^*\eta : \xi \in \mathbb{C}^{1\times r}, \eta \in \mathbb{C}^{1\times R}, \|\xi\| = 1 = \|\eta\|\}$$

and $S_r = \{\text{isometries}\} \cup \{\text{coisometries}\}$ if $r < R$, whereas $S_r = U_r(\mathbb{C})$ if $r = R$. For the Peirce decomposition, write the elements $z \in Z$ as block matrices $z = (u,v)$, where $u \in \mathbb{C}^{r\times r}$ and $v \in \mathbb{C}^{r\times(R-r)}$. For $1 \le k \le r$, consider the partial isometry

$$c = \left(\begin{array}{cccccc|c} 1 & & & & & & \\ & \ddots & & & & & \\ & & 1 & & & & \\ & & & 0 & & & 0 \\ & & & & \ddots & & \\ & & & & & 0 & \end{array}\right) \qquad \text{(k ones).}$$

Write

$$z = \begin{array}{c} \begin{matrix} k & r\text{-}k & R\text{-}r \end{matrix} \\ \begin{pmatrix} u_{11} & u_{12} & v_1 \\ u_{21} & u_{22} & v_2 \end{pmatrix} \end{array} \begin{matrix} k \\ r\text{-}k \end{matrix}$$

Then we have

$$Z_1(c) = \left\{ \begin{pmatrix} u_{11} & 0 & 0 \\ 0 & 0 & 0 \end{pmatrix} : u_{11} \text{ arbitrary} \right\}$$

$$Z_{1/2}(c) = \left\{ \begin{pmatrix} 0 & u_{12} & v_1 \\ u_{21} & 0 & 0 \end{pmatrix} : u_{12}, u_{21}, v_1 \text{ arbitrary} \right\}$$

and

$$Z_0(c) = \left\{ \begin{pmatrix} 0 & 0 & 0 \\ 0 & u_{22} & v_2 \end{pmatrix} : u_{22}, v_2 \text{ arbitrary} \right\}.$$

In the special case $r = R$ (square matrices), this simplifies to

$$Z_1(c) \approx \mathbb{C}^{k\times k}, \; Z_0(c) \approx \mathbb{C}^{(r-k)\times(r-k)},$$

$$Z_{1/2}(c) \approx \mathbb{C}^{k\times(r-k)} \oplus \mathbb{C}^{(r-k)\times k}.$$

For a general Jordan triple Z it is not possible to split the $\frac{1}{2}$-space into two natural summands (as in the associative setting).

1.5.52. EXAMPLE. Consider the complex spin factor $Z = \mathbb{C}^n$ with triple product (1.5.38). By definition, a tripotent $c \in Z$ satisfies

$$c = \{cc^*c\} = 2(c \cdot \bar{c})c - (c \cdot c)\bar{c}. \tag{1.5.53}$$

We now distinguish two cases (for $c \neq 0$).

<u>Case 1</u>: c and $\bar{c}$ are linearly independent. Then (1.5.53) yields $c \cdot \bar{c} = \frac{1}{2}$, $c \cdot c = 0$. The Peirce decomposition of Z associated with c is easily computed:

$$\begin{aligned} &Z_1(c) = \mathbb{C} \cdot c,\ Z_0(c) = \mathbb{C} \cdot \bar{c} \\ &Z_{1/2}(c) = \mathbb{C}<c,\bar{c}>^{\perp} \quad \text{(ortho-complement).} \end{aligned} \tag{1.5.54}$$

If follows that

$$\begin{aligned} S_1 &= \{c \in \mathbb{C}^n : \|c\|_2 = \frac{1}{\sqrt{2}},\ c \perp \bar{c}\} \\ &= \{\frac{x + i\xi}{2} : x, \xi \in \mathbb{S}^{n-1},\ x \cdot \xi = 0\} \approx \mathbb{S}^*(\mathbb{S}^{n-1}) \end{aligned} \tag{1.5.55}$$

can be identified with the *cosphere bundle* of $\mathbb{S}^{n-1}$.

<u>Case 2</u>: c and $\bar{c}$ are linearly dependent. Then $\bar{c} = \lambda c$ for some $\lambda \in \mathbb{C}$. Since $c = \bar{\bar{c}} = \overline{\lambda c} = \bar{\lambda}\bar{c} = \bar{\lambda}\lambda c$ it follows that $|\lambda| = 1$. By (1.5.53), we get

$$c = 2(c \cdot \bar{c})c - |\lambda|^2(c \cdot \bar{c})c = (c \cdot \bar{c})c,$$

i.e., $c \cdot \bar{c} = 1$. Now let $\zeta \in \mathbb{C}$ satisfy $|\zeta| = 1$ and $\bar{\zeta} \cdot \lambda = \zeta$. Then $x := \zeta c$ is a unit vector satisfying $\bar{x} = \bar{\zeta}\bar{c} = \bar{\zeta}\lambda c = \zeta c = x$, i.e., $x \in \mathbb{S}^{n-1}$. Since $c = \bar{\zeta}x$, we get for the set S_2 of all tripotents considered in case 2:

(1.5.56) $$S_2 = \{\zeta x : \zeta \in \mathbb{T}, \bar{x} = x, x \cdot x = 1\} = \mathbb{T} \cdot \mathbb{S}^{n-1}.$$

This space is known as the *Lie sphere.* It is the Shilov boundary of the Lie ball (1.5.39). Every $c \in S_2$ induces a trivial Peirce decomposition

$$Z_1(c) = Z, Z_{1/2}(c) = Z_0(c) = \{0\}.$$

The most important symmetric domains Ω are *irreducible:* they cannot be written as direct products of lower dimensional symmetric domains. The Jordan triple Z associated with an irreducible symmetric domain is irreducible in the algebraic sense. Let Z be an irreducible complex Jordan triple. Two tripotents $c,e \in Z$ are called *orthogonal* if $\{cc^*e\} = 0$. A tripotent $c \neq 0$ is called *primitive* if it is not the sum of two non-zero orthogonal tripotents. A maximal family $e_1, \ldots, e_r$ of orthogonal primitive tripotents is called a *frame* of Z. Its cardinality r depends only on Z and is called the *rank* of Z. Putting

(1.5.57) $$Z_{ij} := \{z \in Z : \{e_k e_k^* z\} = \frac{\delta_{ik} + \delta_{jk}}{2} z \ \forall\ 1 \leq k \leq r\}.$$

we have the *joint Peirce decomposition* [L8, L9]

(1.5.58) $$Z = \sum_{0 \leq i \leq j \leq r}^{\oplus} Z_{ij}.$$

We have $Z_{00} = \{0\}$,

(1.5.59) $$Z_{ii} = \mathbb{C}e_i \qquad (1 \leq i \leq r)$$

and the numbers

(1.5.60) $$a := \dim Z_{ij} \quad (1 \leq i < j \leq r),$$

(1.5.61) $$b := \dim Z_{0j} \quad (1 \leq j \leq r)$$

which depend only on Z are called the *characteristic multiplicities* of Z. By (1.5.58), the dimension n of Z is given by

(1.5.62) $$n = r + \frac{a}{2} r(r - 1) + rb.$$

Another important invariant is the *genus*

(1.5.63) $$p := 2 + r(a - 1) + b.$$

By comparing the Peirce decomposition (1.3.44) and (1.5.58) in the Jordan algebra and Jordan triple case, respectively, we see that a symmetric ball Ω is of tube type (cf. Definition 1.5.18) if and only if $b = 0$. In this case we have $p/2 = n/r$.

For an irreducible complex Jordan triple Z, the positive-definite inner product

(1.5.64) $$(z|w) := \frac{2}{p} \text{ trace } z\Box w^*$$

is called the *hermitian structure* underlying Z.

1.5.65. EXAMPLE. For the matrix space $Z = \mathbb{C}^{r\times R}$ with triple product (1.5.28) the Peirce decomposition reduces to the familiar matrix units. If $r \leq R$, Z is an irreducible Jordan triple of rank r and every $z \in Z$ is a block matrix $z = (u,v)$ with $u \in \mathbb{C}^{r\times r}$ and $v \in \mathbb{C}^{r\times(R-r)}$. For $1 \leq i \leq p$, let

(1.5.66) $$e_i := (E_i,0)$$

with

$$E_i := \begin{pmatrix} 0 & & & & 0 \\ & \ddots & & & \\ & & 0 & & \\ & & & 1 & \\ & & & & 0 \\ 0 & & & & & \ddots \\ & & & & & & 0 \end{pmatrix}$$

having the only entry 1 at the (i,i)-th place. Then the e_i form a frame of Z. For $1 \leq i < j \leq r$, Z_{ij} consists of all matrices $z = (u,0)$ with $u \in \mathbb{C}^{r\times r}$ having non-zero entries only in the (i,j)-th place or the (j,i)-th place (This explains the condition $i < j$). For $1 \leq j \leq r$, Z_{0j} consists of all matrices $z = (0,v)$ with $v \in \mathbb{C}^{r\times(R-r)}$ having non-zero entries only in the j-th row. It follows that $a = 2$ and $b = R - r$. The matrix ball Ω is of tube type if and only if $r = R$, i.e. Z consists of square matrices.

1.5.67. EXAMPLE. The Jordan triple $Z = \mathbb{C}_+^{r\times r}$ of all symmetric matrices has the canonical frame

$$e_i = E_i = \begin{pmatrix} 0 & & & & & \\ & \ddots & & & & \\ & & 0 & & & \\ & & & 1 & & \\ & & & & 0 & \\ & & & & & \ddots \\ & & & & & & 0 \end{pmatrix}$$

for $1 \leq i \leq r$ and is therefore of rank r. In this case we have $Z_{0j} = \{0\}$ for all j, i.e.

$$Z = \sum_{1 \leq i \leq j \leq r}^{\oplus} Z_{ij}$$

with Z_{ij} consisting of all symmetric matrices having non-zero entries only in the (i,j)-position or the (j,i)-position. It follows that $a = 1$ and $b = 0$. The associated domain is of tube type.

1.5.68. EXAMPLE. The Jordan triple $Z = \mathbb{C}^{(2r+\varepsilon)\times(2r+\varepsilon)}_{-}$ of all anti-symmetric matrices has the canonical frame

$$e_i = \begin{matrix} & & \scriptstyle{2i\text{-}1\ 2i} & \\ \begin{pmatrix} \begin{array}{c|cc|c} 0 & 0 & & 0 \\ \hline 0 & 0 & -1 & 0 \\ & 1 & 0 & \\ \hline 0 & 0 & & 0 \end{array} \end{pmatrix} & \begin{matrix} \\ \scriptstyle{2i\text{-}1} \\ \scriptstyle{2i} \\ \ \end{matrix} \end{matrix} \qquad (1 \leq i \leq r).$$

It follows that $\mathrm{rank}(Z) = r$ (regardless whether $\varepsilon = 0$ or $\varepsilon = 1$). One can show that $a = 4$ in this case. In case $\varepsilon = 0$, we have $b = 0$ and the associated unit ball Ω is of tube type. In case $\varepsilon = 1$, we have $b = 2$ and Ω cannot be realized as a tube domain.

1.5.69. EXAMPLE. For the complex spin factor $Z = \mathbb{C}^n$ a frame is defined by the two tripotents

$$e_1 := (\tfrac{1}{2}, \tfrac{i}{2}, 0, ..., 0),$$

(1.5.70)

$$e_2 := (\tfrac{1}{2}, \tfrac{-i}{2}, 0, ..., 0) = \bar{e}_1.$$

Thus the rank is $r = 2$, and (1.5.54) implies $b = 0$ and $a = n - 2$. (This is the only class of irreducible Jordan triples where a can become arbitrarily large.)

The following table summarizes the basic geometric invariants of every irreducible Jordan triple Z:

Jordan triple	rank	multiplicities		dimension	genus
Z	r	a	b	n	p
$\mathbb{C}^{r\times R}$	r	2	$R - r$	$r \cdot R$	$r + R$
$\mathbb{C}_{+}^{r\times r}$	r	1	0	$\frac{r(r+1)}{2}$	$r + 1$
$\mathbb{C}_{-}^{(2r+\varepsilon)\times(2r+\varepsilon)}$	r	4	2ε	$r(2r + 2\varepsilon - 1)$	$4r - 2 + 2\varepsilon$
spin factor $\mathbb{C}^n$	2	$d - 2$	0	n	n
exceptional $\mathbb{C}^{16}$	2	6	4	16	12
exceptional $\mathbb{C}^{27}$	3	8	0	27	26

For domains of tube type Ω, the Shilov boundary $S = S_r$ becomes a compact symmetric quotient space

$$S = K/L$$

where $K = GL(\Omega)^{\circ}$ and

$$L = \{s \in K : se = e\} \tag{1.5.71}$$

is the stabilizer subgroup at the unit element e of the associated Jordan algebra. For domains not of tube type, K is still transitive on S but (K,L) is not a symmetric pair in the sense of Riemannian geometry [H2].

1.5.72. EXAMPLE. (i) Let $X = \mathcal{H}_r(\mathbb{C})$. Then $Z = \mathbb{C}^{r\times r}$ and

$$K = \{z \mapsto uzv^* : u \in U_r(\mathbb{C}),\ v \in U_r(\mathbb{C})\}.$$

The unit element of Z is

$$(1.5.73) \qquad e = \begin{pmatrix} 1 & & 0 \\ & \ddots & \\ 0 & & 1 \end{pmatrix} = (r \times r)\text{-unit matrix.}$$

It follows that $L = \{z \mapsto uzu^*: u \in U_r(\mathbb{C})\}$ showing that

$$S = U_r(\mathbb{C}) \approx (U_r(\mathbb{C}) \times U_r(\mathbb{C}))/U_r(\mathbb{C}).$$

(ii) Let $X = \mathcal{H}_r(\mathbb{R})$. Then $Z = \mathbb{C}_+^{r\times r}$ and

$$K = \{z \mapsto uzu^T : u \in U_r(\mathbb{C})\}.$$

The unit element e of Z is given by (1.5.73). Thus

$$L = \{z \mapsto uzu^T : u \in U_r(\mathbb{R})\}$$

showing that

$$S \approx U_r(\mathbb{C})/U_r(\mathbb{R}).$$

(iii) Let $X = \mathcal{H}_r(\mathbb{H})$. Then $Z \approx \mathbb{C}_-^{2r\times 2r}$ via (1.3.59) and

$$K = \{z \mapsto uzu^T : u \in U_{2r}(\mathbb{C})\}.$$

The unit element of Z is

$$e = \begin{pmatrix} 0 & -1 & & & & & \\ 1 & 0 & & & & & \\ & & 0 & -1 & & & \\ & & 1 & 0 & & & \\ & & & & \ddots & & \\ & & & & & 0 & -1 \\ & & & & & 1 & 0 \end{pmatrix} \quad (r \text{ blocks}).$$

Therefore $L \approx U_r(\mathbb{H})$ showing that

$$S \approx U_{2r}(\mathbb{C})/U_r(\mathbb{H}).$$

(iv) Let $X = \mathbb{R} \times i\mathbb{R}^{n-1}$ = real spin factor. Then $Z = \mathbb{C}^n$ = complex spin factor and

$$K = \{z \mapsto \zeta \cdot \gamma(z) : \zeta \in \mathbb{C}, |\zeta| = 1, \gamma \in SU_n(\mathbb{R})\}.$$

The unit element of Z is $e = (1, 0, ..., 0)$. Therefore $L = SU_{n-1}(\mathbb{R})$ showing that

$$S \approx \mathbb{T} \cdot SU_n(\mathbb{R})/SU_{n-1}(\mathbb{R}).$$

(v) $X = \mathcal{H}_3(\mathbb{O})$ (exceptional Jordan algebra). Then $Z = \mathbb{C}^{27}$ is the exceptional Jordan triple of tube type and one can show

(1.5.74) $$K \approx \mathbb{T} \cdot E_{6(-78)}$$

and $L \approx F_4$. The exceptional Lie groups F_4 and $E_{6(-78)}$ occurring here are related to the Cayley numbers. For background and terminology, cf. [T2].

In the preceding examples a recurrent pattern was that the group K always contains a copy $\mathbb{T}$ of the circle group. This group corresponds to the circular rotations (1.5.2) of Ω. In the irreducible case, this rotation group is the center of K and we have

$$K = \mathbb{T} \cdot K'$$

where K' is the *commutator subgroup* of K. It contains the identity component of L.

1.5.75. PROPOSITION. *If Ω is not of tube type, then K' is still transitive on the Shilov boundary S. If Ω is of tube type and $\Delta : Z \to \mathbb{C}$ is the Jordan algebra determinant of Z (for the unit element $e \in S$), then the orbit*

$$S' := K' \cdot e$$

is the "reduced" Shilov boundary

$$S' = \{z \in S : \Delta(z) = 1\}.$$

1.5.76. EXAMPLE. In the Examples 1.5.72, the reduced Shilov boundary has the following form:

(i) For $X = \mathcal{H}_r(\mathbb{C})$, we have $K' = SU_r(\mathbb{C}) \times SU_r(\mathbb{C})$ and hence

$$S' = SU_r(\mathbb{C}) \approx SU_r(\mathbb{C}) \times SU_r(\mathbb{C})/SU_r(\mathbb{C}).$$

(ii) For $X = \mathcal{H}_r(\mathbb{R})$, we have $K' = SU_r(\mathbb{C})$ and hence

$$S' \approx SU_r(\mathbb{C})/SU_r(\mathbb{R}).$$

(iii) For $X = \mathcal{H}_r(\mathbb{H})$ we have $K' = SU_{2r}(\mathbb{C})$ and hence

$$S' \approx SU_{2r}(\mathbb{C})/SU_r(\mathbb{H}).$$

(iv) For the real spin factor $X = \mathbb{R} \times i\mathbb{R}^{n-1}$ of dimension $n \geq 3$, we have $K' = SU_n(\mathbb{R})$ and hence

$$S' = \mathbb{S}^{n-1} \approx SU_n(\mathbb{R})/SU_{n-1}(\mathbb{R}).$$

Note that S' is not the sphere in X but in the "triple real form" $\mathbb{R}^n = \{x \in \mathbb{C}^n : \bar{x} = x\}$.

(v) For $X = \mathcal{H}_3(\mathbb{O})$ we have $K' = E_{6(-78)}$ (cf. (1.5.74)).

Note that in all cases the group K' and the space S' are (connected and) simply-connected. Moreover, S' becomes an irreducible compact Riemannian symmetric space of rank $r - 1$ (cf. [H2; pp. 346 and 354]).

The joint Peirce decomposition gives rise to a *polar decomposition* of a symmetric ball Ω.

1.5.77. PROPOSITION. *Let* $\Omega \subset Z$ *be an irreducible symmetric ball of rank* r. *Then* $\Omega^{\times} := \{z \in \Omega : \text{rank}(z) = r\}$ *is a dense subdomain of* Ω. *For any frame* $e_1, \ldots, e_r$ *of* Z *there exist continuous mappings*

$$\Omega \xrightarrow{|\cdot|} |\Omega| := \{y \in \mathbb{R}^r : 1 > y_1 \geq \cdots \geq y_r \geq 0\},$$
$$\Omega^{\times} \xrightarrow{\log|\cdot|} \Lambda := \log|\Omega^{\times}| := \{x \in \mathbb{R}^r : 0 > x_1 \geq \cdots \geq x_r\}$$

such that every point $z \in \Omega$ (resp., $z \in \Omega^{\times}$) *has the form*

$$z = s \cdot \sum_{j=1}^{r} y_j e_j \quad (\text{resp., } z = s \cdot \sum_{j=1}^{r} e^{x_j} e_j)$$

where $(y_1, \ldots, y_r) \in |\Omega|$ *and* $(x_1, \ldots, x_r) \in \Lambda$ *are uniquely determined, and* $s \in K$ *(not necessarily unique).*

Proof. By the spectral theorem for complex Jordan triples [FK2, L8, L9] every $z \in Z$ can be written as

$$z = y_1 c_1 + \cdots + y_r c_r \tag{1.5.78}$$

where $c_1, \ldots, c_r$ is a frame of Z and $y_1 \geq \cdots \geq y_r \geq 0$. The "singular numbers" y_j are uniquely determined by z and $z \mapsto |z| := (y_1, \ldots, y_r)$ defines a continuous open mapping from Z onto

$$\vec{\mathbb{R}}^r_+ := \{y \in \mathbb{R}^r : y_1 \geq \cdots \geq y_r \geq 0\}.$$

The spectral norm (1.5.1) of z is given by

$$\|z\| = \max_{1 \leq j \leq r} y_j. \tag{1.5.79}$$

Therefore

$$|\Omega| := \{|z| : z \in \Omega\} = \{y \in \mathbb{R}^r : 1 > y_1 \geq \cdots \geq y_r \geq 0\}.$$

The singular numbers are invariant under the action of K and we have

$$z \in \Omega \Leftrightarrow |z| \in |\Omega|.$$

Since Z is irreducible, the group K acts transitively on the set of all frames [L9]. This implies that, for every $z \in \Omega$, the frame $c_1, \ldots, c_r$ associated with z via (1.5.78) is related to the fixed frame $e_1, \ldots, e_r$ by $c_j = s \cdot e_j$ $(1 \leq j \leq r)$ where $s \in K$ (not necessarily unique). This shows

$$\Omega = K \cdot |\Omega| = \{s \cdot \sum_{j=1}^{r} y_j e_j : (y_1, \ldots, y_r) \in |\Omega|, s \in K\}. \tag{1.5.80}$$

Now consider the dense open subset Z^x consisting of all $z \in Z$ with singular numbers $y_1 \geq \cdots \geq y_r > 0$. Then

$$\log |z| := (\log(y_1), \ldots, \log(y_r))$$

defines a continuous open mapping $z \mapsto \log |z|$ from Z^x onto

$$\vec{\mathbb{R}}^r := \{x \in \mathbb{R}^r : x_1 \geq \cdots \geq x_r\}.$$

Putting $\Omega^x := \Omega \cap Z^x$, it follows that

$$\Lambda := \log|\Omega^x| = \{x \in \mathbb{R}^r : 0 > x_1 \geq \cdots \geq x_r\}$$

is a convex cone in $\vec{\mathbb{R}}^r$ and, by (1.5.80), we have

$$\Omega^x = K \cdot e^\Lambda = \{s \cdot \sum_{j=1}^{r} e^{x_j} e_j : (x_1, \ldots, x_r) \in \Lambda, s \in K\}.$$

Q.E.D.

1.5.81. DEFINITION. Let $\Omega \subset Z$ be an irreducible symmetric ball of rank r. Then

$$|\Omega| := \{|z| : z \in \Omega\} \subset \vec{\mathbb{R}}^r_+ \tag{1.5.82}$$

is called the *absolute domain* of Ω, and

$$\Lambda := \log|\Omega^x| := \{\log|z| : z \in \Omega^x\} \subset \vec{\mathbb{R}}^r \tag{1.5.83}$$

is called the *logarithmic base* of Ω^x.

1.5.84. PROPOSITION. *Let $\Omega \subset Z$ be an irreducible symmetric ball of rank* r, *and let* $e_1, \ldots, e_r$ *be a frame of* Z. *Let* $dV(z)$ *be the Lebesgue measure induced by the hermitian structure of* Z. *Then we have*

$$\int_\Omega f(z)\ dV(z) = \tag{1.5.85}$$

$$\text{const.} \int \cdots \int_{1>y_1>\ldots>y_r>0} \int_K f(s \cdot \sum_{j=1}^{r} y_j e_j)\ ds \prod_{1\leq i<j\leq r} (y_i^2 - y_j^2)^a \prod_{j=1}^{r} y_j^{2b+1}\ dy_1 \cdots dy_r$$

$$= \text{const.} \int \cdots \int_{0>x_1>\ldots>x_r} \int_K f(s \cdot \sum_{j=1}^{r} e^{x_j} e_j)\ ds \prod_{i<j} (e^{2x_i} - e^{2x_j})^a \prod_j (e^{2x_j})^{b+1}\ dx_1 \cdots dx_r$$

for every integrable function f *on* Ω. *Here* a *and* b *are the characteristic multiplicities of* Z.

Proof. Since $dV(z)$ is invariant under the group K we may assume that f is K-invariant, i.e., $f(sz) = f(z)$ for all $z \in \Omega$ and $s \in K$. It is enough to consider the integral on the dense subdomain $\Omega^{xx} := \{z \in \Omega^x : 1 > y_1 > \cdots > y_r > 0\}$. Here $y_1, \ldots, y_r$ are the singular numbers of z. The continuous mappings

(1.5.86) $$\Omega^x \xrightarrow{|\cdot|} |\Omega^x| \xrightarrow{\log} \log |\Omega^x| =: \Lambda,$$

$$s \cdot \sum_j z_j e_j \mapsto (|z_1|, \ldots, |z_r|) \mapsto (\log|z_1|, \ldots, \log|z_r|)$$

associated with $e_1, \ldots, e_r$ give rise to the image measures

$$d|V|(y) = \text{const.} \prod_{1 \le i < j \le r} (y_i^2 - y_j^2)^a \prod_{j=1}^r y_j^{2b+1} \, dy_1 \cdots dy_r ,$$

$$d(\log|V|)(x) = \text{const.} \prod_{1 \le i < j \le r} (e^{2x_i} - e^{2x_j})^a \prod_{j=1}^r (e^{2x_j})^{b+1} \, dx_1 \cdots dx_r$$

as follows from the root decomposition [BK2]. Since f has a factorization via the mappings (1.5.86), the assertion follows. Q.E.D.

Sometimes it is more convenient to express (1.5.85) as

$$\int_\Omega f(z) \; dV(z)$$

$$= \text{const.} \int_0^1 \cdots \int_0^1 \int_K f(s \cdot \sum_{j=1}^r y_j e_j) \, ds \prod_{i<j} |y_i^2 - y_j^2|^a \prod_j y_j^{2b+1} \, dy_1 \cdots dy_r.$$

For integrals over Z we obtain in a similar way

$$\int_Z f(z) \; dV(z)$$

$$= \text{const.} \int_0^\infty \cdots \int_0^\infty \int_K f(s \cdot \sum_{j=1}^r y_j e_j) \, ds \prod_{i<j} |y_i^2 - y_j^2|^a \prod_j y_j^{2b+1} \, dy_1 \cdots dy_r.$$

1.6. K-circular Domains

Any compact Lie group K gives rise to an important class of domains of holomorphy which can be thought of as "non-commutative" analogs of the Reinhardt domains treated in Section 1.4. On the other hand, these domains generalize also the symmetric domains treated in detail in Section 1.5 and thus form a common framework to study Toeplitz operators and Toeplitz C*-algebras for a wide class of complex domains.

Let K be a compact connected Lie group, endowed with an automorphism σ of period 2. Let $K_\sigma := \{s \in K : \sigma s = s\}$ be the fixed point subgroup of σ, and let K_σ^o be its identity component. Let L be a closed subgroup of K satisfying

$$(K^\sigma)^o \subset L \subset K^\sigma.$$

Then the quotient space

$$S := K/L \tag{1.6.1}$$

(consisting of all residue classes sL, $s \in K$) becomes a compact connected Riemannian symmetric space. (Conversely, every such space arises in this way.) Let $e := \{L\}$ denote the "base point" of S. By construction, S carries a K-action

$$K \times S \to S \tag{1.6.2}$$

defined by $(s,tL) \mapsto stL$ for all $s,t \in K$. This action is called the *translation action* of K on S. Using this action, we can write

$$L = \{s \in K : se = e\} \tag{1.6.3}$$

as the stabilizer subgroup of K at the base point e. Now consider the complex Lie groups $K^{\mathbb{C}}$ and $L^{\mathbb{C}}$ obtained via complexification of K and L, respectively [H5]. Then $L^{\mathbb{C}}$ is a closed subgroup of $K^{\mathbb{C}}$, and we can form the complex quotient manifold

$$S^{\mathbb{C}} := K^{\mathbb{C}}/L^{\mathbb{C}}.$$

In analogy to (1.6.3), we have a translation action of $K^{\mathbb{C}}$ on $S^{\mathbb{C}}$ and may consider the restricted action of K on $S^{\mathbb{C}}$.

1.6.4. DEFINITION. A domain $\Omega \subset S^{\mathbb{C}}$ (i.e., an open connected subset) is called K-*circular* if and only if Ω is invariant under the translation action of K, i.e.,

$$z \in \Omega, s \in K \to sz \in \Omega.$$

1.6.5. EXAMPLE. Let $K = \mathbb{T}^r$ be the r-torus (i.e., a compact connected *abelian* Lie group) endowed with the involutive automorphism

$$\theta(s) := s^{-1} \qquad (s \in \mathbb{T}^r).$$

Then we can take L to be trivial and $S = K = \mathbb{T}^r$ is a compact symmetric space, with base point $e = (1, ..., 1)$ and complexification

$$S^{\mathbb{C}} = (\mathbb{C}^{\times})^r = \{z \in \mathbb{C}^r : z_1 \cdots z_r \neq 0\}.$$

The translation action of $\mathbb{T}^r$ on $S^{\mathbb{C}}$ is the restriction of the standard action

$$((s_1, \ldots, s_r), (z_1, \ldots, z_r)) \mapsto (s_1 z_1, \ldots, s_r z_r)$$

of $\mathbb{T}^r$ on $\mathbb{C}^r$. By definition, a domain $\Omega \subset (\mathbb{C}^{\times})^r = S^{\mathbb{C}}$ is $\mathbb{T}^r$-circular if and only if it is polycircular (or a Reinhardt domain) in the sense of Definition 1.4.6.

1.6.6. EXAMPLE. Let Ω be a bounded symmetric domain *of tube type*. By (1.5.1), we may realize Ω as the open unit ball

$$\Omega = \{z \in Z : \|z\| < 1\}$$

of a complex Jordan *-algebra Z. Let

$$S = \partial_{ex}\Omega$$

be the Shilov boundary (= extreme boundary) of Ω. Let $G = \mathrm{Aut}(\Omega)^\circ$ be the identity component of the biholomorphic automorphism group of Ω and put

$$K := \{g \in G : g \cdot 0 = 0\}.$$

Since Ω is simply connected, the compact Lie group K is connected. Define an involutive automorphism $g \mapsto g^\sigma$ of K by putting

$$g^\sigma(y) := (gy^*)^*$$

for all $y \in Z$, using the involution (1.3.2) of Z. Then $L = \{g \in K : g^\sigma = g\}$ and $S = K/L$ becomes a compact symmetric space. Its base point e is the unit element of the Jordan algebra Z, and the complexification $S^{\mathbb{C}}$ can be identified with the open dense subset

(1.6.7) $$S^{\mathbb{C}} = \{z \in Z : \mathrm{rank}(z) = r\}$$

of all invertible elements $z \in Z$. Putting

(1.6.8) $$\Omega^\times := \Omega \cap S^{\mathbb{C}},$$

we obtain a K-circular domain in $S^{\mathbb{C}}$.

Every K-circular domain has a "polar decomposition" given in Lie theoretic terms. Let $\mathfrak{k}$ be the Lie algebra of K and consider the *Cartan decomposition*

(1.6.9) $$\mathfrak{k} = \mathfrak{l} \oplus \mathfrak{s}$$

induced by the differential σ_* of σ. Then

$$\mathfrak{l} = \{\gamma \in \mathfrak{k} : \sigma_*\gamma = \gamma\}$$

is the Lie algebra of L and

$$\mathfrak{s} = \{\gamma \in \mathfrak{k} : \sigma_*\gamma = -\gamma\}$$

can be identified with the tangent space

$$\mathfrak{s} \cong T_e(S)$$

of $S = K/L$ at the base point e. Consider the complexifications

$$\mathfrak{k}^{\mathbb{C}} = \mathfrak{l}^{\mathbb{C}} \oplus \mathfrak{s}^{\mathbb{C}}.$$

Let $\mathfrak{a} \subset i\mathfrak{s}$ be a maximal abelian subspace and let $i\mathfrak{h} \subset \mathfrak{k}$ be a maximal abelian subalgebra containing $i\mathfrak{a}$. Let $\mathfrak{h}^{\mathbb{C}}$ be the complexification of $\mathfrak{h} \subset i\mathfrak{k}$. A non-zero linear form

$$\alpha : \mathfrak{h}^{\mathbb{C}} \to \mathbb{C} \tag{1.6.10}$$

is called a *root* if the corresponding root space

$$\mathfrak{k}^{\mathbb{C}}_{\alpha} := \{B \in \mathfrak{k}^{\mathbb{C}} : [A,B] = \alpha(A)B \quad \forall A \in \mathfrak{h}^{\mathbb{C}}\} \tag{1.6.11}$$

is non-zero. We have

$$\mathfrak{k}^{\mathbb{C}} = \mathfrak{h}^{\mathbb{C}} \oplus \sum_{\alpha}^{\oplus} \mathfrak{k}^{\mathbb{C}}_{\alpha}, \tag{1.6.12}$$

where α ranges over all roots. By [H2; p.496], the roots α are real-valued on $\mathfrak{h}$ and thus can be identified with an element $\alpha \in \mathfrak{h}^{\#}$, the linear dual space of $\mathfrak{h}$. A connected component of the open dense subset

$$\mathfrak{h}^{\times} := \{H \in \mathfrak{h} : \alpha(H) \neq 0 \text{ for all roots } \alpha\}$$

is called a *Weyl chamber* of $\mathfrak{k}$. Similarly, we can consider *restricted roots*

$$\alpha : \mathfrak{a} \to \mathbb{R} \tag{1.6.13}$$

of the pair $(\mathfrak{k},\mathfrak{l})$, and define the restricted Weyl chamber as a connected component of the set

$$\mathfrak{a}^{\times} := \{A \in \mathfrak{a} : \alpha(A) \neq 0 \text{ for all restricted roots } \alpha\}.$$

We denote by $\mathfrak{a}^{\#}$ the real linear dual space of $\mathfrak{a}$.

1.6.14. PROPOSITION. *Let Ω be a K-circular domain in $S^{\mathbb{C}}$, for a compact symmetric space $S = K/L$. Then, for any choice of Weyl chamber $\mathfrak{a}^{<}$, there exist continuous open mappings*

$$\Omega \xrightarrow{|\cdot|} |\Omega| \subset \exp(\mathfrak{a})$$

and

(1.6.15) $$\Omega \xrightarrow{\log|\cdot|} \Lambda := \log|\Omega| \subset \bar{\mathfrak{a}}^{<}$$

such that every point $z \in \Omega$ *has the form*

(1.6.16) $$z = s \cdot \exp(A) \cdot e$$

where $A \in \Lambda$ *is uniquely determined and* $s \in K$.

Proof. The pseudo-Riemannian symmetric space $S^{\mathbb{C}}$ has a Cartan decomposition [L4; p. 315, (iv)]

$$S^{\mathbb{C}} = K \cdot \exp(\bar{\mathfrak{a}}^{<}) \cdot e,$$

i.e., every point $z \in S^{\mathbb{C}}$ can be written as

$$z = s \cdot \exp(A) \cdot e \qquad (s \in K)$$

where $A =: \log|z| \in \bar{\mathfrak{a}}^{<}$ is uniquely determined by z, and $z \mapsto \log|z|$ is a continuous open mapping from $S^{\mathbb{C}}$ into $\bar{\mathfrak{a}}^{<}$. Put

$$|z| := \exp(\log|z|) \in \exp(\mathfrak{a}).$$

The element $s \in K$ is not necessarily unique: we have $s \cdot \exp(A) \cdot e = t \cdot \exp(A) \cdot e$ for $s,t \in K$ if and only if $\ell := s^{-1}t \in L$ satisfies $A = \mathrm{Ad}(\ell)A$. Now define

$$\Lambda := \{\log|z| : z \in \Omega\} \subset \bar{\mathfrak{a}}^{<}$$

and put $|\Omega| := \exp(\Lambda) \subset \exp(\mathfrak{a})$. Q.E.D.

1.6.17. DEFINITION. Let $\Omega \subset S^{\mathbb{C}}$ be a K-circular domain. Then

(1.6.18) $$|\Omega| := \{|z| : z \in \Omega\} \subset \exp(\mathfrak{a})$$

is called the *absolute domain* of Ω, and

(1.6.19) $$\Lambda := \log|\Omega| := \{\log|z| : z \in \Omega\} \subset \bar{\mathfrak{a}}^{<}$$

is called the *logarithmic base* of Ω. Ω is called *log-convex* (resp., *log-conical*) if its logarithmic base Λ is a convex open set (resp. a convex open cone).

Generalizing Theorem 1.4.17, one can show [L4; Théorème C] that a K-circular domain Ω is pseudoconvex, i.e., a domain of holomorphy, if and only if Ω is log-convex.

1.6.20. EXAMPLE. The polar decomposition of a polycircular domain $\Omega \subset (\mathbb{C}^{\times})^r$, for the group $K = \mathbb{T}^r$, is given by

$$\Omega = \{(e^{x_1}s_1, \ldots, e^{x_r}s_r) : (x_1, \ldots, x_r) \in \Lambda, s_1, \ldots, s_r \in \mathbb{T}\},$$

where

$$\Lambda = \{(\log |z_1|, \ldots, \log |z_r|) : (z_1, \ldots, z_r) \in \Omega\}$$

is the logarithmic base. Here we identify $\mathfrak{k} = \mathfrak{s} \cong i\mathbb{R}^r$ and $\mathfrak{a} = i\mathfrak{s} \cong \mathbb{R}^r$. Moreover, the Weyl chamber is

$$\mathfrak{a}^< = \mathbb{R}^r_<.$$

1.6.21. EXAMPLE. The polar decomposition of a symmetric ball Ω of tube type is given as follows: Let $Z = X^{\mathbb{C}}$ be the Jordan *-algebra associated with Ω and let $e \in Z$ be the unit element. Then the Lie algebra $\mathfrak{k}$ of K, consisting of all Jordan triple derivations of Z, has a Cartan decomposition $\mathfrak{k} = \mathfrak{l} \oplus \mathfrak{s}$, where

$$\mathfrak{l} = \{A \in \mathfrak{k} : A \cdot e = 0\} \cong \mathrm{aut}(X)$$

is the Lie algebra of all Jordan algebra derivations of X, and

$$i\mathfrak{s} = \{M_a : a \in X\}$$

is given by the multiplication operators $z \mapsto z \circ a$. Now fix a frame $\{e_1, \ldots, e_r\}$ of X, with $e = e_1 + \cdots + e_r$. Then the multiplication operators

$$M_{e_j} z := z \circ e_j \qquad (1 \le j \le r) \tag{1.6.22}$$

span a maximal abelian subalgebra $\mathfrak{a}$ of $i\mathfrak{s}$. Let

$$M^{\#}_{e_i}(M_{e_j}) := \delta_{ij} \tag{1.6.23}$$

be the dual basis of linear functionals in $\mathfrak{a}^{\#}$. By [U5; Lemma 1.3], the $M^{\#}_{e_i}$ are positive non-compact roots of $\Omega = G/K$ which are strongly orthogonal in the sense of Harish-Chandra. We may assume that $0 < M^{\#}_{e_1} < \cdots < M^{\#}_{e_r}$. Then for $0 \leq i < j \leq r$, the linear forms

(1.6.24) $$\frac{1}{2}(M^{\#}_{e_i} - M^{\#}_{e_j})$$

are precisely the (restricted) positive compact roots. Here we put $M^{\#}_{e_0} := 0$. It follows that

(1.6.25) $$\mathfrak{a}^{<} = \{\sum_{j=1}^{r} x_j M_{e_j} : 0 > x_1 > \cdots > x_r\}$$

is a Weyl chamber in $\mathfrak{a}$, which gives the logarithmic base of Ω (more precisely, of its open dense subset $\Omega^{\times} := \{z \in \Omega : \text{rank}(z) = r\}$) as follows: Since

(1.6.26) $$\exp(\sum_j x_j M_{e_j}) \cdot e = \sum_j e^{x_j} e_j,$$

we obtain

(1.6.27) $$\Omega^{\times} = K \cdot \exp(\Lambda) \cdot e = \{s \cdot \sum_j e^{x_j} e_j : 0 > x_1 \geq \cdots \geq x_r, s \in K\}.$$

1.7 S-bicircular Domains

The class of K-circular domains introduced in Section 1.6 contains an important subclass which is of primary interest in studying the representation theory of compact Lie groups. This class of domains has the property that the "Shilov boundary" S (assumed to be a compact symmetric space in general) is even a compact Lie group. Thus S carries two translation actions (left and right translations) and, accordingly, we consider "bicircular" domains for these actions of S. Let S be a compact connected Lie group. Then the direct product group

(1.7.1) $$K := S \times S$$

is a compact connected Lie group, endowed with the "flip" automorphism

$$\theta(u,v) := (v,u) \qquad (u,v \in S).$$

Let $e \in S$ be the identity element, and consider the translation action $K \times S \to S$ given by

$$((u,v),s) \mapsto usv^{-1} \tag{1.7.2}$$

for all $s,u,v \in S$. Then the fixed point subgroup

$$L := \{(u,u): u \in S\} \tag{1.7.3}$$

of θ coincides with the stabilizer subgroup of K at e. Thus

$$S \cong K/L \tag{1.7.4}$$

becomes a compact symmetric space by identifying the residue class $(u,v) \cdot L$ with uv^{-1}. The symmetry of S at the base point e is

$$s_e(u) = u^{-1} \qquad (u \in S).$$

Now consider the complexification $S^{\mathbb{C}}$ of S, which is a complex connected Lie group. It follows that $S^{\mathbb{C}}$ carries a translation action of K given by (1.7.2). Equivalently, one may think of (1.7.2) as describing a "bi-action" (from the left and the right) of S on $S^{\mathbb{C}}$.

1.7.5. DEFINITION. A domain $\Omega \subset S^{\mathbb{C}}$ is called S-*bicircular* if and only if Ω is invariant under the action (1.7.2) of $S \times S$, i.e.,

$$z \in \Omega,\ s,t \in S \Rightarrow szt^{-1} \in \Omega.$$

1.7.6. EXAMPLE. In the special case where S is abelian, i.e., $S \cong \mathbb{T}^r$ for some r, a domain Ω in $S^{\mathbb{C}} \cong (\mathbb{C}^{\times})^r$ is S-bicircular if and only if Ω is a Reinhardt domain.

1.7.7. EXAMPLE. A bounded symmetric domain Ω of tube type, with Shilov boundary S, is S-bicircular if and only if Ω is the open unit ball of the Jordan algebra $Z = \mathbb{C}^{r \times r}$ of all complex $(r\times r)$-matrices. In this case we have

$$S = U_r(\mathbb{C}),$$

and $K \cong S \times S$ via the action $((u,v),z) \mapsto uzv^{-1}$. L is the diagonal subgroup. The case $r = 1$ gives the unit disk.

For any compact connected Lie group S, there exists a polar decomposition of S-bicircular domains which we will now describe. Let $\mathfrak{s}$ be the Lie algebra of S, identified with the tangent space

$$\mathfrak{s} \cong T_e(S)$$

at the unit element $e \in S$. Consider the complexification $\mathfrak{s}^{\mathbb{C}}$ and let $i\mathfrak{a} \subset \mathfrak{s}$ be a maximal torus. Then $\mathfrak{a} \subset i\mathfrak{s}$ is a maximal abelian subspace, with vector space dual

$$a^{\#} = \{\mathfrak{a} \xrightarrow{\lambda} \mathbb{R} : \lambda \text{ linear}\}.$$

Consider the roots of the pair $(\mathfrak{a}^{\mathbb{C}}, \mathfrak{s}^{\mathbb{C}})$ and choose a Weyl chamber $\mathfrak{a}^{<}$, i.e., a connected component of

$$\mathfrak{a}^{\times} := \{H \in \mathfrak{a} : \alpha(H) \neq 0 \ \forall \text{ roots } \alpha\}.$$

1.7.8. PROPOSITION. *Let Ω be an S-bicircular domain in $S^{\mathbb{C}}$, for a compact Lie group S. Then there exist continuous open mappings*

$$\Omega \xrightarrow{|\cdot|} |\Omega| \subset \exp(\mathfrak{a})$$

and

$$\Omega \xrightarrow{\log|\cdot|} \Lambda := \log|\Omega| \subset \bar{\mathfrak{a}}^{<}$$

such that every point $z \in \Omega$ has the form

$$z = s_1 \exp(A)\, s_2$$

where $A \in \Lambda$ is uniquely determined and $s_1, s_2 \in S$.

Proof. By (1.7.2), the Lie algebra $\mathfrak{k} = \mathfrak{s} \oplus \mathfrak{s}$ of K gives rise to the vector fields

$$(A,B) \cdot s = As - sB \qquad (A,B \in \mathfrak{s})$$

on S. In particular, we have

$$(A,B) \cdot e = A - B \in T_e(S).$$

It follows that $\mathfrak{k}$ has the Cartan decomposition $\mathfrak{k} = \mathfrak{l} \oplus i\mathfrak{m}$, where

$$\mathfrak{l} = \{\frac{1}{2}(A,A) : A \in \mathfrak{s}\},$$
$$i\mathfrak{m} = \{\frac{1}{2}(A, -A) : A \in \mathfrak{s}\}.$$

Thus $\mathfrak{l}$ consists of vector fields vanishing at e, whereas the vector fields in $i\mathfrak{m}$ are uniquely determined by their value $\frac{1}{2}(A, -A)e = A$ at e. A maximal torus $i\mathfrak{a} \subset \mathfrak{s}$ gives rise to a maximal abelian subspace

$$\mathfrak{a} \approx \{\frac{1}{2}(A, -A) : A \in \mathfrak{a}\}$$

of $\mathfrak{m}$. Since

$$\exp(\frac{A}{2}, -\frac{A}{2}) \cdot e = \exp(\frac{A}{2})\, e \exp(-\frac{A}{2})^{-1} = \exp(A),$$

the assertion follows from Proposition 1.6.14. Q.E.D.

1.7.9. DEFINITION. Let $\Omega \subset S^{\mathbb{C}}$ be an S-bicircular domain. Then

(1.7.10) $$|\Omega| := \{|z| : z \in \Omega\} \subset \exp(\mathfrak{a})$$

is called the *absolute domain* of Ω, and

(1.7.11) $$\Lambda := \log|\Omega| := \{\log|z| : z \in \Omega\} \subset \mathfrak{a}$$

is called the *logarithmic base* of Ω.

REMARK. Throughout Chapter 1, the notational conventions for the polar decomposition were chosen such that the cone Λ is "negative", so that the polar cone $\Lambda^\#$ becomes "positive". This explains why we introduced tube domains and Siegel domains (Section 1.3) as generalized *left* half-planes instead of the more familiar right or upper half-planes.

2. Harmonic Analysis on Hilbert Spaces of Holomorphic Functions

2.0 Introduction

For the holomorphic functions of one complex variable, say, on the unit disk, the expansion into a series of monomials (power series) is the crucial analytic tool for the study of Hardy or Bergman type spaces. In the multi-variable setting the fine structure of spaces of holomorphic functions is much more complicated, reflecting the geometry of the underlying domain in $\mathbb{C}^n$. Noting that the classical power series expansion is essentially Fourier analysis on the 1-torus, it is natural to use other Lie group actions in n variables to obtain generalized expansions of holomorphic functions. In general, these Lie groups will be non-abelian so that the standard concepts of Fourier analysis have to be extended to the well-known Peter-Weyl theory. Since we are interested in holomorphic functions, the Fourier analysis has to be combined with a Paley-Wiener type characterization of such functions, and it is here that the geometry of the underlying domains (polar decomposition) plays a crucial role.

The strictly pseudoconvex domains treated in Sections 2.1 (Bergman space) and 2.2 (Hardy space) have no significant group action in general, so instead one uses methods from partial differential equations ($\bar{\partial}$-Neumann problem). We define the Kohn-Laplacian in both settings, and describe the basic results, notably the compactness of the $\bar{\partial}$-Neumann operator, which will be used in the sequel. It should be noted that all other types of domains considered in this book (cf. Chapter 1) don't have a smooth boundary in general so that methods from differential analysis don't apply directly. In fact, it is one of the basic unsolved problems in this area to extend partial differential equation methods to "stratified" non-smooth manifolds.

The tubular domains considered in Section 2.3 (Hardy space) and Section 2.4 (weighted Bergman spaces) are analyzed via the translation action of an abelian (euclidean) group. Using the (non-compact version of) Fourier analysis, we characterize the Hilbert spaces of holomorphic functions via the *polar cone* of the cone defining the tube domain (Paley-Wiener theorem) and express the reproducing kernel functions (in the symmetric case) via the Jordan algebraic determinant function. This yields an explicit description of the orthogonal Szegö (resp., Bergman) projection used in the definition of Toeplitz operators. We also extend the theory to the case of Siegel domains where the translation group is replaced by a nilpotent group of "quasi-translations". As an important special function, the Γ-function associated with a symmetric cone is introduced in Section 2.4. This function can be expressed as a product of ordinary Γ-functions and allows us to compute certain Hilbert norms explicitly.

The polycircular domains studied in Section 2.5 (Hardy space) and 2.6 (Bergman space) are related to (compact, abelian) Fourier analysis on the r-torus but we consider quite arbitrary (non-symmetric) domains which make it impossible to give a closed expression for the reproducing kernel functions. Nevertheless, using a discrete version of polar cone one still has a satisfying Paley-Wiener theory and can expand the Szegö and Bergman kernels into a series of monomial functions.

The theory of holomorphic functions on bounded symmetric domains (which in general are not polycircular and don't have a smooth boundary) relies heavily on a non-commutative extension of Fourier analysis, given by the Peter-Weyl theory of compact Lie groups. While general compact Lie groups are considered later, the groups arising in connection with symmetric domains have a concrete realization as linear isometries of a (Jordan triple) norm on $\mathbb{C}^n$. As a preliminary step we analyze in Section 2.7 the "Segal-Bargmann" (or Fock) space of entire functions on $\mathbb{C}^n$. The basic result is a multiplicity-free decomposition into irreducible subspaces under the action of an isometry group. The basic combinatorial concept used here are integer *partitions* familiar from the representation theory of the matrix groups. For domains "of tube type" we introduce a generalized wave equation and decompose the algebra of polynomials into invariant and harmonic parts. Even for domains of "rank" 2, this gives interesting special functions.

In Sections 2.8 and 2.9, the essentially algebraic theory of polynomial decompositions of the Segal-Bargmann space is then applied to give a detailed account of the Hardy (resp., weighted Bergman) space over any (irreducible) symmetric domain of arbitrary rank. The theory of Jordan algebras and Jordan triples enables us to present the basic results (explicit description of kernel functions, conical and spherical polynomials, and norm computations) in a uniform way independent of the classification of these domains (4 "classical" series and 2 "exceptional" types). As for tubular domains, the basic numerical function is the multi-variable Γ-function. Using the general results, we carry out in detail the decomposition for domains of rank 2 ("Lie balls"), leading to special functions of ultraspherical (or Gegenbauer) type. At the end of Section 2.9 we mention briefly the analytic continuation of the weighted Bergman spaces (constituting the scalar holomorphic discrete series) which yields the Hardy space and other function spaces supported on (part of) the boundary of the domain. While there certainly is a theory of Toeplitz operators on all these spaces it has not been carried out in detail.

The non-commutative Fourier analysis so successful in the symmetric case is used in the remaining Sections 2.10 (K-circular domains) and 2.11 (S-bicircular domains) to outline a more general harmonic analysis, applying to all domains (and even more general manifolds) with a "polar decomposition" under a compact Lie group. The radial part of the domain gives rise to a polar cone which plays the crucial role for the Paley-Wiener theory. As an interesting example which is neither symmetric nor polycircular, we analyze the "non-commutative Hartogs' wedge".

2.1 Bergman Spaces Over Pseudoconvex Domains

Let Ω be a bounded domain in $\mathbb{C}^n$. Let $dV(z)$ be the Lebesgue measure on $\mathbb{C}^n = \mathbb{R}^{2n}$. Consider the corresponding *Lebesgue space* $L^2(\Omega) = L^2(\Omega,dV)$ of square-integrable complex functions on Ω, with inner product

(2.1.1) $$(h|k)_\Omega := \int_\Omega \overline{h(z)}\ k(z)\ dV(z).$$

Throughout the book, we use the convention that inner products on "function spaces" are conjugate-linear in the first variable. Consider the algebra $\mathcal{O}(\Omega)$ of holomorphic functions on Ω and the intersection $L^2(\Omega) \cap \mathcal{O}(\Omega)$, regarded as a subspace of $L^2(\Omega)$.

2.1.2. PROPOSITION. *For any compact subset* $K \subset \Omega$, *the restriction mapping*

$$L^2(\Omega) \cap \mathcal{O}(\Omega) \ni f \mapsto f|_K \in \mathcal{C}(K)$$

is continuous.

Proof. Fix any norm $|\cdot|$ on $\mathbb{C}^n$ and put $2\varepsilon := \text{dist}(K,\partial\Omega) > 0$. Then for any point $o \in K$, we have

$$B_\varepsilon(o) := \{z \in \mathbb{C}^n : |z - o| \le \varepsilon\} \subset \Omega.$$

If $f : \Omega \to \mathbb{C}$ is holomorphic, we have a power series expansion

$$f(z) = \sum_{j\geq 0} f_j(z - o)$$

with f_j a j-homogeneous polynomial, converging uniformly on $B_\varepsilon(o)$. Since homogeneous polynomials of different degree are mutually orthogonal in $L^2(B_\varepsilon(o))$ we obtain

$$\int_\Omega |f(z)|^2 \, dV(z) \geq \int_{B_\varepsilon(o)} |f(z)|^2 \, dV(z) = \sum_{j\geq 0} \int_{B_\varepsilon(o)} |f_j(z)|^2 \, dV(z)$$

$$\geq |f_0|^2 \cdot \text{Vol } B_\varepsilon(o) = |f(o)|^2 \cdot \text{Vol } B_\varepsilon(o).$$

Since $o \in K$ is arbitrary, $||f||_2 \geq \sup_K |f| \cdot (\text{Vol } B_\varepsilon(o))^{1/2}$. Q.E.D.

2.1.3. PROPOSITION. *$L^2(\Omega) \cap \mathcal{O}(\Omega)$ is a closed subspace of $L^2(\Omega)$.*

Proof. Let (f_n) be a Cauchy sequence in $L^2(\Omega) \cap \mathcal{O}(\Omega)$. By Proposition 2.1.2, (f_n) is also a Cauchy sequence in the space $\mathcal{O}(\Omega)$ with respect to compact convergence. Since $\mathcal{O}(\Omega)$ is complete by Weierstrass' Theorem, there exists $f \in \mathcal{O}(\Omega)$ such that $f_n \to f$ uniformly on every compact subset K of Ω. Since $L^2(\Omega)$ is complete, we have also

$$||f_n - g||_2 \to 0$$

for some $g \in L^2(\Omega)$. A subsequence of (f_n) converges almost everywhere towards g. Hence $f = g$ a.e., i.e., $f \in L^2(\Omega) \cap \mathcal{O}(\Omega)$. It follows that $L^2(\Omega) \cap \mathcal{O}(\Omega)$ is a Hilbert space and thus a closed subspace of $L^2(\Omega)$. Q.E.D.

Let $\bar{\Omega}$ denote the closure of Ω, and consider the algebra

$$\mathcal{A}(\Omega) := \{f \in \mathcal{C}(\bar{\Omega}) : f|_\Omega \text{ holomorphic}\} \tag{2.1.4}$$

of all holomorphic functions on Ω which are continuous up to the boundary.

2.1.5. DEFINITION. The L^2-closure

$$H^2(\Omega) := \mathcal{A}(\Omega)^- \subset L^2(\Omega)$$

is called the *Bergman space* over Ω.

By Proposition 2.1.3, $H^2(\Omega)$ is a Hilbert space of holomorphic functions on Ω. The orthogonal projection

$$E_\Omega : L^2(\Omega) \to H^2(\Omega) \tag{2.1.6}$$

is called the *Bergman projection.* By Proposition 2.1.2, the evaluation functional

$$H^2(\Omega) \ni f \mapsto f(w) \in \mathbb{C}$$

at $w \in \Omega$ is continuous. By the Riesz-Fischer Theorem, there exists a vector $E_w \in H^2(\Omega)$ such that

$$f(w) = (E_w|f)_\Omega = \int_\Omega \overline{E_w(z)}\ f(z)\ dV(z)$$

for every $f \in H^2(\Omega)$. The "sesqui-holomorphic" function

$$E_\Omega(z,w) := E_w(z) = \overline{E_z(w)} \tag{2.1.7}$$

is called the *Bergman kernel function* of the domain Ω. With respect to the family of vectors E_w, $w \in \Omega$, the Bergman projection (2.1.6) can be written as an operator integral

$$E_\Omega = \int_\Omega E_w E_w^*\ dV(w).$$

Here, for any vectors $h,k \in H^2(\Omega)$, hk^* denotes the rank ≤ 1 operator defined by

$$(hk^*)f := h \cdot (k|f)_\Omega \tag{2.1.8}$$

for all $f \in H^2(\Omega)$. Note that this operator is $\mathbb{C}$-linear in f.

For strictly pseudo-convex domains Ω, the Bergman projection has a certain regularity that is of fundamental importance in the study of Bergman-Toeplitz operators. This regularity property is related to the so-called $\bar{\partial}$-Neumann problem in partial differential equations [FK3]. For each integer $0 \le q \le n$, consider the space $\mathcal{C}_q^\infty(\bar{\Omega})$ of exterior (0,q)-forms

$$\varphi = \sum_{|I|=q} \varphi_I \; d\bar{z}^I$$

on Ω, with coefficients φ_I which are smooth in a neighborhood of the closure $\bar{\Omega}$ (depending on φ). Here I runs over all q-element sets $1 \le i_1 < \cdots < i_q \le n$ and we put

$$d\bar{z}^I := d\bar{z}_{i_1} \wedge \cdots \wedge d\bar{z}_{i_q}.$$

$\mathcal{C}_q^\infty(\bar{\Omega})$ has an inner product

$$(\varphi|\psi)_\Omega := \sum_{|I|=q} (\varphi_I|\psi_I)_\Omega \tag{2.1.9}$$

for all $\varphi = \sum \varphi_I d\bar{z}^I$, $\psi = \sum \psi_I \, d\bar{z}^I$. Here the inner product on the right-hand side is given by (2.1.1).

2.1.10. DEFINTION. For $0 \le q \le n$, let $L_q^2(\Omega)$ denote the Hilbert space completion of $\mathcal{C}_q^\infty(\bar{\Omega})$, with respect to the inner product (2.1.9). Note that, by the Stone-Weierstrass Theorem, $L_0^2(\Omega) = L^2(\Omega)$ is the usual Lebesgue space of functions. Define the $\bar{\partial}$-operator

$$\bar{\partial}_q : \mathcal{C}_q^\infty(\bar{\Omega}) \to \mathcal{C}_{q+1}^\infty(\bar{\Omega})$$

by

$$\bar{\partial}_q \varphi = \sum_{|I|=q} \bar{\partial}(\varphi_I d\bar{z}^I) := \sum_{|I|=q} \sum_{j=1}^n \frac{\partial \varphi_I}{\partial \bar{z}_j} d\bar{z}_j \wedge d\bar{z}^I. \tag{2.1.11}$$

One can show that for each $q \geq 0$, the operator $\bar{\partial}_q$ is closeable. Let

(2.1.12) $$L^2_q(\Omega) \supset \mathrm{Dom}(\bar{\partial}_q) \xrightarrow{\bar{\partial}_q} L^2_{q+1}(\Omega)$$

be the closure, and define its Hilbert space adjoint

(2.1.13) $$L^2_{q+1}(\Omega) \supset \mathrm{Dom}(\bar{\partial}^*_q) \xrightarrow{\bar{\partial}^*_q} L^2_q(\Omega).$$

As a matter of notation, put $\bar{\partial}_n = \bar{\partial}_{-1} = 0$ and $\bar{\partial}^*_{n+1} = \bar{\partial}^*_0 = 0$.
We can combine the operators (2.1.12) and (2.1.13) to obtain the *Kohn-Laplacian* on Ω

(2.1.14) $$\Box^\Omega_q := \bar{\partial}_{q-1}\bar{\partial}^*_q + \bar{\partial}^*_{q+1}\,\bar{\partial}_q \;:\; \mathrm{Dom}(\Box^\Omega_q) \to L^2_q(\Omega),$$

defined on the subspace

$$\mathrm{Dom}(\Box^\Omega_q) := \{\varphi \in \mathrm{Dom}(\bar{\partial}_q) \cap \mathrm{Dom}(\bar{\partial}^*_q) : \bar{\partial}_q\varphi \in \mathrm{Dom}(\bar{\partial}^*_{q+1}),\ \bar{\partial}^*_q\varphi \in \mathrm{Dom}(\bar{\partial}_{q-1})\}$$

of $L^2_q(\Omega)$. For $q = 0$, (2.1.14) becomes

$$\Box^\Omega_0 := \bar{\partial}^*_1\bar{\partial}_0 \;:\; \mathrm{Dom}(\Box^\Omega_0) \to L^2(\Omega)$$

with

$$\mathrm{Dom}(\Box^\Omega_0) := \{\varphi \in \mathrm{Dom}(\bar{\partial}_0) : \bar{\partial}_0\varphi \in \mathrm{Dom}(\bar{\partial}^*_1)\}.$$

Similarly, for $q = n$ we obtain

$$\Box^\Omega_n := \bar{\partial}_{n-1}\bar{\partial}^*_n : \mathrm{Dom}(\Box^\Omega_n) \to L^2_n(\Omega)$$

with

$$\mathrm{Dom}(\Box^\Omega_n) := \{\varphi \in \mathrm{Dom}(\bar{\partial}^*_n) : \bar{\partial}^*_n\varphi \in \mathrm{Dom}(\bar{\partial}_{n-1})\}.$$

2.1.15. PROPOSITION. *For each* $q \geq 0$, *the null-space*

$$H_q^2(\Omega) := \{\varphi \in \mathrm{Dom}(\square_q^\Omega) : \square_q^\Omega = 0\}$$

$$= \{\varphi \in \mathrm{Dom}(\bar\partial_q) \cap \mathrm{Dom}(\bar\partial_q^*) : \bar\partial_q\varphi = 0 = \bar\partial_q^*\varphi\}$$

is a closed subspace of $L_q^2(\Omega)$.

The elements of $H_q^2(\Omega)$ are called *harmonic* (0,q)-forms on Ω. Let

(2.1.16) $$E_q^\Omega : L_q^2(\Omega) \to H_q^2(\Omega)$$

denote the orthogonal projection. For $q = 0$, we obtain

$$H_0^2(\Omega) = \{\varphi \in \mathrm{Dom}(\bar\partial_0) : \bar\partial_0\varphi = 0\}$$

$$= \{\varphi \in L^2(\Omega) : \varphi \text{ holomorphic}\} = H^2(\Omega)$$

by the Cauchy-Riemann equations. Thus E_0^Ω is the standard Bergman projection. It is shown in [FK3] that $\square_q^\Omega$ has closed range and is bounded away from 0 on $\mathrm{Dom}(\square_q^\Omega) \cap \mathrm{Ker}\, E_q^\Omega$. Thus one can define a bounded operator

(2.1.17) $$N_q^\Omega : L_q^2(\Omega) \to L_q^2(\Omega)$$

to be the inverse of $\square_q^\Omega$ on the range of $\square_q^\Omega$ and zero on its complement. N_q^Ω is called the $\bar\partial$-*Neumann operator*. We have

(2.1.18) $$N_q^\Omega E_q^\Omega = 0 = E_q^\Omega N_q^\Omega,$$

(2.1.19) $$\mathrm{Ran}(N_q^\Omega) \subset \mathrm{Dom}(\square_q^\Omega)$$

and

(2.1.20) $$(I - E_q^\Omega)\varphi = \square_q^\Omega N_q^\Omega \varphi$$

for every $\varphi \in L_q^2(\Omega)$. The most important property of N_q^Ω is [FK3] :

2.1.21. THEOREM. *For* $q \geq 1$, N_q^Ω *is a compact operator.*

2.1.22. LEMMA. *For* $f \in \mathrm{Dom}(\bar\partial_0) \subset L_0^2(\Omega) = L^2(\Omega)$, *the orthogonal projection* $E_0^\Omega f$ *satisfies*

$$(I - E_0^\Omega)f = \bar\partial_1^* N_1^\Omega \bar\partial_0 f. \tag{2.1.23}$$

Proof. By (2.1.19), $N_1^\Omega \bar\partial_0 f \in \mathrm{Dom}(\bar\partial_1^*)$, so that the right-hand side of (2.1.23) is well defined. Specializing (2.1.20) to $q = 0$ we have

$$(I - E_0^\Omega)f = \square_0^\Omega N_0^\Omega f = \bar\partial_1^* \bar\partial_0 N_0^\Omega f.$$

Now $N_\cdot^\Omega$ commutes with $\bar\partial_\cdot$ on $\mathrm{Dom}(\bar\partial_\cdot)$ [FK3]. Therefore $\bar\partial_0 N_0^\Omega f = N_1^\Omega \bar\partial_0 f$. It follows that $(I - E_0^\Omega)f = \bar\partial_1^* N_1^\Omega \bar\partial_0 f$, as required. Q.E.D.

2.1.24. LEMMA. $\bar\partial_1^* N_1^\Omega$ *is a compact (bounded) operator.*

Proof. As an everywhere defined closed operator from $L_1^2(\Omega)$ to $L_0^2(\Omega)$, $\bar\partial_1^* N_1^\Omega$ is bounded by the closed graph theorem. For every $\varphi \in L_1^2(\Omega)$, we have

$$\|\bar\partial_1^* N_1^\Omega \varphi\|_\Omega^2 = (\bar\partial_1^* N_1^\Omega \varphi \mid \bar\partial_1^* N_1^\Omega \varphi)_\Omega = (N_1^\Omega \varphi \mid \bar\partial_0 \bar\partial_1^* N_1^\Omega \varphi)_\Omega.$$

Applying (2.1.20) for $q = 1$ and (2.1.18), we obtain

$$\|\bar\partial_1^* N_1^\Omega \varphi\|_\Omega^2 = (N_1^\Omega \varphi \mid \varphi - E_1^\Omega \varphi - \bar\partial_0^* \bar\partial_1 N_1^\Omega \varphi)$$

$$= (N_1^\Omega \varphi \mid \varphi - \bar\partial_0^* \bar\partial_1 N_1^\Omega \varphi) = (N_1^\Omega \varphi \mid \varphi) - (\bar\partial_1 N_1^\Omega \varphi \mid \bar\partial_1 N_1^\Omega \varphi) \leq (N_1^\Omega \varphi \mid \varphi).$$

Since N_1^Ω is compact by Theorem 2.1.21, it follows easily that $\bar{\partial}_1^* N_1^\Omega$ is also compact. Q.E.D.

2.2 Hardy Spaces Over Strictly Pseudoconvex Domains

Let Ω be a strictly pseudoconvex domain in $\mathbb{C}^n$, with smooth boundary $S = \partial\Omega$ (for the geometry of these domains, cf. Section 1.2). Let $d\sigma$ denote the surface measure on S (i.e., the measure on S considered as a Riemannian submanifold of $\mathbb{C}^n = \mathbb{R}^{2n}$). Let $L^2(S) = L^2(S, d\sigma)$ be the corresponding *Lebesgue space* of square-integrable functions, with inner product

$$(2.2.1) \qquad (h|k)_S := \int_S \overline{h(z)}\, k(z)\, d\sigma(z).$$

2.2.2. PROPOSITION. $S = \partial\Omega$ *is the Shilov boundary of* Ω, *i.e. the smallest closed boundary for the algebra* $\mathcal{A}(\Omega)$.

For the *proof*, cf. [BG6]. Note that a subset $B \subset \partial\Omega$ is called a *boundary* for $\mathcal{A}(\Omega)$ if for every $f \in \mathcal{A}(\Omega)$ we have

$$\sup_{z\in\Omega} |f(z)| = \sup_{z\in B} |f(z)|.$$

By Proposition 2.2.2, the restriction mapping

$$\mathcal{A}(\Omega) \ni f \mapsto f|_S \in C(S)$$

is injective. We can therefore regard $\mathcal{A}(\Omega)$ as a subspace of $L^2(S)$.

2.2.3. DEFINITION. The *Hardy space* $H^2(S)$ is defined as the Hilbert space closure of $\mathcal{A}(\Omega)$ in $L^2(S)$:

$$H^2(S) := \{f|_S : f \in \mathcal{A}(\Omega)\}^-.$$

The orthogonal projection

$$(2.2.4) \qquad E : L^2(S) \to H^2(S)$$

is called the *Cauchy-Szegö projection*.

For strictly pseudo-convex domains Ω with smooth boundary S, the Szegö projection (2.2.4) has a certain regularity property that is of fundamental importance to the study of Hardy-Toeplitz operators. This regularity property is related to the so-called tangential $\bar{\partial}$-Neumann problem in partial differential equations [FK3]. For each integer $0 \leq q < n$, consider the space $\mathcal{C}_q^\infty(S)$ of "tangential" (0,q)-forms

$$\varphi = \sum_{|I|=q} \varphi_I \, d\bar{z}^I$$

on S with smooth coefficients φ_I. Formally, $\mathcal{C}_q^\infty(S)$ is the space of all sections of a locally free sheaf supported on S, namely the quotient of the sheaf of germs of (0,q)-forms whose coefficients are smooth in a neighborhood of $\bar{\Omega}$ modulo the subsheaf of germs of (0,q)-forms φ which are "normal" to the boundary, i.e., satisfy

$$\bar{\partial}\rho \wedge \varphi = 0$$

on $\partial\Omega$. Here ρ is the defining function of Ω (cf. (1.2.13)). $\mathcal{C}_q^\infty(S)$ has an inner product

$$(2.2.5) \qquad (\varphi|\psi)_S := \sum_{|I|=q} (\varphi_I|\psi_I)_S$$

for all $\varphi = \sum \varphi_I \, d\bar{z}^I$, $\psi = \sum \psi_I \, d\bar{z}^I$. Here the inner product on the right-hand side is given by (2.2.1).

2.2.6. DEFINITION. For $0 \leq q < n$, let $L_q^2(S)$ denote the Hilbert space completion of $\mathcal{C}_q^\infty(S)$, with respect to the inner product (2.2.5). Note that, by the Stone-Weierstrass Theorem, $L_0^2(S) = L^2(S)$ is the usual Lebesgue space of functions. The $\bar{\partial}$-operator defined in (2.1.11) induces a well-defined quotient map

$$(2.2.7) \qquad \bar{\partial}_q : \mathcal{C}_q^\infty(S) \to \mathcal{C}_{q+1}^\infty(S)$$

called the *tangential* $\bar\partial$*-operator.*

One can show that for each $q \geq 0$, $\bar\partial_q$ has a closure

(2.2.8)
$$L^2_q(S) \supset \mathrm{Dom}(\bar\partial_q) \xrightarrow{\bar\partial_q} L^2_{q+1}(S)$$

with Hilbert space adjoint

(2.2.9)
$$L^2_{q+1}(S) \supset \mathrm{Dom}(\bar\partial^*_q) \xrightarrow{\bar\partial^*_q} L^2_q(S).$$

As a matter of notation, put $\bar\partial_{n-1} = \bar\partial_{-1} = 0$ and $\bar\partial^*_n = \bar\partial^*_0 = 0.$

We can combine the operators (2.2.8) and (2.2.9) to obtain the *tangential Kohn-Laplacian* on S:

(2.2.10)
$$\Box^S_q := \bar\partial_{q-1}\bar\partial^*_q + \bar\partial^*_{q+1}\bar\partial_q \ : \mathrm{Dom}(\Box^S_q) \to L^2_q(S),$$

defined on the subspace

$$\mathrm{Dom}(\Box^S_q) := \{\varphi \in \mathrm{Dom}(\bar\partial_q) \cap \mathrm{Dom}(\bar\partial^*_q) :$$

$$\bar\partial_q\varphi \in \mathrm{Dom}(\bar\partial^*_{q+1}),\ \bar\partial^*_q\varphi \in \mathrm{Dom}(\bar\partial_{q-1})\}$$

of $L^2_q(S)$. For $q = 0$, (2.2.10) specializes to

$$\Box^S_0 := \bar\partial^*_1\bar\partial_0 \ : \mathrm{Dom}(\Box^S_0) \to L^2(S)$$

with

$$\mathrm{Dom}(\Box^S_0) := \{\varphi \in \mathrm{Dom}(\bar\partial_0) : \bar\partial_0\varphi \in \mathrm{Dom}(\bar\partial^*_1)\}.$$

For $q = n-1$, we obtain

$$\Box^S_{n-1} = \bar\partial_{n-2}\bar\partial^*_{n-1} \ : \mathrm{Dom}(\Box^S_{n-1}) \to L^2_{n-1}(S)$$

with

$$\mathrm{Dom}(\Box^S_{n-1}) := \{\varphi \in \mathrm{Dom}(\bar\partial^*_{n-1}) : \bar\partial^*_{n-1}\varphi \in \mathrm{Dom}(\bar\partial_{n-2})\}.$$

2.2.11. PROPOSITION. *For* $q \geq 0$, *the null-space*

$$H^2_q(S) := \{\varphi \in \mathrm{Dom}(\Box^S_q) : \Box^S_q\varphi = 0\}$$

$$= \{\varphi \in \mathrm{Dom}(\bar\partial_q) \cap \mathrm{Dom}(\bar\partial^*_q) : \bar\partial_q\varphi = 0 = \bar\partial^*_q\varphi)\}$$

is a closed subspace of $L^2_q(S)$.

The elements of $H^2_q(S)$ are called *harmonic* tangential $(0,q)$-forms on S. Let

$$E_q : L^2_q(S) \to H^2_q(S)$$

denote the orthogonal projection. For $q = 0$,

$$H^2_0(S) = \{\varphi \in \mathrm{Dom}(\bar\partial_0) : \bar\partial_0\varphi = 0\} = H^2(S) \tag{2.2.12}$$

is the usual Hardy space, and $E_0 = E$ is the Cauchy-Szegö projection. By easy modifications of the results in [FK3] one can show that $\Box^S_q$ has closed range and is bounded away from 0 on $\{\varphi \in \mathrm{Dom}(\Box^S_q) : E_q\varphi = 0\}$. Thus one can define an operator

$$N^S_q : L^2_q(S) \to L^2_q(S) \tag{2.2.13}$$

to be the inverse of $\Box^S_q$ on the range of $\Box^S_q$ and zero on its complement. This (bounded) operator N^S_q is called the *tangential* $\bar\partial$-*Neumann* operator. It satisfies

$$N^S_q E_q = 0 = E_q N^S_q, \tag{2.2.14}$$

(2.2.15) $$\mathrm{Ran}(N_q^S) \subset \mathrm{Dom}(\Box_q^S),$$

(2.2.16) $$(I - E_q)\varphi = \Box_q^S N_q^S \varphi$$

for every $\varphi \in L_q^2(S)$. Analogous to Theorem 2.1.21, we have [FK3] :

2.2.17. THEOREM. *For* $q \geq 1$, *the tangential* $\bar{\partial}$*-Neumann operator* N_q^S *is compact.*

The following two Lemmas are proved in a similar way as Lemmas 2.1.22 and 2.1.24.

2.2.18. LEMMA. *For* $f \in \mathrm{Dom}(\bar{\partial}_0^S) \subset L^2(S)$, *we have*

$$(I - E)f = \bar{\partial}_1^* N_1^S \bar{\partial}_0 f.$$

2.2.19. LEMMA. $\bar{\partial}_1^* N_1^S$ *is a bounded operator which is compact.*

2.3 Hardy Spaces Over Tubular Domains

In this section we introduce an important Hilbert space of analytic functions, the so-called Hardy space, associated with a tubular domain $\Pi = \Lambda \times iX$ with base Λ being a symmetric cone in a real Jordan algebra X. We will assume that Λ is irreducible. The geometry of tubular domains and the connection with Jordan algebras are discussed in Section 1.3.

Consider the euclidean structure underlying the real Jordan algebra $X \approx \mathbb{R}^n$. Let $d\alpha$ denote the associated Lebesgue measure, and consider the L^2-space $L^2(X) := L^2(X,d\alpha)$ of complex-valued functions, with inner product

(2.3.1) $$(\xi|\eta)_X := \int_X \overline{\xi(\alpha)}\, \eta(\alpha)\, d\alpha$$

for all $\xi, \eta \in L^2(X)$. The *translation action* of the locally compact additive group X on the Hilbert space $L^2(X)$ is defined by

(2.3.2) $$(\alpha_{\#}\xi)(\beta) := \xi(\beta - \alpha)$$

for all $\alpha, \beta \in X$ and $\xi \in L^2(X)$. Now consider the complexification $X \otimes \mathbb{C} \approx \mathbb{C}^n$ and its real subspace iX. For each $z \in iX$, put

$$z^{\#}(\alpha) := e^{-z\cdot\alpha}. \tag{2.3.3}$$

In this way, iX can be identified with the character group of X. Consider the dual Lebesgue measure dz on iX. Let $L^2(iX)$ be the corresponding L^2-space, with inner product

$$(h|k)_{iX} := \int_{iX} \overline{h(z)}\, k(z)\, dz = \int_X \overline{h(i\alpha)}\, k(i\alpha)\, d\alpha. \tag{2.3.4}$$

The *translation action* of iX on $L^2(iX)$ is defined by

$$(z^{\#}h)(w) := h(w - z) \tag{2.3.5}$$

for all $z, w \in iX$ and $h \in L^2(iX)$. For each $\alpha \in X$, put

$$\alpha_{\#}(z) := e^{\alpha\cdot z}. \tag{2.3.6}$$

In this way, X can be identified with the character group of iX.

2.3.7. PROPOSITION. *The Fourier transform*

$$h^{\#}(\alpha) := \frac{1}{(2\pi)^{n/2}} \int_{iX} h(z)\, z^{\#}(\alpha)\, dz = \frac{1}{(2\pi)^{n/2}} \int_X h(i\alpha)\, e^{-i\alpha\cdot x}\, d\alpha \tag{2.3.8}$$

defines a Hilbert space isomorphism

$$L^2(iX) \xrightarrow[\approx]{()^{\#}} L^2(X),$$

with adjoint $L^2(X) \xrightarrow[\approx]{()_{\#}} L^2(iX)$ *given by*

$$\xi_{\#}(z) = \frac{1}{(2\pi)^{n/2}} \int_X \xi(\alpha)\, \alpha_{\#}(z)\, d\alpha = \frac{1}{(2\pi)^{n/2}} \int_X \xi(\alpha)\, e^{\alpha\cdot z}\, d\alpha. \tag{2.3.9}$$

For each $\alpha \in X$ *and* $z \in iX$, *there exist commuting diagrams*

$$\begin{array}{ccccc}
L^2(iX) & \xrightarrow{(\,)^{\#}} & L^2(X) & \xrightarrow{(\,)_{\#}} & L^2(iX) \\
\downarrow z^{\#} & & z^{\#} \downarrow \;\downarrow \alpha_{\#} & & \downarrow \alpha_{\#} \\
L^2(iX) & \xrightarrow[(\,)^{\#}]{} & L^2(X) & \xrightarrow[(\,)_{\#}]{} & L^2(iX)
\end{array}$$

for the respective translation and multiplication actions.

This is just the Fourier-Plancherel Theorem for the abelian group X. Identifying X with iX, we have $h^{\#} = \hat{h}$ and $\xi_{\#} = \check{\xi}$ but we use the #-notation in view of later generalizations.

2.3.10. DEFINITION. The *Hardy space* $H^2(iX)$ (depending on Π) consists of all holomorphic functions $h : \Pi \to \mathbb{C}$ such that

$$||h||^2 := \sup_{a \in \Lambda} \int_{iX} |h(a + z)|^2 \, dz < \infty.$$

By [K5] there exists an embedding $H^2(iX) \subset L^2(iX)$ as a closed subspace such that

$$\lim_{\substack{a \in \Lambda \\ a \to 0}} \int_{iX} |h(a + z) - h(z)|^2 \, dz = 0.$$

This embedding is invariant under the translation action (2.3.5) of iX. The orthogonal projection

(2.3.11) $$E : L^2(iX) \to H^2(iX)$$

is called the *Szegö projection.* We have (cf. Proposition 2.4.10)

2.3.12. PROPOSITION. *The Hardy space* $H^2(iX)$ *has the reproducing "Szegö" kernel*

(2.3.13) $$E(z,w) = \Delta(-z - w^*)^{-n/r}$$

where Δ *is the Jordan algebra determinant of* Z *and* $(x + iy)^* := x - iy$ *is the involution of* Z.

Thus for each $w \in \Pi$ the function

(2.3.14) $$E_w(z) := E(z,w)$$

(which has an extension to $\overline{\Pi}$) belongs to $H^2(iX)$, and the Szegö projection (2.3.11) is given by

(2.3.15) $$(Eh)(z) = (E_z|h)_{iX}$$

for every $h \in L^2(iX)$ and $z \in \Pi$.

2.3.16. DEFINITION. The closed convex cone

(2.3.17) $$\Lambda^\# := \{\alpha \in X : \alpha \cdot a \leq 0 \text{ for all } a \in \Lambda\}$$

is called the *polar cone* of Λ. Define

$$L^2(\Lambda^\#) := \{\xi \in L^2(X) : \xi|_{X\setminus\Lambda^\#} = 0 \text{ [a.e.]}\}$$

as a closed subspace of $L^2(X)$. It is invariant under the multiplication action (2.3.3) of iX. The following result, due to Bochner [B3], is a Paley-Wiener type theorem for tubular domains.

2.3.18. THEOREM. *The Fourier transform* (2.3.8) *induces a Hilbert space isomorphism*

$$H^2(iX) \xrightarrow[\approx]{()^\#} L^2(\Lambda^\#).$$

Conversely, for every $\xi \in L^2(\Lambda^\#)$ *the holomorphic extension of* $\xi_\#$ *to* Π *is given by the compactly convergent integral*

(2.3.19) $$\xi_\#(z) = \frac{1}{(2\pi)^{n/2}} \int_{\Lambda^\#} e^{z\cdot\alpha}\, \xi(\alpha)\, d\alpha.$$

For every $z \in iX$, *there exists a commuting diagram*

$$\begin{array}{ccc} H^2(iX) & \xrightarrow{(\,)^\#} & L^2(\Lambda^\#) \\ \Big\downarrow z^\# & & \Big\downarrow z^\# \\ H^2(iX) & \xrightarrow[(\,)^\#]{} & L^2(\Lambda^\#) \end{array}$$

for the respective translation and multiplication actions.

2.3.20. DEFINITION. The holomorphic function on Π given by the compactly convergent integral

$$E_0(z) = \int_{\Lambda^\#} \alpha_\#(z)\ d\alpha = \int_{\Lambda^\#} e^{z\cdot\alpha}\ d\alpha \tag{2.3.21}$$

is called the *Szegö characteristic function* of Π.

2.3.22. THEOREM. *The Szegö kernel* (2.3.13) *of* $H^2(iX)$ *has an integral representation*

$$E(z,w) = E_0(z + w^*) = \int_{\Lambda^\#} e^{z\cdot\alpha}\ \overline{e^{w\cdot\alpha}}\ d\alpha \tag{2.3.23}$$

converging compactly on $\Pi \times \Pi$.

The Paley-Wiener type realization of the Hardy space extends in a natural way to the more general case of Siegel domains

$$\Pi = \{(u,v) \in U \times V : u + u^* + \Phi(v,v) \in \Lambda\} \tag{2.3.24}$$

introduced in Section 1.3. Here iX is replaced by the *extreme boundary*

$$\Sigma = \{(a - \frac{\Phi(b,b)}{2}, b) : a \in iX,\ b \in V\} \tag{2.3.25}$$

which is a nilpotent Lie group [G1, P2, U3]. Let $da\ db$ denote a Haar measure on Σ. Since

$$\Sigma = \{(u,v) : u + u^* + \Phi(v,v) = 0\}$$

it follows that $(x + u,v) \in \Pi$ whenever $x \in \Lambda$ and $(u,v) \in \Sigma$.

2.3.26. DEFINITION. The *Hardy space* $H^2(\Sigma)$ is the space of all holomorphic functions $h : \Pi \to \mathbb{C}$ such that the family

$$h_x(u,v) := h(x + u,v) \qquad (x \in \Lambda)$$

is bounded in $L^2(\Sigma)$.

We may realize $H^2(\Sigma)$ as a closed subspace of $L^2(\Sigma)$ by taking the boundary values

$$h(u,v) := \lim_{\substack{x \in \Lambda \\ x \to 0}} h(x + u,v).$$

The orthogonal projection

$$E : L^2(\Sigma) \to H^2(\Sigma) \tag{2.3.27}$$

is the *Szegö projection*, and the corresponding *Szegö kernel* $E(z,w)$ is determined by

$$(Eh)(z) = \int_\Sigma E(z,w)h(w)dw \tag{2.3.28}$$

for all $h \in L^2(\Sigma)$ and $z \in \Pi$. Generalizing Proposition 2.3.12, we have [FK3]

2.3.29. PROPOSITION. *The Hardy space* $H^2(\Sigma)$ *has the reproducing Szegö kernel*

$$E(z,w) = \Delta(-z_1 - w_1^* - \Phi(z_2,w_2))^{-n/r} \tag{2.3.30}$$

for all $z = (z_1,z_2) \in \Pi$ *and* $w = (w_1,w_2) \in \Sigma$.

In order to obtain a Paley-Wiener type theorem for $H^2(\Sigma)$, consider the space $L^2_{hol}(\Lambda^\# \times V)$ of all functions $\varphi(\alpha,v)$ on $\Lambda^\# \times V$ which are holomorphic in v and satisfy

$$\int_{\Lambda^\# \times V} |\varphi(\alpha,v)|^2 e^{-\alpha\Phi(v,v)} \, d\alpha \, dv < \infty. \tag{2.3.31}$$

The Hilbert norm on $L^2_{hol}(\Lambda^\# \times V)$ is determined by the integral (2.3.31). Generalizing Theorem 2.3.18, we have [G1]:

2.3.32. THEOREM. *The partial Fourier transform*

$$(2.3.33) \qquad h^\#(\alpha,v) = \frac{1}{(2\pi)^{n_1/2}} \int_X h\left(ix - \frac{\Phi(v,v)}{2}, v\right) e^{-i\alpha\cdot x}\, dx$$

induces a Hilbert space isomorphism

$$(2.3.34) \qquad H^2(\Sigma) \xrightarrow{(\ )^\#} L^2_{hol}(\Lambda^\# \times V),$$

with inverse given by the compactly convergent integral

$$(2.3.35) \qquad \varphi_\#(u,v) = \frac{1}{(2\pi)^{n_1/2}} \int_{\Lambda^\#} e^{\left(u + \frac{\Phi(v,v)}{2}\right)\cdot \alpha} \varphi(\alpha,v)\, d\alpha.$$

Here we put $X := \{x \in U : x^* = x\}$ *and* $n_1 := \dim X$.

Putting, for each fixed $v \in V$, $\varphi_v(\alpha) := \varphi(\alpha,v)$ and

$$h_v(x) := h\left(ix - \frac{\Phi(v,v)}{2}, v\right),$$

the formulas (2.3.33) and (2.3.35) become the usual Fourier transforms $h^\#(\alpha,v) = \hat{h}_v(\alpha)$ and $\varphi_\#(ix - \Phi(v,v)/2,\ v) = \check{\varphi}_v(x)$.

2.4 Bergman Spaces Over Tubular Domains

In this section we introduce a 1-parameter scale of Hilbert spaces of analytic functions, the so-called weighted Bergman spaces, associated with a tubular domain $\Pi = \Lambda \times iX$ over a symmetric cone Λ in a real Jordan algebra X (cf. Section 1.3). We will assume that Λ is irreducible of rank r and dimension n. Then $n = r + \frac{a}{2} r(r-1)$ where a is the characteristic multiplicity (1.5.60) of X. The number

(2.4.1) $$p := 2 + a(r - 1) = \frac{2n}{r}$$

is called the *genus* of X.

2.4.2. DEFINITION. Define the *multi-Γ-function*

(2.4.3) $$\Gamma_\Lambda(\lambda) := (2\pi)^{(n-r)/2} \cdot \prod_{j=1}^{r} \Gamma(\lambda - \frac{a}{2}(j - 1))$$

for $\lambda > \frac{a}{2}(r - 1)$. Here Γ is Euler's Gamma function.

Let $Z = X \oplus iX$ be the complexification of X. Consider the hermitian structure $(z|w)$ underlying Z and let $dV(z)$ be the associated Lebesgue measure. Using the multi-Γ-function (2.4.3), define a measure

(2.4.4) $$d\mu_\Pi(z) := \pi^{-n} \frac{\Gamma_\Lambda(\frac{p}{2})}{\Gamma_\Lambda(p)} \; dV(z)$$

on Π, and consider the associated L^2-space $L^2(\Pi) := L^2(\Pi, d\mu_\Pi)$ of complex functions on Π, with inner product

(2.4.5) $$(h|k)_\Pi := \int_\Pi \overline{h(z)}\, k(z)\, d\mu_\Pi(z).$$

(For the normalization in (2.4.4), cf. (2.9.2)). As in Section 2.3, define the *translation action* of iX on $L^2(\Pi)$ by putting

(2.4.6) $$(z^\# h)(w) := h(w - z)$$

for all $z \in iX$, $h \in L^2(\Pi)$ and $w \in \Pi$, and define for all $\alpha \in X$

(2.4.7) $$z^\#(\alpha) := e^{-z\cdot\alpha}.$$

2.4.8. DEFINITION. The subspace

$$H^2(\Pi) := \{h \in L^2(\Pi) : h \text{ holomorphic}\} = L^2(\Pi) \cap \mathcal{O}(\Pi)$$

of $L^2(\Pi)$ is called the *Bergman space* over Π.

By Proposition 2.1.3, $H^2(\Pi)$ is a closed subspace of $L^2(\Pi)$. It is invariant under the translation action (2.4.6). The orthogonal projection

(2.4.9) $$E_\Pi : L^2(\Pi) \to H^2(\Pi)$$

onto $H^2(\Pi)$ is called the *Bergman projection.*

2.4.10. PROPOSITION. *The Bergman space* $H^2(\Pi)$ *has the reproducing "Bergman" kernel*

(2.4.11) $$E_\Pi(z,w) = \Delta(-z - w^*)^{-p} = \Delta(-z - w^*)^{-2n/r},$$

where Δ *is the Jordan algebra determinant of* Z, *and* $(x + iy)^* := x - iy$ *is the involution of* Z.

Thus, for each fixed $w \in \Pi$, the function

(2.4.12) $$E_w(z) := E_\Pi(z,w)$$

belongs to $H^2(\Pi)$, and the Bergman projection (2.4.9) is given by

(2.4.13) $$(E_\Pi h)(z) = (E_z|h)_\Pi$$

for every $h \in L^2(\Pi)$ and $z \in \Pi$.

Proof. By the transformation rule for Lebesgue integrals, we have

(2.4.14) $$\mathrm{Det}\ g'(z) \cdot E_\Pi(g(z), g(w)) \cdot \overline{\mathrm{Det}\ g'(w)} = E_\Pi(z,w)$$

for all $z,w \in \Pi$ and every biholomorphic automorphism g of Π. Here $g'(z) \in GL(Z)$ is the complex derivative. For any point $z = x + iy \in \Pi$, we have $x \in \Lambda$ and the associated quadratic transformation (cf. (1.3.15))

$$P_x^{1/2} = P_{(-x)^{1/2}} \in GL(\Lambda)$$

extends to a complex-linear automorphism of Π. Let τ_{iy} be the translation by the vector iy, which clearly leaves Π invariant. Then $z = (\tau_{iy} \circ P_x^{1/2})(-e)$ and

$$\mathrm{Det}(\tau_{iy} \circ P_x^{1/2})'(-e) = \mathrm{Det}\ \tau'_{iy}(x) \cdot (\mathrm{Det}\ P_x)^{1/2} = \Delta(-x)^{p/2}$$

by [BK, FK2]. Therefore (2.4.14) gives

$$\Delta(-x)^p\, E_\Pi(z,z) = E_\Pi(-e,-e) = 2^{-2n},$$

where the value at (-e,-e) stems from the normalization (2.4.4). It follows that

$$E_\Pi(z,z) = 2^{-2n}\, \Delta\left(\frac{-z - z^*}{2}\right)^{-p} = \Delta(-z - z^*)^{-p}$$

for all $z \in \Pi$. Since (2.4.11) is sesqui-holomorphic in (z,w), the assertion follows. Q.E.D.

2.4.15. EXAMPLE. Let $X = \mathcal{H}_r(\mathbb{C})$ consist of all self-adjoint (r×r)-matrices over $\mathbb{C}$. Then $Z = \mathbb{C}^{r\times r}$ has dimension $n = r^2$, and

$$\Pi = \{z \in \mathbb{C}^{r\times r} : z + z^* < 0\}$$

(negative-definite). Since $\Delta(z) = \mathrm{Det}(z)$ in this case, we have

$$E_\Pi(z,w) = \mathrm{Det}(-z - w^*)^{-2r}.$$

In particular, for $r = 1$, we have $Z = \mathbb{C}$ and

$$E_\Pi(z,w) = (-z - \overline{w})^{-2} \tag{2.4.16}$$

is the Bergman kernel of the left half-plane Π.

2.4.17. EXAMPLE. The complexification Z of $X := \mathcal{H}_r(\mathbb{R})$ is the space $Z = \{z \in \mathbb{C}^{r\times r} : z^T = z\}$ of all symmetric matrices. The corresponding tube domain

$$\Pi = \{z \in Z : z + \overline{z} < 0\}$$

is called Siegel's (left) half-space. We have $\Delta(z) = \mathrm{Det}(z)$ and $n = \frac{r(r+1)}{2}$. Therefore the Bergman kernel is given by

$$E_\Pi(z,w) = \mathrm{Det}(-z - \bar{w})^{-(r+1)}.$$

For $r = 1$, we recover the case (2.4.16).

We next introduce "weighted" Bergman spaces whose reproducing kernels are powers of the standard Bergman kernel. Fix a parameter $\lambda > p - 1$ and consider the multi-Γ-function defined in (2.4.3). Consider the measure

$$d\mu_\lambda(z) := \pi^{-n} \frac{\Gamma_\Lambda(\lambda)}{\Gamma_\Lambda(\lambda - \frac{p}{2})} \Delta(-z - z^*)^{\lambda-p}\, dV(z) \tag{2.4.18}$$

on Π, and let $L^2_\lambda(\Pi) := L^2(\Pi, d\mu_\lambda)$ be the corresponding L^2-space of complex functions, with inner product

$$(h|k)_\lambda := \int_\Pi \overline{h(z)}\, k(z)\, d\mu_\lambda(z). \tag{2.4.19}$$

For $\lambda = p$, we obtain the space $L^2_p(\Pi) = L^2(\Pi)$ introduced in (2.4.5). Since the measure $d\mu_\lambda$ is invariant under "imaginary" translations, we obtain a translation action of iX on $L^2_\lambda(\Pi)$ defined by (2.4.6).

2.4.20. DEFINITION. For $\lambda > p - 1$, the closed subspace

$$H^2_\lambda(\Pi) = \{h \in L^2_\lambda(\Pi) : h \text{ holomorphic}\} = L^2_\lambda(\Pi) \cap \mathcal{O}(\Pi)$$

of $L^2_\lambda(\Pi)$ is called the λ-*Bergman space* over Π.

The subspaces $H^2_\lambda(\Pi)$ are invariant under the translation action (2.4.6). For $\lambda = p$, $H^2_p(\Pi) = H^2(\Pi)$ is the standard Bergman space. The orthogonal projection

$$E_\lambda : L^2_\lambda(\Pi) \to H^2_\lambda(\Pi) \tag{2.4.21}$$

onto $H^2_\lambda(\Pi)$ is called the λ-*Bergman projection.* Generalizing Proposition 2.4.10 (for $\lambda = p$) we have:

2.4.22. PROPOSITION. *For* $\lambda > p - 1$, *the* λ*-Bergman space* $H^2_\lambda(\Pi)$ *has the reproducing "*λ*-Bergman" kernel*

$$E_\lambda(z,w) = \Delta(-z - w^*)^{-\lambda}, \tag{2.4.23}$$

where Δ *is the Jordan algebra determinant of* Z.

Thus for each $w \in \Pi$, the function

$$E_w(z) := E_\lambda(z,w) \tag{2.4.24}$$

belongs to $H^2_\lambda(\Pi)$, and the λ-Bergman projection (2.4.21) is given by

$$(E_\lambda h)(z) = (E_z | h)_\lambda \tag{2.4.25}$$

for every $h \in L^2_\lambda(\Pi)$ and $z \in \Pi$. Now let $\Lambda^\#$ be the polar cone of Λ, defined in (2.3.17).

2.4.26. THEOREM. *For* $\lambda > p - 1$, *there exists a Hilbert space isomorphism ("Laplace transform")*

$$H^2_\lambda(\Pi) \xrightarrow{()^\#} L^2(\Lambda^\#) \tag{2.4.27}$$

such that its adjoint $L^2(\Lambda^\#) \xrightarrow{()_\#} H^2_\lambda(\Pi)$ *is given by*

$$\xi_\#(z) = \frac{1}{\sqrt{\Gamma_\Lambda(\lambda)}} \int_{\Lambda^\#} e^{z \cdot \alpha}\, \xi(\alpha)\, \Delta(\alpha)^{\lambda/2 - p/4}\, d\alpha \tag{2.4.28}$$

for all $\xi \in L^2(\Lambda^\#)$ *and* $z \in \Pi$. *For each* $z \in iX$, *there exists a commuting diagram*

$$\begin{array}{ccc} H^2_\lambda(iX) & \xrightarrow{()^\#} & L^2(\Lambda^\#) \\ \Big\downarrow z^\# & & \Big\downarrow z^\# \\ H^2_\lambda(iX) & \xrightarrow[()^\#]{} & L^2(\Lambda^\#) \end{array}$$

for the respective translation and multiplication actions.

Proof. For $\lambda > p - 1$, the convergent integral

$$\Gamma_\Lambda(\lambda - \tfrac{p}{2}) := \int_\Lambda e^{x \cdot e}\, \Delta(-x)^{\lambda - p}\, dx \tag{2.4.29}$$

defines the multi-Γ-function [G1, FK2]. More generally [G1], we have for all $\alpha \in \Lambda^\#$

$$\int_\Lambda e^{x \cdot \alpha}\, \Delta(-x)^{\lambda - p}\, dx = \Delta(\alpha)^{(p/2) - \lambda}\, \Gamma_\Lambda(\lambda - \tfrac{p}{2}). \tag{2.4.30}$$

Now let $\xi \in L^2(\Lambda^\#)$. Plancherel's Theorem implies

$$\pi^n \Gamma_\Lambda(\lambda - \tfrac{p}{2}) \cdot \|\xi_\#\|_\lambda^2 = \Gamma_\Lambda(\lambda) \int_\Lambda \Delta(-2x)^{\lambda - p} \int_X |\xi_\#(x + iy)|^2\, dy\, dx$$

$$= \int_\Lambda \Delta(-2x)^{\lambda - p} \int_X \Big| \int_{\Lambda^\#} e^{x \cdot \alpha}\, e^{iy \cdot \alpha}\, \xi(\alpha)\, \Delta(\alpha)^{\lambda/2 - p/4}\, d\alpha \Big|^2\, dy\, dx$$

$$= (2\pi)^n \int_\Lambda \Delta(-2x)^{\lambda - p} \int_{\Lambda^\#} e^{2x \cdot \alpha}\, |\xi(\alpha)|^2\, \Delta(\alpha)^{\lambda - p/2}\, d\alpha\, dx$$

$$= \pi^n \int_\Lambda \Delta(-x)^{\lambda - p} \int_{\Lambda^\#} e^{x \cdot \alpha}\, |\xi(\alpha)|^2\, \Delta(\alpha)^{\lambda - p/2}\, d\alpha\, dx$$

$$= \pi^n\, \Gamma_\Lambda(\lambda - \tfrac{p}{2}) \int_{\Lambda^\#} |\xi(\alpha)|^2\, \Delta(\alpha)^{p/2 - \lambda}\, \Delta(\alpha)^{\lambda - p/2}\, d\alpha = \pi^n\, \Gamma_\Lambda(\lambda - \tfrac{p}{2})\, \|\xi\|^2.$$

This shows that $()_\#$ is isometric. By a, more difficult, Paley-Wiener argument [G1, DG], $()_\#$ is also surjective. Q.E.D.

2.4.31. DEFINITION. For $\lambda > p - 1$, the holomorphic function on Π defined by the compactly convergent integral

$$\chi_\lambda(z) = \frac{1}{\Gamma_\Lambda(\lambda)} \int_{\Lambda^\#} e^{z \cdot \alpha}\, \Delta(\alpha)^{\lambda - p/2}\, d\alpha \tag{2.4.32}$$

is called the *λ-Bergman characteristic function* of Π. For λ = p, we obtain the *Bergman characteristic function*

(2.4.33) $$\chi_\Pi(z) = \frac{1}{\Gamma_\Lambda(p)} \int_{\Lambda^\#} e^{z\cdot\alpha}\, \Delta(\alpha)^{p/2}\, d\alpha.$$

2.4.34. THEOREM. *The λ-Bergman kernel* (2.4.23) *of* $H^2_\lambda(\Pi)$ *has an integral representation*

(2.4.35) $$E_\lambda(z,w) = \chi_\lambda(z + w^*) = \frac{1}{\Gamma_\Lambda(\lambda)} \int_{\Lambda^\#} e^{z\cdot\alpha}\, \overline{e^{w\cdot\alpha}}\, \Delta(\alpha)^{\lambda-p/2}\, d\alpha$$

converging compactly on Π × Π.

Proof. With Proposition 2.4.22 and (2.4.32) we obtain

$$E_\lambda(z,w) = \Delta(-z - w^*)^{-\lambda} = \frac{1}{\Gamma_\Lambda(\lambda)} \int_{\Lambda^\#} e^{(z+w^*)\cdot\alpha}\, \Delta(\alpha)^{\lambda-p/2}\, d\alpha.$$

Q.E.D.

Now consider the more general symmetric Siegel domains (2.3.24), again assumed to be irreducible. Putting

$$n_1 := \dim_{\mathbb{R}} X = \dim_{\mathbb{C}} U,\ n_2 := \dim_{\mathbb{C}} V,\ n := n_1 + n_2\ ,$$

$$p_1 := 2n_1/r\ , \quad p_2 := n_2/r$$

we have

2.4.36. PROPOSITION. *Define the partial Fourier-Laplace transform*

(2.4.37) $$\hat{\varphi}(u,v) = \frac{1}{(2\pi)^{n_1/2}} \int_{\Lambda^\#} e^{u\cdot\alpha}\, \varphi(\alpha,v)\, d\alpha$$

of a compactly supported function φ *on* $\Lambda^\#\times V$, *where* (u,v) ∈ Π. *Then we have*

(2.4.38) $$\int_\Pi |\hat{\varphi}(u,v)|^2\, \Delta(-u - u^* - \Phi(v,v))^{\lambda-p_1-p_2}\, du\, dv$$

$$= 2^{-n_1}\,\Gamma_\Lambda(\lambda - \frac{p_1}{2} - p_2) \int_{\Lambda^\# \times V} |\varphi(\alpha,v)|^2 \, e^{-\Phi(v,v)\cdot\alpha}\, \Delta(\alpha)^{-\lambda+\frac{p_1}{2}+p_2}\, d\alpha\, dv$$

whenever $\lambda > p_1 + p_2 - 1$.

Proof. Putting $u = x + iy$ and $t := 2x + \Phi(v,v) \in \Lambda$, the classical Plancherel Theorem in the y-variable and (2.4.30) (cf. [G1; Proposition 2.3]) imply

$$\int_\Pi |\hat{\varphi}(u,v)|^2\, \Delta(-u - u^* - \Phi(v,v))^{\lambda-p_1-p_2}\, du\, dv =$$

$$\frac{1}{(2\pi)^{n_1}} \int\int\int \Big| \int_{\Lambda^\#} e^{x\cdot\alpha+iy\cdot\alpha}\, \varphi(\alpha,v)\, d\alpha\Big|^2\, \Delta(-2x - \Phi(v,v))^{\lambda-p_1-p_2}\, dy\, dx\, dv$$

$$= \int\int \int_{\Lambda^\#} e^{2x\cdot\alpha}\, |\varphi(\alpha,v)|^2\, \Delta(-2x - \Phi(v,v))^{\lambda-p_1-p_2}\, d\alpha\, dx\, dv$$

$$= 2^{-n_1} \int_V \int_\Lambda \int_{\Lambda^\#} e^{t\cdot\alpha}\, e^{-\Phi(v,v)\cdot\alpha}\, |\varphi(\alpha,v)|^2\, \Delta(-t)^{\lambda-p_1-p_2}\, d\alpha\, dt\, dv$$

$$= 2^{-n_1} \int_V \int_{\Lambda^\#} |\varphi(\alpha,v)|^2\, e^{-\Phi(v,v)\cdot\alpha} \int_\Lambda e^{t\cdot\alpha}\, \Delta(-t)^{\lambda-p_1-p_2}\, dt\, d\alpha\, dv$$

$$= 2^{-n_1}\,\Gamma_\Lambda(\lambda - \frac{p_1}{2} - p_2) \int_V \int_{\Lambda^\#} |\varphi(\alpha,v)|^2\, e^{-\Phi(v,v)\cdot\alpha}\, \Delta(\alpha)^{-\lambda+\frac{p_1}{2}+p_2}\, d\alpha\, dv\, .$$

Q.E.D.

As a consequence of Proposition 2.4.36, it follows that the Hilbert space $L^2_{hol}(\Lambda \times V)$ of all functions $\varphi(\alpha,v)$ on $\Lambda \times V$ which are holomorphic in v and square-integrable under the measure

(2.4.39) $$d\mu_\lambda(\alpha,v) = \pi^{-n}\, 2^{-n_1}\, \Gamma_\Lambda(\lambda)\, e^{-\Phi(v,v)\cdot\alpha}\, \Delta(\alpha)^{-\lambda+\frac{p_1}{2}+p_2}\, d\alpha\, dv$$

is mapped isometrically under the transform (2.4.37) into the *weighted Bergman space* $H^2_\lambda(\Pi)$, consisting of all holomorphic functions $h(u,v)$ on Π which are square-integrable under the measure

$$(2.4.40)\quad d\mu_\lambda(u,v) = \pi^{-n} \frac{\Gamma_\Lambda(\lambda)}{\Gamma_\Lambda(\lambda - \frac{p_1}{2} - p_2)} \Delta(-u - u^* - \Phi(v,v))^{\lambda - p_1 - p_2}\, du\, dv.$$

One can show [G1] that this embedding is surjective. Therefore

$$(2.4.41)\quad H^2_\lambda(\Pi) \approx L^2_{hol}(\Lambda \times V)$$

under the transform (2.4.37). For tube domains ($V = \{0\}$) we have $p_2 = 0$ and (2.4.41) specializes to Theorem 2.4.26. In order to compute the reproducing kernel of $H^2_\lambda(\Pi)$ we need

2.4.42. LEMMA. *For* $z = (z_1,z_2)$ *and* $s = (s_1,s_2)$ *in* Π, *we have*

$$(2.4.43)\quad \int_\Pi \overline{\Delta(-s_1 - w_1^* - \Phi(s_2,w_2))}^{-\lambda} \Delta(-w_1 - w_1^* - \Phi(w_2,w_2))^\mu \cdot$$

$$\cdot \Delta(-z_1 - w_1^* - \Phi(z_2,w_2))^{-\lambda}\, dw_1\, dw_2 =$$

$$\pi^{n_1+n_2} \frac{\Gamma_\Lambda(\mu + \frac{p_1}{2})\Gamma_\Lambda(2\lambda - p_1 - p_2 - \mu)}{\Gamma_\Lambda(\lambda)^2} \Delta(-z_1 - s_1^* - \Phi(z_2,s_2))^{p_1+p_2+\mu-2\lambda}.$$

Proof. Putting $s_1 = \sigma + i\tau$, $z_1 = x + iy$ and $w_1 = u + iv$ we have, applying (2.4.30) to $\Lambda^\# = -\bar{\Lambda}$,

$$(2.4.44)\quad \Gamma_\Lambda(\lambda)^2 \int_\Pi \overline{\Delta(-s_1 - w_1^* - \Phi(s_2,w_2))}^{-\lambda} \Delta(-z_1 - w_1^* - \Phi(z_2,w_2))^{-\lambda} \cdot$$

$$\cdot \Delta(-w_1 - w_1^* - \Phi(w_2,w_2))^\mu\, dw_1\, dw_2$$

$$= \Gamma_\Lambda(\lambda)^2 \int \int \int \overline{\Delta(-\sigma - u - \operatorname{Re}\Phi(s_2,w_2) + i(-\tau + v - \operatorname{Im}\Phi(s_2,w_2)))}^{-\lambda} \cdot$$

$$\cdot\, \Delta(-x - u - \mathrm{Re}\, \Phi(z_2,w_2) + i(-y + v - \mathrm{Im}\, \Phi(z_2,w_2)))^{-\lambda} \cdot$$

$$\cdot\, \Delta(-2u - \Phi(w_2,w_2))^{\mu}\, dw_2\, dv\, du$$

$$= \int \int \int \int_{\Lambda^\#} e^{(\sigma+u+\mathrm{Re}\ \Phi(s_2,w_2))\cdot\alpha}\, e^{-i(\tau-v+\mathrm{Im}\ \Phi(s_2,w_2))\cdot\alpha}\, \Delta(\alpha)^{\lambda-\frac{p_1}{2}}\, d\alpha\ \cdot$$

$$\cdot \int_{\Lambda^\#} e^{(x+u+\mathrm{Re}\ \Phi(z_2,w_2))\cdot\beta}\, e^{i(y-v+\mathrm{Im}\ \Phi(z_2,w_2))\cdot\beta}\, \Delta(\beta)^{\lambda-\frac{p_1}{2}}\, d\beta\ \cdot$$

$$\cdot\, \Delta(-2u - \Phi(w_2,w_2))^{\mu}\, dw_2\, dv\, du.$$

Integrating over the v-variable (in $X \approx \mathbb{R}^{n_1}$), the Fourier inversion theorem yields for (2.4.44)

$$(2\pi)^{n_1} \int \int \int_{\Lambda^\#} e^{(\sigma+x+2u+\mathrm{Re}\ \Phi(s_2+z_2,w_2))\cdot\alpha}\, e^{-i(\tau-y-\mathrm{Im}\ \Phi(z_2-s_2,w_2))\cdot\alpha}$$

$$\cdot\, \Delta(\alpha)^{2\lambda-p_1}\, d\alpha \cdot \Delta(-2u - \Phi(w_2,w_2))^{\mu}\, dw_2\, du$$

(2.4.45)

$$= \pi^{n_1} \int_V \int_\Lambda \int_{\Lambda^\#} e^{(\sigma+x+t-\Phi(w_2,w_2)+\mathrm{Re}\ \Phi(s_2+z_2,w_2))\cdot\alpha}\ \cdot$$

$$\cdot\, e^{-i(\tau-y-\mathrm{Im}\ \Phi(z_2-s_2,w_2))\cdot\alpha}\, \Delta(\alpha)^{2\lambda-p_1}\, \Delta(-t)^{\mu}\, d\alpha\, dt\, dw_2$$

where we put, for any $w_2 \in V$, $t := 2u + \Phi(w_2,w_2) \in \Lambda$. Identifying the inner product on V with

$$z_2 \cdot \overline{w}_2 := \Phi(z_2,w_2) \cdot e \tag{2.4.46}$$

(where $e \in -\Lambda$ is the unit element), we have the well-known relation

$$\int_V \overline{e^{\Phi(s_2,w_2)\cdot e}}\, e^{\Phi(z_2,w_2)\cdot e}\, e^{-\Phi(w_2,w_2)\cdot e}\, dw_2 = \pi^{n_2}\, e^{\Phi(z_2,s_2)\cdot e} \tag{2.4.47}$$

which yields the reproducing kernel for the Fock (or Segal-Bargmann) space over V (cf. Section 2.7). Since the linear change of coordinates $w_2 \mapsto w_2'$ given by

$$P_\alpha^{1/2}\, \Phi(w_2,w_2) = \Phi(w_2', w_2')$$

satisfies $dw_2' = \Delta(\alpha)^{p_2}\, dw_2$ for the Jacobian, we obtain more generally

$$(2.4.48) \qquad \int_V \overline{e^{\Phi(s_2,w_2)\cdot\alpha}}\, e^{\Phi(z_2,w_2)\cdot\alpha}\, e^{-\Phi(w_2,w_2)\cdot\alpha}\, dw_2 = \pi^{n_2}\, \Delta(\alpha)^{-p_2}\, e^{\Phi(z_2,s_2)\cdot\alpha}$$

for every $\alpha \in \Lambda$. Thus (2.4.45) equals

$$\pi^{n_1+n_2} \int_\Lambda \int_{\Lambda^\#} e^{(\sigma+x+t)\cdot\alpha}\, e^{-i(\tau-y)\cdot\alpha}\, \Delta(\alpha)^{2\lambda-p_1-p_2}\, \Delta(-t)^\mu\, e^{\Phi(z_2,s_2)\cdot\alpha}\, d\alpha\, dt$$

$$= \pi^{n_1+n_2}\, \Gamma_\Lambda(\mu + \frac{p_1}{2}) \int_\Lambda e^{(\sigma+x)\cdot\alpha}\, e^{-i(\tau-y)\cdot\alpha}\, \Delta(\alpha)^{2\lambda-\frac{3}{2}p_1-p_2-\mu}\, e^{\Phi(z_2,s_2)\cdot\alpha}\, d\alpha$$

$$= \pi^{n_1+n_2}\, \Gamma_\Lambda(\mu + \frac{p_1}{2})\, \Gamma_\Lambda(2\lambda - p_1 - p_2 - \mu)\, \Delta(-z_1 - s_1^* - \Phi(z_2,s_2))^{p_1+p_2+\mu-2\lambda}.$$

Here we used (2.4.30) twice. Q.E.D.

2.4.49. COROLLARY. *For $\lambda > p_1 + p_2 - 1$, the weighted Bergman space $H_\lambda^2(\Pi)$ has the reproducing kernel*

$$E_\lambda(z,w) = \Delta(-z_1 - w_1^* - \Phi(z_2,w_2))^{-\lambda}$$

for all $z = (z_1,z_2)$ and $w = (w_1,w_2)$ in Π.

Proof. Putting $\mu = \lambda - p_1 - p_2$ in (2.4.43), we obtain

$$\int_\Pi \overline{E_\lambda(s,w)}\, E_\lambda(z,w)\, d\mu_\lambda(w) =$$

$$= \pi^{-(n_1+n_2)} \frac{\Gamma_\Lambda(\lambda)}{\Gamma_\Lambda(\lambda-\frac{p_1}{2}-p_2)} \int_\Pi \overline{E_\lambda(s,w)}\, E_\lambda(z,w)\, \Delta(-w_1 - w_1^* - \Phi(w_2,w_2))^{\mu}\, dw_1\, dw_2$$

$$= \frac{\Gamma_\Lambda(\lambda)}{\Gamma_\Lambda(\lambda-\frac{p_1}{2}-p_2)} \frac{\Gamma_\Lambda(\lambda-\frac{p_1}{2}-p_2)\,\Gamma_\Lambda(\lambda)}{\Gamma_\Lambda(\lambda)^2} E_\lambda(z,s) = E_\lambda(z,s).$$

Q.E.D.

For tube domains ($V = \{0\}$) we obtain (2.4.23).

2.5 Hardy Spaces Over Polycircular Domains

In this section we introduce an important Hilbert space of analytic functions, the so-called Hardy space, associated with a polycircular domain $\Omega = e^\Lambda \mathbb{T}^r \subset \mathbb{C}^r$ with conical base $\Lambda \subset \mathbb{R}^r_<$. The geometry of polycircular domains is discussed in Section 1.4. Endow the r-torus $\mathbb{T}^r$ with the normalized Haar measure dz. Define the L^2-space $L^2(\mathbb{T}^r) := L^2(\mathbb{T}^r, dz)$ of complex-valued functions, with inner product

$$(2.5.1) \qquad (h|k)_{\mathbb{T}^r} := \int_{\mathbb{T}^r} \overline{h(z)}\, k(z)\, dz$$

for all $h,k \in L^2(\mathbb{T}^r)$. The *translation action* of $\mathbb{T}^r$ on $L^2(\mathbb{T}^r)$ is defined by

$$(2.5.2) \qquad (z^\# h)(w) := h(\bar{z}w)$$

for all $z,w \in \mathbb{T}^r$ and $h \in L^2(\mathbb{T}^r)$. Here we put $\bar{z}w := (\bar{z}_1 w_1, \ldots, \bar{z}_r w_r)$. For each $\alpha \in \mathbb{Z}^r$, put

$$(2.5.3) \qquad \alpha_\#(z) = z^\alpha := z_1^{\alpha_1} \cdots z_r^{\alpha_r}.$$

In this way, $\mathbb{Z}^r$ can be identified with the character group of $\mathbb{T}^r$. Let $d\alpha$ be the counting measure on $\mathbb{Z}^r$ and consider the corresponding L^2-space $L^2(\mathbb{Z}^r) := L^2(\mathbb{Z}^r, d\alpha)$ with inner product

$$(\xi|\eta)_{\mathbb{Z}^r} := \sum_{\alpha\in\mathbb{Z}^r} \overline{\xi(\alpha)}\ \eta(\alpha). \tag{2.5.4}$$

The *translation action* of $\mathbb{Z}^r$ on $L^2(\mathbb{Z}^r)$ is defined by

$$(\alpha_{\#}\xi)(\beta) := \xi(\beta - \alpha) \tag{2.5.5}$$

for all $\alpha,\beta \in \mathbb{Z}^r$ and $\xi \in L^2(\mathbb{Z}^r)$. For each $z \in \mathbb{T}^r$, put

$$z^{\#}(\alpha) := \overline{z}^{\alpha} = \overline{z}_1^{\alpha_1} \cdots \overline{z}_r^{\alpha_r}. \tag{2.5.6}$$

In this way, $\mathbb{T}^r$ can be identified with the character group of $\mathbb{Z}^r$.

2.5.7. PROPOSITION. *The Fourier transform*

$$h^{\#}(\alpha) := \int_{\mathbb{T}^r} h(z)\ z^{\#}(\alpha)\ dz = \int_{\mathbb{T}^r} h(z)\ \overline{z}^{\alpha}\ dz \tag{2.5.8}$$

defines a Hilbert space isomorphism

$$L^2(\mathbb{T}^r) \xrightarrow[\approx]{()^{\#}} L^2(\mathbb{Z}^r)$$

whose adjoint $()_{\#}$ *is given by*

$$\xi_{\#}(z) = \sum_{\alpha\in\mathbb{Z}^r} \xi(\alpha)\ \alpha_{\#}(z) = \sum_{\alpha\in\mathbb{Z}^r} \xi(\alpha)\ z^{\alpha}. \tag{2.5.9}$$

For each $\alpha \in \mathbb{Z}^r$ *and* $z \in \mathbb{T}^r$, *there exist commuting diagrams*

$$\begin{array}{ccccc}
L^2(\mathbb{T}^r) & \xrightarrow{()^{\#}} & L^2(\mathbb{Z}^r) & \xrightarrow{()_{\#}} & L^2(\mathbb{T}^r) \\
\downarrow z^{\#} & & z^{\#}\downarrow \ \downarrow \alpha_{\#} & & \downarrow \alpha_{\#} \\
L^2(\mathbb{T}^r) & \xrightarrow[()^{\#}]{} & L^2(\mathbb{Z}^r) & \xrightarrow[()_{\#}]{} & L^2(\mathbb{T}^r)
\end{array}$$

for the respective translation and multiplication actions.

Proof. This is the Fourier-Plancherel Theorem for $\mathbb{T}^r$ and its dual group $\mathbb{Z}^r$. In more elementary terms, consider the natural orthonormal basis

(2.5.10) $$\alpha(\beta) := \delta_{\alpha,\beta} \qquad \text{(Kronecker delta)}$$

of $L^2(\mathbb{Z}^r)$. For each fixed $\alpha \in \mathbb{Z}^r$, the function (2.5.10) on $\mathbb{Z}^r$ has the inverse Fourier transform $\alpha_{\#}(z) = z^\alpha$ which yields an orthonormal basis of $L^2(\mathbb{T}^r)$. Q.E.D.

2.5.11. DEFINITION. The *Hardy space* $H^2(\mathbb{T}^r)$ (depending on Ω) consists of all holomorphic functions $h : \Omega \to \mathbb{C}$ such that

$$||h||^2 := \sup_{a\in\Lambda} \int_{\mathbb{T}^r} |h(e^a z)|^2 \, dz < \infty.$$

By [L4] there exists an embedding $H^2(\mathbb{T}^r) \subset L^2(\mathbb{T}^r)$ as a closed subspace such that

$$\lim_{\substack{a\in\Lambda \\ a\to 0}} \int_{\mathbb{T}^r} |h(e^a z) - h(z)|^2 \, dz = 0.$$

This embedding is invariant under the translation action (2.5.2) of $\mathbb{T}^r$. The orthogonal projection

(2.5.12) $$E : L^2(\mathbb{T}^r) \to H^2(\mathbb{T}^r)$$

is called the *Szegö projection.*

2.5.13. DEFINITION. The closed convex cone

(2.5.14) $$\Lambda^{\#} := \{\alpha \in \mathbb{R}^r : \alpha \cdot a \le 0 \text{ for all } a \in \Lambda\}$$

is called the *polar cone* of Λ. The closed subspace

$$L^2(\mathbb{Z}^r \cap \Lambda^{\#}) := \{\xi \in L^2(\mathbb{Z}^r) : \xi(\alpha) = 0 \ \ \forall \alpha \in \mathbb{Z}^r \backslash \Lambda^{\#}\}$$

of $L^2(\mathbb{Z}^r)$ is invariant under the multiplication action (2.5.6) of $\mathbb{T}^r$.

2.5.15. EXAMPLE. For the Hartogs' wedge $\Omega_{\delta,\varepsilon}$ in $\mathbb{C}^2$ defined in Example 1.4.22 the logarithmic base $\Lambda = \log |\Omega_{\delta,\varepsilon}|$ is given by

$$\Lambda = \{a \in \mathbb{R}^2_< : \varepsilon a_1 < a_2 < \delta a_1\}.$$

The polar cone $\Lambda^\#$ of Λ is bounded by the half-lines $L_{-1/\delta}$ and $L_{-1/\varepsilon}$ of slope $-1/\delta$ and $-1/\varepsilon$, respectively:

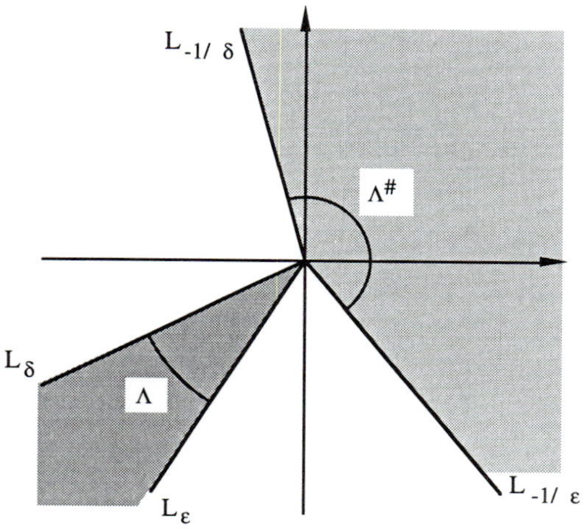

In the extreme case $\delta = 0, \varepsilon = +\infty$ we have $\Lambda^\# = \mathbb{R}^2_+$.

The following result [L4] is a Paley-Wiener type theorem for polycircular domains.

2.5.16. THEOREM. *The Fourier transform* (2.5.8) *induces a Hilbert space isomorphism*

$$H^2(\mathbb{T}^r) \xrightarrow[\approx]{()^\#} L^2(\mathbb{Z}^r \cap \Lambda^\#).$$

Conversely, for every $\xi \in L^2(\mathbb{Z}^r \cap \Lambda^\#)$ *the holomorphic extension of* $\xi_\#$ *to* Ω *is given by the compactly convergent series*

(2.5.17) $$\xi_{\#}(z) = \sum_{\alpha \in \mathbb{Z}^r \cap \Lambda^{\#}} \alpha_{\#}(z) \cdot \xi(\alpha) = \sum_{\alpha \in \mathbb{Z}^r \cap \Lambda^{\#}} z^{\alpha} \cdot \xi(\alpha).$$

For every $z \in \mathbb{T}^r$, *there exists a commuting diagram*

$$\begin{array}{ccc} H^2(\mathbb{T}^r) & \xrightarrow{\ ()^{\#}\ } & L^2(\mathbb{Z}^r \cap \Lambda^{\#}) \\ {\scriptstyle z^{\#}} \downarrow & & \downarrow {\scriptstyle z^{\#}} \\ H^2(\mathbb{T}^r) & \xrightarrow[\ ()^{\#}\ ]{} & L^2(\mathbb{Z}^r \cap \Lambda^{\#}) \end{array}$$

for the respective translation and multiplication actions.

2.5.18. DEFINITION. The holomorphic function on Ω given by the compactly convergent series

(2.5.19) $$E_e(z) = \sum_{\alpha \in \mathbb{Z}^r \cap \Lambda^{\#}} \alpha_{\#}(z) = \sum_{\alpha \in \mathbb{Z}^r \cap \Lambda^{\#}} z^{\alpha}$$

is called the *Szegö characteristic function* of Ω.

2.5.20. THEOREM. *The Hardy space* $H^2(\mathbb{T}^r)$ *has a reproducing "Szegö" kernel with a series representation*

(2.5.21) $$E(z,w) = E_e(z\bar{w}) = \sum_{\alpha \in \mathbb{Z}^r \cap \Lambda^{\#}} z^{\alpha} \bar{w}^{\alpha}$$

converging compactly on $\Omega \times \Omega$.

Thus, for each $w \in \Omega$, the function

(2.5.22) $$E_w(z) := E(z,w)$$

belongs to $H^2(\mathbb{T}^r)$, and the Szegö projection (2.5.12) is given by

(2.5.23) $$(Eh)(z) := (E_z | h)_{\mathbb{T}^r}$$

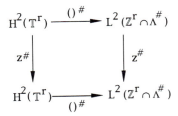

for all $h \in L^2(\mathbb{T}^r)$ and $z \in \Omega$.

Proof. By Theorem 2.5.16, the monomials $\{z^\alpha : \alpha \in \mathbb{Z}^r \cap \Lambda^\#\}$ form an orthonormal basis of $H^2(\mathbb{T}^r)$. Q.E.D.

2.6 Bergman Spaces Over Polycircular Domains

In this section we introduce an important Hilbert space of analytic functions, the so-called Bergman space, associated with a polycircular domain $\Omega = e^\Lambda \mathbb{T}^r \subset \mathbb{C}^r$ with logarithmic base Λ. We assume that $\Omega \subset \mathbb{B}^r$ is pseudoconvex, i.e., Λ is a convex open subset of $\mathbb{R}^r_<$. Note that Λ is not necessarily conical. We also assume that Ω contains the origin.

Let $dV(z)$ denote the Lebesgue measure on $\mathbb{C}^r \approx \mathbb{R}^{2r}$. Consider the corresponding Lebesgue space $L^2(\Omega) := L^2(\Omega, dV)$ of square-integrable functions, with inner product

(2.6.1) $$(h|k)_\Omega := \int_\Omega \overline{h(z)}\; k(z)\; dV(z).$$

As in Section 2.5, define the *translation action* of $\mathbb{T}^r$ on $L^2(\Omega)$ by putting

(2.6.2) $$(z^\# h)(w) := h(\bar{z}w)$$

for all $z \in \mathbb{T}^r$, $h \in L^2(\Omega)$ and $w \in \Omega$, and define for all $\alpha \in \mathbb{Z}^r$

(2.6.3) $$z^\#(\alpha) := \bar{z}^\alpha .$$

2.6.4. DEFINITION. The subspace

$$H^2(\Omega) := \{h \in L^2(\Omega) : h \text{ holomorphic}\} = L^2(\Omega) \cap \mathcal{O}(\Omega)$$

of $L^2(\Omega)$ is called the *Bergman space* over Ω. By Proposition 2.1.3, $H^2(\Omega)$ is a closed subspace of $L^2(\Omega)$. It is invariant under the translation action (2.6.2). The orthogonal projection

(2.6.5) $$E_\Omega : L^2(\Omega) \to H^2(\Omega)$$

onto $H^2(\Omega)$ is called the *Bergman projection.* The following result is a Paley-Wiener type characterization for Bergman spaces over polycircular domains (containing the origin).

2.6.6. THEOREM. *There exists a Hilbert space isomorphism*

$$H^2(\Omega) \xrightarrow[\approx]{()^{\#}} L^2(\mathbb{N}^r) \tag{2.6.7}$$

with adjoint $L^2(\mathbb{N}^r) \xrightarrow[\approx]{()_{\#}} H^2(\Omega)$, *such that for each* $\alpha \in \mathbb{N}^r$ *the function*

$$\alpha(\beta) = \delta_{\alpha,\beta} \qquad \textit{(Kronecker symbol)}$$

on $\mathbb{N}^r$ *satisfies*

$$\alpha_{\#}(z) = \frac{z^\alpha}{\|z^\alpha\|_\Omega}. \tag{2.6.8}$$

For each $z \in \mathbb{T}^r$, *there exists a commuting diagram*

$$\begin{array}{ccc} H^2(\Omega) & \xrightarrow{()^{\#}} & L^2(\mathbb{N}^r) \\ \downarrow{\scriptstyle z^{\#}} & & \downarrow{\scriptstyle z^{\#}} \\ H^2(\Omega) & \xrightarrow[()^{\#}]{} & L^2(\mathbb{N}^r) \end{array}$$

for the respective translation and multiplication action.

Proof. Since Ω is bounded and contains the origin, Proposition 1.4.8 implies that $H^2(\Omega)$ contains the polynomial algebra $\mathcal{P}(\mathbb{C}^r)$ as a dense subspace. Hence the monomials

$$z^\alpha := z_1^{\alpha_1} \cdots z_r^{\alpha_r}$$

for $\alpha \in \mathbb{N}^r$ are total in $H^2(\Omega)$. Since Ω is polycircular, poly-rotational invariance of $dV(z)$ implies $(z^\alpha | z^\beta)_\Omega = 0$ if $\alpha \neq \beta$. Hence the monomials (2.6.8) form an orthonormal basis of $H^2(\Omega)$. For the last statement, let $z \in \mathbb{T}^r$ and $\alpha \in \mathbb{N}^r$. Then we have for all $w \in \Omega$

$$(z^{\#}\alpha_{\#})(w) = \alpha_{\#}(\bar{z}w) = \frac{(\bar{z}w)^{\alpha}}{||z^{\alpha}||_{\Omega}} = \frac{\bar{z}^{\alpha}w^{\alpha}}{||z^{\alpha}||_{\Omega}}$$
$$= \bar{z}^{\alpha}\ \alpha_{\#}(w) = z^{\#}(\alpha)\alpha_{\#}(w).$$

Q.E.D.

2.6.9. DEFINITION. The holomorphic function on Ω defined by the compactly convergent series

(2.6.10)
$$\chi_{\Omega}(z) = \sum_{\alpha \in \mathbb{N}^r} \frac{z^{\alpha}}{||z^{\alpha}||^2_{\Omega}}$$

is called the *Bergman characteristic function* of Ω.

2.6.11. THEOREM. *The Bergman space* $H^2(\Omega)$ *has the reproducing "Bergman" kernel with a series representation*

(2.6.12)
$$E_{\Omega}(z,w) = \chi_{\Omega}(z\bar{w}) = \sum_{\alpha \in \mathbb{N}^r} \frac{z^{\alpha}\bar{w}^{\alpha}}{||z^{\alpha}||^2_{\Omega}}$$

which converges compactly on $\Omega \times \Omega$.

Thus for each $w \in \Omega$, the function

(2.6.13)
$$E_w(z) := E_{\Omega}(z,w)$$

belongs to $H^2(\Omega)$, and the Bergman projection (2.6.5) is given by

(2.6.14)
$$(E_{\Omega}h)(z) = (E_z|h)_{\Omega}$$

for all $h \in L^2(\Omega)$ and $z \in \Omega$.

2.7 The Segal-Bargmann Space of a Hermitian Vector Space

In this section we introduce an important Hilbert space of entire functions, the so-called Segal-Bargmann space, associated with a complex vector space Z endowed with a hermitian inner product $(z|w)$. In view of later applications we assume that Z is the hermitian vector space underlying an irreducible complex Jordan triple Z of rank r and dimension n. For background on Jordan triples, cf. Section 1.5. Let $dV(z)$ be the Lebesgue measure, and consider the Gauss probability measure

$$d\mu_Z(z) := \pi^{-n} e^{-(z|z)} dV(z) \tag{2.7.1}$$

on Z. Define the L^2-space $L^2(Z) := L^2(Z, d\mu_Z)$ of complex functions on Z, with inner product

$$(h|k)_Z := \int_Z \overline{h(z)}\, k(z)\, d\mu_Z(z). \tag{2.7.2}$$

The group K defined in (1.5.3) consists of unitary transformations of Z and leaves the measure (2.7.1) invariant. Thus we obtain a *translation action* of K on $L^2(Z)$ defined by

$$(\lambda_s h)(z) = h(s^{-1}z) \tag{2.7.3}$$

for all $s \in K$, $h \in L^2(Z)$ and $z \in Z$.

2.7.4. DEFINITION. The subspace

$$H^2(Z) := \{h \in L^2(Z) : h \text{ holomorphic}\} = L^2(Z) \cap \mathcal{O}(Z)$$

of $L^2(Z)$ is called the *Segal-Bargmann space* over Z.

One can show that $H^2(Z)$ is a closed subspace of $L^2(Z)$. It is invariant under the right translation action (2.7.3) of K. The orthogonal projection

$$E_Z : L^2(Z) \to H^2(Z) \tag{2.7.5}$$

onto $H^2(Z)$ is called the *Segal-Bargmann projection.*

2.7.6. PROPOSITION. *The Hilbert space* $H^2(Z)$ *has the reproducing "Segal-Bargmann" kernel*

$$E_Z(z,w) := e^{(z|w)} \tag{2.7.7}$$

for all $z,w \in Z$.

Thus for every $w \in Z$ the function

(2.7.8) $$E_w(z) := E_Z(z,w)$$

belongs to $H^2(Z)$, and the Segal-Bargmann projection (2.7.5) is given by

(2.7.9) $$(E_Z h)(z) = (E_z | h)_Z$$

for all $h \in L^2(Z)$ and $z \in Z$.

Consider the algebra $\mathcal{P}(Z)$ of all holomorphic polynomials on Z, endowed with the inner product

(2.7.10) $$(p|q)_Z = (\partial_p q)(0)$$

for all $p,q \in \mathcal{P}(Z)$. Here ∂_p is the constant coefficient holomorphic differential operator on Z uniquely determined by

$$\partial_p E_w = \overline{p(w)}\, E_w$$

for all $w \in Z$. The group K acts by algebra automorphisms on $\mathcal{P}(Z)$ via (2.7.3) and leaves the positive definite scalar product (2.7.10) invariant. The canonical splitting

$$\mathcal{P}(Z) = \sum_{j \in \mathbb{N}} \mathcal{P}^j(Z) \qquad \text{(algebraic direct sum)}$$

by the total degree j is invariant under the action of K, and the K-modules $\mathcal{P}^j(Z)$ are pairwise orthogonal under (2.7.10) (use invariance under the circle group $z \mapsto e^{it}z$).

2.7.11. EXAMPLE. Let $p \in \mathcal{P}^j(Z)$ and $a \in Z$. Then

(2.7.12) $$((z|a)^j | p)_Z = j!\; p(a).$$

By [S2, J2, U5], there exists a decomposition

(2.7.13) $$\mathcal{P}(Z) = \sum_{\alpha \in \vec{\mathbb{N}}^r} \mathcal{P}^\alpha(Z) \qquad \text{(algebraic direct sum)}$$

into *irreducible* K-modules $\mathcal{P}^\alpha(Z) \subset \mathcal{P}(Z)$, where $\vec{\mathbb{N}}^r$ denotes the set of all multi-indices $\alpha = (\alpha_1, ..., \alpha_r)$ of integers

(2.7.14) $$\alpha_1 \geq \alpha_2 \geq \cdots \geq \alpha_r \geq 0.$$

These multi-indices are called *signatures* (or partitions) of length r, and the polynomials in the finite-dimensional unitary K-module $\mathcal{P}^\alpha(Z)$ are said to be of *type* α. They are homogeneous of degree $|\alpha| := \alpha_1 + \cdots + \alpha_r$. Consider the *Hilbert sum*

$$\sum_{\alpha \in \vec{\mathbb{N}}^r}^{\oplus} \mathcal{P}^\alpha(Z)$$

of all square-summable families $(\xi_\alpha)_{\alpha \in \vec{\mathbb{N}}^r}$, with inner product

(2.7.15) $$((\xi_\alpha)|(\eta_\alpha))_{\vec{\mathbb{N}}^r} = \sum_{\alpha \in \vec{\mathbb{N}}^r} (\xi_\alpha|\eta_\alpha)_Z.$$

2.7.16. THEOREM. *There exists a Hilbert space isomorphism*

(2.7.17) $$H^2(Z) \xrightarrow[\approx]{()^\#} \sum_{\alpha \in \vec{\mathbb{N}}^r}^{\oplus} \mathcal{P}^\alpha(Z)$$

such that the adjoint isomorphism $(\,)_\#$ *is given by*

(2.7.18) $$((\xi_\alpha))_\# := \sum_{\alpha \in \vec{\mathbb{N}}^r} \xi_\alpha$$

for each square-summable family (ξ_α) *of polynomials* ξ_α *of type* α. *The isomorphism* (2.7.17) *is K-equivariant.*

Proof. Since the inner products (2.7.2) and (2.7.10) agree on $\mathcal{P}(Z)$ the embedding

(2.7.19) $$\mathcal{P}(Z) \subset H^2(Z)$$

as a K-invariant subspace is isometric. The decomposition (2.7.13) of $\mathcal{P}(Z)$ is orthogonal since the irreducible K-modules $\mathcal{P}^\alpha(Z)$, $\alpha \in \vec{\mathbb{N}}^r$, are pairwise inequivalent. It follows that $()_\#$ defines an isometric mapping into $H^2(Z)$. To show that $()_\#$ is surjective, let $h \in H^2(Z)$. By Proposition 1.5.42, applied to $\Omega = Z$, there is a Taylor expansion

$$h(z) = \sum_{j \in \mathbb{N}} p_j(z)$$

into a series of j-homogeneous polynomials $p_j \in \mathcal{P}^j(Z)$ which converges compactly on Z. By (2.7.12) or the fact that (2.7.1) is invariant under the circle group $z \mapsto e^{it}z$ we have $(p_j|p_k)_Z = 0$ whenever $j \neq k$. This implies

$$||h||_Z^2 = \sum_{j \in \mathbb{N}} ||p_j||_Z^2 < \infty$$

and hence

$$||h - \sum_{j<k} p_j||_Z^2 = \sum_{j \geq k} ||p_j||_Z^2 \to 0$$

as $k \to \infty$. Therefore $\mathcal{P}(Z)$ is a dense subspace of $H^2(Z)$, and $()_\#$ is surjective. Q.E.D.

2.7.20. DEFINITION. For each partition $\alpha \in \vec{\mathbb{N}}^r$, let $E^\alpha(z,w)$ denote the reproducing kernel of $\mathcal{P}^\alpha(Z)$.

Thus, for every $w \in Z$, the function

$$E_w^\alpha(z) := E^\alpha(z,w) \tag{2.7.21}$$

is a polynomial of type α, and the orthogonal projection $E^\alpha : H^2(Z) \to \mathcal{P}^\alpha(Z)$ onto the finite-dimensional subspace $\mathcal{P}^\alpha(Z)$ is given by

$$(E^\alpha h)(z) = (E_z^\alpha|h)_Z \tag{2.7.22}$$

for all $h \in H^2(Z)$ and $z \in Z$. In particular,

$$(E_z^\alpha \mid E_w^\alpha)_Z = E^\alpha(z,w) \tag{2.7.23}$$

for all $z,w \in Z$.

2.7.24. THEOREM. *The Segal-Bargmann kernel* (2.7.7) *has a series representation*

(2.7.25) $$E_Z(z,w) = \sum_{\alpha \in \vec{\mathbb{N}}^r} E^\alpha(z,w)$$

which converges compactly on $Z \times Z$.

Proof. This expresses the fact that $H^2(Z)$ is the Hilbert sum of $\mathcal{P}^\alpha(Z)$, $\alpha \in \vec{\mathbb{N}}^r$. Q.E.D.

For the rest of this section we study the special case that the complex Jordan triple Z is actually the complexification $Z = X \oplus iX$ of an irreducible real Jordan algebra X. Let $\Delta : Z \to \mathbb{C}$ be the Jordan algebra determinant of Z, and consider the associated constant coefficient differential operator ∂_Δ called the *generalized wave operator*. By [U5] the polynomial algebra $\mathcal{P}(Z)$ is the free tensor product

(2.7.26) $$\mathcal{P}(Z) = \mathbb{C}[\Delta] \otimes \mathcal{H}(Z)$$

of the polynomial algebra $\mathbb{C}[\Delta]$ generated by Δ and the subspace

(2.7.27) $$\mathcal{H}(Z) := \{q \in \mathcal{P}(Z) : \partial_\Delta q = 0\}$$

of all *harmonic* polynomials ("separation of variables"). Thus every $p \in \mathcal{P}(Z)$ has a unique finite expansion

(2.7.28) $$p = \sum_{k \in \mathbb{N}} \Delta^k q_k$$

where $q_k \in \mathcal{H}(Z)$ is a harmonic polynomial for every k. Let K' denote the *commutator subgroup* of K (cf. Section 1.5). By [S5], the determinant Δ is invariant under K'. Since $K = K' \cdot \mathbb{T}$ it follows that there exists a character $\chi : K \to U(\mathbb{C})$ satisfying

(2.7.29) $$\Delta(sz) = \Delta(z)\chi(s)$$

for all $z \in Z$ and $s \in K$. A similar relation holds for the differential operator ∂_Δ. Therefore $\mathcal{H}(Z)$ is invariant under K. Since Δ is a homogeneous polynomial we have

$$\mathcal{H}(Z) = \sum_{j \in \mathbb{N}} \mathcal{H}^j(Z)$$

where

(2.7.30) $$\mathcal{H}^j(Z) := \mathcal{H}(Z) \cap \mathcal{P}^j(Z).$$

One can show [U5] that $\mathcal{H}^j(Z)$ is spanned by the powers $z \mapsto (z|w)^j$ where $w \in Z$ satisfies $\Delta(w) = 0$. In general, the K-modules $\mathcal{H}^j(Z)$ are not irreducible.

2.7.31. DEFINITION. Consider the algebraic hypersurface

$$Z' := \{z \in Z : \Delta(z) = 1\}.$$

The *reduced Segal-Bargmann space* is defined as the closed subspace

$$H^2(Z') := \overline{\mathcal{H}(Z)} \subset H^2(Z)$$

of $H^2(Z)$ generated by all harmonic polynomials. The orthogonal projection

$$\mathcal{H} : H^2(Z) \to H^2(Z')$$

is called the *harmonic projection*. For example, $\mathcal{H}(p) := q_0$ if $p \in \mathcal{P}(Z)$ is given by (2.7.28). Now consider the natural identification

$$\vec{\mathbb{N}}^{r-1} = \{(\alpha_1, \ldots, \alpha_r) \in \vec{\mathbb{N}}^r : \alpha_r = 0\}.$$

2.7.32. THEOREM. *The Fourier transform (2.7.17) induces a Hilbert space isomorphism*

(2.7.33) $$H^2(Z') \xrightarrow[\approx]{()^\#} \sum_{\alpha \in \vec{\mathbb{N}}^{r-1}}^{\oplus} \mathcal{P}^\alpha(Z).$$

Proof. By (2.7.29) the polynomial differential operator $\Delta\partial_\Delta$ is K-invariant and thus acts as a scalar operator on each irreducible component $\mathcal{P}^\alpha(Z)$. By [U5], we have

(2.7.34) $$\Delta\partial_\Delta p = \prod_{j=1}^{r} (\alpha_j + (r - j) \frac{a}{2}) p$$

for every $p \in \mathcal{P}^\alpha(Z)$ and $\alpha \in \vec{\mathbb{N}}^r$. Here a is given by (1.5.60). Therefore $\partial_\Delta p = 0$ if and only if $\alpha_r = 0$. Q.E.D.

Writing $\vec{\mathbb{N}}^{r-k} := \{(\alpha_1, \ldots, \alpha_r) \in \vec{\mathbb{N}}^r : \alpha_{k+1} = \alpha_{k+2} = \cdots = \alpha_r = 0\}$, one has a similar "harmonic" characterization of

$$\sum_{\alpha\in\vec{\mathbb{N}}^{r-k}}^{\oplus} \mathcal{P}^\alpha(Z).$$

2.7.35. EXAMPLE. Let Z be the complex spin factor of dimension d. Thus Z has an inner product $z \cdot \bar{w}$ and a conjugation $z \mapsto \bar{z}$. By (1.5.40), we have

(2.7.36) $$\Delta(z) = z \cdot z,$$

(2.7.37) $$(z|w) := 2z \cdot \bar{w}$$

for the normalized inner product. Since ∂_Δ is computed via $(z|w)$, we obtain

(2.7.38) $$\partial_\Delta = \frac{1}{4} \sum_{j=1}^{n} \frac{\partial^2}{\partial z_j^2}.$$

Thus $\mathcal{H}(Z)$ consists of all "complex-harmonic" polynomials in the usual sense. By (2.7.28), every $p \in \mathcal{P}^\ell(Z)$ has a unique representation

(2.7.39) $$p(z) = \sum_{k=0}^{[\ell/2]} (z \cdot z)^k \, q_k(z)$$

where $q_k \in \mathcal{H}^{\ell-2k}(Z)$. For every $q \in \mathcal{H}^m(Z)$ we have

$$\partial_\Delta(\Delta^k q) = k(k + m + \frac{a}{2})\, \Delta^{k-\ell} q$$

where $a := n - 2$. More generally,

$$\partial_\Delta^j(\Delta^k q) = \frac{k!}{(k-j)!} \frac{\Gamma(k+m+\frac{a}{2}+1)}{\Gamma(k+m+\frac{a}{2}-j+1)}\, \Delta^{k-j} q$$

for all $0 \le j \le k$. Using (2.7.39) we obtain

$$\Delta^j \cdot \partial_\Delta^j p = \sum_{k=0}^{[\ell/2]} a_{jk}\, \Delta^k q_k$$

where (a_{jk}) is the triangular matrix

$$a_{jk} = \frac{k!}{(k-j)!} \frac{\Gamma(\ell-k+\frac{a}{2}+1)}{\Gamma(\ell-k+\frac{a}{2}-j+1)}$$

for $0 \le j \le k \le [\ell/2]$. For $0 \le j \le [\ell/2]$ define

$$b_{0j} = \frac{(-1)^j}{j!} \frac{\Gamma(\frac{a}{2}+\ell-j)}{\Gamma(\frac{a}{2}+\ell)} .$$

Then

$$\sum_{j=0}^{k} b_{0j}\, a_{jk} = \delta_{0k} \qquad \text{(Kronecker symbol)}$$

for all $0 \le k \le [\ell/2]$ showing that (b_{0j}) is the first row of the inverse of the matrix (a_{jk}). Therefore the harmonic projection of $p \in \mathcal{P}^\ell(Z)$ is given by

(2.7.40)
$$\mathcal{H}(p) = q_0 = \sum_{j=0}^{[\ell/2]} b_{0j}\, \Delta^j \partial_\Delta^j\, p$$
$$= \sum_{j=0}^{[\ell/2]} \frac{(-1)^j}{j!} \frac{\Gamma(\frac{a}{2} + \ell - j)}{\Gamma(\frac{a}{2} + \ell)} \Delta^j \cdot \partial_\Delta^j\, p.$$

Now assume in particular that $p(z) = (z|\bar{w}) \cdot q(z)$ where $w \in Z$ is fixed and $q \in \mathcal{H}^{\ell-1}(Z)$. Writing

$$w = \sum_{i=1}^{n} (w \cdot b_i)\, b_i$$

for the standard basis b_i of $Z \approx \mathbb{C}^n$ we see that

$$\partial_\Delta p = \sum_i b_i \cdot w \frac{\partial q}{\partial z_i} = \partial_w\, q$$

since $\partial_\Delta q = 0$. For $j \geq 2$ we have

$$\partial_\Delta^j p = \partial_\Delta^{j-1}\, \partial_w\, q = \partial_w \partial_\Delta^{j-1} q = 0.$$

Thus (2.7.40) simplifies to

(2.7.41)
$$\mathcal{H}((z|\bar{w}) \cdot q) = (z|\bar{w})\, q - \frac{\Gamma(\frac{a}{2} + \ell - 1)}{\Gamma(\frac{a}{2} + \ell)} \Delta \cdot \partial_\Delta p$$
$$= (z|\bar{w})\, q - \frac{\Delta(z) \cdot \partial_w q}{\ell - 1 + \frac{a}{2}}.$$

2.7.42. DEFINITION. The holomorphic function on Z defined by the compactly convergent series

(2.7.43)
$$\chi_Z(z) = \sum_{\alpha \in \vec{\mathbb{N}}^r} E^\alpha(z,e) = e^{(z|e)}$$

is called the *Segal-Bargmann characteristic function* of Z.

2.7.44. PROPOSITION. *The Segal-Bargmann kernel (2.7.7) satisfies*

(2.7.45) $$E_Z(z,w) = \chi_Z(z \circ w^*)$$

for all $z,w \in Z = X^{\mathbb{C}}$.

Proof. The "associativity" property [L8, L9] of $(z|w)$ implies

$$(z|w) = (z|\{e(w^*)^*e\}) = (\{ze^*w^*\}|e) = (z \circ w^*|e).$$

Taking exponentials, the assertion follows. Q.E.D.

2.8 Hardy Spaces Over Symmetric Domains

In this section we introduce an important Hilbert space of analytic functions, the so-called Hardy space, associated with a symmetric domain. As explained in Section 1.5, every symmetric domain can be realized as the open unit ball

$$\Omega = \{z \in Z : \|z\| < 1\}$$

of a complex Jordan triple Z. We will assume that Z is irreducible of rank r and dimension n. Let S be the Shilov boundary of Ω. Then S = K/L where $L = \{\ell \in K : \ell e = e\}$. Let a and b denote the characteristic multiplicities of Z.

For any signature $\alpha \in \vec{\mathbb{N}}^r$ (cf. (2.7.14)) define the *multi-Pochhammer symbol*

(2.8.1) $$((\lambda))_\alpha := \prod_{j=1}^{r} (\lambda - \frac{a}{2}(j-1))_{\alpha_j}$$

as a polynomial of degree $|\alpha|$ in $\lambda \in \mathbb{C}$. Here $(x)_n := x(x+1) \cdots (x+n-1)$ is the usual Pochhammer symbol. Since the group $K = GL(\Omega)$ acts transitively on S, there exists a unique K-invariant probability measure dz on S. Define the L^2-space $L^2(S) := L^2(S,dz)$ of complex functions on S, with inner product

(2.8.2) $$(h|k)_S := \int_S \overline{h(z)}\ k(z)\ dz.$$

The *translation action* of K on $L^2(S)$ is defined for all $s \in K$, $h \in L^2(S)$ and $z \in S$ by

(2.8.3) $$(\lambda_s h)(z) := h(s^{-1}z)\ .$$

2.8.4. DEFINITION. The *Hardy space* $H^2(S)$ consists of all holomorphic functions $h : \Omega \to \mathbb{C}$ such that

$$||h||^2 := \sup_{r\to 1} \int_S |h(rz)|^2\ dz < \infty.$$

By [K5] there exists an embedding $H^2(S) \subset L^2(S)$ as a closed subspace such that

$$\lim_{r\to 1} \int_S |h(rz)-h(z)|^2\ dz = 0.$$

This embedding is invariant under the left translation action (2.8.3) of K. The orthogonal projection

(2.8.5) $$E : L^2(S) \to H^2(S)$$

is called the *Szegö projection*.

2.8.6. PROPOSITION. *The Hilbert space* $H^2(S)$ *has the reproducing "Szegö" kernel*

(2.8.7) $$E(z,w) = \Delta(z,w)^{-n/r}$$

where Δ *is the Jordan triple determinant* (1.5.17) *of* Z.

Thus for every $w \in S$ the holomorphic function

(2.8.8) $$E_w(z) := E(z,w)$$

on Ω belongs to $H^2(S)$, and the Szegö projection (2.8.5) is given by

(2.8.9) $$(Eh)(z) = (E_z|h)_S$$

for all $h \in L^2(S)$ and $z \in \Omega$. The *proof* follows by analytic continuation from the corresponding result for the (weighted) Bergman spaces studied in Section 2.9. For details, cf. [FK1].

2.8.10. THEOREM. *There exists a Hilbert space isomorphism*

$$H^2(S) \xrightarrow[\approx]{()^\#} \sum_{\alpha \in \vec{\mathbb{N}}^r}^{\oplus} \mathcal{P}^\alpha(Z) \tag{2.8.11}$$

such that the adjoint isomorphism $()_\#$ *is given by*

$$((\xi_\alpha))_\#(z) := \sum_{\alpha \in \vec{\mathbb{N}}^r} ((n/r))_\alpha^{1/2}\, \xi_\alpha(z) \tag{2.8.12}$$

for all square-summable families (ξ_α) *and all* $z \in S$. *The mapping* (2.8.11) *is K-equivariant.*

Proof. The complexification $K^{\mathbb{C}}$ of K is a complex Lie subgroup of $GL(Z)$ which acts on $\mathcal{P}(Z)$ via

$$(\lambda_g p)(z) := p(g^{-1}z) \tag{2.8.13}$$

for all $g \in K^{\mathbb{C}}$, $p \in \mathcal{P}(Z)$ and $z \in Z$. For every $g \in K^{\mathbb{C}}$, the adjoint $g^* \in GL(Z)$ with respect to $(z|w)$ belongs to $K^{\mathbb{C}}$. We claim that the kernel function (2.7.21) of $\mathcal{P}^\alpha(Z)$, for $\alpha \in \vec{\mathbb{N}}^r$, satisfies

$$\lambda_{g^*} E_z^\alpha = E_{g^{-1}z}^\alpha \tag{2.8.14}$$

for all $g \in K^{\mathbb{C}}$ and $z \in Z$. In fact we have for all $p \in \mathcal{P}(Z)$

$$(E_{g^{-1}z}^\alpha \mid p)_Z = p(g^{-1}z) = (\lambda_g p)(z) = (E_z^\alpha \mid \lambda_g p)_Z = (\lambda_{g^*} E_z^\alpha \mid p)_Z$$

where the last equation follows from the fact that the inner product (2.7.10) is defined in terms of the hermitian structure of Z. Since p is arbitrary, the assertion (2.8.14) follows. Now fix a frame $e_1, \ldots, e_r$ of Z and put $e := e_1 + \cdots + e_r$. Consider the associated Peirce decomposition (1.5.58) and define

(2.8.15) $$Z_\ell := \sum_{1 \le i \le j \le \ell} Z_{ij}$$

for each $1 \le \ell \le r$. Z_ℓ is a Jordan algebra of rank ℓ with unit element $e_1 + \cdots + e_\ell$. For $\ell = r$, $Z_r = Z_1(e)$ is the Peirce 1-space of e. Let

$$\Delta_{Z_\ell} : Z_\ell \to \mathbb{C}$$

be the corresponding Jordan algebra determinant. Defining

(2.8.16) $$\Delta_\ell\Big(\sum_{0 \le i \le j \le r} z_{ij}\Big) := \Delta_{Z_\ell}\Big(\sum_{1 \le i \le j \le \ell} z_{ij}\Big)$$

we obtain a polynomial $\Delta_\ell : Z \to \mathbb{C}$ of degree ℓ called the ℓ-th *minor* of Z. By [U5], the K-module $\mathcal{P}^\alpha(Z)$ is spanned by the translates of the *conical polynomial*

(2.8.17) $$\Delta_\alpha(z) := \Delta_1(z)^{\alpha_1 - \alpha_2}\, \Delta_2(z)^{\alpha_2 - \alpha_3} \cdots \Delta_r(z)^{\alpha_r}.$$

Define the *spherical polynomial*

(2.8.18) $$\phi_\alpha(z) := \int_L \Delta_\alpha(sz)\, ds \in \mathcal{P}^\alpha(Z).$$

By definition of the Shilov boundary, every polynomial is uniquely determined by its restriction to S. Thus we obtain a K-equivariant embedding $\mathcal{P}(Z) \to H^2(S)$. Since $\mathcal{P}^\alpha(Z)$ has multiplicity one in $L^2(S)$ [S2], it is known that (2.8.18) is the unique L-invariant polynomial of type α satisfying $\phi_\alpha(e) = 1$. Thus

(2.8.19) $$E^\alpha_e(z) = E^\alpha_e(e) \cdot \phi_\alpha(z).$$

Now put $X := \{x \in Z_1(e) : \{ex^*e\} = x\}$ and let Λ be the symmetric cone of X. For every $x \in -\Lambda$, the quadratic representation P_x is positive definite and $g := P_x^{1/2} \in K^{\mathbb{C}}$ is self-adjoint. Therefore (2.8.14) implies

$$E^\alpha(x,x) = (E^\alpha_x \mid E^\alpha_x)_Z = (E^\alpha_x \mid E^\alpha_{ge})_Z = (E^\alpha_x \mid \lambda_g^{-1} E^\alpha_e)_Z$$

$$= (\lambda_g^{-1} E^\alpha_x \mid E^\alpha_e)_Z = (E^\alpha_{gx} \mid E^\alpha_e)_Z = (E^\alpha_{x^2} \mid E^\alpha_e)_Z = E^\alpha(x^2, e).$$

Since $\Lambda \subset X$ is open we obtain

$$E^{\alpha}(x,x) = E^{\alpha}(x^2,e) \tag{2.8.20}$$

for all $x \in X$. Put $d_\alpha := \dim \mathcal{P}^{\alpha}(Z)$. Applying Schur orthogonality [FK1] to the irreducible K-module $\mathcal{P}^{\alpha}(Z)$ we obtain

$$\int_K |E^{\alpha}_e(s \cdot x)|^2 \, ds = \int_K |(E^{\alpha}_{s\cdot x} | E^{\alpha}_e)_Z|^2 \, ds = \int_K |(\lambda_s E^{\alpha}_x | E^{\alpha}_e)_Z|^2 \, ds$$

$$= \frac{1}{d_\alpha} (E^{\alpha}_x | E^{\alpha}_x)_Z \cdot (E^{\alpha}_e | E^{\alpha}_e)_Z = \frac{E^{\alpha}(x^2,e)\, E^{\alpha}(e,e)}{d_\alpha}.$$

Combined with (2.8.19) this implies

$$\int_K |\phi_\alpha(sx)|^2 \, ds = \frac{1}{d_\alpha} \phi_\alpha(x^2) \tag{2.8.21}$$

for all $x \in X$. In particular,

$$(\phi_\alpha | \phi_\alpha)_S = \int_K |\phi_\alpha(se)|^2 \, ds = \frac{1}{d_\alpha}. \tag{2.8.22}$$

In order to compute the norm of ϕ_α in $H^2(Z)$, let $\equiv$ denote equality up to a factor independent of α. Integrating in polar coordinates (Proposition 1.5.84) and changing variables $y_j = x_j^2$ we obtain from (2.8.21)

$$d_\alpha(\phi_\alpha | \phi_\alpha)_Z \equiv d_\alpha \int_Z |\phi_\alpha(z)|^2 \, e^{-(z|z)} \, dV(z)$$

$$\equiv d_\alpha \int_{\mathbb{R}^r_+} \int_K |\phi_\alpha(t \cdot \sum_{j=1}^{r} x_j e_j)|^2 \exp(-\sum_{j=1}^{r} x_j^2) \cdot \prod_{1 \le i < j \le r} |x_i^2 - x_j^2|^a \prod_{j=1}^{r} x_j^{2b+1} \, dt \, dx_1 \cdots dx_r$$

$$\equiv d_\alpha \int_{\mathbb{R}^r_+} \phi_\alpha(\sum_{j=1}^{r} x_j^2 e_j) \exp(-\sum_{j=1}^{r} x_j^2) \cdot \prod_{1 \le i < j \le r} |x_i^2 - x_j^2|^a \prod_{j=1}^{r} x_j^{2b+1} \, dx_1 \cdots dx_r$$

$$\equiv d_\alpha \int_{\mathbb{R}^r_+} \phi_\alpha(\sum_{j=1}^r y_j e_j) \exp(-\sum_{j=1}^r y_j) \cdot \prod_{1 \le i < j \le r} |y_i - y_j|^a \prod_{j=1}^r y_j^b \, dy_1 \cdots dy_r$$

$$\equiv \int_{-\Lambda} \phi_\alpha(y)\, e^{-(y|e)} \Delta(y)^b \, dy.$$

Here Δ is the Jordan algebra determinant of X. For $y \in -\Lambda$, we have

$$\phi_\alpha(y) = \int_{L'} \Delta_\alpha(sy)\, ds$$

where $L' = \mathrm{Aut}(X)$ is the automorphism group of the Jordan algebra X. (This group differs from L only if $b > 0$, i.e., Ω is not of tube type). Since the functions $e^{-(y|e)}$ and $\Delta(y)$ and the measure dy are L'-invariant, it follows from a result of Gindikin [G1] that

$$d_\alpha(\phi_\alpha|\phi_\alpha)_Z \equiv \int_{-\Lambda} \Delta_\alpha(y)\, e^{-(y|e)} \Delta(y)^b \, dy \equiv \Gamma_\Lambda(\alpha + n/r)$$

where Γ_Λ is the multi-Γ-function defined in (2.4.2). Evaluating for $\alpha = (0,\ldots,0)$, we obtain

(2.8.23) $$d_\alpha(\phi_\alpha|\phi_\alpha)_Z = \frac{\Gamma_\Lambda(\alpha + n/r)}{\Gamma_\Lambda(n/r)} = ((n/r))_\alpha.$$

Comparing with (2.8.22) it follows that

$$(\phi_\alpha|\phi_\alpha)_Z = ((n/r))_\alpha\, (\phi_\alpha|\phi_\alpha)_S.$$

Since the K-invariant inner products (2.7.10) and (2.8.2) are proportional on $\mathcal{P}^\alpha(Z)$ we obtain

(2.8.24) $$(p|q)_Z = ((n/r))_\alpha\, (p|q)_S$$

for all $p,q \in \mathcal{P}^\alpha(Z)$. This show that $()_\#$ defined by (2.8.12) is an isometry. Since Ω is a circular domain, every $h \in H^2(S)$ has a Taylor expansion

$$h(z) = \sum_{j \in \mathbb{N}} p_j(z)$$

into a series of j-homogeneous polynomials $p_j \in \mathcal{P}^j(Z)$ which converges compactly on Ω. Since S is invariant under the circular group action (1.5.2) we have $(p_j|p_k)_S = 0$ whenever $j \neq k$. As in the proof of Theorem 2.7.16, this shows that

$$\|h - \sum_{j<k} p_j\|_S \to 0$$

as $k \to \infty$. Thus $\mathcal{P}(Z)$ is dense in $H^2(S)$, and $()_\#$ is surjective. Q.E.D.

2.8.25. EXAMPLE. Let Z be an irreducible Jordan triple of rank r. Consider signatures of the form $(m, 0, ..., 0)$. Since $\Delta_1(z) = (z|e_1)$ we have

$$\Delta_{m,0,\ldots,0}(z) = (z|e_1)^m \tag{2.8.26}$$

and $\mathcal{P}^{(m,0,\ldots,0)}(Z)$ is the linear span of polynomials $z \mapsto (z|w)^m$ where $w \in Z$ has (Jordan algebraic) rank 1. Since

$$\|(z|w)^m\|_Z^2 = m!\ (w|w)^m$$

by Example 2.7.11, it follows from (2.8.24) that

$$\|(z|w)^m\|_S^2 = \frac{m!\ (w|w)^m}{((n/r))_{(m,0,\ldots,0)}} = \frac{m!\ (w|w)^m}{(n/r)_m}.$$

Since $(e_1|e_1) = 1$ we obtain in particular

$$\|\Delta_{m,0,\ldots,0}\|_S^2 = \frac{m!}{(n/r)_m}. \tag{2.8.27}$$

2.8.28. EXAMPLE. Consider the complex Jordan triple $Z = \mathbb{C}^{r\times(r+b)}$ with canonical frame (1.5.66). Writing the elements of Z as matrices

$$z = \begin{pmatrix} z_{10} & z_{11} & \cdots & z_{1r} \\ \vdots & \vdots & & \vdots \\ z_{r0} & z_{r1} & \cdots & z_{rr} \end{pmatrix}$$

with (1×b)-vectors $z_{10}, \ldots, z_{r0}$ and scalars z_{ij} $(1 \leq i, j \leq r)$, we obtain

(2.8.29)
$$\Delta_\ell(z) = \operatorname{Det} \begin{pmatrix} z_{11} & z_{1\ell} \\ z_{\ell 1} & z_{\ell\ell} \end{pmatrix}.$$

In particular $\Delta_1(z) = z_{11}$, $\Delta_2(z) = z_{11}z_{22} - z_{12}z_{21}$ and

$$\Delta_r(z) = \operatorname{Det} \begin{pmatrix} z_{11} & \cdots & z_{1r} \\ \vdots & & \vdots \\ z_{r1} & \cdots & z_{rr} \end{pmatrix}.$$

2.8.30. THEOREM. *The Szegö kernel (2.8.7) has a series expansion*

(2.8.31)
$$E(z,w) = \sum_{\alpha \in \vec{\mathbb{N}}^r} ((n/r))_\alpha \, E^\alpha(z,w)$$

which converges compactly on $\Omega \times \Omega$. *Here* $E^\alpha(z,w)$ *is the reproducing kernel of* $\mathcal{P}^\alpha(Z)$ *in* $H^2(Z)$.

Proof. Combine Theorem 2.7.24 and (2.8.24). Q.E.D.

For the rest of this section we study the special case where Ω is of tube type. In algebraic terms this means that the associated Jordan triple Z is the complexification $Z = X \oplus iX$ of a real Jordan algebra X. Let $e \in X$ be the unit element, and consider the Jordan algebra determinant $\Delta : Z \to \mathbb{C}$. Since Ω is supposed to be of tube type, its Shilov boundary $S = K/L$ is a compact symmetric quotient space (cf. Section 1.5). Thus the general Fourier theory of symmetric spaces [H2] applies, resulting in a Fourier decomposition of the full L^2-space $L^2(S)$ instead of its subspace $H^2(S)$ considered in Theorem 2.8.10. In the 1-dimensional case we have

$$L^2(S) = H^2(S) + \overline{H^2(S)}$$

with a 1-dimensional intersection consisting of all constant functions. In the higher rank case the relationship between $H^2(S)$ and $L^2(S)$ is more complicated. Let $\vec{\mathbb{Z}}^r$ denote the set of all multi-indices $\alpha = (\alpha_1, \ldots, \alpha_r)$ of integers

(2.8.32) $$\alpha_1 \geq \cdots \geq \alpha_r.$$

Note that we do not require $\alpha_r \geq 0$, a condition which defines the subset $\vec{\mathbb{N}}^r$ of $\vec{\mathbb{Z}}^r$. Given $\alpha \in \vec{\mathbb{Z}}^r$ define a subspace $H_\alpha \subset L^2(S)$ as follows. In case $\alpha_r \geq 0$, i.e., $\alpha \in \vec{\mathbb{N}}^r$, we put

(2.8.33) $$H_\alpha := \{p|_S : p \in \mathcal{P}^\alpha(Z)\}$$

where $\mathcal{P}^\alpha(Z) \subset \mathcal{P}(Z)$ is the irreducible K-module of type α defined in (2.7.13). In case $\alpha_r < 0$, i.e. $\alpha \in \vec{\mathbb{Z}}^r \setminus \vec{\mathbb{N}}^r$, we define

$$\alpha - \alpha_r := (\alpha_1 - \alpha_r, \alpha_2 - \alpha_r, \ldots, \alpha_{r-1} - \alpha_r, 0) \in \vec{\mathbb{N}}^r$$

and put

(2.8.34) $$H_\alpha := H_{\alpha-\alpha_r} \cdot \bar{\Delta}^{-\alpha_r}.$$

Here $\bar{\Delta}$ is the complex conjugate of the determinant Δ (restricted to S).

2.8.35. PROPOSITION. *For each* $\alpha \in \vec{\mathbb{Z}}^r$ *the subspace* $H_\alpha \subset L^2(S)$ *is invariant under the action (2.8.3) of* K.

Proof. Suppose first that $\alpha \in \vec{\mathbb{N}}^r$. Since $\mathcal{P}^\alpha(Z)$ is a K-module and S is K-invariant, it is clear that H_α is a K-module. Now let $\alpha_r < 0$. Using (2.7.29) and taking complex conjugates, we see that

(2.8.36) $$\lambda_s \bar{\Delta}^{-\alpha_r} = \bar{\Delta}^{-\alpha_r} \chi(s)^{\alpha_r}$$

for every $s \in K$. Since $H_{\alpha-\alpha_r}$ is a K-module by the first part of the proof, the assertion follows. Q.E.D.

Consider the Hilbert sum

$$\sum_{\alpha \in \vec{\mathbb{Z}}^r}^{\oplus} H_\alpha$$

of all square-summable families $(\xi_\alpha)_{\alpha \in \vec{\mathbb{Z}}^r}$, with inner product

$$((\xi_\alpha)|(\eta_\alpha))_{\vec{\mathbb{Z}}^r} := \sum_{\alpha \in \vec{\mathbb{Z}}^r} (\xi_\alpha|\eta_\alpha)_S. \tag{2.8.37}$$

2.8.38. THEOREM. *There exists a Hilbert space isomorphism*

$$L^2(S) \xrightarrow[\approx]{()^\#} \sum_{\alpha \in \vec{\mathbb{Z}}^r}^{\oplus} H_\alpha \tag{2.8.39}$$

such that the adjoint $()_\#$ *is given by*

$$((\xi_\alpha))_\# := \sum_{\alpha \in \vec{\mathbb{Z}}^r} \xi_\alpha \tag{2.8.40}$$

for all square-summable families (ξ_α). *The isomorphism (2.8.39) is K-invariant.*

Proof. For $\alpha \in \vec{\mathbb{N}}^r$, the K-module $\mathcal{P}^\alpha(Z)$ is the linear span of the translates

$$\Delta_\alpha(sz) = \Delta_1(sz)^{\alpha_1-\alpha_2} \cdots \Delta_{r-1}(sz)^{\alpha_{r-1}-\alpha_r}\ \Delta_r(sz)^{\alpha_r}$$

where $\Delta_1, \ldots, \Delta_r$ are the minors of Z (cf. (2.7.16)). Since Ω is of tube type, we have $\Delta_r = \Delta$ and (2.7.29) implies

$$\Delta_\alpha(sz) = \Delta_{\alpha-\alpha_r}(sz) \cdot \Delta(z)^{\alpha_r}\ \chi(s)^{\alpha_r}.$$

Therefore $\mathcal{P}^\alpha(Z) = \mathcal{P}^{\alpha-\alpha_r}(Z) \cdot \Delta^{\alpha_r}$ whenever $\alpha \in \vec{\mathbb{N}}^r$. Restricting to S we obtain

$$H_\alpha = H_{\alpha-\alpha_r} \cdot \Delta^{\alpha_r} \tag{2.8.41}$$

for $\alpha \in \vec{\mathbb{N}}^r$. Also, (2.7.29) implies $|\Delta(sz)| = |\Delta(z)| \cdot |\chi(s)| = |\Delta(s)|$ for all $z \in Z$ and $s \in K$. Since $\Delta(e) = 1$ and $S = K \cdot e$ it follows that

$$|\Delta(z)| = 1 \tag{2.8.42}$$

for all $z \in S$. Thus $\Delta\bar{\Delta} = 1$ on S and (2.8.41) holds for all $\alpha \in \vec{\mathbb{Z}}^r$. Now let $\alpha,\beta \in \vec{\mathbb{Z}}^r$ and suppose there exist $\varphi \in H_\alpha$, $\psi \in H_\beta$ with $(\varphi|\psi)_S \neq 0$. According to (2.8.41) write $\varphi = p \cdot \Delta^{\alpha_r}$, $\psi = q \cdot \Delta^{\beta_r}$ as functions on S, where $p \in H_{\alpha-\alpha_r}$, $q \in H_{\beta-\beta_r}$. We may assume $\alpha_r \geq \beta_r$. Then (2.8.42) gives

$$0 \neq (\varphi|\psi)_S = (p\Delta^{\alpha_r}|q\Delta^{\beta_r})_S = (p\Delta^{\alpha_r-\beta_r}|q)_S.$$

Since $p\Delta^{\alpha_r-\beta_r} \in H_{\alpha-\alpha_r}$ and $\alpha - \alpha_r \in \vec{\mathbb{N}}^r$, it follows from Theorem 2.8.10 that $\alpha - \beta_r = \beta - \beta_r$, i.e., $\alpha = \beta$. Thus we have shown $(H_\alpha|H_\beta)_S = 0$ whenever $\alpha,\beta \in \vec{\mathbb{Z}}^r$ are distinct. This shows that (2.8.40) defines an isometry into $L^2(S)$. In order to show that $()_\#$ is surjective, consider the "standard" bilinear form [S5]

$$\langle z|w\rangle := (z|w^*)$$

of Z defined in terms of the hermitian structure and the involution of Z. Define the *gradient* of Δ as the Z-valued polynomial $\mathrm{grad}_z\Delta$ on Z with

$$(\partial_w\Delta)(z) = \langle \mathrm{grad}_z\Delta|w\rangle \tag{2.8.44}$$

for all $z,w \in Z$. Here

$$(\partial_w\Delta)(z) = \lim_{t\to 0} \frac{\Delta(z + tw) - \Delta(z)}{t}$$

is the complex directional derivative. Then "Cramer's rule" (1.3.17) gives

$$z^{-1} = \frac{\mathrm{grad}_z\Delta}{\Delta(z)} \tag{2.8.45}$$

whenever $z \in Z$ is invertible. If $z \in S$, then z is invertible and [L9] implies $z^{-1} = z^*$. It follows that

$$\Delta(z)^{-1}(\partial_w\Delta)(z) = \left\langle \frac{\mathrm{grad}_z\Delta}{\Delta(z)} \middle| w\right\rangle = \langle z^{-1}|w\rangle = \langle z^*|w\rangle = (z^*|w^*) = (w|z) = \overline{(z|w)}.$$

With (2.8.44), this implies for every $w \in Z$

$$\overline{(z|w)} = (\partial_w\Delta)(z) \cdot \overline{\Delta(z)} \tag{2.8.46}$$

for $z \in S$. Thus every real-analytic polynomial p on Z, when restricted to S, can be written as $p = q \cdot \bar{\Delta}^m$ where $q \in \mathcal{P}(Z)$ and $m \geq 0$. This shows that the algebraic direct sum of H_α $(\alpha \in \vec{\mathbb{Z}}^r)$ contains all real-analytic polynomials, restricted to S. By the Stone-Weierstrass Theorem, this implies that $()_\#$ is surjective. Q.E.D.

2.8.47. COROLLARY. *The Fourier transform (2.8.39) induces a Hilbert space isomorphism*

$$H^2(S) \xrightarrow[\approx]{()^\#} \sum_{\alpha\in\vec{\mathbb{N}}^r}^{\oplus} H_\alpha \tag{2.8.48}$$

whose adjoint $()_\#$ *is given by*

$$((\xi_\alpha))_\#(z) = \sum_{z\in\vec{\mathbb{N}}^r} \xi_\alpha(z)$$

for all $z \in S$.

Proof. By Theorem 2.8.10, the direct sum of H_α, $\alpha \in \vec{\mathbb{N}}^r$, is dense in $H^2(S)$. Therefore (2.8.43) implies

$$H_\alpha \subset H^2(S)^\perp$$

whenever $\alpha_r < 0$. Q.E.D.

Note that, for $\alpha \in \vec{\mathbb{N}}^r$, the K-modules $\mathcal{P}^\alpha(Z)$ and H_α are isomorphic (via the restriction mapping) but their inner products $(|)_Z$ and $(|)_S$ differ by the proportionality constant $((n/r))_\alpha$. Since the irreducible

K-modules H_α, $\alpha \in \vec{\mathbb{Z}}^r$, are pairwise inequivalent, Frobenius reciprocity [BD] implies that for each $\alpha \in \vec{\mathbb{Z}}^r$ there exists a unique *spherical function*

(2.8.49) $$\phi_\alpha \in H_\alpha$$

which is L-invariant and satisfies

$$\phi_\alpha(e) = 1.$$

If $\alpha \in \vec{\mathbb{N}}^r$, ϕ_α is the restriction to S of the *spherical polynomial* defined in (2.8.18). If $\alpha \in \vec{\mathbb{Z}}^r \setminus \vec{\mathbb{N}}^r$ we have

(2.8.50) $$\phi_\alpha(z) = \phi_{\alpha-\alpha_r}(z) \cdot \Delta(z)^{\alpha_r}$$

for all $z \in S$, since Δ is L-invariant and $\Delta(e) = 1$. In particular, we obtain for all $m \in \mathbb{Z}$

$$\phi_{(m,\ldots,m)}(z) = \Delta(z)^m.$$

2.8.51. EXAMPLE. Let Z be a complex Jordan algebra with unit e. Consider the expansion

$$\Delta(e + tz) = \sum_{j=0}^{r} t^j \phi_j(z)$$

into j-homogeneous polynomials $\phi_j : Z \to \mathbb{C}$. Then

$$\phi_{(1,\ldots,1,0,\ldots,0)}(z) = \binom{r}{j}^{-1} \phi_j(z)$$

is the spherical polynomial of type (1, ..., 1, 0, ..., 0) (j ones). In particular, we have the *reduced trace*

$$\phi_{(1,0,\ldots,0)}(z) = \frac{1}{r}\phi_1(z) = \frac{(z|e)}{r}$$

and the determinant

$$\phi_{(1,\ldots,1)}(z) = \phi_r(z) = \Delta(z).$$

2.8.52. EXAMPLE. Consider the complex spin factor $Z = \mathbb{C}^n$, $n \geq 3$, with canonical frame $e_1, \bar{e}_1$ defined in (1.5.70). Then

$$(2.8.53) \quad \Delta_1(z) = (z|e_1) = 2\,(z_1, \ldots, z_n)\,(\tfrac{1}{2}, \tfrac{i}{2}, 0, \ldots, 0)^* = z_1 - iz_2,$$

$$(2.8.54) \quad \Delta_2(z) = z_1^2 + \cdots + z_n^2.$$

It follows that

$$(2.8.55) \quad \Delta_{(j+h,j)}(z) = (z_1^2 + \cdots + z_n^2)^j\,(z_1 - iz_2)^h$$

is the conical polynomial of type $(j + h, j)$. In order to compute the spherical polynomial, note that $p(z) := (z|e)^\ell = 2^\ell z_1^\ell$ satisfies

$$\partial_\Delta^j p = \frac{\ell!}{(\ell - 2j)!}\,(z|e)^{\ell-2j}$$

for all $0 \leq j \leq [\ell/2]$. By (2.7.40), p has the harmonic projection

$$(2.8.56) \quad \mathcal{H}(p)(z) = \ell! \sum_{j=0}^{[\ell/2]} \frac{(-1)^j}{j!(\ell - 2j)!}\,\frac{\Gamma(\frac{a}{2} + \ell - j)}{\Gamma(\frac{a}{2} + \ell)}\,\Delta(z)^j (z|e)^{\ell-2j}$$

where $a = n - 2$. Since p is L-invariant, $\mathcal{H}(p)$ is also L-invariant. Since $\mathcal{H}(p)$ belongs to $\mathcal{H}^\ell(Z) = \mathcal{P}^{\ell,0}(Z)$ this implies

$$\phi_{(\ell,0)} = \frac{1}{c_\ell}\,\mathcal{H}(p)$$

where

$$c_\ell = \mathcal{H}(p)(e) = \ell! \sum_{j=0}^{[\ell/2]} \frac{(-1)^j}{j!(\ell - 2j)!}\,\frac{\Gamma(\frac{a}{2} + \ell - j)}{\Gamma(\frac{a}{2} + \ell)}\,2^{\ell-2j}$$

$$= \ell!\,\frac{\Gamma(\frac{a}{2})}{\Gamma(\frac{a}{2} + \ell)}\,C_\ell^{a/2}(1) = \ell!\,\frac{\Gamma(\frac{n}{2})}{\Gamma(\frac{n}{2} + \ell)}$$

and

$$C^{a/2}_{\ell}(t) := \sum_{j=0}^{[\ell/2]} \frac{(-1)^j}{j!(\ell-2j)!} \frac{\Gamma(\frac{a}{2}+\ell-j)}{\Gamma(\frac{a}{2})} (2t)^{\ell-2j}$$

is the *Gegenbauer polynomial* [H6] which is known to satisfy $C^{a/2}_{\ell}(1) = \frac{a}{2}(\ell+\frac{a}{2})^{-1}$. If $x \in \mathbb{R}^n \subset \mathbb{C}^n$, (2.8.56) implies

$$\mathcal{H}(p)(x) = \ell! \frac{\Gamma(\frac{a}{2})}{\Gamma(\frac{a}{2}+\ell)} C^{a/2}_{\ell}\left(\frac{x \cdot e}{\sqrt{x \cdot x}}\right)(x \cdot x)^{\ell/2} \tag{2.8.57}$$

so that

$$\phi_{(\ell,0)}(x) = \frac{\ell+\frac{a}{2}}{\frac{a}{2}} (x \cdot x)^{\ell/2} C^{a/2}_{\ell}\left(\frac{x \cdot e}{\sqrt{x \cdot x}}\right). \tag{2.8.58}$$

Since Δ is L-invariant, we have

$$\phi_{(\alpha_1,\alpha_2)}(z) = \phi_{(\alpha_1-\alpha_2,0)}(z) \cdot \Delta(z)^{\alpha_2}, \tag{2.8.59}$$

for all $(\alpha_1,\alpha_2) \in \vec{\mathbb{N}}^2$, and [CW; p. 39] together with (2.8.23) imply

$$\begin{aligned} \|\phi_{(\alpha_1,\alpha_2)}\|_S^2 &= \|\phi_{(\alpha_1-\alpha_2,0)}\|_S^2 = \dim \mathcal{H}^{\alpha_1-\alpha_2}(Z)^{-1} \\ &= \frac{a!\,(\alpha_1-\alpha_2)!}{(\alpha_1-\alpha_2+a-1)!\,(2(\alpha_1-\alpha_2)+a)}. \end{aligned} \tag{2.8.60}$$

2.8.61. DEFINITION. The holomorphic L-invariant function on Ω defined by the compactly convergent series

$$E_e(z) := \sum_{\alpha \in \vec{\mathbb{N}}^r} ((n/r))_\alpha \, E^\alpha(z,e) = \sum_{\alpha \in \vec{\mathbb{N}}^r} d_\alpha \, \phi_\alpha(z) \tag{2.8.62}$$

is called the *Szegö characteristic function* of Ω. Here $d_\alpha := \dim \mathcal{P}^\alpha(Z)$.

2.8.63. PROPOSITION. *The Szegö kernel (2.8.7) satisfies*

$$E(x,x) = E_e(x^2) \tag{2.8.64}$$

for all $x \in X$.

Proof. Apply Theorem 2.8.30 and (2.8.20). Q.E.D.

The *reduced Shilov boundary*

$$S' := \{w \in S : \Delta(w) = 1\} = S \cap Z'$$

satisfies $S = S' \cdot \mathbb{T}$ and we have

$$\int_S |f(z)|^2 \, dz = \int_{S'} \int_{\mathbb{T}} |f(w \cdot \zeta)|^2 \, d\zeta \, dw$$

for the probability measures dz on S and dw on S', which are invariant under K and K', respectively. This implies

(2.8.65) $$L^2(S) \cong L^2(\mathbb{T}) \otimes L^2(S').$$

Now consider the Hardy space $H^2(S)$ which contains $\mathcal{P}(Z)$ as a dense subspace. Writing

$$p = \sum_{k \geq 0} \Delta^k q_k$$

with $q_k \in \mathcal{H}(Z)$ according to (2.7.28) we put

$$\Phi(p) := \sum_{k \geq 0} \zeta^k \otimes q_k|_{S'} \in H^2(\mathbb{T}) \otimes L^2(S').$$

Here ζ is the variable in $\mathbb{T}$. By [U5], Φ extends to an isomorphism

(2.8.66) $$H^2(S) \xrightarrow[\cong]{\Phi} H^2(\mathbb{T}) \otimes L^2(S')$$ (Hilbert space tensor product)

which can be regarded as the "completion" of the algebraic isomorphism (2.7.26). In particular, the restriction mapping

(2.8.67) $$\mathcal{H}(Z) \ni q \mapsto q|_{S'} \in L^2(S')$$

is injective and dense. The harmonic projection

$$\mathcal{H} : H^2(S) \to L^2(S')$$

is given by $\mathcal{H} = P \otimes \mathrm{id}$ where $P : H^2(\mathbb{T}) \to \mathbb{C} \cdot 1$ is the projection onto the constants.

2.8.68. THEOREM. *There exists a Hilbert space isomorphism*

$$L^2(S') \xrightarrow{()^{\#}} \sum_{\alpha \in \vec{\mathbb{N}}^{r-1}} H_\alpha \tag{2.8.69}$$

such that the adjoint $()_{\#}$ *satisfies*

$$((\xi_\alpha))_{\#}(w) = \sum_{\alpha \in \vec{\mathbb{N}}^{r-1}} \xi_\alpha(w) \tag{2.8.70}$$

for all $w \in S'$. *The mapping (2.8.69) is* K'*-equivariant.*

Proof. By (2.8.42), $L^2(S')$ is the Hilbert sum of the subspaces H_α, $\alpha \in \vec{\mathbb{N}}^{r-1}$, restricted to S'. Q.E.D.

2.9. Bergman Spaces Over Symmetric Domains

In this section we introduce an important family of Hilbert spaces of analytic functions, the (weighted) Bergman spaces, associated with a symmetric ball $\Omega \subset Z$ of an irreducible complex Jordan triple Z of rank r and dimension n (cf. Section 1.5 and the preceding Section 2.8). Then $n = r + \frac{a}{2} r(r - 1) + b$ where a and b are the characteristic multiplicities. The number

$$p := 2 + a(r - 1) + b \tag{2.9.1}$$

is called the *genus*. Let $(z|w)$ be the hermitian structure underlying Z and let $dV(z)$ be the corresponding Lebesgue measure. It is invariant under the group $K = GL(\Omega)$. Our first goal is to compute the volume of Ω (note that Ω is not the hermitian ball unless $r = 1$). By [K6; p. 131],

$$\pi^{-n} \int_\Omega dV(z) = \prod_{k=1}^{r} \frac{\Gamma(1 + (k - 1)\frac{a}{2})}{\Gamma(b + 2 + (r + k - 2)\frac{a}{2})} \tag{2.9.2}$$

$$= \prod_{j=1}^{r} \frac{\Gamma(1 + (r - 1)\frac{a}{2} - (j - 1)\frac{a}{2})}{\Gamma(b + 2 + (r - 1)a - (j - 1)\frac{a}{2})}$$

$$= \frac{\Gamma_\Lambda(1 + (r - 1)\frac{a}{2})}{\Gamma_\Lambda(b + 2 + (r - 1)a)} = \frac{\Gamma_\Lambda(p - \frac{n}{r})}{\Gamma_\Lambda(p)}$$

where Γ_Λ is the multi-Γ-function (2.4.2). It follows that

$$d\mu_\Omega(z) := \pi^{-n} \frac{\Gamma_\Lambda(p)}{\Gamma_\Lambda(p - \frac{n}{r})} dV(z) \tag{2.9.3}$$

is a probability measure on Ω. Define the L^2-space $L^2(\Omega) := L^2(\Omega, d\mu_\Omega)$ of complex functions on Ω, with inner product

$$(h|k)_\Omega := \int_\Omega \overline{h(z)}\, k(z)\, d\mu_\Omega(z). \tag{2.9.4}$$

The *translation action* of K on $L^2(\Omega)$ is defined by

$$(\lambda_s h)(z) := h(s^{-1}z) \tag{2.9.5}$$

for all $s \in K, h \in L^2(\Omega)$ and $z \in \Omega$.

2.9.6. DEFINITION. The subspace

$$H^2(\Omega) := \{h \in L^2(\Omega) : h \text{ holomorphic}\} = L^2(\Omega) \cap \mathcal{O}(\Omega)$$

of $L^2(\Omega)$ is called the *Bergman space* over Ω.

By Proposition 2.1.3, $H^2(\Omega)$ is a closed subspace of $L^2(\Omega)$, and is therefore a Hilbert space with inner product (2.9.4). It is invariant under the translation action (2.9.5). The orthogonal projection

$$E_\Omega : L^2(\Omega) \to H^2(\Omega) \tag{2.9.7}$$

onto $H^2(\Omega)$ is called the *Bergman projection.*

2.9.8. THEOREM. *The Bergman space* $H^2(\Omega)$ *has the reproducing "Bergman" kernel*

$$E_\Omega(z,w) = \Delta(z,w)^{-p}, \tag{2.9.9}$$

where $\Delta(z,w)$ *is the Jordan triple determinant of* Z *and* p *is the genus.*

Thus, for each fixed $w \in \Omega$, the function

$$E_w(z) := E_\Omega(z,w) \tag{2.9.10}$$

belongs to $H^2(\Omega)$, and the Bergman projection (2.9.7) is given by

$$(E_\Omega h)(z) = (E_z|h)_\Omega \tag{2.9.11}$$

for every $h \in L^2(\Omega)$ and $z \in \Omega$.

Proof. By the transformation rule for Lebesgue integrals, we have

$$\operatorname{Det} g'(z) \cdot E_\Omega(g(z),g(w)) \cdot \overline{\operatorname{Det} g'(w)} = E_\Omega(z,w) \tag{2.9.12}$$

for all $z,w \in \Omega$ and all g in the holomorphic automorphism group $\operatorname{Aut}(\Omega)$. Here $g'(z) \in GL(Z)$ is the complex derivative. Now fix $\zeta \in \Omega$ and consider the transformation $g_\zeta \in \operatorname{Aut}(\Omega)$ defined in (1.5.13). Then

$$g_\zeta'(z) = B(\zeta,\zeta)^{1/2} B(z,\zeta)^{-1}, \tag{2.9.13}$$

$$\operatorname{Det} g_\zeta'(0) = \operatorname{Det} B(\zeta,\zeta)^{1/2} = \Delta(\zeta,\zeta)^{p/2}. \tag{2.9.14}$$

Since $E_\Omega(0,0) = 1$ by (2.9.2), (2.9.12) implies

$$E_\Omega(-\zeta,-\zeta) = \Delta(\zeta,\zeta)^{-p} = \Delta(-\zeta,-\zeta)^{-p}.$$

Since both sides in (2.9.9) are sesqui-holomorphic in (z,w), the assertion follows. Q.E.D.

2.9.15. EXAMPLE. For the hyperbolic matrix ball $\Omega = \Omega_{r,r+b} := \{z \in \mathbb{C}^{r\times(r+b)} : zz^* < I_r\}$ we obtain

$$E_\Omega(z,w) = \operatorname{Det}(I_r - zw^*)^{-(2r+b)} \tag{2.9.16}$$

by (1.5.28). As special cases, we have

$$E_\Omega(z,w) = (1 - z \cdot \bar{w})^{-(n+1)}$$

for the Hilbert ball $\Omega \subset \mathbb{C}^n$, and

$$E_\Omega(z,w) = (1 - z\bar{w})^{-2}$$

for the unit disk $\Omega \subset \mathbb{C}$.

As a consequence of (2.9.12), it follows that

$$d\mu(z) = E_\Omega(z,z)\, dV(z) = \Delta(z,z)^{-p}\, dV(z) \tag{2.9.17}$$

is an (infinite) measure on Ω which is invariant under the action of $\mathrm{Aut}(\Omega)$. The corresponding L^2-space does not contain any non-zero polynomial. In order to get finite (K-invariant) measures on Ω, we choose a real parameter λ and consider densities of the form $\Delta(z,z)^{\lambda-p}$. Since $\Delta(z,z) > 0$ for all $z \in \Omega$, the powers are well defined and positive. For $\lambda \leq p - 1$, the function $\Delta(z,z)^{\lambda-p}$ is not integrable over Ω. For $\lambda > p - 1$, $\Delta(z,z)^{\lambda-p}$ is integrable and, in generalization of (2.9.2), we have

2.9.18. LEMMA. *Let* $\lambda > p - 1$. *Then*

$$\int_\Omega \Delta(z,z)^{\lambda-p}\, dV(z) = \pi^n \frac{\Gamma_\Lambda(\lambda - \frac{n}{r})}{\Gamma_\Lambda(\lambda)}. \tag{2.9.19}$$

Proof. Let $\equiv$ denote equality up to a factor independent of λ. Integrating in polar coordinates [FK1] and changing variables $y_j = x_j^2$, we obtain

$$\int_\Omega \Delta(z,z)^{\lambda-p}\, dV(z) \equiv \int_{[0,1)^r} \prod_{j=1}^r (1 - x_j^2)^{\lambda-p} \prod_{1\leq i<j\leq r} |x_i^2 - x_j^2|^a \prod_{j=1}^r x_j^{2b+1}\, dx_1 \cdots dx_r$$

$$\equiv \int_{[0,1)^r} \prod_{j=1}^r (1 - y_j)^{\lambda-p} \prod_{1\leq i<j\leq r} |y_i - y_j|^a \prod_{j=1}^r y_j^b\, dy_1 \cdots dy_r$$

$$\equiv \int_{-\Lambda\cap(e+\Lambda)} \Delta(e - y)^{\lambda-p}\, \Delta(y)^b\, dy$$

$$\equiv \frac{\Gamma_\Lambda(\lambda - p + 1 + \frac{a}{2}(r-1))\, \Gamma_\Lambda(b + 1 + \frac{a}{2}(r-1))}{\Gamma_\Lambda(\lambda - p + 2 + b + a(r-1))}$$

by [G1]. Using (2.9.1), we see that

$$\int_\Omega \Delta(z,z)^{\lambda-p}\, dV(z) \equiv \pi^n \frac{\Gamma_\Lambda(\lambda - \frac{n}{r})}{\Gamma_\Lambda(\lambda)}.$$

Evaluating at $\lambda = p$, (2.9.19) follows. Q.E.D.

By Lemma 2.9.18,

(2.9.20) $$d\mu_\lambda(z) := \pi^{-n} \frac{\Gamma_\Lambda(\lambda)}{\Gamma_\Lambda(\lambda - \frac{n}{r})} \Delta(z,z)^{\lambda-p}\, dV(z)$$

defines a probability measure on Ω. Define the L^2-space $L^2_\lambda(\Omega) := L^2(\Omega, d\mu_\lambda)$ of complex-valued functions on Ω, with inner product

(2.9.21) $$(h|k)_\lambda := \int_\Omega \overline{h(z)}\, k(z)\, d\mu_\lambda(z).$$

For $\lambda = p$, we get the measure (2.9.3) and the L^2-space $L^2_p(\Omega) = L^2(\Omega)$. Since $d\mu_\lambda$ is K-invariant, the translation action (2.9.5) preserves the space $L^2_\lambda(\Omega)$ and its inner product.

2.9.22. DEFINITION. For $\lambda > p - 1$, the closed subspace

$$H^2_\lambda(\Omega) := \{h \in L^2_\lambda(\Omega) : h \text{ holomorphic}\} = L^2_\lambda(\Omega) \cap \mathcal{O}(\Omega)$$

of $L^2_\lambda(\Omega)$ is called the λ-*Bergman space* (or "weighted" Bergman space) over Ω.

The subspace $H^2_\lambda(\Omega)$ is invariant under the translation action (2.9.5). For $\lambda = p$, $H^2_\lambda(\Omega) = H^2(\Omega)$ is the standard Bergman space. In general, the orthogonal projection

(2.9.23) $$E_\lambda : L^2_\lambda(\Omega) \to H^2_\lambda(\Omega)$$

onto $H^2_\lambda(\Omega)$ is called the *λ-Bergman projection.*

2.9.24. PROPOSITION. *For* $\lambda > p - 1$, *the λ-Bergman space* $H^2_\lambda(\Omega)$ *has the reproducing "λ-Bergman" kernel*

(2.9.25) $$E_\lambda(z,w) = \Delta(z,w)^{-\lambda},$$

where $\Delta(z,w)$ *is the Jordan triple determinant of* Z.

Thus, for each fixed $w \in \Omega$, the function

(2.9.26) $$E_w(z) := E_\lambda(z,w)$$

belongs to $H^2_\lambda(\Omega)$, and the λ-Bergman projection (2.9.23) is given by

(2.9.27) $$(E_\lambda h)(z) = (E_z|h)_\lambda$$

for every $h \in L^2_\lambda(\Omega)$ and $z \in \Omega$.

Proof. By the transformation rule for Lebesgue integrals, the formula

(2.9.28) $$U_\lambda(g^{-1})h(z) := h(g(z))(\text{Det } g'(z))^{\lambda/p}$$

defines a continuous projective representation of $\text{Aut}(\Omega)^\circ$ (identity component) on $H^2_\lambda(\Omega)$. Here $h \in H^2_\lambda(\Omega)$ and, for every fixed g, one has chosen a holomorphic branch of $z \mapsto (\text{Det } g'(z))^{\lambda/p}$ on the simply-connected domain Ω. It follows that the λ-Bergman kernel satisfies

(2.9.29) $$(\text{Det } g'(z))^{\lambda/p}\, E_\lambda(g(z),g(w))\, \overline{\text{Det } g'(w)}^{\lambda/p} = E_\lambda(z,w)$$

for all $z,w \in \Omega$ and all $g \in \text{Aut}(\Omega)^\circ$. Since $d\mu_\lambda$ has total mass 1 we have $E_\lambda(0,0) = 1$, and (2.9.14) gives

$$E_\lambda(z,z) = |\text{Det } g'(0)|^{-2\lambda/p} = \Delta(z,z)^{-\lambda}$$

where $g \in \mathrm{Aut}(\Omega)^\circ$ satisfies $g(0) = z$. Since both sides in (2.9.25) are sesqui-holomorphic in (z,w), the assertion follows. Q.E.D.

2.9.30. THEOREM. *For $\lambda > p - 1$ there exists a Hilbert space isomorphism*

(2.9.31)
$$H^2_\lambda(\Omega) \xrightarrow[\cong]{()^\#} \sum^{\oplus}_{\alpha \in \vec{\mathbb{N}}^r} \mathcal{P}^\alpha(Z)$$

such that the adjoint $()_\#$ is given by

(2.9.32)
$$((\xi_\alpha))_\#(z) := \sum_{\alpha \in \vec{\mathbb{N}}^r} ((\lambda))_\alpha^{1/2} \, \xi_\alpha(z)$$

for all $z \in \Omega$. Here $((\lambda))_\alpha$ denotes the multi-Pochhammer symbol (2.8.1). The mapping (2.9.31) is K-equivariant.

Proof. In order to compute the norm of the spherical polynomial ϕ_α of type $\alpha \in \vec{\mathbb{N}}^r$ (cf. (2.8.18)) in $H^2_\lambda(\Omega)$, let $\equiv$ denote equality up to a factor independent of α and put $d_\alpha := \dim \mathcal{P}^\alpha(Z)$. Integrating in polar coordinates [FK1] and changing variables $y_j = x_j^2$ we obtain from (2.8.22)

$$d_\alpha (\phi_\alpha | \phi_\alpha)_\lambda \equiv d_\alpha \int_\Omega |\phi_\alpha(z)|^2 \, \Delta(z,z)^{\lambda - p} \, dV(z)$$

$$\equiv d_\alpha \int_{[0,1)^r} \int_K |\phi_\alpha(t \cdot \sum_{j=1}^r x_j e_j)|^2 \prod_{j=1}^r (1 - x_j^2)^{\lambda - p} \prod_{1 \le i < j \le r} |x_i^2 - x_j^2|^a \prod_{j=1}^r x_j^{2b+1} dt \, dx_1 \cdots dx_r$$

$$\equiv \int_{[0,1)^r} \phi_\alpha(\sum_{j=1}^r x_j^2 e_j) \prod_{j=1}^r (1 - x_j^2)^{\lambda - p} \prod_{1 \le i < j \le r} |x_i^2 - x_j^2|^a \prod_{j=1}^r x_j^{2b+1} \, dx_1 \cdots dx_r$$

$$\equiv \int_{[0,1)^r} \phi_\alpha(\sum_{j=1}^r y_j e_j) \prod_{j=1}^r (1 - y_j)^{\lambda - p} \prod_{1 \le i < j \le r} |y_i - y_j|^a \prod_{j=1}^r y_j^b \, dy_1 \cdots dy_r$$

$$\equiv \int_{-\Lambda \cap (e + \Lambda)} \phi_\alpha(y) \, \Delta(e - y)^{\lambda - p} \, \Delta(y)^b \, dy.$$

For each $y \in -\Lambda \cap (e + \Lambda)$ we can write $\phi_\alpha(y)$ in the form (2.8.24), for the subgroup L' of L. Since the function $\Delta(e - y)^{\lambda-p}$ and the measure dy on $-\Lambda \cap (e + \Lambda)$ are L'-invariant, we obtain

$$d_\alpha(\phi_\alpha|\phi_\alpha)_\lambda = \int_{-\Lambda\cap(e+\Lambda)} \Delta_\alpha(y)\ \Delta(e - y)^{\lambda-p}\ \Delta(y)^b\ dy = \frac{\Gamma_\Lambda(\alpha + \frac{n}{r})}{\Gamma_\Lambda(\alpha + \lambda)}$$

by [G1]. Comparing with (2.8.23), we obtain $(\phi_\alpha|\phi_\alpha)_Z = \Gamma_\Lambda(\alpha + \lambda)\ (\phi_\alpha|\phi_\alpha)_\lambda$. Evaluating at $\alpha = (0, ..., 0)$, this implies

$$\frac{(\phi_\alpha|\phi_\alpha)_Z}{(\phi_\alpha|\phi_\alpha)_\lambda} = \frac{\Gamma_\Lambda(\alpha + \lambda)}{\Gamma_\Lambda(\lambda)} = ((\lambda))_\alpha.$$

By proportionality of (2.7.10) and (2.9.21) on $\mathcal{P}^\alpha(Z)$, we have

$$(p|q)_Z = ((\lambda))_\alpha (p|q)_\lambda \tag{2.9.33}$$

for all $p,q \in \mathcal{P}^\alpha(Z)$. This shows that $()_\#$ is an isometry. Since Ω is a circular domain, every $h \in H^2_\lambda(\Omega)$ has a Taylor expansion

$$h(z) = \sum_{j\in\mathbb{N}} p_j(z)$$

into a series of j-homogeneous polynomials $p_j \in \mathcal{P}^j(Z)$ which converges compactly on Ω. Since Ω is invariant under the circle group action (1.5.2) we have $(p_j|p_k)_\lambda = 0$ whenever $j \neq k$. As in the proof of Theorem 2.7.16 it follows that

$$\|h - \sum_{j\geq k} p_j\|_\lambda \to 0$$

as $k \to \infty$. Thus $\mathcal{P}(Z)$ is dense in $H^2_\lambda(\Omega)$, and $()_\#$ is surjective Q.E.D.

2.9.34. THEOREM. *The λ-Bergman kernel (2.9.25) has a series expansion*

(2.9.35) $$E_\lambda(z,w) = \sum_{\alpha \in \vec{\mathbb{N}}^r} ((\lambda))_\alpha \, E^\alpha(z,w)$$

which converges compactly on $\Omega \times \Omega$.

The weighted Bergman spaces $H^2_\lambda(\Omega)$ which are defined in terms of a probability measure on Ω make sense for parameters $\lambda > p - 1$, where p is the genus. On the other hand, the Hardy space $H^2(S)$ which, by Proposition 2.8.7, corresponds to the parameter

$$\lambda = \frac{n}{r} = 1 + \frac{a}{2}(r - 1) + b \leq p - 1 = 1 + a(r - 1) + b,$$

also belongs to a probability measure which is supported on $S \subset \partial\Omega$. In order to understand this relationship in more detail it is useful to regard these spaces as completions of $\mathcal{P}(Z)$ with respect to different inner products. The relevant completions are labeled by a parameter λ, and the corresponding Hilbert spaces are said to form the "analytic continuation" of the (scalar) holomorphic discrete series, which is by definition the family of weighted Bergman spaces $H^2_\lambda(\Omega)$ endowed with the projective representation (2.9.28) of the holomorphic automorphism group $\mathrm{Aut}(\Omega)^\circ$. Following the computation (2.9.35) and (2.8.30) of the Bergman and Szegö kernel, respectively, we consider the compactly convergent series expansion

(2.9.36) $$\Delta(z,w)^{-\lambda} = \sum_{\alpha \in \vec{\mathbb{N}}^r} ((\lambda))_\alpha \, E^\alpha(z,w)$$

on $\Omega \times \Omega$, for *all* values $\lambda \in \mathbb{C}$. The crucial property is now that one requires

(2.9.37) $$((\lambda))_\alpha \geq 0$$

for all signatures $\alpha \in \vec{\mathbb{N}}^r$. The values of λ having this property form the so-called *Wallach set.* In case (2.9.37) is satisfied, the series (2.9.36) defines a positive kernel function

(2.9.38) $$E_\lambda(z,w) := \Delta(z,w)^{-\lambda}$$

in the sense that the matrix

$$(E_\lambda(z_i,z_j))_{1\le i,j\le m}$$

is positive for every choice of points $z_1, \ldots, z_m \in \Omega$.

2.9.39. DEFINITION. For a parameter λ in the Wallach set, the Hilbert space $H^2_\lambda(\Omega)$ associated with the positive kernel (2.9.36) is defined as the Hausdorff completion of the linear span of the holomorphic functions

$$E_w(z) = E_\lambda(z,w) \qquad (w \in \Omega) \tag{2.9.40}$$

on Ω, with respect to the positive inner product $(\varphi|\psi)_\lambda$ determined by the property

$$(E_z \mid E_w)_\lambda = E_\lambda(z,w) \tag{2.9.41}$$

for all $z,w \in \Omega$.

By construction, $E_\lambda(z,w)$ becomes the reproducing kernel of $H^2_\lambda(\Omega)$ in the sense that for every $w \in \Omega$, the function E_w belongs to $H^2_\lambda(\Omega)$ and for every $h \in H^2_\lambda(\Omega)$, the value of h at $z \in \Omega$ is given by

$$h(z) = (E_z \mid h)_\lambda.$$

One can show that $H^2_\lambda(\Omega)$ carries a projective unitary representation of $\mathrm{Aut}(\Omega)^\circ$ given by the formula (2.9.28). This is the analytic continuation of the holomorphic discrete series given by the weighted Bergman spaces for $\lambda > p - 1$. Restricted to K this action is just the translation action (2.9.5). Following [FK1, L5] we will now analyze the condition (2.9.37) more closely in order to determine the precise Wallach set. Analyzing the polynomials $((\lambda))_\alpha$ defined in (2.8.1) one can show that the Wallach set splits into two parts:

(i) *Continuous part:* $\lambda > \frac{a}{2}(r - 1)$: In this case $((\lambda))_\alpha > 0$ for all signatures $\alpha \in \vec{\mathbb{N}}^r$ since $\lambda - (r - 1)\frac{a}{2} > 0$ and all other factors in (2.8.1) are $> \lambda - (r - 1)\frac{a}{2}$. Thus the kernel $E_\lambda(z,w)$ is even strictly positive and

$$H^2_\lambda(\Omega) = \mathcal{P}(Z)^-$$

is a completion of the full polynomial algebra $\mathcal{P}(Z)$.

(ii) *Discrete Part:* $\lambda = (j-1)\frac{a}{2}$ for some integer $1 \le j \le r$: In this case $((\lambda))_\alpha > 0$ only for signatures $\alpha \in \vec{\mathbb{N}}^r$ satisfying $\alpha_j = 0$. Thus the isotypic components $\mathcal{P}^\alpha(Z)$ with $\alpha_j > 0$ vanish under the Hausdorff completion and

$$H^2_\lambda(\Omega) = \sum_{\alpha\in\vec{\mathbb{N}}^{j-1}}^{\oplus} \mathcal{P}^\alpha(Z) \qquad \text{(Hilbert sum)}.$$

One can show that no other values of λ satisfy the positivity condition (2.9.37). We will be mainly interested in the continuous part $\lambda > \frac{a}{2}(r-1)$ of the Wallach set.

2.9.42. PROPOSITION. *For λ in the Wallach set, the inner product $(|)_\lambda$ on $H^2_\lambda(\Omega)$ satisfies*

$$\frac{(p|q)_Z}{(p|q)_\lambda} = ((\lambda))_\alpha \tag{2.9.43}$$

for all $p,q \in \mathcal{P}^\alpha(Z)$, *provided* $((\lambda))_\alpha > 0$.

2.9.44. REMARK. For $\lambda > p-1$ $(> (r-1)\frac{a}{2})$, the Hilbert space completion coincides (isometrically) with the weighted Bergman space $H^2_\lambda(\Omega)$ defined in 2.9.22. For the special case $\lambda = p$, we get the standard Bergman space $H^2_p(\Omega) \cong H^2(\Omega)$. Note that these functional Hilbert spaces are defined in terms of a measure on the interior Ω. For the value $\lambda = \frac{n}{r}$ (which satisfies $\frac{a}{2}(r-1) < \lambda \le p-1$), the Hilbert space completion coincides (isometrically) with the Hardy space $H^2_{n/r}(\Omega) \cong H^2(S)$. A graphical picture of the set of admissible values of λ is as follows

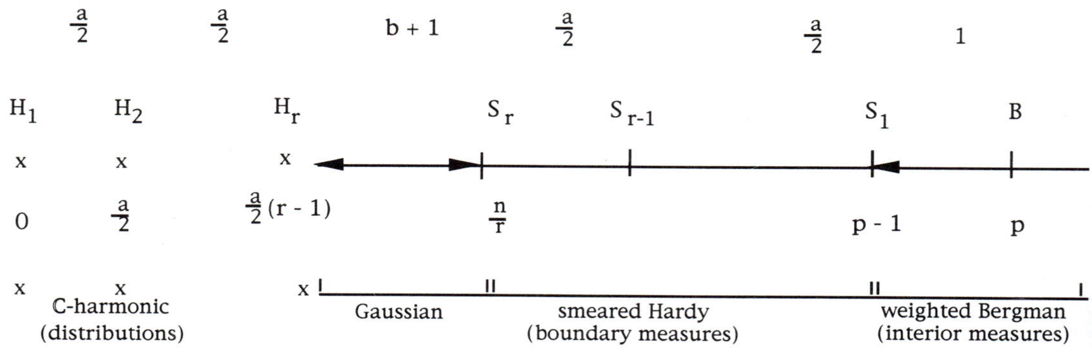

Here B = Bergman, S_r = Hardy, $S_1, \ldots, S_{r-1}$ denote Hardy-type spaces on other parts of the boundary $\partial\Omega$, $H_1, \ldots, H_r$ are completions of subspaces of polynomials characterized by certain "harmonicity" conditions, H_1 = constants.

2.9.45. EXAMPLE. Let Ω be the unit ball in the complexification $Z = X^{\mathbb{C}}$ of the real matrix Jordan algebra $X = \mathcal{H}_r(\mathbb{K})$ over $\mathbb{K} \in \{\mathbb{R}, \mathbb{C}, \mathbb{H}\}$. By Example 1.3.49, we have $b = 0$, $a = \dim_{\mathbb{R}} \mathbb{K} \in \{1, 2, 4\}$ and $p = 2 + a(r - 1)$. The admissible parameters λ are given by the following diagram

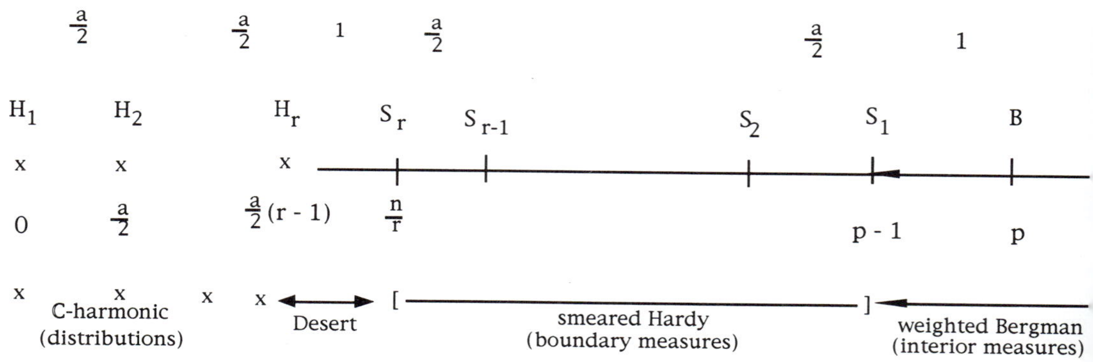

2.9.46. EXAMPLE. For the Lie ball Ω in $\mathbb{C}^n$, we have $r = 2$, $a = n - 2$ and $b = 0$. Thus the Wallach set has the form

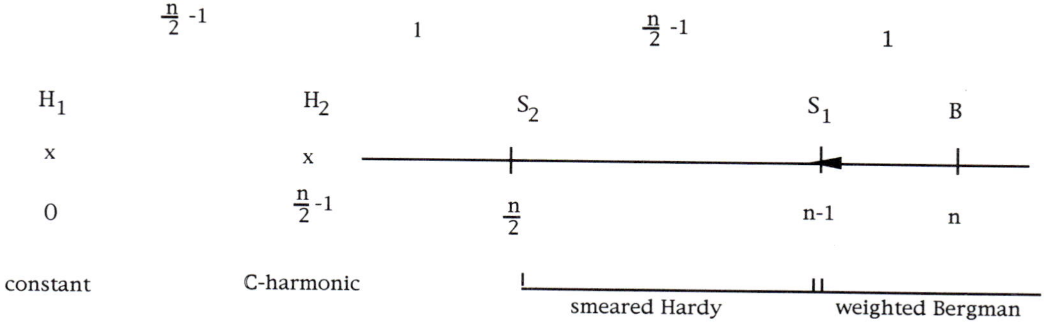

2.9.47. EXAMPLE. For the unit disk $\Omega = \Delta_{1,1}$ in $Z = \mathbb{C}$ with boundary $S = U(\mathbb{C})$ we have $r = n = 1$, $a = 2$, $b = 0$, and $p = 2$. By Example 1.5.22, we have $\Delta(z,w) = 1 - z\bar{w}$. Thus

$$E_\Omega(z,w) = (1 - z\bar{w})^{-2} \qquad \text{(Bergman kernel)},$$

$$E(z,w) = (1 - z\bar{w})^{-1} \qquad \text{(Szegö kernel)}.$$

The Wallach set consists of the parameters $\lambda > 0$ (continuous part) and $\lambda = 0$ (discrete part). The Hardy space is $\lambda = 1$, weighted Bergman spaces correspond to $\lambda > 1$, with $\lambda = 2$ the standard Bergman space.

2.9.48. EXAMPLE. For the matrix ball $\Omega = \Omega_{r,r+b}$ with Shilov boundary S (= partial isometries of rank r), we have $a = 2$, $n = r(r + b)$ and $p = 2r + b$. By Example 1.5.24, we have $\Delta(z,w) = \text{Det}(I - zw^*)$. Thus

$$E_\Omega(z,w) = \text{Det}(I - zw^*)^{-2r-b} \qquad \text{(Bergman kernel)},$$

$$E(z,w) = \text{Det}(I - zw^*)^{-r-b} \qquad \text{(Szegö kernel)}.$$

The Wallach set consists of the parameters $\lambda > r - 1$ (continuous part) and $\lambda = 0, 1, \ldots, r - 1$ (discrete part). The Hardy space is $\lambda = r + b$, the weighted Bergman spaces correspond to $\lambda > 2r + b - 1$, with $\lambda = 2r + b$ the standard Bergman space. Setting $r = 1$, Ω is the Hilbert ball in $\mathbb{C}^n$ for $n = 1 + b$ and we get for the Wallach set: $\lambda > 0$ (continuous part) and $\lambda = 0$ (discrete part). The Hardy space is $\lambda = n$, the weighted

Bergman spaces correspond to $\lambda > n$, with $\lambda = n + 1$ the standard Bergman space.

For the rest of this section assume that Ω is of tube type, i.e., Z is the complexification

$$Z = X \oplus iX$$

of an irreducible real Jordan algebra X . of rank r and dimension n. Let e be the unit of X. Consider the genus (2.4.1) and the weighted Bergman spaces for $\lambda > p - 1$.

2.9.49. DEFINITION. The holomorphic L-invariant function on Ω defined by the compactly convergent series

$$\chi_\lambda(z) := \sum_{\alpha \in \vec{\mathbb{N}}^r} ((\lambda))_\alpha \; E^\alpha(z,e) \tag{2.9.50}$$

is called the *λ-Bergman characteristic function* of Ω.

In particular, for $\lambda = p$, we obtain the Bergman characteristic function

$$\chi_\Omega(z) = \sum_{\alpha \in \vec{\mathbb{N}}^r} ((p))_\alpha \; E^\alpha(z,e).$$

2.9.51. PROPOSITION. *The λ-Bergman kernel (2.9.25) satisfies*

$$E_\lambda(x,x) = \chi_\lambda(x^2)$$

for all $x \in X$. *In particular,* $E_\Omega(x,x) = \chi_\Omega(x^2)$.

Proof. Apply Theorem 2.9.34 and (2.8.20). Q.E.D.

2.10 Hardy Spaces Over K-circular Domains

In this section we introduce an important Hilbert space of analytic functions, the so-called Hardy space, associated with a K-circular Domain

$$\Omega = e \cdot \exp(\Lambda) \cdot K$$

for a compact Lie group K with symmetric quotient $S = L/K$. K-circular domains have been introduced in Section 1.6. (In this and the following sections we write the K-action from the right in accordance with notations from C*-duality). We will assume that Ω is a log-conical domain, i.e., the logarithmic base Λ of Ω is a convex open cone in $\mathfrak{a}$. Let ds be the Haar measure on K, and define the L^2-space $L^2(K) := L^2(K,ds)$ of complex-valued functions, with inner product

$$(2.10.1) \qquad (h|k)_K := \int_K \overline{h(s)}\, k(s)\, ds.$$

The *right translation action* of K on $L^2(K)$ is defined by

$$(2.10.2) \qquad (s^{\#}h)(t) := h(ts)$$

for all $s,t \in K$ and $h \in L^2(K)$. We also have a *left translation action* of K on $L^2(K)$ given by

$$(2.10.3) \qquad (\lambda_s h)(t) := h(s^{-1}t).$$

Let $K^{\#}$ be the unitary dual of K, i.e., the set of all equivalence classes of irreducible continuous unitary representations. For each $\alpha \in K^{\#}$, we select a representation

$$(2.10.4) \qquad \alpha : K \to U(H_\alpha) \qquad \text{(unitary group)}.$$

Here H_α is a complex Hilbert space with inner product $(|)_\alpha$, conjugate-linear in the first variable. Since K is compact, $d_\alpha := \dim(H_\alpha) < \infty$. Let $\bar{\alpha}$ be the contragredient representation acting on the dual space $\bar{H}_\alpha$. Let

$$(2.10.5) \qquad \mathcal{L}^2(H_\alpha) \cong H_\alpha \otimes \bar{H}_\alpha$$

be the Hilbert space of all endomorphisms of H_α with inner product

$$(2.10.6) \qquad (A|B)_{\alpha\otimes\bar{\alpha}} = \operatorname{trace}(A^*B).$$

Consider the Hilbert sum

$$\sum_{\alpha\in K^\#}^{\oplus} \mathcal{L}^2(H_\alpha)$$

of all square-summable families $(A^\alpha)_{\alpha\in K^\#}$ of endomorphisms, with inner product

(2.10.7) $$((A^\alpha)|(B^\alpha))_{K^\#} := \sum_{\alpha\in K^\#} (A^\alpha|B^\alpha)_{\alpha\otimes\bar{\alpha}} \cdot$$

For $h \in \mathcal{L}^2(K)$ and $\alpha \in K^\#$, define the *α-th Fourier coefficient*

(2.10.8) $$h^\#_\alpha := \int_K h(s)\ \alpha(s)^*\, ds \in \mathcal{L}^2(H_\alpha).$$

Conversely, define the *Fourier symbol* of $A \in \mathcal{L}^2(H_\alpha)$ by

(2.10.9) $$A_\#(s) := \text{trace } A \cdot \alpha(s)$$

for all $s \in K$.

2.10.10. THEOREM. *There exists a Hilbert space isomorphism*

(2.10.11) $$L^2(K) \xrightarrow[\approx]{()^\#} \sum_{\alpha\in K^\#}^{\oplus} \mathcal{L}^2(H_\alpha)$$

such that

(2.10.12) $$h^\# = (\sqrt{d_\alpha} \cdot h^\#_\alpha)_{\alpha\in K^\#}$$

for all $h \in L^2(K)$, *and the adjoint* $()_\#$ *of (2.10.11) is given by*

(2.10.13) $$((A^\alpha)_{\alpha\in K^\#})_\# := \sum_{\alpha\in K^\#} \sqrt{d_\alpha}\, A^\alpha_\#$$

for all square-summable families (A^α).

Proof. By the Peter-Weyl theory (cf. [HLW; Theorem 2.4]) we have for all $\alpha,\beta \in K^\#$, $A \in \mathcal{L}^2(H_\alpha)$ and $B \in \mathcal{L}^2(H_\beta)$

(2.10.14)
$$(A_\#)^\#_{\beta\otimes\bar\beta} = \begin{cases} \frac{1}{d_\alpha} A & \alpha = \beta \\ 0 & \alpha \neq \beta \end{cases},$$

(2.10.15)
$$(A_\# | B_\#)_K = \begin{cases} \frac{1}{d_\alpha} (A|B)_{\alpha\otimes\bar\alpha} & \alpha = \beta \\ 0 & \alpha \neq \beta \end{cases}.$$

It follows that

$$((A^\alpha)_\# | (B^\beta)_\#)_K = \sum_{\alpha,\beta\in K^\#} \sqrt{d_\alpha}\sqrt{d_\beta}\,(A^\alpha_\# \mid B^\beta_\#)_K = \sum_{\alpha\in K^\#} d_\alpha (A^\alpha_\# \mid B^\alpha_\#)_K$$

$$= \sum_{\alpha\in K^\#} (A^\alpha | B^\alpha)_{\alpha\otimes\bar\alpha} = ((A^\alpha)|(B^\alpha)).$$

Therefore $()_\#$ is an isometry. On the other hand, [HLW; (11)] shows that every $h \in L^2(K)$ has a Fourier series expansion

(2.10.16)
$$h = \sum_{\alpha\in K^\#} d_\alpha (h^\#_\alpha)_\#$$

converging in the L^2-sense. Thus $()_\#$ is also surjective. Q.E.D.

We now pass to quotient spaces, with K acting on the right. Consider the closed subgroup $L \subset K$ with quotient $S = L\backslash K$. Then $e := \{L\}$ is the "base point" of S. Endow S with the unique K-invariant probability measure dz. Define the L^2-space $L^2(S) := L^2(S,dz)$ of complex-valued functions on S, with inner product

(2.10.17)
$$(h|k)_S := \int_S \overline{h(z)}\, k(z)\, dz.$$

Via the pull-back along the canonical projection $K \to S$, we may identify $L^2(S)$ with the closed subspace

(2.10.18)
$$L^2(S) = \{h \in L^2(K) : h(\ell s) = h(s)\ \forall \ell \in L\}$$

of all left *L-invariant* functions in $L^2(K)$. This subspace is invariant under the translation action (2.10.3). The orthogonal projection $P : L^2(K) \to L^2(S)$ is given by

$$(Ph)(s) = \int_L h(\ell s)\, d\ell. \tag{2.10.19}$$

Let $S^\#$ denote the set of all equivalence classes $\alpha \in K^\#$ such that H_α contains an L-invariant unit vector

$$\varepsilon_\alpha \in H_\alpha \tag{2.10.20}$$

(which is unique up to a phase factor). For $\alpha \in S^\#$, the orthogonal projection

$$Q_\alpha := \int_L \alpha(\ell)\, d\ell \tag{2.10.21}$$

onto the subspace of all L-invariant vectors in H_α satisfies

$$Q_\alpha\, \alpha(\ell) = Q_\alpha = \alpha(\ell)\, Q_\alpha \tag{2.10.22}$$

for all $\ell \in L$, and is given as the rank 1 projection

$$Q_\alpha = \varepsilon_\alpha \varepsilon_\alpha^*. \tag{2.10.23}$$

Here ε_α^* is the linear form on H_α induced by ε_α. Consider the Hilbert sum

$$\sum_{\alpha \in S^\#}^{\oplus} H_\alpha$$

of all square-integrable families $(\xi^\alpha)_{\alpha \in S^\#}$, with inner product

$$((\xi^\alpha)|(\eta^\alpha))_{S^\#} := \sum_{\alpha \in S^\#} (\xi^\alpha|\eta^\alpha)_\alpha. \tag{2.10.24}$$

For every $\xi \in H_\alpha$ define its "symbol"

$$\xi_\#(z) = (\xi\varepsilon_\alpha^*)_\#(s) = (\varepsilon_\alpha|\alpha(s)\xi)_\alpha \tag{2.10.25}$$

for all $z = es \in S$. Since ε_α is L-invariant, the dexter side of (2.10.25) depends only on z and not on the particular choice of $s \in K$.

2.10.26. THEOREM. *There exists a Hilbert space isomorphism*

(2.10.27) $$L^2(S) \xrightarrow[\approx]{()^\#} \sum_{\alpha \in S^\#}^{\oplus} H_\alpha$$

such that

(2.10.28) $$h^\# = (\sqrt{d_\alpha}\, h^\#_\alpha \varepsilon_\alpha)_{\alpha \in S^\#}$$

for all $h \in L^2(S) \subset L^2(K)$, *and the adjoint* $()_\#$ *of (2.10.27) is given by*

(2.10.29) $$((\xi^\alpha))_\# = \sum_{\alpha \in S^\#} \sqrt{d_\alpha}\, \xi^\alpha_\#.$$

Proof. Since $h \in L^2(S)$ is left L-invariant, we have

$$h^\#_\alpha Q_\alpha = \int_K h(s)\ \alpha(s)^*\ ds \cdot \int_L \alpha(\ell)\ d\ell = \int_K \int_L h(s)\ \alpha(s^{-1}\ell)\ d\ell\ ds$$

$$= \int_K \int_L h(\ell t^{-1})\ \alpha(t)\ d\ell\ dt = \int_K h(t^{-1})\ \alpha(t)\ dt = \int_K h(s)\ \alpha(s^{-1})\ ds = h^\#_\alpha$$

for all $\alpha \in K^\#$. Therefore $h^\#_\alpha = h^\#_\alpha \cdot 0 = 0$ if $\alpha \notin S^\#$. On the other hand, if $\alpha \in S^\#$ and $A \in \mathcal{L}^2(H_\alpha)$ we have

$$(A|h^\#_\alpha)_{\alpha\otimes\bar\alpha} = \text{trace}\ h^\#_\alpha\ A^* = \text{trace}\ h^\#_\alpha\ \varepsilon_\alpha\ \varepsilon^*_\alpha\ A^*$$

$$= \text{trace}(h^\#_\alpha \varepsilon_\alpha)(A\varepsilon_\alpha)^* = (A\varepsilon_\alpha | h^\#_\alpha \varepsilon_\alpha)_\alpha.$$

In particular, $(h^\#_\alpha \varepsilon_\alpha | h^\#_\alpha \varepsilon_\alpha)_\alpha = (h^\#_\alpha | h^\#_\alpha)_{\alpha\otimes\bar\alpha}$, and Theorem 2.10.10 implies that $()_\#$ is an isometry. Now let $h \in L^2(S)$ and $s \in K$. Then (2.10.16) implies

$$h(s) = \sum_{\alpha \in K^\#} d_\alpha\ (h^\#_\alpha)_\#(s) = \sum_{\alpha \in S^\#} d_\alpha\ (\alpha(s)^* | h^\#_\alpha)_{\alpha\otimes\bar\alpha}$$

$$= \sum_{\alpha \in S^{\#}} d_\alpha \, (\alpha(s)^* \varepsilon_\alpha | h^{\#}_\alpha \varepsilon_\alpha)_\alpha = \sum_{\alpha \in S^{\#}} d_\alpha \, (h^{\#}_\alpha \varepsilon_\alpha)_{\#}(s).$$

Therefore $()_{\#}$ is also surjective. Q.E.D.

As a special case of (2.10.25), we obtain the *spherical function*

(2.10.30) $$\phi_\alpha(z) := (\varepsilon_\alpha | \alpha(s)\, \varepsilon_\alpha)_\alpha$$

for all $z = es \in S$. This is a smooth function on S which is right L-invariant, i.e.,

$$\phi_\alpha(z\ell) = \phi_\alpha(z) \qquad \forall \ell \in L.$$

Note that, in general, the function (2.10.30) does not depend on the particular choice of L-invariant unit vector $\varepsilon_\alpha \in H_\alpha$.

2.10.31. EXAMPLE. Let $K = S = \mathbb{T}^r$ be the r-torus. Then $K^{\#} = S^{\#} = \mathbb{Z}^r$ via (2.5.8), and for $\alpha \in \mathbb{Z}^r$ the corresponding representation

$$\phi_\alpha(s) = s^\alpha$$

acts on $H_\alpha = \mathbb{C}$. Put $\varepsilon_\alpha := 1$ in this case. For $h \in L^2(\mathbb{T}^r)$ and $\alpha \in \mathbb{Z}^r$, we have

$$h^{\#}_\alpha = \int_{\mathbb{T}^r} h(s)\overline{\phi_\alpha(s)}\, ds = h^{\#}(\alpha).$$

Hence the isomorphism (2.10.26) reduces to the classical Fourier transform (2.5.8).

2.10.32. PROPOSITION. *The Fourier transforms (2.10.11) and (2.10.27) induce a commuting diagram*

$$\begin{array}{ccc}
L^2(K) & \xrightarrow[\approx]{()^{\#}} & \sum^{\oplus}_{\alpha \in K^{\#}} \mathcal{L}^2(H_\alpha) \\
\Big\downarrow P & & \Big\downarrow \sum^{\oplus}_{\alpha} P_\alpha \\
L^2(S) & \xrightarrow[()^{\#}]{\approx} & \sum^{\oplus}_{\alpha \in S^{\#}} H_\alpha
\end{array}$$

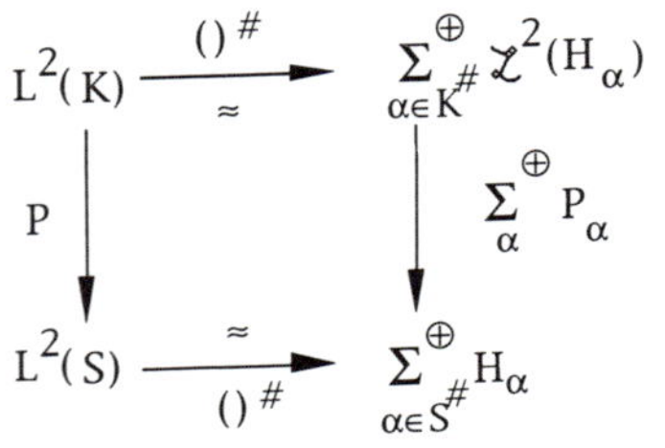

where P *is the orthogonal projection and we define*

$$P_\alpha : \mathcal{L}^2(H_\alpha) \to H_\alpha,\ A \mapsto A\varepsilon_\alpha$$

in case $\alpha \in S^\#$ *and* $P_\alpha := 0$ *in case* $\alpha \in K^\# \setminus S^\#$.

Proof. Let $h \in L^2(K)$ and put $k := Ph$. For each $\alpha \in S^\#$, we have

$$\begin{aligned} k_\alpha^\# &= \int_K k(s)\ \alpha(s)^*\ \varepsilon_\alpha\ ds = \int_K \int_L h(\ell s)\ \alpha(s)^*\ \varepsilon_\alpha\ d\ell\ ds \\ &= \int_K \int_L h(t)\ \alpha(t^{-1}\ell)\ \varepsilon_\alpha\ d\ell\ dt = \int_K h(t)\ \alpha(t^{-1})\ \varepsilon_\alpha\ dt = h_\alpha^\# \varepsilon_\alpha \end{aligned}$$

since ε_α is L-invariant. Therefore

$$\Big(\sum_\alpha^\oplus P_\alpha\Big)h^\# = \big(\sqrt{d_\alpha}\ h_\alpha^\#\ \varepsilon_\alpha\big)_{\alpha \in S^\#} = \big(\sqrt{d_\alpha}\ k_\alpha^\#\ \varepsilon_\alpha\big)_{\alpha \in S^\#} = k^\# = (Ph)^\#.$$

Q.E.D.

2.10.34. DEFINITION. The *Hardy space* $H^2(S)$ (depending on Ω) consists of all holomorphic functions $h : \Omega \to \mathbb{C}$ such that

$$||h||^2 := \sup_{a \in \Lambda} \int_K |h(e\ \exp(a)\ s)|^2\ ds < \infty.$$

By [L4; Théorème 4] there exists an embedding $H^2(S) \subset L^2(S)$ as a closed subspace such that

$$\lim_{\substack{a \in \Lambda \\ a \to 0}} \int_K |h(e\ \exp(a)\ s) - h(es)|^2\ ds = 0.$$

This embedding is invariant under the left translation action (2.10.3) of K. The orthogonal projection

(2.10.35) $$E : L^2(S) \to H^2(S)$$

is called the *Szegö projection*.

In order to obtain a Fourier transform characterization of the Hardy space $H^2(S)$ associated with a K-circular log-conical domain Ω, we need a "linear" realization of the abstract spaces $S^\#$ and $K^\#$. This involves the theory of "highest weights". Let $\mathfrak{k}$ be the Lie algebra of K, with Cartan decomposition $\mathfrak{k} = \mathfrak{l} \oplus \mathfrak{s}$. Let $\mathfrak{a} \subset i\mathfrak{s}$ be a maximal abelian subspace and let $i\mathfrak{h} \subset \mathfrak{k}$ be a maximal abelian subalgebra containing $i\mathfrak{a}$.

2.10.36. LEMMA. $\mathfrak{h} = (\mathfrak{h} \cap i\mathfrak{l}) \oplus \mathfrak{a}$.

Proof. Let $A \in \mathfrak{h}$ have the Cartan decomposition $A = B + C$ with $B \in i\mathfrak{l}$ and $C \in i\mathfrak{s}$. Then we have for all $D \in \mathfrak{a}$:

$$0 = [A,D] = [B,D] + [C,D] .$$

Since $[B,D] \in [i\mathfrak{l},\mathfrak{a}] \subset \mathfrak{s}$ and $[C,D] \in [\mathfrak{s},\mathfrak{s}] \subset \mathfrak{l}$, we have $[B,D] = 0 = [C,D]$ for all $D \in \mathfrak{a}$. Therefore $C \in \mathfrak{a}$ by maximality. Hence also $B = A - C \in \mathfrak{h}$.
Q.E.D.

By the theory of highest weights [H2; Theorem V.13], every $\alpha \in K^\#$ is uniquely determined by its *highest weight*, a linear form $\alpha : \mathfrak{h} \to \mathbb{R}$ characterized by the property

$$d\alpha(A)\delta_\alpha = \alpha(A)\delta_\alpha \qquad \forall A \in \mathfrak{h} \tag{2.10.37}$$

where

$$d\alpha(A) := \frac{d}{dt}\Big|_{t=0} \alpha(\exp(tA)) \qquad (A \in \mathfrak{k}) \tag{2.10.38}$$

is the infinitesimal representation of $\mathfrak{k}$ on H_α associated with (2.10.4), and $\delta_\alpha \in H_\alpha$ is a "highest weight" unit vector satisfying

$$d\alpha(B)\delta_\alpha = 0 \tag{2.10.39}$$

for all $B \in \mathfrak{k}^{\mathbb{C}}$ belonging to the positive root subalgebra $\mathfrak{n}_+$ with respect to $\mathfrak{h}^{\mathbb{C}}$. In this way we may identify

$$K^\# \subset \mathfrak{h}^\# \tag{2.10.40}$$

with a discrete subset of the real-linear dual space $\mathfrak{h}^{\#}$ of $\mathfrak{h}$. Now consider a symmetric quotient space $S = L\backslash K$ and the corresponding subset $S^{\#} \subset K^{\#}$.

2.10.41. LEMMA. *Let* $\alpha \in S^{\#}$ *have the highest weight* $\alpha : \mathfrak{h} \to \mathbb{R}$. *Then* $\alpha|\mathfrak{h} \cap i\mathfrak{l} = 0$.

Proof. Let $\delta_\alpha \in H_\alpha$ be a highest weight vector. As a consequence of the Iwasawa decomposition [H2], the translates $\alpha(\ell)\delta_\alpha$ $(\ell \in L)$ span H_α. It follows that $Q_\alpha\delta_\alpha \in H_\alpha$ is non-zero and L-invariant. Now let $A \in \mathfrak{h} \cap i\mathfrak{l}$. Then

$$0 = d\alpha(A)Q_\alpha\delta_\alpha = Q_\alpha d\alpha(A)\delta_\alpha = \alpha(A)Q_\alpha\delta_\alpha.$$

Since $Q_\alpha\delta_\alpha \neq 0$, the assertion $\alpha(A) = 0$ follows. Q.E.D.

As a consequence of Lemma 2.10.41, it follows that every $\alpha \in S^{\#}$ is uniquely determined by its *restricted highest weight*, a linear form $\alpha : \mathfrak{a} \to \mathbb{R}$ characterized by the property

(2.10.42) $$d\alpha(A)\delta_\alpha = \alpha(A)\delta_\alpha \qquad \forall A \in \mathfrak{a}$$

where $\delta_\alpha \in H_\alpha$ is a highest weight unit vector. In this way we identify

(2.10.43) $$S^{\#} \subset \mathfrak{a}^{\#}$$

with a discrete subset of the real-linear dual space $\mathfrak{a}^{\#}$ of $\mathfrak{a}$. By Proposition 1.6.14, the logarithmic base Λ of a K-circular domain Ω is realized as an open subset of $\mathfrak{a}$. Let

(2.10.44) $$\Lambda^{\#} := \{\alpha \in \mathfrak{a}^{\#} : \alpha(A) \leq 0 \ \forall A \in \Lambda\}$$

denote the *polar cone*. We have the following basic result [L5]:

2.10.45. THEOREM. *The Fourier transform (2.10.28) induces a Hilbert space isomorphism*

(2.10.46) $$H^2(S) \xrightarrow[\approx]{()^{\#}} \sum_{\alpha \in S^{\#} \cap \Lambda^{\#}}^{\oplus} H_\alpha.$$

2.10.47. EXAMPLE. Let Ω be an irreducible symmetric domain of tube type, realized as the open unit ball of a complex Jordan algebra $Z = X^{\mathbb{C}}$ with unit element e. Then the Shilov boundary S of Ω can be realized as a symmetric quotient of K, where

$$K = GL(\Omega)^\circ$$

is the identity component of all linear automorphisms of Z preserving Ω. Its Lie algebra $\mathfrak{k}$ has the Cartan decomposition $\mathfrak{k} = \mathfrak{l} \oplus i\mathfrak{q}$ described in Example 1.6.21, and the maximal abelian subspace $\mathfrak{a} \subset \mathfrak{q}$ is spanned by the multiplication operators M_{e_j} $(1 \le j \le r)$ for a frame $e_1, \ldots, e_r$ of X. Using the dual basis

$$M^{\#}_{e_i}(M_{e_j}) := \delta_{ij}$$

of linear forms on $\mathfrak{a}$, we may identify $\mathfrak{a}^{\#} \cong \mathbb{R}^r$. As in Example 1.6.21 we define

$$\bar{\mathfrak{a}}^{<} \cap \Lambda := \{\sum_{j=1}^{r} a_j M_{e_j} : 0 > a_1 \ge \cdots \ge a_r\}.$$

Now fix $\alpha \in \vec{\mathbb{Z}}^r$ and consider the rational function

$$\Delta_\alpha(z) := \Delta_1(z)^{\alpha_1 - \alpha_2}\, \Delta_2(z)^{\alpha_2 - \alpha_3} \cdots \Delta_r(z)^{\alpha_r}$$

on the open dense subset $\Omega^\times := \{z \in \Omega : \Delta_r(z) \neq 0\}$. Let

$$(\partial_A h)(z) := h'(z)(Az)$$

be the infinitesimal translation action of $\mathfrak{k}^{\mathbb{C}}$ on the rational function h on $\Omega^\times$. By [U5; Lemmas 3.4 and 3.6] we have

$$\partial_B \Delta_\ell = 0 \qquad \forall\ 1 \le \ell \le r$$

whenever B belongs to $\mathfrak{h} \cap i\mathfrak{l}$ or to the positive root spaces of $\mathfrak{k}^{\mathbb{C}}$ relative to $\mathfrak{h}^{\mathbb{C}}$. By [U5; Lemma 3.3], the basis vectors of $\mathfrak{a}$ satisfy

$$\partial_{M_{e_j}} \Delta_\ell = \begin{cases} \Delta_\ell & j \le \ell \\ 0 & j > \ell \end{cases} .$$

Putting $m_{r+1} := 0$ it follows that

$$\partial_{\Sigma a_j M_{e_j}} \Delta_\alpha = \sum_{j=1}^{r} a_j \, \partial_{M_{e_j}} \Delta_\alpha = \sum_{j=1}^{r} a_j \sum_{\ell \ge j} (\alpha_\ell - \alpha_{\ell+1}) \Delta_\alpha = (\sum_{j=1}^{r} a_j \alpha_j) \cdot \Delta_\alpha .$$

Thus Δ_α is the highest weight vector of an irreducible K-module H_α with highest weight

(2.10.48)
$$\alpha = \sum_{j=1}^{r} \alpha_j M_{e_j}^{\#} .$$

For $\alpha \in \vec{\mathbb{N}}^r$, i.e., $\alpha_r \ge 0$, H_α coincides with $\mathcal{P}^\alpha(Z)$. One can show [S2] that the linear forms (2.10.48) constitute all restricted highest weights in $S^{\#}$. Thus we may identify

(2.10.49)
$$S^{\#} = \vec{\mathbb{Z}}^r \subset \mathfrak{a}^{\#} = \mathbb{R}^r .$$

By Example 1.6.21, we have $\Lambda = \mathfrak{a}^<$ and obtain the polar cone

(2.10.50)
$$\Lambda^{\#} := \{ \sum_{j=1}^{r} \alpha_j M_{e_j}^{\#} : \alpha_1 \ge \alpha_2 \ge \cdots \ge \alpha_r \ge 0 \} .$$

In particular,

(2.10.51)
$$S^{\#} \cap \Lambda^{\#} = \vec{\mathbb{Z}}^r \cap \Lambda^{\#} = \vec{\mathbb{N}}^r .$$

Thus we see that the Fourier transforms (2.10.27) and (2.10.46) agree with (2.8.39) and (2.8.48), respectively.

2.10.52. EXAMPLE. For $n \ge 3$, the Lie sphere

$$S = \mathbb{T} \cdot \mathbb{S}^{n-1}$$

in $Z = \mathbb{C}^n$ is a compact symmetric quotient space arising as the Shilov boundary of the n-dimensional Lie ball (1.5.39). Put $K = \mathbb{T} \cdot SO(n)$. Let $\{e_1, e_2\}$ be the canonical frame of Z (Example 1.5.69) and let

$$M_{e_j} z = z \circ e_j \qquad (j = 1,2)$$

be the corresponding basis of $\mathfrak{a}$. Identifying $\mathfrak{a} \approx \mathbb{R}^2$ via the basis $\{M_{e_1}, M_{e_2}\}$, we obtain

(2.10.53) $$\Lambda \cap \bar{\mathfrak{a}}^{<} = \{(a_1, a_2) \in \mathbb{R}^2 : 0 > a_1 \geq a_2\}.$$

Similarly, we identify $\mathfrak{a}^{\#} \approx \mathbb{R}^2$ using the dual basis $\{M^{\#}_{e_1}, M^{\#}_{e_2}\}$ and obtain, via (2.10.51)

$$S^{\#} = \{(\alpha_1, \alpha_2) \in \mathbb{Z}^2 : \alpha_1 \geq \alpha_2\} = \vec{\mathbb{Z}}^2.$$

Now define a convex cone $\Lambda_\varepsilon \subset \mathfrak{a}$ by the slope ε of its non-trivial face F :

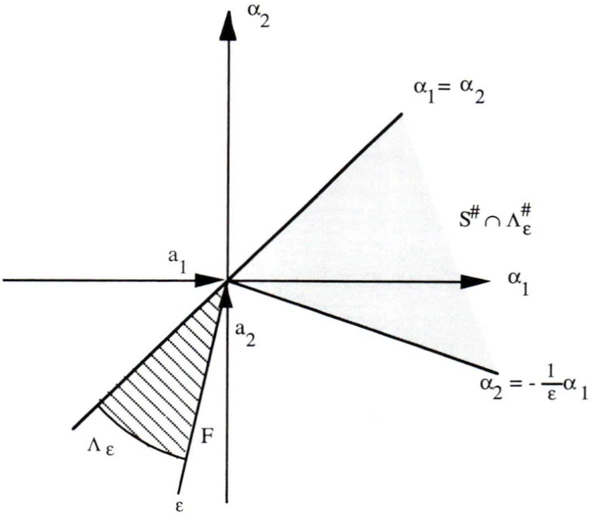

Here $1 < \varepsilon \leq \infty$ and we put

(2.10.54) $$\Lambda_\varepsilon \cap \bar{\mathfrak{a}}^{<} = \{(a_1, a_2) : \varepsilon a_1 < a_2 \leq a_1 < 0\}.$$

Let

(2.10.55) $$\Omega_\varepsilon := e \exp(\Lambda_\varepsilon)\, K$$

be the corresponding K-circular domain. In the degenerate case $\varepsilon = +\infty$, Ω_ε is the full Lie ball (1.5.39). In general, we have

(2.10.56) $$S^\# \cap \Lambda_\varepsilon^\# = \{(\alpha_1,\alpha_2) \in \mathbb{Z}^2 : \alpha_1 \geq \alpha_2 \geq -\frac{\alpha_1}{\varepsilon}\}$$

which reduces to $S^\# \cap \Lambda_\infty^\# = \vec{\mathbb{N}}^2$ in case $\varepsilon = +\infty$. For $\alpha = (\alpha_1,\alpha_2) \in S^\# \cap \Lambda_\varepsilon^\#$ the corresponding K-module $H_\alpha \subset L^2(S)$ consists of all rational functions

$$p(z) \cdot \Delta_2(z)^{\alpha_2},\ p \in \mathcal{P}^{\alpha_1-\alpha_2,0}(\mathbb{C}^n)$$

restricted to S. These rational functions are homogeneous of total degree

$$\alpha_1 + \alpha_2 \geq \alpha_1 - \frac{\alpha_1}{\varepsilon} = \alpha_1(1 - \frac{1}{\varepsilon}) \geq 0.$$

Since

$$\mathcal{P}^{j,0}(\mathbb{C}^n) = \mathcal{H}^j(\mathbb{C}^n) \qquad \text{(harmonic polynomials)}$$

by Theorem 2.7.32, we obtain from [CW; p. 39]

$$\dim H_\alpha = \dim \mathcal{P}^{\alpha_1-\alpha_2,0}(\mathbb{C}^n) = \dim \mathcal{H}^{\alpha_1-\alpha_2}(\mathbb{C}^n)$$

$$= \frac{(\alpha_1 - \alpha_2 + n - 3)!(2(\alpha_1 - \alpha_2) + n - 2)}{(n - 2)!(\alpha_1 - \alpha_2)!}$$

$$= \binom{\alpha_1 - \alpha_2 + n - 2}{n - 2} \frac{2(\alpha_1 - \alpha_2) + n - 2}{\alpha_1 - \alpha_2 + n - 2}.$$

If $n = 4$, we obtain in particular $\dim H_\alpha = (\alpha_1 - \alpha_2 + 1)^2$.

2.10.57. PROPOSITION. *For each* $\alpha \in S^\# \cap \Lambda^\#$, *let* B_α *be an orthonormal basis of* H_α. *Then the series*

(2.10.58) $$E(z,w) := \sum_{\alpha \in S^{\#} \cap \Lambda^{\#}} d_\alpha \sum_{\xi \in B_\alpha} \xi_{\#}(z)\, \overline{\xi_{\#}(w)}$$

converges compactly on $\Omega \times \Omega$, *and defines a reproducing kernel (called the "Szegö kernel") for* $H^2(S)$.

Thus for each fixed $w \in \Omega$, the function

(2.10.59) $$E_w(z) := E(z,w)$$

belongs to $H^2(S)$, and the Szegö projection (2.10.35) is given by

(2.10.60) $$(Eh)(z) = (E_z|h)_S$$

for all $h \in L^2(S)$ and $z \in \Omega$. The Szegö kernel $E(z,w)$ is K-invariant in the following sense: For all $s \in K$ we have

(2.10.61) $$E(zs, ws) = E(z,w).$$

Proof. By Theorem 2.10.45, the functions

$$\{\sqrt{d_\alpha} \cdot \xi_{\#}(z) : \alpha \in S^{\#} \cap \Lambda^{\#}, \xi \in B_\alpha\}$$

form an orthonormal basis of $H^2(S)$. Thus every $h \in H^2(S)$ has a generalized Laurent expansion

(2.10.62) $$h(z) = \sum_{\alpha \in S^{\#} \cap \Lambda^{\#}} d_\alpha \sum_{\xi \in B_\alpha} h^{\#}_{\xi}(\alpha) \xi_{\#}(z),$$

where for $\xi \in B_\alpha$

(2.10.63) $$h^{\#}_{\xi}(\alpha) := (\xi_{\#}|h)_S = \int_S \overline{\xi_{\#}(z)}\, h(z)\, dz$$

is the (α,ξ)-th Laurent coefficient. Q.E.D.

2.10.64. DEFINITION. The holomorphic L-invariant function E_e on Ω defined by the compactly convergent series

(2.10.65) $$E_e(z) := \sum_{\alpha\in S^{\#}\cap\Lambda^{\#}} d_\alpha\, \phi_\alpha(z)$$

is called the *Szegö characteristic function* of Ω.

2.10.66. PROPOSITION. *We have for all* $z \in \Omega$

(2.10.67) $$E_e(z) = E(z,e).$$

Proof. For every $\alpha \in S^{\#} \cap \Lambda^{\#}$, there exists an orthonormal basis B_α of H_α containing ε_α. We have for all $\xi \in B_\alpha\backslash\{\varepsilon_\alpha\}$

$$\xi_{\#}(e) = (\varepsilon_\alpha|\alpha(e)\ \xi)_\alpha = (\varepsilon_\alpha|\xi)_\alpha = 0.$$

Now the assertion follows from Proposition 2.10.57. Q.E.D.

2.11 Hardy Spaces Over S-bicircular Domains

In this section we study Hardy spaces over K-circular domains in the special case that $K = S \times S$ is the direct product of a compact connected Lie group S. The corresponding domains

$$\Omega = S\ \exp(\Lambda)\ S$$

in the complexified Lie group $S^{\mathbb{C}}$ are called *S-bicircular* and have been studied in Section 1.7. Let dz be the Haar measure on S, and define the L^2-space $L^2(S) := L^2(S,dz)$ of complex-valued functions, with inner product

(2.11.1) $$(h|k)_S := \int_S \overline{h(z)}\ k(z)\ dz.$$

The *right translation action* of $S\times S$ on S is defined by

(2.11.2) $$w \cdot (z_1,z_2) := z_2^{-1} w z_1$$

for all $w, z_1, z_2 \in S$. Similarly, we have a left translation action

(2.11.3) $$(z_1,z_2)\cdot w := z_1 w z_2^{-1}$$

of $S \times S$ on S, and obtain a corresponding left translation action

(2.11.4) $$\lambda_{(z_1,z_2)}h(w) = h(z_1^{-1} w z_2)$$

of $S \times S$ on $L^2(S)$. Let $S^\#$ be the unitary dual of S, i.e., the set of all equivalence classes of irreducible continuous unitary representations. For each $\alpha \in S^\#$, we select a representative

(2.11.5) $$\alpha : S \to U(H_\alpha) \qquad \text{(unitary group).}$$

Here H_α is a complex Hilbert space of dimension

$$d_\alpha := \dim H_\alpha < \infty,$$

with inner product $(|)_\alpha$ conjugate-linear in the first variable. Let $\bar{\alpha}$ be the contragredient representation acting on the dual space $\overline{H}_\alpha$. For $\alpha,\beta \in S^\#$, consider the Hilbert space

$$H_{\beta,\bar{\alpha}} := \mathcal{L}^2(H_\alpha,H_\beta) = H_\beta \otimes \overline{H}_\alpha$$

of all endomorphisms $H_\beta \xleftarrow{A} H_\alpha$, with inner product

$$(A|B)_{\beta\otimes\bar{\alpha}} := \operatorname{trace} A^*B.$$

Define an irreducible continuous unitary representation $(\beta,\bar{\alpha}) : S \times S \to U(H_{\beta,\bar{\alpha}})$ by putting $(\beta,\bar{\alpha})(z,w)A := \beta(z)\, A\, \alpha(w)^*$ for all $z,w \in S$ and $A \in H_{\beta,\bar{\alpha}}$. It is known [D1; Problem XXI.1.12] that the mapping $S^\# \times S^\# \to (S \times S)^\#$ given by $\alpha,\beta \mapsto (\beta,\bar{\alpha})$ is bijective.

The right translation action (2.11.2) of $K := S \times S$ on S has the stabilizer subgroup

$$L := \{(z,z) : z \in S\}$$

at the identity $e \in S$. For $\alpha, \beta \in S^\#$, the representation $(\beta,\bar{\alpha})$ of K admits a non-zero L-invariant vector if and only if $\alpha = \beta$. In this case

$$H_{\alpha,\bar\alpha} := \mathcal{Z}^2(H_\alpha) = H_\alpha \otimes \overline{H}_\alpha$$

contains the L-invariant unit vector

(2.11.6) $$\varepsilon_{\alpha,\bar\alpha} := \frac{1}{\sqrt{d_\alpha}}\ \mathrm{Id}.$$

Thus the mapping $\alpha \mapsto (\alpha,\bar\alpha)$ identifies $S^\#$ with the subset of $K^\#$ defined in Section 2.10. By (2.10.30), the spherical function on S corresponding to (2.11.6) is given by

$$\phi_{\alpha,\bar\alpha}(z) = (\varepsilon_{\alpha,\bar\alpha} \mid (\alpha,\bar\alpha)(z,e)\ \varepsilon_{\alpha,\bar\alpha})_{\alpha\otimes\bar\alpha} = \frac{1}{d_\alpha}(\mathrm{Id} \mid \alpha(z)\ \mathrm{Id})_{\alpha\otimes\bar\alpha} = \frac{1}{d_\alpha}\ \mathrm{trace}\ \alpha(z)$$

for all $z \in S$ and thus coincides with the normalized *character* of α. For $h \in L^2(S)$ and $\alpha \in S^\#$, define the α-th *Fourier coefficient*

(2.11.7) $$h^\#_\alpha := \int_S h(z)\ \alpha(z)^*\ dz \in \mathcal{Z}^2(H_\alpha).$$

2.11.8. THEOREM. *There exists a Hilbert space isomorphism*

(2.11.9) $$L^2(S) \xrightarrow[\approx]{()^\#} \sum_{\alpha\in S^\#}^{\oplus} \mathcal{Z}^2(H_\alpha)$$

such that for all $h \in L^2(S)$

(2.11.10) $$h^\# = (\sqrt{d_\alpha}\ h^\#_\alpha)_{\alpha\in S^\#}.$$

Proof. This is just a reformulation of Theorem 2.10.10. However, we want to check that the Fourier isomorphism (2.11.9) agrees with the transformation (2.10.27) defined in the general case (i.e., K not necessarily a direct product). To this end, note that the canonical embedding $L^2(S) \subset L^2(K)$ is given by $h(z,w) := h(e \cdot (z,w)) = h(w^{-1}z)$ for all $z,w \in S$. Therefore (2.11.4) and (2.11.6) imply for $h \in L^2(S)$

$$h^\#_{\alpha,\bar\alpha}\,\varepsilon_{\alpha,\bar\alpha} = \int_S\int_S h(z,w)((\alpha,\bar\alpha)(z,w))^*\ \varepsilon_{\alpha,\bar\alpha}\ dz\ dw$$

$$= \frac{1}{\sqrt{d_\alpha}} \int_S \int_S h(w^{-1}z)\, \alpha(z)^* \, \mathrm{Id}\, \alpha(w)\, dz\, dw$$

$$= \frac{1}{\sqrt{d_\alpha}} \int_S \int_S h(w^{-1}z)\, \alpha(w^{-1}z)^* \, dz\, dw$$

$$= \frac{1}{\sqrt{d_\alpha}} \int_S h(z)\, \alpha(z)^* \, dz = \frac{1}{\sqrt{d_\alpha}} h^\#_\alpha.$$

Since $d_{\alpha,\bar{\alpha}} = d_\alpha^2$, we obtain

$$\sqrt{d_{\alpha,\bar{\alpha}}}\; h^\#_{\alpha,\bar{\alpha}}\, \varepsilon_{\alpha,\bar{\alpha}} = \sqrt{d_\alpha}\, h^\#_\alpha. \qquad \text{Q.E.D.}$$

Let $\mathfrak{t}$ be a maximal abelian subalgebra of the Lie algebra $\mathfrak{s}$ of S and put $\mathfrak{a} := i\mathfrak{t}$. Consider the logarithmic base $\Lambda \subset \mathfrak{a}$ of Ω.

2.11.11. DEFINITION. The *Hardy space* $H^2(S)$ (depending on Ω) consists of all holomorphic functions $h : \Omega \to \mathbb{C}$ such that

$$\|h\|^2 := \sup_{a \in \Lambda} \int_S \int_S |h(w^{-1} \exp(a)\, z)|^2 \, dz\, dw < \infty.$$

By [L4] there exists an embedding $H^2(S) \subset L^2(S)$ as a closed subspace such that

$$\lim_{\substack{a \in \Lambda \\ a \to 0}} \int_S \int_S |h(w^{-1} \exp(a)\, z) - h(w^{-1}z)|^2 \, dz\, dw = 0.$$

This embedding is invariant under the right translation action (2.11.4) of K. The orthogonal projection

$$(2.11.12) \qquad E : L^2(S) \to H^2(S)$$

is called the *Szegö projection*. The Lie algebra $\mathfrak{k} = \mathfrak{s} \oplus \mathfrak{s}$ of $K = S \times S$ has the Cartan decomposition $\mathfrak{k} = \mathfrak{l} \oplus i\mathfrak{q}$ where

$$\mathfrak{l} = \{(A,A) : A \in \mathfrak{s}\}, \quad i\mathfrak{q} = \{(A,-A) : A \in \mathfrak{s}\}.$$

Identify

$$\mathfrak{a} = \{(A,-A) : A \in i\mathfrak{t}\} \approx i\mathfrak{t}$$

via the mapping $\frac{1}{2}(A,-A) \mapsto A$. By the theory of highest weights [BD], every $\alpha \in S^{\#}$ is uniquely determined by its *highest weight*, a linear form $\alpha : \mathfrak{a} \to \mathbb{R}$ characterized by the property

(2.11.13) $$d\alpha(A)\delta_\alpha = \alpha(A)\delta_\alpha \qquad \forall A \in \mathfrak{a},$$

where

(2.11.14) $$d\alpha(A) := \frac{d}{dt}\Big|_{t=0} \alpha(\exp(tA)) \qquad (A \in \mathfrak{s})$$

is the infinitesimal representation of $\mathfrak{s}$ on H_α associated with (2.11.5), and $\delta_\alpha \in H_\alpha$ is a highest weight unit vector satisfying $d\alpha(B)\delta_\alpha = 0$ for all $B \in \mathfrak{s}^{\mathbb{C}}$ belonging to the positive root spaces with respect to $\mathfrak{t}^{\mathbb{C}}$. In this way we may identify

(2.11.15) $$S^{\#} \subset \mathfrak{a}^{\#}$$

with a discrete subset of the real-linear dual space $\mathfrak{a}^{\#}$ of $\mathfrak{a}$. Consider the polar cone

(2.11.16) $$\Lambda^{\#} := \{\alpha \in \mathfrak{a}^{\#} : \alpha(A) \le 0 \ \forall A \in \Lambda\}$$

of $\Lambda \subset \mathfrak{a}$. As a special case of Theorem 2.10.45, we have

2.11.17. THEOREM. *The Fourier transform (2.11.9) induces a Hilbert space isomorphism*

(2.11.18) $$H^2(S) \xrightarrow[\approx]{()^{\#}} \sum_{\alpha \in S^{\#} \cap \Lambda^{\#}}^{\oplus} \mathcal{L}^2(H_\alpha).$$

2.11.19. PROPOSITION. *For each* $\alpha \in S^{\#} \cap \Lambda^{\#}$ *and* $\xi,\eta \in H_\alpha$ *let*

(2.11.20) $$\alpha_{\xi,\eta}(z) := (\xi|\alpha(z)\eta)$$

be the corresponding "matrix coefficient". Choose an orthonormal basis B_α *of* H_α. *Then the series*

(2.11.21) $$E(z,w) := \sum_{\alpha\in S^\#\cap\Lambda^\#} d_\alpha \sum_{\xi,\eta\in B_\alpha} \alpha_{\xi,\eta}(z)\,\overline{\alpha_{\xi,\eta}(w)}$$

converges compactly on $\Omega \times \Omega$, *and defines the Szegö kernel for* $H^2(S)$.

Proof. Let $\alpha \in S^\#$ and $\xi,\eta \in H_\alpha$. Then the rank 1 operator

$$\xi\eta^* \in \mathcal{Z}^2(H_\alpha) = H_{\alpha,\bar\alpha}$$

has the Fourier symbol (cf. (2.10.9))

$$(\eta\xi^*)_\#(z) = (\varepsilon_{\alpha,\bar\alpha} \mid (\alpha,\bar\alpha)(z,e)\eta\xi^*)_{\alpha\otimes\bar\alpha} = (\varepsilon_{\alpha,\bar\alpha} \mid (\alpha(z)\,\eta)\xi^*)_{\alpha\otimes\bar\alpha}$$

$$= \frac{1}{\sqrt{d_\alpha}} \text{ trace } (\alpha(z)\eta)\xi^* = \frac{1}{\sqrt{d_\alpha}} (\xi \mid \alpha(z)\eta)_\alpha = \frac{1}{\sqrt{d_\alpha}} \alpha_{\xi,\eta}(z)$$

for all $z \in S$. Since $\{\eta\xi^*: \xi,\eta \in B_\alpha\}$ is an orthonormal basis of $H_{\alpha,\bar\alpha}$, Proposition 2.10.57 yields

$$E(z,w) = \sum_{\alpha\in S^\#\cap\Lambda^\#} d_\alpha^2 \sum_{\xi,\eta\in B_\alpha} \frac{1}{\sqrt{d_\alpha}} \alpha_{\xi,\eta}(z) \frac{1}{\sqrt{d_\alpha}} \overline{\alpha_{\xi,\eta}(w)}.$$

Q.E.D.

2.11.22. DEFINITION. The holomorphic central function E_e on Ω defined by the compactly convergent series

(2.11.23) $$E_e(z) := \sum_{\alpha\in S^\#\cap\Lambda^\#} d_\alpha \text{ trace } \alpha(z)$$

is called the *Szegö characteristic function* of Ω.

Here $\alpha(z)$ is the *holomorphic* extension of $\alpha \in S^\# \cap \Lambda^\#$ to a representation of $S^{\mathbb{C}}$, and central means $E_e(w^{-1}zw) = E_e(z)$ for all $w \in S$. The series (2.11.23) agrees with (2.10.65) since

$$\sum_{\alpha\in S^\#\cap\Lambda^\#} d_{\alpha,\bar\alpha}\,(\alpha,\bar\alpha)(z) = \sum_{\alpha\in S^\#\cap\Lambda^\#} d_\alpha^2 \frac{1}{d_\alpha} \text{ trace } \alpha(z) = \sum_{\alpha\in S^\#\cap\Lambda^\#} d_\alpha \text{ trace } \alpha(z).$$

3. Multiplier C^*-Algebras and Their Representations

3.0. Introduction

For strictly pseudoconvex domains with smooth boundary (and the more general smooth domains of "finite type" [BDT]), Toeplitz operators and their associated C^*-algebras can be studied directly using a generalization of the pseudodifferential calculus (cf. Sections 4.1 and 4.2). For all other types of domains studied in this book the boundary is in general not smooth but has only a stratification given by certain fibrations or foliations. Our approach towards this more complicated geometric setting is to introduce an intermediary C^*-algebra of "multipliers" (or convolution operators under Fourier transform) which arises as a certain completion of a group C^*-algebra and contains the Hardy (or Bergman) projection. Thus this multiplier C^*-algebra is a convenient tool to study this orthogonal projection in an algebraic setting. The basic result concerning the multiplier C^*-algebra is the determination of its spectrum, i.e., the set of all characters (in the abelian case).

The first four Sections 3.1–3.4 introduce the multiplier C^*-algebra in the setting of tubular domains and polycircular domains. The common feature here is that the canonical group acting is commutative, namely a euclidean translation group in the first case and the r-torus rotation group in the second case. Therefore the completion of the (abelian) group C^*-algebra can be described explicitly in terms of functions on the dual group. This makes the determination of all characters of the multiplier C^*-algebra a problem in integration theory. For tubular domains (over symmetric cones) the relevant integrals are computed via the explicit knowledge of the underlying cones. In the polycircular case the cone can be quite arbitrary and estimating the relevant integrals is more difficult. In both cases the final result asserts that the *facial structure* of the radial cone, describing the geometry of the underlying domain, gives a geometric realization of the C^*-algebraic spectrum.

The remaining Sections 3.5-3.7 treat the non-commutative case of K-circular domains and the subclass of symmetric domains. In this situation the multiplier C^*-algebra is non-commutative (consisting of "block diagonal" operators instead of diagonal operators) but the theory of "spherical functions" allows one to identify a commutative C^*-subalgebra which contains enough information for the later study of Toeplitz operators. While for general K-circular domains we give only the overall construction, the symmetric case is carried out in full detail. Here methods from microlocal analysis (Hermite operators) combine in an interesting way with the representation theoretic arguments. The author hopes that a similar proof can be given for arbitrary K-circular domains.

3.1 Hardy Multipliers Over Tubular Domains

In this section we introduce a commutative C^*-algebra whose spectrum plays a crucial role in the analysis of Hardy-Toeplitz operators over a given tubular domain $\Pi = \Lambda \times iX$ in $Z = X \oplus iX$. For the harmonic analysis of the Hardy space over the Shilov boundary iX of Π see Section 2.3. Let $\mathcal{L}(L^2(iX))$ be the C^*-algebra of all bounded operators on $L^2(iX)$.

3.1.1. DEFINITION. For any integrable function $u \in L^1(iX)$, the *convolution operator* with *symbol* u is the bounded operator $u^\# : L^2(iX) \to L^2(iX)$ defined by

$$(3.1.2) \qquad (u^\# h)(z) := \int_{iX} h(z - w)\, u(w)\, dw$$

for all $h \in L^2(iX)$ and $z \in iX$. The multiplication action (2.3.6) of X on $L^2(iX)$ induces an adjoint action of X on $\mathcal{L}(L^2(iX))$ which satisfies for every $\beta \in X$

$$(3.1.3) \qquad Ad(\beta_\#)u^\# = (\beta_\# \cdot u)^\# \qquad \text{(convolution operator)}$$

where $\beta_\#(z) = e^{\beta \cdot z}$ belongs to $L^\infty(iX)$. Generalizing (3.1.2), we define a convolution operator $u^\# : \mathcal{C}^\infty_c(iX) \to \mathcal{C}^\infty_c(iX)$ for any *distribution* u on iX by putting

$$(3.1.4) \qquad (u^\# h)(z) := \int_{iX} h(z - w)\, du(w).$$

Then the covariance (3.1.3) holds by putting

$$(3.1.5) \qquad d(\beta_\# u)(z) = e^{\beta \cdot z}\, du(z).$$

3.1.6. PROPOSITION. *Let $\Lambda \subset X$ be a symmetric cone. There exists a distribution E_0 on iX called the "characteristic convolutor" of Λ such that*

(3.1.17) $$\int_{iX} h(z)\, dE_0(z) = \lim_{\substack{a\in\Lambda \\ a\to 0}} \int_{iX} h(z)\, E_0(a+z)\, dz$$

for all $h \in C_c^\infty(iX)$. *Here* $E_0(a+z)$ *is the Szegö characteristic function (2.3.21) at* $a + z \in \Pi$.

3.1.8. PROPOSITION. *The convolution operator* $E_0^\#$ *is the Szegö projection* $E_0^\# : L^2(iX) \to H^2(iX)$.

Proof. By (2.3.15) and (2.3.23), the Szegö projection E satisfies

$$(Eh)(z) = (E_z \mid h)_{iX} = \int_{iX} \overline{E(w,z)}\, h(w)\, dw = \int_{iX} E(z,w)\, h(w)\, dw$$
$$= \int_{iX} E_0(z - w)\, h(w)\, dw$$

for all $h \in L^2(iX)$ and $z \in \Pi$. This implies for $z \in iX$ and $h \in C_c^\infty(iX)$

$$(Eh)(z) = \lim_{\substack{a\in\Lambda \\ a\to 0}} Eh(z+a) = \lim_{\substack{a\in\Lambda \\ a\to 0}} \int_{iX} E_0(z + a - y)\, h(y)\, dy$$

$$= \lim_{\substack{a\in\Lambda \\ a\to 0}} \int_{iX} E_0(w + a)\, h(z - w)\, dw = \int_{iX} h(z - w)\, dE_0(w).$$

Q.E.D.

3.1.9. DEFINITION. For any bounded function $\varphi \in L^\infty(X)$, the *multiplication operator* with *symbol* φ is the bounded operator $\varphi : L^2(X) \to L^2(X)$ defined for all $\xi \in L^2(X)$ and $\alpha \in X$ by

$$(\varphi\xi)(\alpha) := \varphi(\alpha)\xi(\alpha)\ .$$

The translation action (2.3.2) of X on $L^2(X)$ induces an adjoint action of X on $\mathcal{L}(L^2(X))$ which satisfies for every $\beta \in X$

(3.1.11) $$\mathrm{Ad}(\beta_\#)\varphi = \beta_\#\varphi \qquad \text{(multiplication operator)}$$

where $(\beta_\#\varphi)(\alpha) := \varphi(\alpha - \beta)$ belongs to $L^\infty(X)$.

3.1.12. DEFINITION. Let $\Lambda^\# \subset X$ denote the polar cone of a symmetric cone $\Lambda \subset X$. Define the *characteristic multiplier* $\chi \in L^\infty(X)$ by

$$\chi(\alpha) := \begin{cases} 1 & \alpha \in \Lambda^\# \\ 0 & \alpha \in X \setminus \Lambda^\# \end{cases}.$$

3.1.13. PROPOSITION. *The multiplication operator* χ *coincides with the orthogonal projection* $\chi : L^2(X) \to L^2(\Lambda^\#)$.

3.1.14. PROPOSITION. *The Fourier transform (2.3.8) induces a commuting diagram*

$$\begin{array}{ccc} L^2(iX) & \xrightarrow{\;()^\#\;} & L^2(X) \\ {\scriptstyle E_0^\#}\downarrow & & \downarrow{\scriptstyle \chi} \\ H^2(iX) & \xrightarrow[\;()^\#\;]{} & L^2(\Lambda^\#) \end{array}$$

Proof. Since $()^\#$ is a Hilbert space isomorphism mapping $H^2(iX)$ onto $L^2(\Lambda^\#)$ by Theorem 2.3.18, the assertion follows from Proposition 3.1.13. Q.E.D.

For every $\mu \in L^1(X)$ the inverse Fourier transform

$$\mu_\#(z) := \int_X e^{z\cdot\alpha}\, \mu(\alpha)\, d\alpha \qquad (z \in iX) \tag{3.1.15}$$

is a smooth function on iX vanishing at ∞. Thus we may form the multiplication $\mu_\# \cdot E_0$ with the characteristic convolutor E_0 on iX, and obtain a distribution on iX. We may also form the convolution

$$(\mu_\#\chi)(x) = \int_X \chi(x-y)\, \mu(y)\, dy = \int_{x-\Lambda^\#} \mu(y)\, dy$$

with the characteristic multiplier χ on X, and obtain a bounded uniformly continuous function on X.

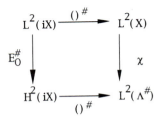

3.1.16. PROPOSITION. *For every* $\mu \in L^1(X)$, *the Fourier transform* (2.3.8) *induces a commuting diagram*

$$\begin{array}{ccc} L^2(iX) & \xrightarrow{\;()^{\#}\;} & L^2(X) \\ {\scriptstyle (\mu_{\#}\cdot E_0)^{\#}}\Big\downarrow & & \Big\downarrow{\scriptstyle \mu_{\#}\chi} \\ L^2(iX) & \xrightarrow[\;()^{\#}\;]{} & L^2(X) \end{array}$$

for the respective convolution and multiplication operators.

Proof. For every $h \in L^2(iX)$ (or rather belonging to a dense subspace), we have by standard Fourier theory

$$((\mu_{\#} \cdot E_0)^{\#} h)^{\#} = (\mu_{\#} \cdot E_0)^{\#} \cdot h^{\#},$$

where $(\mu_{\#} \cdot E_0)^{\#} = (\mu_{\#}^{\#})_{\#}(E_0^{\#}) = \mu_{\#}\chi.$

Q.E.D.

3.1.17. DEFINITION. The *Hardy multiplier algebra* associated with Π is the non-unital C^*-algebra

$$\mathcal{D}(X) := C^*(\mu_{\#}\chi : \mu \in L^1(X)) \tag{3.1.18}$$

of multiplication operators on $L^2(X)$. Since $\beta_{\#}(\mu_{\#} \cdot E_0) = (\beta_{\#}\mu)_{\#} \cdot E_0$ and $\beta_{\#}(\mu_{\#}\chi) = (\beta_{\#}\mu)_{\#}\chi$ for all $\beta \in X$, the adjoint action of X on $\mathcal{Z}(L^2(X))$ leaves the C^*-subalgebra $\mathcal{D}(X)$ invariant, and we obtain a restricted action of X on $\mathcal{D}(X)$. Identifying $\mathcal{D}(X)$ with a C^*-subalgebra of $L^\infty(X)$, this action coincides with the translation action of X. The *spectrum* (= character space) Spec $\mathcal{D}(X)$ of the abelian Banach algebra (3.1.18) is a locally compact Hausdorff space which is not compact since $\mathcal{D}(X)$ is non-unital. Being a subalgebra of $L^\infty(X)$, $\mathcal{D}(X)$ has the "elementary" characters α_A $(\alpha \in X)$ defined by

$$\alpha_A \cdot \varphi := \varphi(\alpha) \tag{3.1.19}$$

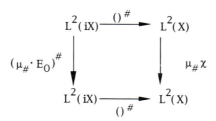

for all $\varphi \in \mathcal{D}(X)$. Here we put $A := \bar{\Lambda}$. Since $\mathcal{D}(X)$ separates the points of X, we obtain an embedding $X \subset \operatorname{Spec} \mathcal{D}(X)$ given by $\alpha \mapsto \alpha_A$.

In the following we consider *faces* of the closed convex cone $A = \bar{\Lambda} \subset X$. By Theorem 1.3.35, every face of A has the form

$$B = \{x \in A : x \cdot c = 0\} = A \cap X_0(c), \tag{3.1.20}$$

where $c \in X$ is an idempotent, i.e. $c^2 = c$. Then

$$T(B) := X_0(c)$$

is the corresponding tangent space. Let $P_B : X \to T(B)$ be the orthogonal Peirce projection.

3.1.21. THEOREM. *Let $\alpha = \alpha_n$ be a sequence in $\Lambda^\#$ such that there exist orthogonal minimal idempotents $c_1, \ldots, c_k \in X$ with the property*

$$P_{j-1}^{\perp}\alpha/\|P_{j-1}^{\perp}\alpha\| \to c_j \qquad (1 \leq j \leq k)$$

and $P_B\alpha \to \beta$. Here $P_j^{\perp}$ is the orthogonal projection onto $\langle c_1, \ldots, c_j\rangle^{\perp}$. Let $B = A \cap X_0(c_1 + \cdots + c_k)$ denote the corresponding face. Then the character

$$\beta_B := w^* - \lim \alpha_A \in \operatorname{Spec} \mathcal{D}(X) \tag{3.1.22}$$

exists and satisfies for all $\mu \in L^1(X)$

$$\beta_B(\mu_\#\chi) := \int_{\{P_B x \leq \beta\}} \mu(x)\ dx. \tag{3.1.23}$$

Proof. For every $\mu \in L^1(X)$, we have

$$\begin{aligned} \alpha_A \cdot (\mu_\#\chi) &= \mu_\#\chi(\alpha) = \int_X \chi(\alpha - \beta)\, \mu(\beta)\, d\beta \\ &= \int_{\alpha-\Lambda^\#} \mu(\beta)\, d\beta = \int_{\{x \leq \alpha\}} \mu(x)\ dx \end{aligned} \tag{3.1.24}$$

whenever $\alpha \in X$. This agrees with (3.1.23) in case $k = 0$. Now consider sequences $\alpha = \alpha_n$ in $\Lambda^{\#}$ with $\|\alpha_n\| \to \infty$. Then $k \geq 1$. It suffices to prove (3.1.22) for the generators of $\mathcal{D}(X)$. Let $e_1, \ldots, e_r$ be a frame of idempotents of X and suppose first that

$$\alpha_n = \sum_{j=1}^{r} x_j(n) e_j \tag{3.1.25}$$

for all n. Then $x_j(n) \geq 0$ for every j and, after reordering, we may assume $x_j(n) \to +\infty$ for $1 \leq j \leq k$ and $x_j(n) \to x_j \in \mathbb{R}$ for $k < j \leq r$, where $0 \leq k \leq r$. Then $c := e_1 + \cdots + e_k$ is an idempotent, with corresponding face $B = A \cap X_0(c)$. Consider the Peirce decomposition

$$X = X_1(c) \oplus X_{1/2}(c) \oplus X_0(c) \tag{3.1.26}$$

and let $x = u + v + w$ be the corresponding Peirce coordinates. Then $\alpha_n = u_n + w_n$ with

$$u_n := \sum_{j \leq k} x_j(n) e_j \to +\infty \qquad \text{(in } X_1(c)\text{)},$$

$$w_n := \sum_{j>k} x_j(n) e_j \to \beta := \sum_{j>k} x_j e_j. \tag{3.1.27}$$

We will now show

$$\overline{\lim}\, (\alpha_n - \Lambda^{\#}) := \bigcap_{m \geq 1} \bigcup_{n \geq m} (\alpha_n - \Lambda^{\#}) \subset \{P_B x \leq \beta\}. \tag{3.1.28}$$

In fact if $x = u + v + w \in \overline{\lim}\, (\alpha_n - \Lambda^{\#})$, then $x \in \alpha_n - \Lambda^{\#}$, i.e., $x \leq \alpha_n$, for infinitely many n. Applying the Peirce projections gives $u \leq u_n$ and $w \leq w_n$ for those n. For $n \to \infty$, we obtain $P_B x = w \leq \beta$. By [B1; p. 64], (3.1.28) implies

$$\overline{\lim} \int_{\alpha_n - \Lambda^{\#}} \mu \leq \int_{\overline{\lim}\, (\alpha_n - \Lambda^{\#})} \mu \leq \int_{\{P_B x \leq \beta\}} \mu \tag{3.1.29}$$

whenever $\mu \in L^1(X)$ is positive. For the converse we show that for every $t > 0$

$$(3.1.30) \quad \{P_B x \leq \beta - t(e - c)\} \subset \underline{\lim}\,(\alpha_n - \Lambda^\#) = \bigcup_{m \geq 1} \bigcap_{n \geq m} (\alpha_n - \Lambda^\#).$$

In fact, there exists $m \geq 1$ such that $w_n \geq \beta - \frac{t}{2}(e - c)$ for all $n \geq m$. If $x = u + v + w$ satisfies $w = P_B x \leq \beta - t(e - c)$ then

$$w_n - w \geq \beta - \frac{t}{2}(e - c) - w \geq \frac{t}{2}(e - c).$$

Since $u_n - u \to +\infty$ we may choose m such that

$$\alpha_n - x = (u_n - u) - v + (w_n - w) \geq (u_n - u) - v + \frac{t}{2}(e - c)$$

belongs to $\Lambda^\#$ for all $n \geq m$. This proves (3.1.30). Since the union

$$\bigcup_{t>0} \{P_B x \leq \beta - t(e - c)\} \subset \{P_B x \leq \beta\}$$

is a dense convex set, its boundary has measure zero and (3.1.30) implies

$$(3.1.31) \quad \int_{\{P_B x \leq \beta\}} \mu \leq \int_{\underline{\lim}(\alpha_n - \Lambda^\#)} \mu \leq \underline{\lim} \int_{\alpha_n - \Lambda^\#} \mu .$$

Combining (3.1.29) and (3.1.31), we obtain $\alpha_A \to \beta_B \in \operatorname{Spec} \mathcal{D}(X)$ provided $\alpha = \alpha_n$ has the form (3.1.25). For every $g \in L := \operatorname{Aut}(X)$, $B \cdot g$ is a face of A, $\beta \cdot g \in T(B \cdot g)$ and we have

$$(\alpha \cdot g)_A = \alpha_A \cdot g \to \beta_B \cdot g = (\beta \cdot g)_B \in \operatorname{Spec} \mathcal{D}(X) ,$$

because L acts continuously on $\mathcal{D}(X)$ since L leaves Λ invariant. This proves (3.1.22) in general since every sequence $\alpha = \alpha_n$ has the form $\alpha_n = \beta_n \cdot g_n$ where β_n is of the form (3.1.25) and g_n belongs to the compact group L.

Q.E.D.

Using the notation (3.1.23) we define for any face $B \subset A$

(3.1.32) $$\mathrm{Spec}_B\, \mathcal{D}(X) := \{\beta_B : \beta \in P_B\Lambda^\#\}.$$

In particular

$$\mathrm{Spec}_A\, \mathcal{D}(X) = \{\alpha_A : \alpha \in \Lambda^\#\}.$$

3.1.33. PROPOSITION. *The character sets (3.1.32) are pairwise disjoint. Each such set is open in its closure*

(3.1.34) $$\mathrm{Spec}_B\, \mathcal{D}(X)^{cl} = \bigcup_{C \subset B} \mathrm{Spec}_C\, \mathcal{D}(X)$$

which is compact. In particular,

(3.1.35) $$\mathrm{Spec}_+\, \mathcal{D}(X) := \mathrm{Spec}_A\, \mathcal{D}(X)^{cl} = \bigcup_{B \subset A} \mathrm{Spec}_B\, \mathcal{D}(X)$$

is compact and contains $\mathrm{Spec}_A\, \mathcal{D}(X)$ *as an open subset.*

Proof. Following [MR; §6] we will give an explicit realization of Spec $\mathcal{D}(X)$. By Theorem 3.1.21, every sequence $\alpha = \alpha_n \in \Lambda^\#$ gives rise, after passing to a subsequence, to a character

(3.1.36) $$\beta_B := w^* - \lim_{n\to\infty} \alpha_A \in \mathrm{Spec}\, \mathcal{D}(X)$$

where $\beta = \lim P_B\alpha \in X_0(c)$ and P_B is the orthogonal projection onto the tangent space $T(B) = X_0(c)$ for a face $B \subset A := \bar{\Lambda}$ determined by the idempotent $c \in X$. It follows that we may identify

(3.1.37) $$\mathrm{Spec}_+\, \mathcal{D}(X) \approx \{(c,\beta) : c = c^2 \in X,\ \beta \in X_0^+(c)\},$$

where $X_0^+(c) = P_B\Lambda^\#$ is the closed positive cone of $X_0(c)$. More generally (considering sequences $\alpha = \alpha_n$ not necessarily in $\Lambda^\#$) we may identify

(3.1.38) $$\mathrm{Spec}\, \mathcal{D}(X) \approx \{(c,\beta) : c = c^2 \in X,\ \beta \in X_0(c)\}.$$

By (3.1.23), the character (3.1.36) has the explicit form

$$\beta_B(\mu_\# \chi) = \int_{\{x_0 \leq \beta\}} \mu(x)\ dx \qquad (\mu \in L^1(X))$$

where x_0 is the Peirce 0-component of x. The set $\{x_0 \leq \beta\}$ coincides with the closure $N := \overline{\beta + X_1(c) + \bar{\Lambda}}$. In fact, if $x = \beta + y_1 + p$, with $p \in \bar{\Lambda}$, we have $x_0 = P_0 x = \beta + P_0 p$ with $P_0 p \in \bar{\Lambda}_c$. Thus $x_0 \leq \beta$. Conversely if $x = x_1 + x_{1/2} + x_0$ satisfies $x_0 < \beta$, then we may write $x = \beta + (x_1 + \lambda c) + [x_0 - \beta + x_{1/2} - \lambda c]$ and $x_0 - \beta + x_{1/2} - \lambda c \in \Lambda$ if $\lambda > 0$ is large enough. It follows that we have

$$\beta_B(\mu_\# \chi) = \int_N \mu(x)\ dx$$

for all $\mu \in L^1(X)$. According to (3.1.38), we regard $\mu_\# \chi$ as a function on Spec $\mathcal{D}(X)$ by writing

$$(\mu_\# \chi)(c,\beta) := \int_N \mu(x)\ dx. \tag{3.1.39}$$

If $\beta \in X$ is arbitrary, a similar argument as above shows $N = \overline{\beta_0 + X_1(c) + \bar{\Lambda}}$ (β_0 = Peirce 0-component), so that (3.1.39) gives

$$(\mu_\# \chi)(c,\beta_0) = \int_N \mu(x)\ dx \tag{3.1.40}$$

for any $\beta \in X$. Following [MR; 6.3] we define a topology on Spec $\mathcal{D}(X)$, generated by the basic open sets

$$\langle U,V\rangle = \{(c, P_0^c(\beta + P_1^e y)) : e \in U, c \leq e, \beta \in V, y \in -\Lambda\} \tag{3.1.41}$$

where U is open in the compact space P_k of all rank k idempotents e, P_1^e is the corresponding Peirce 1-projection, c is an idempotent of rank $\leq k$ contained in $P_1^e(X)$, and V is open in X. Using (3.1.40) and [MR; Lemma 6.2] one shows that all functions $\mu_\# \chi$, $\mu \in L^1(X)$, are continuous on Spec $\mathcal{D}(X)$. By [MR; Theorem 6.4], the topology generated by the sets (3.1.41) coincides with the weak* topology on Spec $\mathcal{D}(X)$. Therefore Proposition 3.1.33 follows from the facial structure of Λ (cf. Theorem 1.3.35). Q.E.D.

3.2 Bergman Multipliers Over Tubular Domains

In this section we introduce a commutative C^*-algebra whose spectrum plays a crucial role in the analysis of Bergman-Toeplitz operators over a tubular domain $\Pi = \Lambda \times iX$. For the harmonic analysis of the weighted Bergman spaces over Π, indexed by a real parameter λ, cf. Section 2.4.

3.2.1. DEFINITION. Let $\Lambda^\# \subset X$ denote the polar cone of Λ. For each $\gamma \in \Lambda^\#$ and $\lambda > p - 1$ define the *λ-characteristic multiplier about* γ by putting

$$(3.2.2) \qquad \chi_\gamma(\alpha) := \begin{cases} \left(\dfrac{\Delta(\alpha)}{\Delta(\gamma + \alpha)}\right)^{\lambda/2 - p/4} & \text{if} \quad \alpha \in \Lambda^\# \\ 0 & \text{if} \quad \alpha \in X \backslash \Lambda^\# . \end{cases}$$

Here Δ is the Jordan algebra determinant. Note that $\gamma + \alpha \geq \alpha$ in the $\Lambda^\#$-ordering which implies $\Delta(\gamma + \alpha) \geq \Delta(\alpha)$. Thus $0 \leq \chi_\gamma \leq 1$ on X. In particular, $\chi_\gamma \in L^\infty(X)$. Given $\mu \in L^1(X)$, we may form the convolution $\mu_\# \chi_\gamma$ and obtain a bounded uniformly continuous function on X. In the degenerate case $\lambda = p/2$ (corresponding to the Hardy space), χ_γ is independent of γ and coincides with the characteristic multiplier χ defined in 3.1.12.

3.2.3. DEFINITION. The *λ-Bergman multiplier algebra* associated with Π is the non-unital C^*-algebra

$$(3.2.4) \qquad \mathcal{D}_\lambda(X) := C^*(\mu_\# \chi_\gamma : \mu \in L^1(X), \gamma \in \Lambda^\#)$$

of multiplication operators on $L^2(X)$.

Since $\beta_\#(\mu_\# \chi_\gamma) = (\beta_\# \mu)_\# \chi_\gamma$ for all $\beta \in X$, the adjoint action of X on $\mathcal{L}(L^2(X))$ leaves the C^*-subalgebra $\mathcal{D}_\lambda(X)$ invariant, and we obtain a restricted action of X on $\mathcal{D}_\lambda(X)$. Identifying $\mathcal{D}_\lambda(X)$ with a C^*-subalgebra of $L^\infty(X)$, this action coincides with the translation action of X. The *spectrum* (= character space) Spec $\mathcal{D}_\lambda(X)$ of the abelian Banach algebra (3.2.4) is a locally compact Hausdorff space which is not compact since $\mathcal{D}_\lambda(X)$ is non-unital. Being a subalgebra of $L^\infty(X)$, $\mathcal{D}_\lambda(X)$ has the "elementary" characters α_A $(\alpha \in X)$ defined by

$$\alpha_A \cdot \varphi := \varphi(\alpha) \tag{3.2.5}$$

for all $\varphi \in \mathcal{D}_\lambda(X)$. Here we put $A := \bar{\Lambda}$. Since $\mathcal{D}_\lambda(X)$ separates the points of X, we obtain an embedding $X \subset \text{Spec}\ \mathcal{D}_\lambda(X)$ given by $\alpha \mapsto \alpha_A$. Analogous to Theorem 3.1.21 we have

3.2.6. THEOREM. *Let* $\alpha = \alpha_n$ *be a sequence in* $\Lambda^\#$ *such that there exists orthogonal minimal idempotents* $c_1, \ldots, c_k \in X$ *with the property*

$$P_{j-1}^\perp \alpha / \|P_{j-1}^\perp \alpha\| \to c_j \qquad (1 \le j \le k)$$

and $P_k^\perp \alpha \to \beta$. *Here* $P_j^\perp$ *is the orthogonal projection onto* $\langle c_1, \ldots, c_j \rangle^\perp$. *Let* $B = A \cap X_0(c_1 + \cdots + c_k)$ *denote the corresponding face. Then*

$$\beta_B := w^* - \lim \alpha_A \in \text{Spec}\ \mathcal{D}_\lambda(X) \tag{3.2.7}$$

exists and satisfies for all $\mu \in L^1(X)$ *and* $\gamma \in \Lambda^\#$

$$\beta_B(\mu_\# \chi_\gamma) := \int_{\{P_B x \le \beta\}} \mu(x) \left[\frac{\Delta(\beta - x)^{\lambda - p/2}}{\Delta(\beta - x + P_B \gamma)^{\lambda - p/2}}\right]^{1/2} dx. \tag{3.2.8}$$

Proof. For every $\mu \in L^1(X)$ and $\gamma \in \Lambda^\#$, we have

$$\alpha_A \cdot (\mu_\# \chi_\gamma) = (\mu_\# \chi_\gamma)(\alpha) = \int_X \chi_\gamma(\alpha - x)\, \mu(x)\ dx$$
$$= \int_{\alpha - \Lambda^\#} \left(\frac{\Delta(\alpha - x)^{\lambda - p/2}}{\Delta(\alpha - x + \gamma)^{\lambda - p/2}}\right)^{1/2} \mu(x)\ dx$$

whenever $\alpha \in X$. This agrees with (3.2.8) in case $k = 0$. Now consider sequences $\alpha = \alpha_n$ in $\Lambda^\#$ with $\|\alpha\| \to \infty$. Then $k \ge 1$. It suffices to prove

(3.2.7) for the generators of $\mathcal{D}_\lambda(X)$. As in the proof of Theorem 3.1.21 we may assume $\alpha_n = \sum x_j(n)e_j$ for some frame of idempotents $e_1, \ldots, e_r$ of X and $x_j(n) \to +\infty$ for $j \leq k$, $x_j(n) \to x_j \in \mathbb{R}$ for $j > k$. Put $c := e_1 + \cdots + e_k$, and consider the Peirce decomposition $x = u + v + w$, $\alpha_n = u_n + w_n$ relative to (3.1.26). Then

$$w_n \to \beta := \sum_{j>k} x_j e_j.$$

According to (3.1.28) and (3.1.30), we have for the characteristic functions

(3.2.9)
$$\chi_{(\alpha_n - \Lambda^\#)} \to \chi_{\{P_B x \leq \beta\}}$$

almost everywhere. Here $B := A \cap X_0(c)$ is the face corresponding to c. We have

$$\frac{\Delta(\alpha_n - x)}{\Delta(\alpha_n - x + \gamma)} = \frac{\Delta((u_n - u) - v + (w_n - w))}{\Delta((u_n - u + \gamma_1) + (\gamma_{1/2} - v) + (w_n - w + \gamma_0))}$$

$$= \frac{\Delta(u_n - u + e - c)\,\Delta(c - P^{-1/2}_{u_n - u + e - c} v + w_n - w)}{\Delta(u_n - u + \gamma_1 + e - c)\,\Delta(c + P^{-1/2}_{u_n - u + \gamma_1 + e - c}(\gamma_{1/2} - v) + w_n - w + \gamma_0)}$$

where $\gamma = \gamma_1 + \gamma_{1/2} + \gamma_0$ is the Peirce decomposition and $P_x y = \{xyx\}$ is the quadratic representation. Since $u_n \to +\infty$, we have

$$\frac{\Delta(u_n - u + e - c)}{\Delta(u_n - u + \gamma_1 + e - c)} \to 1,$$

$$\lim P^{-1/2}_{u_n - u + e - c} = \lim P^{-1/2}_{u_n - u + \gamma_1 + e - c} = 0.$$

as $n \to \infty$. Therefore

$$\frac{\Delta(\alpha_n - x)}{\Delta(\alpha_n - x + \gamma)} \to \frac{\Delta(c + \beta - w)}{\Delta(c + \beta - w + \gamma_0)}.$$

Multiplying by (3.2.9), we obtain

$$\int_{\alpha_n-\Lambda^\#} \left(\frac{\Delta(\alpha_n - x)^{\lambda-p/2}}{\Delta(\alpha_n - x + \gamma)^{\lambda-p/2}}\right)^{1/2} \mu(x)\ dx$$

$$\to \int_{\{P_B x\leq\beta\}} \left[\frac{\Delta(c + \beta - w)^{\lambda-p/2}}{\Delta(c + \beta - w + \gamma_0)^{\lambda-p/2}}\right]^{1/2} \mu(x)\ dx.$$

Since $P_B\gamma = \gamma_0$, the assertion follows.Q.E.D.

Using the notation (3.2.7) we define for any face $B \subset A$

$$\text{Spec}_B\ \mathcal{D}_\lambda(X) := \{\beta_B : \beta \in P_B\Lambda^\#\}. \tag{3.2.10}$$

In particular

$$\text{Spec}_A\ \mathcal{D}_\lambda(X) = \{\alpha_A : \alpha \in \Lambda^\#\}.$$

Using similar geometric arguments as in the proof of Proposition 3.1.33, we obtain

3.2.11. PROPOSITION. *The character sets (3.2.10) are pairwise disjoint. Each such set is open in its closure*

$$\text{Spec}_B\ \mathcal{D}_\lambda(X)^{c\ell} = \bigcup_{C\subset B} \text{Spec}_C\ \mathcal{D}_\lambda(X) \tag{3.2.12}$$

which is compact. In particular,

$$\text{Spec}_+\ \mathcal{D}_\lambda(X) := \text{Spec}_A\ \mathcal{D}_\Lambda(X)^{c\ell} = \bigcup_{C\subset B} \text{Spec}_B\ \mathcal{D}_\lambda(X) \tag{3.2.13}$$

is compact and contains $\text{Spec}_A\ \mathcal{D}_\lambda(X)$ *as an open subset.*

3.3 Hardy Multipliers Over Polycircular Domains

In this section we introduce a commutative C^*-algebra whose spectrum plays a crucial role in the analysis of Hardy-Toeplitz operators over a polycircular domain $\Omega = e^\Lambda \cdot \mathbb{T}^r$ in $\mathbb{C}^r$. We assume that Λ is a convex cone, so that $\mathbb{T}^r$ is the Shilov boundary of Ω. The harmonic analysis of the corresponding Hardy space is discussed in Section 2.5.

3.3.1. DEFINITION. For any integrable function $u \in L^1(\mathbb{T}^r)$, the *convolution operator* with *symbol* u is the bounded operator $u^\# : L^2(\mathbb{T}^r) \to L^2(\mathbb{T}^r)$ defined by

$$(u^\# h)(z) := \int_{\mathbb{T}^r} h(\bar{w}z)\, u(w)\, dw \tag{3.3.2}$$

for all $h \in L^2(\mathbb{T}^r)$ and $z \in \mathbb{T}^r$. The multiplication action (2.5.3) of $\mathbb{Z}^r$ on $L^2(\mathbb{T}^r)$ induces an adjoint action of $\mathbb{Z}^r$ on $\mathcal{L}(L^2(\mathbb{T}^r))$ which satisfies for every $\beta \in \mathbb{Z}^r$

$$\mathrm{Ad}(\beta_\#)u^\# = (\beta_\# \cdot u)^\# \tag{3.3.3}$$

where $\beta_\#(z) := z^\beta$ belongs to $L^\infty(\mathbb{T}^r)$. Generalizing (3.3.2), we define a convolution operator $u^\# : \mathcal{C}^\infty(\mathbb{T}^r) \to \mathcal{C}^\infty(\mathbb{T}^r)$ for any *distribution* on $\mathbb{T}^r$ by putting

$$(u^\# h)(z) := \int_{\mathbb{T}^r} h(\bar{w}z)\, du(w). \tag{3.3.4}$$

Then the covariance property (3.3.3) holds with

$$d(\beta_\# u)(z) = z^\beta \cdot du(z). \tag{3.3.5}$$

3.3.6. PROPOSITION. *There exists a distribution* E_e *on* $\mathbb{T}^r$, *called the "characteristic convolutor" of* Ω, *such that*

$$\int_{\mathbb{T}^r} h(z)\, dE_e(z) = \lim_{\substack{a \in \Lambda \\ a \to 0}} \int_{\mathbb{T}^r} h(z)\, E_e(e^a z)\, dz$$

for all $h \in \mathcal{C}^\infty(\mathbb{T}^r)$. *Here* $E_e(e^a z)$ *is the Szegö characteristic function (2.5.19) at* $e^a z \in \Omega$.

3.3.7. PROPOSITION. *The convolution operator* $E_e^\#$ *with symbol* E_e *coincides with the Szegö projection* $E_e^\# : L^2(\mathbb{T}^r) \to H^2(\mathbb{T}^r)$.

Proof. By (2.5.23) and (2.5.21), we have

$$(Eh)(z) = (E_z|h)_{\mathbb{T}^r} = \int_{\mathbb{T}^r} \overline{E_z(w)}\ h(w)\ dw$$

$$= \int_{\mathbb{T}^r} E(z,w)\ h(w)\ dw = \int_{\mathbb{T}^r} E_e(z\bar{w})\ h(w)\ dw$$

for all $h \in L^2(\mathbb{T}^r)$ and $z \in \Omega$. Now fix $z \in \mathbb{T}^r$. Then we get for all $h \in \mathcal{C}^\infty(\mathbb{T}^r)$

$$(Eh)(z) = \lim_{\substack{a\in\Lambda \\ a\to 0}} (Eh)(e^a z) = \lim_{\substack{a\in\Lambda \\ a\to 0}} \int_{\mathbb{T}^r} E_e(e^a z\bar{s})\ h(s)\ ds$$

$$= \lim_{\substack{a\in\Lambda \\ a\to 0}} \int_{\mathbb{T}^r} E_e(e^a w)\ h(\bar{w}z)\ dw = \int_{\mathbb{T}^r} h(\bar{w}z)\ dE_e(w) = (E_e^{\#}h)(z)$$

Q.E.D.

3.3.8. DEFINITION. For any bounded function $\varphi \in L^\infty(\mathbb{Z}^r)$, the *multiplication operator* with symbol φ is the bounded operator $\varphi : L^2(\mathbb{Z}^r) \to L^2(\mathbb{Z}^r)$ defined by

(3.3.9) $$(\varphi\xi)(\alpha) := \varphi(\alpha)\xi(\alpha)$$

for all $\xi \in L^2(\mathbb{Z}^r)$ and $\alpha \in \mathbb{Z}^r$. The translation action (2.5.5) of $\mathbb{Z}^r$ on $L^2(\mathbb{Z}^r)$ induces an adjoint action of $\mathbb{Z}^r$ on $\mathfrak{L}(L^2(\mathbb{Z}^r))$ which satisfies for every $\beta \in \mathbb{Z}^r$

(3.3.10) $$\mathrm{Ad}(\beta_\#)\varphi = \beta_\#\varphi \quad \text{(multiplication operator)}$$

where $(\beta_\#\varphi)(\alpha) := \varphi(\alpha - \beta)$ belongs to $L^\infty(\mathbb{Z}^r)$.

3.3.11. DEFINITION. Let $\Lambda^\# \subset \mathbb{R}^r$ denote the polar cone of Λ. Define the *characteristic multiplier* $\chi \in L^\infty(\mathbb{Z}^r)$ *by*

$$\chi(\alpha) := \begin{cases} 1 & \alpha \in \mathbb{Z}^r \cap \Lambda^\# \\ 0 & \alpha \in \mathbb{Z}^r \setminus \Lambda^\#. \end{cases}$$

3.3.12. PROPOSITION. *The multiplication operator (3.3.9) with symbol* χ *coincides with the orthogonal projection* $\chi : L^2(\mathbb{Z}^r) \to L^2(\mathbb{Z}^r \cap \Lambda^\#)$.

3.3.13. PROPOSITION. *The Fourier transform (2.5.8) induces a commuting diagram*

$$\begin{array}{ccc} L^2(\mathbb{T}^r) & \xrightarrow[\approx]{(\,)^\#} & L^2(\mathbb{Z}^r) \\ {\scriptstyle E_e^\#}\downarrow & & \downarrow{\scriptstyle \chi} \\ H^2(\mathbb{T}^r) & \xrightarrow[(\,)^\#]{\approx} & L^2(\mathbb{Z}^r \cap \Lambda^\#) \end{array} .$$

For every $\mu \in L^1(\mathbb{Z}^r)$ the inverse Fourier transform

$$\mu_\#(z) := \sum_{\alpha \in \mathbb{Z}^r} z^\alpha \, \mu(\alpha) \tag{3.3.14}$$

is a continuous function on $\mathbb{T}^r$. Every smooth function $f \in \mathcal{C}^\infty(\mathbb{T}^r)$ is of the form $f = \mu_\#$. Thus we may form the multiplication $\mu_\# \cdot E_e$ with the characteristic convolutor $E_e = \chi_\#$ of Ω, and obtain a distribution on $\mathbb{T}^r$. We may also form the convolution $\mu_\# \chi$ with the characteristic multiplier χ and obtain a bounded function on $\mathbb{Z}^r$.

3.3.15. THEOREM. *For every* $\mu \in L^1(\mathbb{Z}^r)$, *the Fourier transform (2.5.8) induces a commuting diagram*

$$\begin{array}{ccc} L^2(\mathbb{T}^r) & \xrightarrow{(\,)^\#} & L^2(\mathbb{Z}^r) \\ {\scriptstyle (\mu_\# \cdot \chi_\#)^\#}\downarrow & & \downarrow{\scriptstyle \mu_\# \chi} \\ L^2(\mathbb{T}^r) & \xrightarrow[(\,)^\#]{} & L^2(\mathbb{Z}^r) \end{array}$$

for the respective convolution and multiplication operators.

Proof. For $\alpha, \beta \in \mathbb{Z}^r$ and $z \in \mathbb{T}^r$, we have

$$(z^\beta E_e)^\#(z^\alpha) = \int_{\mathbb{T}^r} (\bar{w}z)^\alpha\, w^\beta\, dE_e(w) = \sum_{\gamma\in\mathbb{Z}^r\cap\Lambda^\#} \int_{\mathbb{T}^r} (\bar{w}z)^\alpha\, w^\beta\, w^\gamma\, dw$$

(3.3.16)

$$= \sum_{\gamma\in\mathbb{Z}^r\cap\Lambda^\#} z^\alpha \int_{\mathbb{T}^r} w^{\beta+\gamma-\alpha}\, dw = z^\alpha \cdot \chi(\alpha - \beta).$$

Now consider the functions $\beta(\alpha) = \delta_{\alpha,\beta}$ (Kronecker symbol) which are total in $L^1(\mathbb{Z}^r)$. We have $\beta_\#(z) = z^\beta$ and (3.3.16) implies

$$(\beta_\# \cdot E_e)^\#(z^\alpha) = (z^\alpha \cdot \chi(\alpha - \beta))^\# = \alpha \cdot \chi(\alpha - \beta) = (\beta_\#\chi) \cdot \alpha = (\beta_\#\chi)(z^\alpha)^\#.$$

Since $\{z^\alpha : \alpha \in \mathbb{Z}^r\}$ is total in $L^2(\mathbb{T}^r)$ by Weierstrass' Theorem, the assertion follows. Q.E.D.

3.3.17. DEFINITION. The *Hardy multiplier algebra* associated with Ω is the non-unital C^*-algebra

(3.3.18) $$\mathcal{D}(\mathbb{Z}^r) := C^*(\mu_\#\chi : \mu \in L^1(\mathbb{Z}^r)) = C^*(\beta_\#\chi : \beta \in \mathbb{Z}^r)$$

of multiplication operators on $L^2(\mathbb{Z}^r)$.

Since $\beta_\#(\mu_\# \cdot E_e) = (\beta_\#\mu)_\# \cdot E_e$ and $\beta_\#(\mu_\#\chi) = (\beta_\#\mu)_\#\chi$ for all $\beta \in \mathbb{Z}^r$, the adjoint action of $\mathbb{Z}^r$ on $\mathcal{L}(L^2(\mathbb{Z}^r))$ leaves the C^*-subalgebra $\mathcal{D}(\mathbb{Z}^r)$ invariant, and we obtain a restricted action of $\mathbb{Z}^r$ on $\mathcal{D}(\mathbb{Z}^r)$. Identifying $\mathcal{D}(\mathbb{Z}^r)$ with a C^*-subalgebra of $L^\infty(\mathbb{Z}^r)$, this action coincides with the translation action of $\mathbb{Z}^r$. The *spectrum* (= character space) Spec $\mathcal{D}(\mathbb{Z}^r)$ of the abelian Banach algebra (3.3.18) is a locally compact Hausdorff space which is not compact since $\mathcal{D}(\mathbb{Z}^r)$ is non-unital. Being a subalgebra of $L^\infty(\mathbb{Z}^r)$, $\mathcal{D}(\mathbb{Z}^r)$ has the "elementary" characters α_A ($\alpha \in \mathbb{Z}^r$) defined by

(3.3.19) $$\alpha_A \cdot \varphi := \varphi(\alpha)$$

for all $\varphi \in \mathcal{D}(\mathbb{Z}^r)$. Here we put $A := \bar{\Lambda}$. Since $\mathcal{D}(\mathbb{Z}^r)$ separates the points of $\mathbb{Z}^r$, we obtain an embedding $\mathbb{Z}^r \subset$ Spec $\mathcal{D}(\mathbb{Z}^r)$ given by $\alpha \mapsto \alpha_A$.

In the following we consider *faces* of the closed convex cone $A = \bar{\Lambda} \subset \mathbb{R}^r$. Every face $B \subset A$ is a closed convex cone with *tangent space*

$$T(B) = B - B = \mathbb{R}\langle B\rangle$$

and orthogonal projection $P_B : \mathbb{R}^r \to T(B)$. We write $B \underset{c}{\supset} C$ for faces $B \supset C$ of A, if c is a unit vector in $T(B)$ such that $B \cdot c \leq 0$ and

$$C = \{b \in B : b \cdot c = 0\}. \tag{3.3.20}$$

Thus C is the "exposed" face of B given by the supporting vector c. In this case we have $T(C) \subset c^{\perp}$. Every face $B \subset A$ can be successively obtained via a chain of relatively exposed faces

$$A \underset{c_1}{\supset} A_1 \underset{c_2}{\supset} \cdots \underset{c_k}{\supset} A_k = B, \tag{3.3.22}$$

for orthogonal unit vectors $c_1, \ldots, c_k$. In this case $T(B) \subset \langle c_1, \ldots, c_k\rangle^{\perp}$.

3.3.23. THEOREM. *Let* $\alpha = \alpha_n$ *be a sequence in* $\Lambda^{\#}$ *such that there exist orthogonal unit vectors* $c_1, \ldots, c_k \in \mathbb{R}^r$ *with the property*

$$P_{j-1}^{\perp}\alpha/\|P_{j-1}^{\perp}\alpha\| \to c_j \qquad (1 \leq j \leq k)$$

and $P_k^{\perp}\alpha \to \beta$. *Here* $P_j^{\perp}$ *is the orthogonal projection onto* $\langle c_1, \ldots, c_j\rangle^{\perp}$. *Let*

$$B = A_k \underset{c_k}{\subset} A_{k-1} \underset{c_{k-1}}{\subset} \cdots \subset A_2 \underset{c_2}{\subset} A_1 \underset{c_1}{\subset} A$$

denote the corresponding tower of relatively exposed faces. Then

$$\beta_B := w^*\text{-}\lim \alpha_A \in \operatorname{Spec} \mathcal{D}(\mathbb{Z}^r) \tag{3.3.24}$$

exists, and is given for all $\mu \in L^1(\mathbb{Z}^r)$ *by*

$$\beta_B(\mu_{\#}\chi) = \sum_{\{P_k^{\perp}x \leq \beta\}} \mu(x). \tag{3.3.25}$$

Proof. For every $\alpha \in \mathbb{Z}^r$ and $\beta \in \mathbb{Z}^r$ we have $(\beta_\# \chi)(\alpha) = \chi(\alpha - \beta)$ and therefore

$$(\mu_\# \chi)(\alpha) = \sum_\beta \chi(\alpha - \beta)\, \mu(\beta) = \sum_{\alpha - \Lambda^\#} \mu \tag{3.3.26}$$

whenever $\mu \in L^1(\mathbb{Z}^r)$. This agrees with (3.3.25) in case $k = 0$. Now consider sequences $\alpha = \alpha_n$ in $\Lambda^\#$ with $\|\alpha_n\| \to \infty$. Then $k \geq 1$. It suffices to prove (3.3.24) for the generators of $\mathcal{D}(\mathbb{Z}^r)$. We will first show

$$\overline{\lim_n}\, (\alpha_n - \Lambda^\#) := \bigcap_{m \geq 1} \bigcup_{n \geq m} (\alpha_n - \Lambda^\#) \subset \{P_k^\perp x \leq \beta\}\,. \tag{3.3.27}$$

In fact if $x \in \overline{\lim}\, (\alpha_n - \Lambda^\#)$, then $x \in \alpha_n - \Lambda^\#$, i.e. $x \leq \alpha_n$ (rel. $\Lambda^\#$) for infinitely many n. Applying the orthogonal projection $P_k^\perp$, we obtain

$$P_k^\perp x \leq P_k^\perp \alpha_n \qquad \text{(rel. } P_k^\perp \Lambda^\#)$$

for these n. Passing to the limit, it follows that

$$P_k^\perp x \leq \beta \qquad \text{(rel. } \overline{P_k^\perp \Lambda^\#}\,),$$

as asserted. By [B2; p. 64], (3.3.27) implies

$$\overline{\lim_n} \sum_{\alpha_n - \Lambda^\#} \mu(x) \leq \sum_{\overline{\lim}(\alpha_n - \Lambda^\#)} \mu(x) \leq \sum_{\{P_k^\perp x \leq \beta\}} \mu(x) \tag{3.3.28}$$

whenever $\mu \in L^1(\mathbb{Z}^r)$ is positive. In order to show equality in (3.3.28), as asserted in (3.3.25), one has to use the facial structure of the cone Λ. This is carried out in Theorem 3.4.9, for the case of Bergman spaces over polycircular domains containing the origin, at least in dimensions 2 and 3. Q.E.D.

Using the notation (3.3.25) we define for any face $B \subset A$

$$\mathrm{Spec}_B\, \mathcal{D}(\mathbb{Z}^r) := \{\beta_B : \beta \in (P_B \Lambda^\#)^{c\ell}\}. \tag{3.3.29}$$

In particular

$$\text{Spec}_A\, \mathcal{D}(\mathbb{Z}^r) = \{\alpha_A : \alpha \in \Lambda^\#\}. \tag{3.3.30}$$

3.3.31. THEOREM. *The character sets (3.3.30) are pairwise disjoint. Each such set is open in its closure*

$$\text{Spec}_B\, \mathcal{D}(\mathbb{Z}^r)^{c\ell} = \bigcup_{E \subset B} \text{Spec}_E\, \mathcal{D}(\mathbb{Z}^r) \tag{3.3.32}$$

which is compact. In particular,

$$\text{Spec}_+\, \mathcal{D}(\mathbb{Z}^r) := \text{Spec}_A\, \mathcal{D}(\mathbb{Z}^r)^{c\ell} = \bigcup_{B \subset A} \text{Spec}_B\, \mathcal{D}(\mathbb{Z}^r) \tag{3.3.33}$$

is compact and contains $\text{Spec}_A\, \mathcal{D}(\mathbb{Z}^r)$ *as an open subset.*

3.4 Bergman Multipliers Over Polycircular Domains

In this section we introduce a commutative C^*-algebra whose spectrum plays a crucial role in the analysis of Bergman-Toeplitz operators over a polycircular domain $\Omega = e^\Lambda \mathbb{T}^r \subset \mathbb{C}^r$. We assume in the following that Ω is log-convex, contains the origin $0 \in \Omega$ and is contained in the unit polydisc $\mathbb{B}^r := \{z \in \mathbb{C}^r : |z_i| < 1 \text{ for all } i\}$. Thus Λ is a convex open subset of $\mathbb{R}^r_<$. However, we do not assume that Λ is conical. For the harmonic analysis of the Bergman space over Ω, we refer to Section 2.6.

3.4.1. DEFINITION. For each $\gamma \in \mathbb{N}^r$ define the *characteristic multiplier* about γ by putting

$$\chi_\gamma(\alpha) := \begin{cases} \|z^{\alpha+\gamma}\|_\Omega / \|z^\alpha\|_\Omega & \text{if } \alpha \in \mathbb{N}^r \\ 0 & \text{if } \alpha \in \mathbb{Z}^r \setminus \mathbb{N}^r. \end{cases} \tag{3.4.2}$$

Since $\Omega \subset \mathbb{B}^r$ we have $|z^{\alpha+\gamma}| = |z^\alpha|\,|z^\gamma| \le |z^\alpha|$ for each $z \in \Omega$ which shows that $0 \le \chi_\gamma \le 1$ on $\mathbb{Z}^r$. In particular, $\chi_\gamma \in L^\infty(\mathbb{Z}^r)$. For every $\mu \in L^1(\mathbb{Z}^r)$, we may form the convolution $\mu_\# \chi_\gamma$ and obtain a bounded function on $\mathbb{Z}^r$.

The special case $\gamma = 0$ gives rise to the Hardy multipliers introduced in Section 3.3.

3.4.3. DEFINITION. The *Bergman multiplier algebra* associated with Ω is the non-unital C^*-algebra

$$(3.4.4) \qquad \mathcal{D}_\Omega(\mathbb{Z}^r) := C^*(\mu_\# \chi_\gamma : \mu \in L^1(\mathbb{Z}^r), \gamma \in \mathbb{N}^r) = C^*(\beta_\# \chi_\gamma : \beta \in \mathbb{Z}^r, \gamma \in \mathbb{N}^r)$$

of multiplication operators on $L^2(\mathbb{Z}^r)$.

Since $\beta_\#(\mu_\#\chi_\gamma) = (\beta_\#\mu)_\#\chi_\gamma$ and $\beta_\#(\alpha_\#\chi_\gamma) = (\beta + \alpha)_\#\chi_\gamma$ for all $\beta, \alpha \in \mathbb{Z}^r$, the adjoint action of $\mathbb{Z}^r$ on $\mathcal{L}(L^2(\mathbb{Z}^r))$ leaves the C^*-subalgebra $\mathcal{D}_\Omega(\mathbb{Z}^r)$ invariant, and we obtain a restricted action of $\mathbb{Z}^r$ on $\mathcal{D}_\Omega(\mathbb{Z}^r)$. Identifying $\mathcal{D}_\Omega(\mathbb{Z}^r)$ with a C^*-subalgebra of $L^\infty(\mathbb{Z}^r)$, this action coincides with the translation action of $\mathbb{Z}^r$. The *spectrum* (= character space) Spec $\mathcal{D}_\Omega(\mathbb{Z}^r)$ of the abelian Banach algebra (3.4.4) is a locally compact Hausdorff space which is not compact since $\mathcal{D}_\Omega(\mathbb{Z}^r)$ is non-unital. Being a subalgebra of $L^\infty(\mathbb{Z}^r)$, $\mathcal{D}_\Omega(\mathbb{Z}^r)$ has the "elementary" characters α_A $(\alpha \in \mathbb{Z}^r)$ defined by

$$(3.4.5) \qquad \alpha_A \cdot \varphi := \varphi(\alpha)$$

for all $\varphi \in \mathcal{D}_\Omega(\mathbb{Z}^r)$. Here we put $A := \bar{\Lambda}$. Since $\mathcal{D}_\Omega(\mathbb{Z}^r)$ separates the points of $\mathbb{Z}^r$, we obtain an embedding $\mathbb{Z}^r \subset \text{Spec}\ \mathcal{D}_\Omega(\mathbb{Z}^r)$ given by $\alpha \mapsto \alpha_A$.

In the following we consider *faces* of the closed convex set $A = \bar{\Lambda} \subset \mathbb{R}^r$. Given a face $B \subset A$, let

$$T(B) = \mathbb{R}\langle B - o\rangle$$

denote its *tangent space*. Here $o \in B$ is arbitrary. Let

$$P_B : \mathbb{R}^r \to T(B)$$

denote the orthogonal projection.

3.4.6. DEFINITION. We write $B \underset{c}{\supset} C$ if $B \supset C$ are faces of A, $c \in T(B)$ is a unit vector and

(3.4.7) $$C = \{b \in B : b \cdot c = \sup B \cdot c\}.$$

Thus C is an "exposed" face of B, with supporting vector c (not necessarily unique). In this case we have $T(C) \subset c^\perp$. Although a face of A need not be exposed, every face $B \subset A$ can be successively obtained via a chain of relatively exposed faces

(3.4.8) $$A \underset{c_1}{\supset} A_1 \underset{c_2}{\supset} \cdots \underset{c_k}{\supset} A_k = B,$$

for orthogonal unit vectors $c_1, \ldots, c_k$. In this case

$$T(B) \subset \langle c_1, \ldots, c_k \rangle^\perp.$$

For example, if A is bounded by parallel straight lines and semi-circles, we have the following situation:

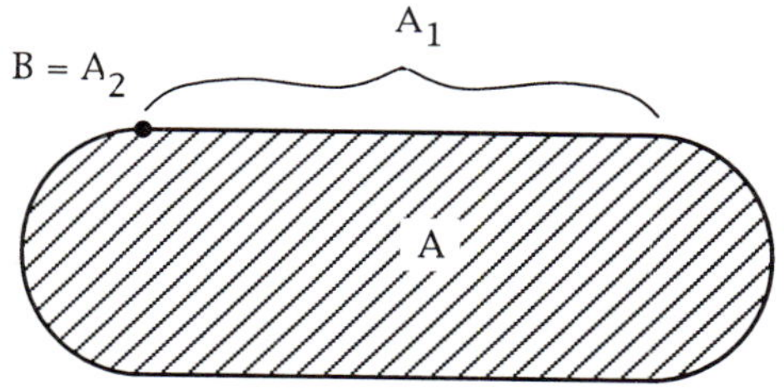

where A_1 is a straight line with endpoint B.

3.4.9. THEOREM. *Let* $\alpha = \alpha_n$ *be a sequence in* $\Lambda^\#$ *such that there exist orthogonal unit vectors* $c_1, \ldots, c_k \in \mathbb{R}^r$ *with the property*

(3.4.10) $$P_{j-1}^\perp \alpha / \|P_{j-1}^\perp \alpha\| \to c_j \qquad (1 \le j \le k)$$

and $P_k^\perp \alpha \to \beta$. *Here* $P_j^\perp$ *is the orthogonal projection onto* $\langle c_1, \ldots, c_j \rangle^\perp$. *Let*

(3.4.11) $$B = A_k \underset{c_k}{\subset} A_{k-1} \subset \cdots \subset A_2 \underset{c_2}{\subset} A_1 \underset{c_1}{\subset} A := \bar{\Lambda}$$

denote the corresponding tower of relatively exposed faces. Then the weak limit*

$$(3.4.12) \qquad \beta_B := w^* - \lim_{\alpha} \alpha_A \in \operatorname{Spec} \mathcal{D}_\Omega(\mathbb{Z}^r)$$

exists, and satisfies

$$(3.4.13) \qquad \beta_B \cdot (\mu_{\#}\chi_\gamma) = \sum_{\{P_B x \le \beta\}} \mu(x) \left(\frac{\int_B e^{2(\beta - x + \gamma)\cdot b}\, d^* b}{\int_B e^{2(\beta - x)\cdot b}\, d^* b} \right)^{1/2}$$

for all $\mu \in L^1(\mathbb{Z}^r)$ *and* $\gamma \in \mathbb{N}^r$. *Here* $d^* a = e^{2\mathbb{1}\cdot a}\, da$ *with* $\mathbb{1} :=$ $(1, 1, \ldots, 1)$.

Proof. This theorem is proved in [SSU] for the case $r = 2$, in which the faces of $\bar{\Lambda}$ are either line segments or points. The argument given below is more general but the details are carried out only for dimension ≤ 3. By 3.4.2 and Proposition 1.4.24, we have for $A := \bar{\Lambda}$

$$(\beta_{\#}\chi_\gamma)(\alpha)^2 = \chi_\gamma(\alpha - \beta)^2 = \|z^{\alpha-\beta+\gamma}\|^2_\Omega / \|z^{\alpha-\beta}\|^2_\Omega$$

$$= \int_\Omega |z^{\alpha-\beta+\gamma}|^2 \, dV(z) / \int_\Omega |z^{\alpha-\beta}|^2 \, dV(z) = \int_A e^{2(\alpha-\beta+\gamma)\cdot a}\, d^* a / \int_A e^{2(\alpha-\beta)\cdot a}\, d^* a$$

whenever $\alpha - \beta \in \mathbb{N}^r$. This implies for $\alpha \in \mathbb{Z}^r$

$$(3.4.14) \qquad (\mu_{\#}\chi_\gamma)(\alpha) = \sum_x \mu(x)(x_{\#}\chi_\gamma)(\alpha) = \sum_{x \in \alpha - \mathbb{N}^r} \mu(x) \left(\frac{\int_A e^{2(\alpha - x + \gamma)\cdot a}\, d^* a}{\int_A e^{2(\alpha - x)\cdot a}\, d^* a} \right)^{1/2}$$

whenever $\mu \in L^1(\mathbb{Z}^r)$. This agrees with (3.4.13) in case $k = 0$.

Now consider sequences $\alpha = \alpha_n$ in $\Lambda^\#$ with $\|\alpha_n\| \to \infty$. Then $k \ge 1$. It suffices to prove (3.4.12) for the generators of $\mathcal{D}_\Omega(\mathbb{Z}^r)$. By (3.4.8), we have

$$(3.4.15) \qquad A_1 = \{a \in A : a \cdot c_1 = M_1 := \sup A \cdot c_1\}$$

for a unit vector c_1 and $\alpha/\|\alpha\| \to c_1$. Since $\alpha = \alpha \cdot c_1 c_1 + P_1^{\perp}\alpha$, this implies $\alpha \cdot c_1/\|\alpha\| \to 1$ and $P_1^{\perp}(\alpha/\|\alpha\|) \to 0$. Since $t_1 := a \cdot c_1 - M_1$ is ≤ 0 on A and $\alpha \cdot c_1 \to +\infty$,

$$\psi_\alpha^1(a) := e^{2\alpha \cdot c_1 t_1}$$

is d^*a-integrable if α is large. We show for every positive $h \in \mathcal{C}_c(A)$ with compact support K :

$$(3.4.16) \qquad \overline{\lim_\alpha} \int_A h(a)\, \psi_\alpha^1(a)\, d^*a \Big/ \int_A \psi_\alpha^1(a)\, d^*a \leq \sup_{A_1} h.$$

In fact, let $\varepsilon > \sup_{A_1} h$. Then $U := \{a \in A : h(a) < \varepsilon\}$ is an open neighborhood of $A_1 \subset A$. By convexity, there exist $r_1 > 0$ and an open neighborhood V_1 of $A_1 \subset U$ such that

$$\sup_{K \setminus U} t_1 \leq -r_1 < -\frac{r_1}{2} \leq \inf_{V_1} t_1.$$

Since $\alpha \cdot c_1 \to +\infty$, this implies

$$(3.4.17) \qquad \sup_{K\setminus U} \psi_\alpha^1 / \inf_{V_1} \psi_\alpha^1 \leq e^{-\alpha \cdot c_1 r_1} \to 0.$$

We have

$$\int_A h(a)\, e^{2\alpha \cdot c_1 t_1}\, d^*a \Big/ \int_A e^{2\alpha \cdot c_1 t_1}\, d^*a$$

$$\leq \int_U h(a)\, e^{2\alpha \cdot c_1 t_1}\, d^*a \Big/ \int_U e^{2\alpha \cdot c_1 t_1}\, d^*a$$

$$+ \int_{K\setminus U} h(a)\, e^{2\alpha \cdot c_1 t_1}\, d^*a \Big/ \int_{V_1} e^{2\alpha \cdot c_1 t_1}\, d^*a.$$

The first term is $\leq \varepsilon$ and the second term tends to 0 by (3.4.17). This proves (3.4.16). Now suppose $k \geq 2$. Then

(3.4.18) $$A_2 = \{a \in A_1 : a \cdot c_2 = M_2 := \sup A_1 \cdot c_2\}$$

and c_1 and c_2 are orthogonal unit vectors. We have $\alpha/\|a\| \to c_1$, $\|P_1^{\perp}\alpha\| \to \infty$, and $P_1^{\perp}\alpha/\|P_1^{\perp}\alpha\| \to c_2$. Since $\alpha = \alpha \cdot c_1 c_1 + \alpha \cdot c_2 c_2 + P_2^{\perp}\alpha$, we obtain $\alpha \cdot c_1/\|\alpha\| \to 1$, $\alpha \cdot c_2/\|\alpha\| \to 0$, $\alpha \cdot c_2/\|P_1^{\perp}\alpha\| \to 1$ and $P_2^{\perp}(\alpha/\|P_1^{\perp}\alpha\|) \to 0$. Put $t_2 := a \cdot c_2 - M_2$. Since $t_1 \le 0$ on A and $\alpha \cdot c_2/\alpha \cdot c_1 \to 0$ it follows that

$$\psi_\alpha^2(a) := e^{2\alpha \cdot c_1 t_1} e^{2\alpha \cdot c_2 t_2}$$

is a d^*a-integrable function on A when α is large. We show

(3.4.19) $$\overline{\lim_\alpha} \int_A h(a)\, \psi_\alpha^2(a)\, d^*a \Big/ \int_A \psi_\alpha^2(a)\, d^*a \le \sup_{A_2} h$$

in this case. In fact, by convexity there exist $r_1 > 0$ and $r_2 > 0$ such that $W := \{a \in A : t_1 \ge -2r_1\}$ satisfies $W \subset U \cup V$ where $V = \{a \in W : t_2 \le -r_2\}$. Hence

$$\sup_{A \setminus U \cup V} t_1 \le -2r_1.$$

Since $\alpha \cdot c_2/\alpha \cdot c_1 \to 0$ and $t_1 = t_2 = 0$ on A_2, there exists an open neighborhood V_2 of $A_2 \subset A$ such that

$$\sup_{K \setminus U \cup V} t_1 + \frac{\alpha \cdot c_2}{\alpha \cdot c_1} t_2 \le -r_1 < -\frac{r_1}{2} \le \inf_{V_2} t_1 + \frac{\alpha \cdot c_2}{\alpha \cdot c_1} t_2.$$

Therefore

(3.4.20) $$\sup_{K \setminus U \cup V} \psi_\alpha^2 / \inf_{V_2} \psi_\alpha^2 \le e^{-\alpha \cdot c_1 r_1} \to 0.$$

We have

(3.4.21) $$\int_A h(a)\, \psi_\alpha^2(a)\, d^*a \Big/ \int_A \psi_\alpha^2(a)\, d^*a$$

$$\leq \int_U h(a)\ \psi_\alpha^2(a) d^*a \Big/ \int_U \psi_\alpha^2(a)\ d^*a$$

$$+ \int_{K \setminus U \cup V} h(a)\ \psi_\alpha^2(a) d^*a \Big/ \int_{V_2} \psi_\alpha^2(a)\ d^*a.$$

$$+ \int_{K \cap V} h(a)\ \psi_\alpha^2(a) d^*a \Big/ \int_{K \cap W} \psi_\alpha^2(a)\ d^*a.$$

The first term is $\leq \varepsilon$ and the second term tends to 0 by (3.4.20). For the third term write

$$W = \bigcup_{w \in W'} I_w \times \{w\}$$

where $I_w = \{m_w \leq t_1 \leq M_w\}$ is an interval and W' is a convex open set in $c_1^\perp$. Integrating over t_1, we obtain

$$\int_W \psi_\alpha^2(a)\ d^*a = \frac{1}{2(\alpha \cdot c_1 + 1)} \int_{W'} \phi_\alpha(w)\ dw,$$

where

$$\phi_\alpha(w) := e^{2(\alpha \cdot c_2 + 1)t_2} (e^{2(\alpha \cdot c_1 + 1)M_w} - e^{2(\alpha \cdot c_1 + 1)m_w}).$$

For $w \in V'$ we have $t_2 \leq -r_2$ and may assume $M_w \leq -\varepsilon$. Therefore

$$\phi_\alpha(w) \leq e^{2(\alpha \cdot c_2 + 1)t_2}\ e^{2(\alpha \cdot c_1 + 1)M_w} \leq e^{-2(\alpha \cdot c_2 + 1)r_2}\ e^{-2(\alpha \cdot c_1 + 1)\varepsilon}.$$

On the other hand, we have $0 \geq t_2 \geq \frac{-r_2}{2}$, $M_w \geq -\frac{\varepsilon}{2}$ and $M_w - m_w \geq \delta > 0$ in a non-empty open subset W_0 of W. Therefore

$$\phi_\alpha(w) = e^{2(\alpha \cdot c_2 + 1)t_2}\ e^{2(\alpha \cdot c_1 + 1)M_w} (1 - e^{-2(\alpha \cdot c_1 + 1)(M_w - m_w)})$$

$$\geq \frac{1}{2} e^{2(\alpha \cdot c_2 + 1)t_2}\ e^{2(\alpha \cdot c_1 + 1)M_w} \geq \frac{1}{2} e^{-(\alpha \cdot c_2 + 1)r_2}\ e^{-(\alpha \cdot c_1 + 1)\varepsilon}.$$

It follows that

$$\sup_{V'} \phi_\alpha / \inf_{W_0'} \phi_\alpha \le 2e^{-(\alpha\cdot c_2+1)r_2}\, e^{-(\alpha\cdot c_1+1)\varepsilon} \to 0. \tag{3.4.22}$$

This proves that the third term in (3.4.21) converges to 0. Iterating the above procedure we see that in general the function

$$\psi_\alpha(a) := e^{2\alpha\cdot c_1 t_1}\, e^{2\alpha\cdot c_2 t_2} \dots e^{2\alpha\cdot c_k t_k}$$

with $t_j := a \cdot c_j - M_j$ and $M_j := \sup A_{j-1} \cdot c_j$ is d^*a-integrable over A when α is large, and satisfies

$$\overline{\lim_\alpha} \int_A h(a)\ \psi_\alpha(a)\ d^*a / \int_A \psi_\alpha(a)\ d^*a \le \sup_B h \tag{3.4.23}$$

for every positive $h \in \mathcal{C}_c(A)$. It follows that every weak cluster point $m \in \mathcal{M}_1^+(A)$ of the sequence of probability measures

$$dm_\alpha(a) := \psi_\alpha(a)\ d^*a / \int_A \psi_\alpha(a)\ d^*a \tag{3.4.24}$$

on A has support in B, i.e., $m \in \mathcal{M}_1^+(B)$. We now show that $e^{-2\,\mathbb{1}\cdot a}\, dm(a)$ is a Lebesgue measure on B by arguing as follows: For any $\varrho \in B$ let $C_\varrho(B)$ denote the *tangent cone*, i.e., the intersection of all half-spaces containing B and having ϱ in the boundary. If $b \in C_\varrho(B)$ and $t > 0$ we have $\psi_\alpha(a + tb) = \psi_\alpha(a)$ for all $a \in A$ since $b \cdot c_j = 0$ for all $1 \le j \le k$. Let $h : B \to \mathbb{R}_+$ be differentiable, have support near ϱ and vanish on $\varrho + H_b$ where

$$H_b := \{a \in \mathbb{R}^r : b \cdot a \le 0\}.$$

Define a continuous function $\tilde{h}$ on the closed set $B \cup [A \cap (\varrho + H_b)]$ by putting $\tilde{h}|_B := h$ and $h|_{A\cap(\varrho+H_b)} := 0$. By a standard extension theorem, there exists a continuous extension $\hat{h} : A \to \mathbb{R}_+$ of $\tilde{h}$ which also has support near ϱ. It follows that

$$\int_A (\hat{h}(a+\tau b) - \hat{h}(a))\, da = \int_{A\cap(A+\tau b)} \hat{h} - \int_A \hat{h} = - \int_{A\setminus(A+\tau b)} \hat{h}$$

and, letting $\tau \to 0$,

$$\int_A \partial_b \hat{h}(a)\, da = \lim_\tau \frac{-1}{\tau} \int_{A\setminus(A+\tau b)} \hat{h} = -\int_\Sigma \hat{h}(a)\, d\sigma(a) = 0$$

where $\Sigma \subset \partial A \cap (\wp + H_b)$ is endowed with the surface measure σ. Letting $\alpha \to \infty$, we obtain (for a subsequence)

$$\int_B \partial_b h(a)\, e^{-2\,\mathbb{1}\cdot a}\, dm(a) = \lim_\alpha \int_A \partial_b \hat{h}(a)\, e^{-2\,\mathbb{1}\cdot a}\, \psi_\alpha(a)\, d^*a \Big/ \int_A \psi_\alpha(a)\, d^*a$$

$$= \lim_\alpha \int_A \partial_b \hat{h}(a)\, \psi_\alpha(a)\, da \Big/ \int_A \psi_\alpha(a)\, d^*a = 0.$$

Since $b \in C_\wp(B)$ and h (vanishing on $\wp + H_b$ and having support near $\wp$) were arbitrary, it follows that $e^{-2\,\mathbb{1}\cdot b}\, dm(b) = \text{const.}\ d_B b$ for a suitable constant. Normalizing, we obtain

$$(3.4.25) \qquad \frac{\psi_\alpha(a)\, d_A^*a}{\int_A \psi_\alpha(a)\, d_A^*a} \longrightarrow \frac{d_B^*b}{\int d_B^*b}$$

in the weak topology on $\mathcal{M}_+^1(A)$. Since $P_k^\perp\alpha \to \beta$ by assumption, we have for every $x \in \mathbb{Z}^r$ and $\gamma \in \mathbb{N}^r$

$$e^{2(P_k^\perp\alpha - x+\gamma)\cdot a} \to e^{2(\beta - x+\gamma)\cdot a}$$

compactly on A. Therefore

$$(x_\#\varepsilon_\gamma)(\alpha)^2 = \int_A e^{2(\alpha-x+\gamma)\cdot a}\, d^*a \Big/ \int_A e^{2(\alpha-x)\cdot a}\, d^*a$$

$$= \int_A e^{2(P_k^\perp\alpha-x+\gamma)\cdot a}\, \psi_\alpha(a)\, d^*a \Big/ \int_A e^{2(P_k^\perp\alpha-x)\cdot a}\, \psi_\alpha(a)\, d^*a$$

$$\to \int_B e^{2(\beta-x+\gamma)\cdot b}\, d^*b \Big/ \int_B e^{2(\beta-x)\cdot b}\, d^*b. \qquad \text{Q.E.D.}$$

Using the notation (3.4.13) we define for any face $B \subset A$

$$\text{Spec}_B\, \mathcal{D}_\Omega(\mathbb{Z}^r) := \{\beta_B : \beta \in (P_B\Lambda^\#)^{c\ell}\}. \tag{3.4.26}$$

In particular

$$\text{Spec}_A\, \mathcal{D}_\Omega(\mathbb{Z}^r) = \{\alpha_A : \alpha \in \Lambda^\#\}.$$

As a consequence of Theorem 3.4.9 we obtain

3.4.27. PROPOSITION. *The character sets (3.4.26) are pairwise disjoint. Each such set is open in its closure*

$$\text{Spec}_B\, \mathcal{D}_\Omega(\mathbb{Z}^r)^{c\ell} = \bigcup_{E \subset B} \text{Spec}_E\, \mathcal{D}_\Omega(\mathbb{Z}^r) \tag{3.4.28}$$

which is compact. In particular,

$$\text{Spec}_+\, \mathcal{D}_\Omega(\mathbb{Z}^r) = \text{Spec}_A\, \mathcal{D}_\Omega(\mathbb{Z}^r)^{c\ell} = \bigcup_{B \subset A} \text{Spec}_B\, \mathcal{D}_\Omega(\mathbb{Z}^r) \tag{3.4.29}$$

is compact and contains $\text{Spec}_A\, \mathcal{D}_\Omega(\mathbb{Z}^r)$ *as an open subset.*

3.5 Hardy Multipliers Over K-circular Domains

In this section we introduce a commutative C^*-algebra whose spectrum plays a crucial role in the analysis of Hardy-Toeplitz operators over a K-circular domain $\Omega = e \cdot \exp(\Lambda)K \subset S^{\mathbb{C}}$ for a compact symmetric space $S = L\backslash K$. Note that in this section, as in the following ones, we let the group K act on the *right* in order to conform to standard conventions in non-commutative duality theory. We assume that Ω is bounded and log-conical. The Fourier analysis of the Hardy space over S is discussed in Section 2.10.

3.5.1. DEFINITION. For any integrable function $u \in L^1(K)$, the *convolution operator* with *symbol* u is the bounded operator $u^\#: L^2(K) \longrightarrow L^2(K)$ defined by

(3.5.2) $$(u^{\#}h)(t) := \int_K h(s^{-1}t)\ u(s)\ ds$$

for all $h \in L^2(K)$ and $t \in K$.

We have $u^{\#}v^{\#} = (u^{\#}v)^{\#}$ for the convolution product

$$(u^{\#}v)(t) := \int_K v(s^{-1}t)\ u(s)\ ds$$

of functions. By Young's inequality, $u^{\#}$ is a bounded operator on $L^2(K)$ with operator norm

$$\|u\|_1 := \int_K |u(s)|\ ds.$$

3.5.3. DEFINITION. The *spatial group C^*-algebra* of K is the C^*-algebra

(3.5.4) $$C^*(K) := C^*(u^{\#} : u \in L^1(K))$$

generated by all convolution operators (3.5.2) on $L^2(K)$.

Since K is a non-trivial compact connected Lie group, $C^*(K)$ is non-unital. Now consider the space $\mathcal{C}(K)$ of all complex-valued continuous functions on K, and its Banach dual space

(3.5.5) $$\mathcal{M}(K) := \mathcal{C}(K)^{\#}$$

consisting of all *complex measures* on K. For $u \in \mathcal{M}(K)$, we may define a convolution operator $u^{\#} : \mathcal{C}(K) \longrightarrow \mathcal{C}(K)$ by putting

(3.5.6) $$(u^{\#}h)(t) \int_K h(s^{-1}t)\ du(s)$$

for all $h \in \mathcal{C}(K)$ and $t \in K$. More generally, for any *distribution* u on K there is a convolution operator $u^{\#} : \mathcal{C}^{\infty}(K) \longrightarrow \mathcal{C}^{\infty}(K)$ defined by (3.5.6). We have $u^{\#}v^{\#} = (u^{\#}v)^{\#}$ for the convolution product

(3.5.7) $$\int_K f(s)\ d(u^{\#}v)(s) = \int_K \int_K f(st)\ du(s)\ dv(t)$$

of measures (resp., distributions) on K.

3.5.8. DEFINITION. The *spatial group von Neumann algebra* of K is the W^*-algebra

(3.5.9) $$W^*(K) := W^*(u^{\#} : u \in \mathcal{M}(K))$$

generated by all convolution operators (3.5.6) with measure symbol u.

The unit element of $W^*(K)$ is the convolution operator $e^{\#}$ for the Dirac measure at $e \in K$. Now let $L \subset K$ be a closed subgroup such that $S := L\backslash K$ is a compact symmetric space. Let $P : L^2(K) \to L^2(S)$ be the orthogonal projection onto the closed subspace of all left L-invariant functions on K. Since

(3.5.10) $$Ph(s) = \int_L h(\ell s)\ d\ell$$

it follows that $P : \mathcal{C}^\infty(K) \to \mathcal{C}^\infty(S)$. A measure [resp., a distribution] u on K is called L-*biinvariant* if

(3.5.11) $$\int_K h(s)\ du(s) = \int_K h(\ell_1 s \ell_2)\ du(s)$$

for every pair $(\ell_1,\ell_2) \in L \times L$ and all $h \in \mathcal{C}(K)$ [resp., all $h \in \mathcal{C}^\infty(K)$]. In this case the associated convolution operator $u^{\#}$ satisfies

(3.5.12) $$Pu^{\#} = u^{\#}P = u^{\#}$$

on $L^2(K)$ [resp., on $\mathcal{C}^\infty(K)$]. The convolution product (3.5.7) of L-biinvariant measures (or distributions) u and v on K is again L-biinvariant.

3.5.13. PROPOSITION. *There exists an L-biinvariant distribution* E_e *on* K, *called the "characteristic convolutor" of* Ω, *such that*

(3.5.14) $$\int_K h(s)\ dE_e(s) = \lim_{\substack{a \in \Lambda \\ a \to 0}} \int_K E_e(e \cdot \exp(a)s)\ h(s)\ ds$$

for all test functions $h \in \mathcal{C}^\infty(K)$. *Here* $E_e(e \cdot \exp(a)s)$ *is the Szegö characteristic function (2.10.65) at the point* $e \cdot \exp(a)s \in \Omega$ *(written with* K *acting on the right).*

Proof. For each $\alpha \in S^\# \cap \Lambda^\#$, let ϕ_α be the L-invariant spherical function on S corresponding to α. Let d_α be the dimension of H_α. Put

$$(3.5.15) \qquad dE_e(s) := \sum_{\alpha \in S^\# \cap \Lambda^\#} d_\alpha \cdot \phi_\alpha(s) \cdot ds. \qquad \text{Q.E.D.}$$

3.5.16. PROPOSITION. *The convolution operator* $E_e^\#$ *is the Szegö projection* $E_e^\# : L^2(S) \to H^2(S)$.

Proof. By (2.10.60), (2.10.61) and (2.10.67), the Szegö projection E satisfies

$$(Eh)(z) = (E_z | h)_S = \int_S \overline{E(w,z)}\, h(w)\, dw = \int_S E(z,w)\, h(w)\, dw$$

$$= \int_K E(z,es)\, h(es)\, ds = \int_K E(zs^{-1},e)\, h(es)\, ds = \int_K E_e(zs^{-1})\, h(es)\, ds$$

for all $h \in L^2(S)$ and $z \in \Omega$. This implies for $t \in K$ and $h \in \mathcal{C}^\infty(K)$

$$(Eh)(et) = \lim_{\substack{a \in \Lambda \\ a \to 0}} (Eh)(e \cdot \exp(a)t) = \lim_{\substack{a \in \Lambda \\ a \to 0}} \int_K E_e(e \cdot \exp(a)ts^{-1})\, h(s)\, ds$$

$$= \lim_{\substack{a \in \Lambda \\ a \to 0}} \int_K E_e(e \cdot \exp(a)x)\, h(x^{-1}t)\, dx = \int_K h(s^{-1}t)\, dE_e(s).$$

Q.E.D.

3.5.17. DEFINITION. For any bounded family $(B_\alpha)_{\alpha \in K^\#}$ of endomorphisms $B_\alpha \in \mathcal{L}(H_\alpha)$, the associated *block multiplication operator* is the bounded operator

$$(3.5.18) \qquad \sum_{\alpha \in K^\#}^{\oplus} \mathcal{L}^2(H_\alpha) \xrightarrow{(B_\alpha)} \sum_{\alpha \in K^\#}^{\oplus} \mathcal{L}^2(H_\alpha)$$

defined as the componentwise *right* multiplication $(A_\alpha) \mapsto (A_\alpha B_\alpha)$ by (B_α).

Note that we have $\|A_\alpha B_\alpha\|_2 \le \|A_\alpha\|_2 \cdot \|B_\alpha\|$ for the Hilbert-Schmidt norm $\|\cdot\|_2$ (resp., the operator norm $\|\cdot\|$) on $\mathcal{L}(H_\alpha)$. For every $u \in \mathcal{M}(K)$ and $\alpha \in K^\#$, we define the α-th *Fourier coefficient* of u to be the linear endomorphism

$$u^\#_\alpha := \int_K \alpha(s)^* \, du(s) \in \mathcal{L}(H_\alpha) \tag{3.5.19}$$

on the (finite dimensional) representation space H_α of α. In particular for $u \in L^1(K) \subset \mathcal{M}(K)$, we obtain the α-th Fourier coefficient

$$u^\#_\alpha := \int_K \alpha(s)^* \, u(s) \, ds. \tag{3.5.20}$$

For $u \in L^2(K) \subset L^1(K)$ this agrees with (2.10.8).

3.5.21. PROPOSITION. *For every $u \in \mathcal{M}(K)$ the Fourier transform (2.10.11) induces a commuting diagram*

$$\begin{array}{ccc}
L^2(K) & \xrightarrow[\approx]{()^\#} & \sum^{\oplus}_{\alpha \in K^\#} \mathcal{L}^2(H_\alpha) \\
\Big\downarrow u^\# & & \Big\downarrow (u^\#_\alpha) \\
L^2(K) & \xrightarrow[()^\#]{\approx} & \sum^{\oplus}_{\alpha \in K^\#} \mathcal{L}^2(H_\alpha)
\end{array}$$

of convolution and multiplication operators, resp. If u is a distribution, a similar diagram exists when restricting to smooth functions.

Proof. For every $h \in L^2(K)$, we have

$$h^\#_\alpha u^\#_\alpha = \int_K h(x)\, \alpha(x)^* \, dx \int_K \alpha(s)^* \, du(s) = \int_K \int_K h(x)\, \alpha(sx)^* \, dx \, du(s)$$

$$= \int_K \int_K h(s^{-1}t)\, \alpha(t)^* \, dt \, du(s) = \int_K (u^\# h)(t)\, \alpha(t)^* \, dt = (u^\# h)^\#_\alpha.$$

Q.E.D.

3.5.22. PROPOSITION. *There exists an anti-homomorphism*

$$\Phi : W^*(K) \to \sum_{\alpha\in K^\#}^{\oplus} \mathcal{L}(H_\alpha)$$

of W^**-algebras such that we have for every* $u \in \mathcal{M}(K)$

$$\Phi(u) = (u_\alpha^\#)_{\alpha\in K^\#}. \tag{3.5.23}$$

Proof. Consider the Fourier transform

$$\mathcal{F} = ()^\# : L^2(K) \to \sum_{\alpha\in K^\#}^{\oplus} \mathcal{L}^2(H_\alpha).$$

Then $\mathrm{Ad}(\mathcal{F})T := \mathcal{F}T\mathcal{F}^*$, $T \in \mathcal{L}(L^2(K))$, defines a W^*-homomorphism. By Proposition 3.5.21, $\mathrm{Ad}(\mathcal{F})u^\#$ is a direct sum of right multiplication operators by $u_\alpha^\#$, $\alpha \in K^\#$. Identifying this operator with $u_\alpha^\# \in \mathcal{L}(H_\alpha)$ (this is a W^*-anti-isomorphism), we obtain the anti-homomorphism Φ satisfying (3.5.23). Q.E.D.

3.5.24. PROPOSITION. *Via the anti-homomorphism* Φ, *the* C^**-subalgebra* $C^*(K) \subset W^*(K)$ *can be identified with the* C^**-algebra*

$$C^*(K) \approx \{(A_\alpha)_{\alpha\in K^\#} : \alpha \mapsto \|A_\alpha\| \text{ vanishes at } \infty\} \tag{3.5.25}$$

of block-diagonal operators on $\sum_{\alpha\in K^\#}^{\oplus} H_\alpha$.

Proof. For every $u \in L^1(K)$, we have

$$\Phi(u^\#) = \sum_{\alpha\in K^\#}^{\oplus} u_\alpha^\#$$

acting on $\sum_{\alpha}^{\oplus} H_\alpha$. By [D1; 18.2.4] or [H2; Proposition V.2.2], the set $\{\alpha \in K^\# : \|u_\alpha^\#\| \geq \varepsilon\}$ is finite for every $\varepsilon > 0$. Thus $\alpha \mapsto \|u_\alpha^\#\|$ vanishes at

∞. Conversely let $\alpha \in K^{\#}$ be fixed. For every $A \in \mathcal{L}(H_\alpha)$ the Fourier symbol $A_{\#}$ defined in (2.10.9) belongs to $L^1(K)$ and, by (2.10.14), satisfies

$$\Phi(A_{\#}) = \frac{1}{d_\alpha} A. \tag{3.5.26}$$

Thus $\Phi(C^*(K))$ contains all single blocks $\mathcal{L}(H_\alpha), \alpha \in K^{\#}$. Since these blocks are C^*-dense in the right-hand side of (3.5.25), the assertion follows. Q.E.D.

3.5.27. COROLLARY. *Via the anti-homomorphism* Φ, $W^*(K)$ *can be identified with the direct product* W^**-algebra*

$$W^*(K) = \{(A_\alpha)_{\alpha \in K^{\#}} : \alpha \mapsto \|A_\alpha\| \text{ bounded}\} \tag{3.5.28}$$

of bounded block-diagonal operators on $\sum_\alpha^{\oplus} H_\alpha$.

Proof. Clearly, the right hand side of (3.5.28) is the W^*-closure of the right hand side of (3.5.25). Q.E.D.

3.5.29. COROLLARY. $C^*(K)$ *is an ideal in* $W^*(K)$, *and we have*

$$W^*(K) = C^*(K)^{\#\#} \qquad \textit{(double dual).}$$

3.5.30. COROLLARY. $C^{\#}(K) \subset \mathcal{K}(L^2(K))$ *(compact operators).*

3.5.31. PROPOSITION. *The convolution operator* $E_e^{\#}$ *with symbol* E_e *belongs to* $W^*(K)$ *and satisfies*

$$\Phi(E_e^{\#})_\alpha = \begin{cases} Q_\alpha = \int_L \alpha(\ell)\, d\ell & \text{if } \alpha \in S^{\#} \cap \Lambda^{\#}, \\ 0 & \text{if } \alpha \in K^{\#} \setminus (S^{\#} \cap \Lambda^{\#}). \end{cases}$$

Proof. By Proposition 3.5.16, $E_e^{\#}$ is a bounded operator on $L^2(K)$ which commutes with all right translations

$$(\rho_s f)(t) := f(ts) \qquad (s \in K) \tag{3.5.32}$$

since the right translation action of K on Ω preserves the holomorphic structure. Now [S5; p. 261] implies $E_e^\# \in W^*(K)$. For every $\alpha \in K^\#$, the α-th Fourier coefficient

$$(E_e)_\alpha^\# := \int_K \alpha(s)^* \, dE_e(s) \in \mathcal{Z}(H_\alpha)$$

is a projection satisfying

$$(E_e)_\alpha^\# Q_\alpha = (E_e)_\alpha^\# = Q_\alpha (E_e)_\alpha^\#.$$

For $\alpha \in K^\# \setminus S^\#$, $Q_\alpha = 0$ and hence $(E_e)_\alpha^\# = 0$. For $\alpha \in S^\# \setminus \Lambda^\#$, ϕ_α belongs to $H^2(S)^\perp$ by Theorem 2.10.45, and $(E_e)_\alpha^\# = 0$. For $\alpha \in S^\# \cap \Lambda^\#$, $\phi_\alpha \in H^2(S)$ and $(E_e)_\alpha^\# = Q_\alpha$. Q.E.D.

3.5.33. DEFINITION. For any bounded function $\varphi \in L^\infty(S^\#)$, the *multiplication operator* with *symbol* φ is the bounded operator

$$\sum_{\alpha \in S^\#}^{\oplus} H_\alpha \xrightarrow{(\varphi(\alpha))} \sum_{\alpha \in S^\#}^{\oplus} H_\alpha \tag{3.5.34}$$

given by $(\xi_\alpha) \mapsto (\varphi(\alpha)\xi_\alpha)$.

For any L-biinvariant measure (or distribution) u on S and $\alpha \in S^\#$, define the α-th *Fourier coefficient* of u as the scalar

$$u^\#(\alpha) := \int_S \overline{\phi_\alpha(z)} \, du(z), \tag{3.5.35}$$

where $\phi_\alpha \in \mathcal{C}^\infty(S)$ is the α-th spherical function.

3.5.36. PROPOSITION. *For every L-biinvariant measure* u *on* K, *the Fourier transforms (2.10.11) and (2.10.27) induce a commuting diagram*

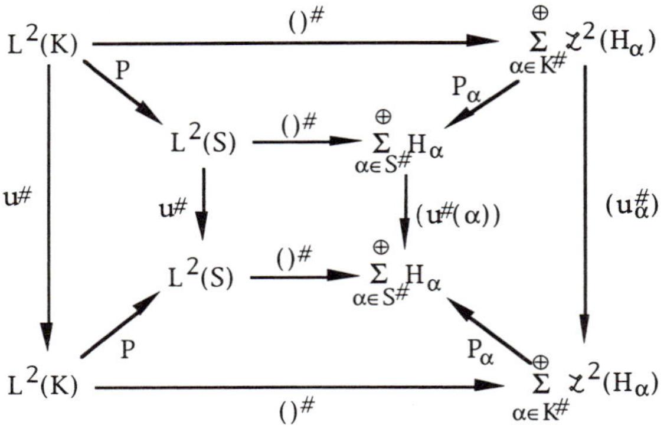

Here P *is the orthogonal projection and* P_α *is defined by (2.10.33). If* u *is a distribution, a similar diagram exists when restricting to smooth functions.*

Proof. For every $\alpha \in S^\#$ let $\varepsilon_\alpha \in H_\alpha$ be an L-invariant unit vector. Then $u^\#_\alpha \varepsilon_\alpha \in H_\alpha$ is L-invariant. Since $S = L\backslash K$ is a symmetric quotient, there exists a constant c such that $u^\#_\alpha \varepsilon_\alpha = c \cdot \varepsilon_\alpha$. Since $(\varepsilon_\alpha | \varepsilon_\alpha)_\alpha = 1$, we have

$$c = (\varepsilon_\alpha | u^\#_\alpha \varepsilon_\alpha)_\alpha = (\varepsilon_\alpha | \int_K \alpha(s)^* \, \varepsilon_\alpha \; du(s))_\alpha$$

$$= \int_K (\varepsilon_\alpha | \alpha(s)^* \varepsilon_\alpha)_\alpha \; du(s) = \int_K (\alpha(s)\varepsilon_\alpha | \varepsilon_\alpha)_\alpha \; du(s)$$

$$= \int_K \overline{(\varepsilon_\alpha | \alpha(s)\varepsilon_\alpha)_\alpha} \; du(s) = \int_K \overline{\phi_\alpha(es)} \; du(s) = u^\#(\alpha).$$

It follows that for every $f \in L^2(K)$ we have

$$f^\#_\alpha u^\#_\alpha \varepsilon_\alpha = f^\#_\alpha \, u^\#(\alpha) \, \varepsilon_\alpha = u^\#(\alpha) \, f^\#_\alpha \, \varepsilon_\alpha.$$

By definition of P_α, the assertion follows. Q.E.D.

3.5.37. DEFINITION. Let $\Lambda^\# \subset \mathbf{a}^\#$ denote the polar cone of Λ. Define the *characteristic multiplier* $\chi \in L^\infty(S^\#)$ by

$$\chi(\alpha) := \begin{cases} 1 & \alpha \in S^{\#} \cap \Lambda^{\#} \\ 0 & \alpha \in S^{\#} \backslash \Lambda^{\#} \end{cases} .$$

3.5.38. PROPOSITION. *The multiplication operator (3.5.34) with symbol χ coincides with the orthogonal projection*

$$\sum_{\alpha \in S^{\#}}^{\oplus} H_{\alpha} \xrightarrow{(\chi(\alpha))} \sum_{\alpha \in S^{\#} \cap \Lambda^{\#}}^{\oplus} H_{\alpha} .$$

3.5.39. PROPOSITION. *The Fourier transform (2.10.27) induces a commuting diagram*

$$\begin{array}{ccc} L^2(S) & \xrightarrow[\approx]{()^{\#}} & \sum\limits_{\alpha \in S^{\#}}^{\oplus} H_{\alpha} \\ E_e^{\#} \Big\downarrow & & \Big\downarrow (\chi(\alpha)) \\ H^2(S) & \xrightarrow[()^{\#}]{\approx} & \sum\limits_{\alpha \in S^{\#} \cap \Lambda^{\#}}^{\oplus} H_{\alpha} \end{array} .$$

Now consider the *Fourier algebra*

$$A(K) := (f \in \mathcal{C}(K) : \sum_{\alpha \in K^{\#}} d_{\alpha} \, \|f_{\alpha}^{\#}\|_1 < \infty), \tag{3.5.40}$$

where for each $\alpha \in K^{\#}$ and $A \in \mathcal{L}(H_{\alpha})$ we define the trace-norm

$$\|A\|_1 := \text{trace}(AA^*)^{1/2}. \tag{3.5.41}$$

It is known [E1] that $A(K)$ can be realized as a dense $*$-subalgebra of $\mathcal{C}(K)$ and the inclusion mapping $A(K) \subset \mathcal{C}(K)$ is continuous. Moreover, $A(K)$ is a Banach $*$-algebra for the norm

$$\|f\| := \sum_{\alpha \in K^{\#}} d_{\alpha} \, \|f_{\alpha}^{\#}\|_1. \tag{3.5.42}$$

3.5.43. PROPOSITION. *There exists a pairing* $\langle | \rangle : W^*(K) \times A(K) \to \mathbb{C}$ *such that*

$$\langle u^{\#} | f \rangle = \int_K f(s) \quad du(s) \tag{3.5.44}$$

for all $f \in A(K)$ *and* $u \in \mathcal{M}(K)$. *Via this pairing we may identify*

$$A(K) = C^*(K)^\#, \tag{3.5.45}$$

$$W^*(K) = A(K)^\# \tag{3.5.46}$$

as Banach dual spaces.

Proof. For each $\alpha \in K^\#$ let $\mathcal{L}^1(H_\alpha)$ (resp., $\mathcal{L}^\infty(H_\alpha)$) denote the vector space $\mathcal{L}(H_\alpha)$ endowed with the trace norm (3.5.4) (resp., with the operator norm). Then we have

$$[\mathcal{L}^1(H_\alpha)]^\# = \mathcal{L}^\infty(H_\alpha), \ [\mathcal{L}^\infty(H_\alpha)]^\# = \mathcal{L}^1(H_\alpha)$$

isometrically via the pairing $\langle A|B\rangle :=$ trace AB for all $A,B \in \mathcal{L}(H_\alpha)$. Now the assertion follows from Proposition 3.5.24 and Corollary 3.5.27.
Q.E.D.

3.5.47. PROPOSITION. $\mathcal{C}^\infty(K) \subset A(K)$.

Proof. Identify $K^\#$ with a discrete subset of the dual space $\mathfrak{h}^\#$ of the abelian subalgebra $\mathfrak{h} \subset i\mathfrak{k}$ by assigning to each $\alpha \in K^\#$ its highest weight (cf. Section 2.10). Let $R := \dim_{\mathbb{R}} \mathfrak{h}$ and choose any norm $\|\cdot\|$ on $\mathfrak{h}^\#$. It is known ([H2; p. 548] or [S6]) that

$$\mathcal{C}^\infty(K) = \{f \in \mathcal{C}(K) : \lim_{\|\alpha\|\to\infty} \|\alpha\|^k \cdot \|f_\alpha^\#\|_1 \to 0 \ \ \forall k \in \mathbb{N}\}. \tag{3.5.48}$$

Writing $\alpha = \sum_{j=1}^{R} \alpha_j \delta_j$ in terms of a basis $\{\delta_1, ..., \delta_R\}$ of $\mathfrak{h}^\#$ we may take $\|\alpha\| := \max(|\alpha_1|, ..., |\alpha_R|)$. Now let $f \in \mathcal{C}^\infty(K)$. Excluding finitely many α, we have

$$\sum_\alpha \|f_\alpha^\#\|_1 \le \sum_\alpha \frac{1}{\|\alpha\|^{2R}} \le \sum_\alpha \frac{1}{\alpha_1^2 \cdots \alpha_R^2} \le \sum_{\alpha_1} \frac{1}{\alpha_1^2} \cdots \sum_{\alpha_R} \frac{1}{\alpha_R^2} < \infty$$

since $\|\alpha\|^R = \max(|\alpha_1|^R, ..., |\alpha_R|^R) \ge |\alpha_1 \cdots \alpha_R|$. Therefore $f \in A(K)$. Q.E.D.

3.5.49. PROPOSITION. *For every* $g \in A(K)$ *there exists a bounded operator* $(E_e g)^\# \in W^*(K)$ satisfying

(3.5.50) $$(E_e g)^{\#}h(t) = \int_K h(s^{-1}t)\ g(s)\ dE_e(s)\ ,$$

(3.5.51) $$(E_e g)^{\#}_{\alpha} = \int_K \alpha(s)^*\ g(s)\ dE_e(s).$$

Proof. Since $H^2(S)$ is a closed subspace of $L^2(K)$ invariant under right translations, Proposition 3.5.16 implies that $E_e^{\#}$ is a bounded operator on $L^2(K)$ commuting with right translations. By [S5], $E_e^{\#} \in W^*(K)$. Since $A(K)$ is a Banach algebra [E1], its dual space $W^*(K)$ becomes a right Banach $A(K)$-module by putting

(3.5.52) $$\langle a \rtimes g, h\rangle := \langle a, gh\rangle$$

for all $a \in W^*(K)$ and $g,h \in A(K)$. In particular, $E_e^{\#} \rtimes g \in W^*(K)$ satisfies

(3.5.53) $$\langle E_e^{\#} \rtimes g, h\rangle = \int_K g(s)\ h(s)\ dE_e(s)$$

and is therefore the convolution operator with symbol $g(s)\ dE_e(s)$. Q.E.D.

3.5.54. DEFINITION. The *Hardy block multiplier algebra* associated with Ω is the non-unital C^*-algebra

(3.5.55) $$\mathcal{D}(K) := C^*(((E_e g)^{\#}_{\alpha})_{\alpha\in K^{\#}} : g \in A(K))$$

generated by all block multiplication operators (3.5.18).

Via the anti-isomorphism Φ, $\mathcal{D}(K)$ can be identified with the C^*-algebra generated by all convolution operators (3.5.50) with $g \in A(K)$. By Proposition 3.5.49,

(3.5.56) $$\mathcal{D}(K) \subset W^*(K).$$

For any L-biinvariant $f \in \mathcal{C}^{\infty}(S)$, the distribution $E_e f$ on K is L-biinvariant, and we may consider the convolution operator $(E_e f)^{\#} : L^2(S) \to L^2(S)$ defined by

(3.5.57) $$(E_e f)^{\#}h(t) := \int_K h(s^{-1}t)\ f(s)\ dE_e(s)$$

for all $h \in L^2(S)$ and $t \in K$. By Proposition 3.5.36, we obtain the corresponding bounded function on $S^\#$ given by

$$(3.5.58) \qquad (E_e f)^\#(\alpha) := \int_S \overline{\phi_\alpha(z)}\; f(z)\, dE_e(z)$$

3.5.59. DEFINITION. The *Hardy multiplier algebra* associated with Ω is the non-unital abelian C^*-algebra

$$(3.5.60) \qquad \mathcal{D}^L(S) := C^*(((E_e f)^\#(\alpha)) : f \in \mathcal{C}^\infty(S) \quad \text{L-biinvariant})$$

generated by the multiplication operators (3.5.58).

As a special case of Proposition 3.5.36 we have a commuting diagram

$$\begin{array}{ccc} L^2(S) & \xrightarrow{()^\#} & \sum\limits_{\alpha \in S}^{\oplus} H_\alpha \\ {\scriptstyle (E_e f)^\#}\downarrow & & \downarrow {\scriptstyle ((E_e f)^\#(\alpha))} \\ L^2(S) & \xrightarrow[()^\#]{} & \sum\limits_{\alpha \in S}^{\oplus} H_\alpha \end{array}$$

for every L-biinvariant $f \in \mathcal{C}^\infty(S)$. Therefore $\mathcal{D}^L(S)$ can be identified with the C^*-algebra generated by the convolution operators (3.5.57).

3.5.61. LEMMA. *Let* $P : L^2(K) \to L^2(S)$ *be the orthogonal projection. Then* $P\mathcal{D}(K)P = \mathcal{D}^L(S)$.

Proof. For every $g \in A(K)$, we have $P(E_e g)^\# P = (E_e f)^\#$ where

$$(3.5.62) \qquad f(t) := \int_L \int_L g(\ell_1 t \ell_2)\, d\ell_1 d\ell_2 \in \mathcal{C}^\infty(S)$$

is L-biinvariant. Q.E.D.

The *spectrum* (= character space) Spec $\mathcal{D}^L(S)$ of the abelian Banach algebra (3.5.60) is a locally compact Hausdorff space which is not compact since $\mathcal{D}^L(S)$ has no unit. In the following section we will determine this spectrum in the important special case of symmetric spaces. The case $S = K = \mathbb{T}^r$ was treated in Section 3.3.

3.6 Hardy Multipliers Over Symmetric Domains

In this section we introduce a commutative C^*-algebra whose spectrum plays a crucial role in the analysis of Hardy-Toeplitz operators over a symmetric domain $\Omega \subset Z$ of tube type. Let S be the Shilov boundary of Ω. The Fourier analysis of $H^2(S)$ is discussed in Section 2.8. As in Section 1.6, we may identify

$$\mathfrak{a} := \{\sum_{j=1}^{r} a_j M_{e_j} : a_j \in \mathbb{R}\},$$

$$\Lambda \cap \bar{\mathfrak{a}}^< := \{\sum_{j=1}^{r} a_j M_{e_j} : 0 > a_1 \geq \cdots \geq a_r\}.$$

Then Ω has a polar decomposition $\Omega = e \cdot \exp(\Lambda) \cdot K$, with K acting on the right. As in Section 3.5, introduce the left convolution operators $u^\# : L^2(K) \to L^2(K)$ and $u^\# : \mathcal{C}^\infty(K) \to \mathcal{C}^\infty(K)$ where u is an L^1-function (resp., a distribution) on K. Let

$$C^*(K) := C^*(u^\# : u \in L^1(K)) ,$$

$$W^*(K) := W^*(u^\# : u \in \mathcal{M}(K))$$

be the corresponding spatial group C^*-algebra (resp., group von Neumann algebra) on $L^2(K)$. Since Ω is of tube type,

$$S = L \backslash K \qquad (3.6.1)$$

is a compact symmetric quotient space. Consider the orthogonal projection $P : L^2(K) \to L^2(S)$ given by (3.5.10) and define L-biinvariant distributions by (3.5.11).

3.6.2. PROPOSITION. *There exists an L-biinvariant distribution* E_e *on* K, *called the "characteristic convolutor" of* Ω, *such that*

$$\int_K h(s)\, dE_e(s) = \lim_{\rho \uparrow 1} \int_K E_e(\rho \cdot es)\, h(s)\, ds \qquad (3.6.3)$$

for all test functions $h \in \mathcal{C}^\infty(K)$. *Here* $E_e(\rho \cdot es)$ *is the Szegö characteristic function (2.8.62) at the point* $\rho \cdot es \in \Omega$.

Proof. For every $\rho < 1$, the integral

$$(3.6.4) \quad h \mapsto \int_K h(es)\ \Delta(e, \rho es)^{-n/r}\ ds = \int_K h(es)\ \Delta(e - \rho es)^{-n/r}\ ds$$

defines a distribution on K which is clearly L-biinvariant. Define E_e as the distribution limit, for $\rho \to 1$, of (3.6.4). Q.E.D.

3.6.5. PROPOSITION. *The convolution operator* $E_e^\#$ *with symbol* E_e *coincides with the Szegö projection* $E_e^\# : L^2(S) \to H^2(S)$.

Proof. Writing E for the orthogonal projection, we have by (2.8.9) and (2.8.64)

$$(Eh)(z) = (E_z|h)_S = \int_S \overline{E(w,z)}\ h(w)\ dw = \int_S E(z,w)\ h(w)\ dw$$

$$= \int_K E(z,e \cdot s)\ h(e \cdot s)\ ds = \int_K E(z \cdot s^{-1},e)\ h(es)\ ds = \int_K E_e(zs^{-1})\ h(es)\ ds$$

for $h \in L^2(S)$ and $z \in \Omega$. Now let $t \in K$ and suppose $h \in \mathcal{C}^\infty(S)$. Then

$$(Eh)(et) = \lim_{\rho \uparrow 1} (Eh)(\rho \cdot et) = \lim_{\rho \uparrow 1} \int_K E_e(\rho \cdot et\sigma^{-1})\ h(e\sigma)\ d\sigma$$

$$= \lim_{\rho \uparrow 1} \int_K E_e(\rho \cdot es)\ h(e \cdot s^{-1}t)\ ds = \int_K h(e \cdot s^{-1}t)\ dE_e(s) = (E_e^\# h)(et).$$

Q.E.D.

By Theorem 2.8.38, the subset $S^\# \subset K^\#$, realized in $\mathfrak{a}^\# \cong \mathbb{R}^r$, can be identified with

$$\vec{\mathbb{Z}}^r := \{(\alpha_1, \ldots, \alpha_r) \in \mathbb{Z}^r : \alpha_1 \geq \cdots \geq \alpha_r\}.$$

For each $\alpha \in \vec{\mathbb{Z}}^r$ the associated K-module in $L^2(S)$ is denoted by $\mathcal{P}^\alpha(S)$. It consists of (restrictions of) holomorphic polynomials on Z in case $\alpha_r \geq 0$.

3.6.6. DEFINITION. For any bounded function $\varphi \in L^\infty(\vec{\mathbb{Z}}^r)$, the *multiplication operator* with *symbol* φ is the bounded operator

$$\sum_{\alpha \in \vec{\mathbb{Z}}^r}^{\oplus} \mathcal{P}^\alpha(S) \xrightarrow{(\varphi(\alpha))} \sum_{\alpha \in \vec{\mathbb{Z}}^r}^{\oplus} \mathcal{P}^\alpha(S) \tag{3.6.7}$$

given by $(\xi_\alpha) \mapsto (\varphi(\alpha)\xi_\alpha)$.

3.6.8. PROPOSITION. *For every L-biinvariant measure* u *on* K, *the Fourier transform (2.8.39) induces a commuting diagram*

$$\begin{array}{ccc} L^2(S) & \xrightarrow[\approx]{()^\#} & \sum\limits_{\alpha \in \vec{\mathbb{Z}}^r}^{\oplus} \mathcal{P}^\alpha(S) \\ {\scriptstyle u^\#}\big\downarrow & & \big\downarrow{\scriptstyle (u^\#(\alpha))} \\ L^2(S) & \xrightarrow[()^\#]{\approx} & \sum\limits_{\alpha \in \vec{\mathbb{Z}}^r}^{\oplus} \mathcal{P}^\alpha(S) \end{array}$$

where

$$u^\#(\alpha) := \int_S \overline{\Delta_\alpha(z)}\, du(z) = \int_S \overline{\phi_\alpha(z)}\, du(z)$$

is the α*-th (scalar) Fourier coefficient of* u. *If* u *is an L-biinvariant distribution, a similar diagram exists when restricting to smooth functions.*

By Theorem 2.8.10, the polar cone $\Lambda^\# \subset \mathbf{a}^\# \approx \mathbb{R}^r$ of the cone $\Lambda \subset \mathbf{a}$ satisfies

$$\vec{\mathbb{N}}^r := \{\alpha \in \mathbb{N}^r : \alpha_1 \geq \ldots \geq \alpha_r\} = \vec{\mathbb{Z}}^r \cap \Lambda^\#. \tag{3.6.9}$$

3.6.10. DEFINITION. Define the *characteristic multiplier* $\chi \in L^\infty(\vec{\mathbb{Z}}^r)$ by

$$\chi(\alpha) := \begin{cases} 1 & \text{if } \alpha \in \vec{\mathbb{N}}^r \\ 0 & \text{if } \alpha \in \vec{\mathbb{Z}}^r \setminus \vec{\mathbb{N}}^r. \end{cases}$$

Hence $\chi(\alpha) = 0$ if and only if $\alpha_r < 0$.

3.6.11. PROPOSITION. *The multiplication operator (3.6.7) with symbol* χ *coincides with the orthogonal projection*

$$\sum_{\alpha\in\vec{\mathbb{Z}}^r}^{\oplus} \mathcal{P}^\alpha(S) \xrightarrow{\chi(\alpha)} \sum_{\alpha\in\vec{\mathbb{N}}^r}^{\oplus} \mathcal{P}^\alpha(S).$$

3.6.12. PROPOSITION. *The Fourier transform (2.8.39) induces a commuting diagram*

$$\begin{array}{ccc} L^2(S) & \xrightarrow[\approx]{()^\#} & \sum\limits_{\alpha\in\vec{\mathbb{Z}}^r}^{\oplus} \mathcal{P}^\alpha(S) \\ E_e^\# \big\downarrow & & \big\downarrow (\chi(\alpha)) \\ H^2(S) & \xrightarrow[()^\#]{\approx} & \sum\limits_{\alpha\in\vec{\mathbb{N}}^r}^{\oplus} \mathcal{P}^\alpha(S) \end{array}$$

3.6.13. DEFINITION. The *Hardy block multiplier algebra* associated with Ω is the non-unital C^*-algebra

(3.6.14) $$\mathcal{D}(K) := C^*((E_e g)^\# : g \in A(K))$$

generated by all convolution operators

(3.6.15) $$(E_e g)^\# h(t) := \int_K h(s^{-1}t)\ g(s)\ dE_e(s)$$

on $L^2(K)$, with $g \in A(K)$.

3.6.16. PROPOSITION. $C^*(K) \subset \mathcal{D}(K) \subset W^*(K)$.

Proof. Let $u \in \mathcal{C}^\infty(K)$ be arbitrary. Since

(3.6.17) $$\Delta(e - s)^{n/r}\, dE_e(s) = ds$$

by Proposition 2.8.6, we have

(3.6.18) $$u^{\#} = (u(s)ds)^{\#} = (u(s)\, \Delta(e - s)^{n/r}\, \chi_{\#})^{\#} \in \mathcal{D}(K).$$

Since $C^*(K)$ is generated by operators of the form $u^{\#}$, the first inclusion follows. The second inclusion follows from (3.5.56). Q.E.D.

3.6.19. DEFINITION. The *Hardy multiplier algebra* associated with Ω is the non-unital abelian C^*-algebra

(3.6.20) $$\mathcal{D}^L(\vec{\mathbb{Z}}^r) := C^*(((E_e g)^{\#}(\alpha)) : g \in A(K) \text{ L-biinvariant}\}$$

generated by the multiplication operators (3.6.7), for the bounded functions

(3.6.21) $$(E_e g)^{\#}(\alpha) := \int_S \overline{\phi_\alpha(z)}\; g(z)\, dE_e(z)$$

on $\vec{\mathbb{Z}}^r$. As a special case of Proposition 3.6.8 we have a commuting diagram

$$\begin{array}{ccc}
L^2(S) & \xrightarrow{\ ()^{\#}\ } & \sum\limits_{\alpha\in\vec{\mathbb{Z}}^r}^{\oplus} \mathcal{P}^\alpha(S) \\
\Big\downarrow {\scriptstyle (E_e g)^{\#}} & & \Big\downarrow {\scriptstyle ((E_e g)^{\#}(\alpha))} \\
L^2(S) & \xrightarrow[\ ()^{\#}\ ]{} & \sum\limits_{\alpha\in\vec{\mathbb{Z}}^r}^{\oplus} \mathcal{P}^\alpha(S)
\end{array}$$

for every L-biinvariant function $g \in A(K)$. Therefore $\mathcal{D}^L(\vec{\mathbb{Z}}^r)$ can be identified with the C^*-algebra generated by the convolution operators

(3.6.22) $$(E_e g)^{\#} h(t) := \int_K h(s^{-1}t)\; g(s)\; dE_e(s).$$

As in Lemma 3.5.61, the orthogonal projection P onto $L^2(S)$ satisfies

(3.6.23) $$P\,\mathcal{D}(K)\,P = \mathcal{D}^L(\vec{\mathbb{Z}}^r).$$

3.6.24. PROPOSITION. $\mathcal{C}_0(\vec{\mathbb{Z}}^r) \subset \mathcal{D}^L(\vec{\mathbb{Z}}^r) \subset L^\infty(\vec{\mathbb{Z}}^r)$.

Proof. This follows from Proposition 3.6.15 but can also be directly seen as follows: For any fixed $\beta \in \vec{\mathbb{Z}}^r$, the smooth function $g(z) := \phi_\beta(z)\, \Delta(z,e)^{n/r}$ on S is L-invariant, and we have for all $\alpha \in \vec{\mathbb{Z}}^r$

$$(E_e g)^\#(\alpha) = \int_S \overline{\phi_\alpha(z)}\ \phi_\beta(z)\ \Delta(z,e)^{n/r}\ dE_e(z)$$

$$= \int_S \overline{\phi_\alpha(z)}\ \phi_\beta(z)\ dz = c_\beta\, \beta(\alpha)\ \text{(Kronecker symbol)}.$$

Since $\mathcal{C}_0(\vec{\mathbb{Z}}^r)$ is generated (as a C^*-algebra) by the functions $\beta(\alpha) := \delta_{\alpha,\beta}$, the assertion follows. Q.E.D.

The *spectrum* (= character space) Spec $\mathcal{D}^L(\vec{\mathbb{Z}}^r)$ of the abelian Banach algebra (3.6.20) is a locally compact Hausdorff space which is not compact since $\mathcal{D}^L(\vec{\mathbb{Z}}^r)$ has no unit. Being a subalgebra of $L^\infty(\vec{\mathbb{Z}}^r)$, $\mathcal{D}^L(\vec{\mathbb{Z}}^r)$ has the "elementary" characters α_0 $(\alpha \in \mathbb{Z}^r)$ defined by

$$\alpha_0 \cdot \varphi := \varphi(\alpha) \tag{3.6.25}$$

for all $\varphi \in \mathcal{D}^L(\vec{\mathbb{Z}}^r)$. Since $\mathcal{D}^L(\vec{\mathbb{Z}}^r)$ separates the points of $\vec{\mathbb{Z}}^r$ by Proposition 3.6.24, we obtain an embedding $\vec{\mathbb{Z}}^r \subset \text{Spec}\ \mathcal{D}^L(\vec{\mathbb{Z}}^r)$ given by $\alpha \mapsto \alpha_0$. We will now determine the full spectrum of $\mathcal{D}^L(\vec{\mathbb{Z}}^r)$, showing that the characters not given by (3.6.25) are obtained by taking limits along the faces of the polar cone (3.6.9).

3.6.26. THEOREM. *Let* $\alpha = \alpha(n) = (\alpha_1(n),\ldots,\alpha_r(n))$ *be a sequence in* $\vec{\mathbb{N}}^r$ *such that there exists* $k \le r$ *with the property* $\alpha_j(n) \to \infty$ $(1 \le j \le k)$ *and*

$$(\alpha_{k+1}(n),\ \ldots,\ \alpha_r(n)) \to \beta := (\beta_{k+1},\ \ldots,\ \beta_r) \in \vec{\mathbb{N}}^{r-k}. \tag{3.6.27}$$

Then the weak* *limit*

$$\beta_k := w^*\text{-}\lim_\alpha \alpha_0 \in \text{Spec}\ \mathcal{D}^L(\vec{\mathbb{Z}}^r) \tag{3.6.28}$$

exists, and satisfies

(3.6.29) $$\beta_k(E_e g)^\# = \int_{S_c} \overline{\phi_\beta(w)}\, g_c(w)\, dE_c(w)$$

for all L-invariant $f \in \mathcal{C}^\infty(S)$. *Here*

(3.6.30) $$c := e_1 + \cdots + e_k,$$

$g_c(w) := g(c + w)$ *for all* $w \in S_c$, ϕ_β *is the spherical polynomial of type* β *in* Z_c *and* E_c *is the characteristic convolutor of the symmetric space* $\Omega_c \subset Z_c$ (cf. 1.5.48).

The *proof* of Theorem 3.6.26 requires a series of Lemmas. Consider the subset

(3.6.31) $$F := \{\sum_{i=1}^{k} \xi_i M^\#_{e_i} : \xi_1 \geq \ldots \geq \xi_k \geq 0\}$$

of the polar cone $\Lambda^\#$ (cf. (3.6.9)). Embed

(3.6.32) $$K_c' := \text{Aut}\, Z_0(c)' \qquad \text{(commutator subgroup)}$$

as a subgroup of K, and put $A := \exp(a)$. Then the centralizer of F in K, denoted by K_F, is generated by K_c, A and the centralizer of A in L (where $S = L\backslash K$). It follows that

$$S_F := e \cdot K_F = \{\sum_{i=1}^{k} u_i e_i + w : u_i \in \mathbb{T},\ w \in S_c\} \approx \mathbb{T}^k \times S_c.$$

3.6.33. LEMMA. *Let* $\varphi \in C^\infty(S)$ *vanish on* S_F. *Then*

$$\lim_{\alpha_k \to \infty} \int_S \overline{\Delta_{\alpha_1,\ldots,\alpha_k,0,\ldots,0}(z)\varphi(z)}\, d\mu(z) = 0$$

for every distribution μ *on* S *defining a bounded convolution operator.*

Proof. Let $E \subset L^2(S)$ denote the closed linear span of Δ_α, $\alpha \in \vec{\mathbb{N}}^r$. Let f be a smooth function on the face F which is homogeneous of degree 0 and has support contained in the complement of a neighborhood of ∂F (relative to the span of F). Define a bounded linear operator $\pi_f : L^2(S) \to E$ by putting $\pi_f \Delta_\beta := f(\beta)\Delta_\beta$ for all $\beta \in \vec{\mathbb{N}}^k = \vec{\mathbb{N}}^r \cap F$, and $\pi_f := 0$ on the orthocomplement of $\langle \Delta_\beta : \beta \in \vec{\mathbb{N}}^k \rangle$. By [G3; Theorem 8.10], π_f is a "Hermite operator" with symbol in $H^0(S \times S, \Sigma_F^D)$, where $\Sigma_F^D \subset T^*S \times (-T^*S)$ (opposite symplectic structure) projects onto $S_F \times S_F$. Suppose first that $\varphi \in C_0^\infty(S \backslash S_F)$. Then $\varphi \pi_f$ is a smoothing operator, and the same holds for $P_\ell := \varphi \pi_f \Delta^\ell$, where $\ell \geq 0$ and Δ is the Laplace-Beltrami operator on S. Applying [G3; Proposition II.3.8] we have for $z \in S$ and $\alpha = (\alpha_1, \ldots, \alpha_k, 0, \ldots, 0)$

$$(P_\ell \Delta_\alpha)(z) = (\varphi \pi_f \Delta^\ell \Delta_\alpha)(z) = \varphi(z)\ (|\alpha + \rho|^2 - |\rho|^2)^\ell\ (\pi_f \Delta_\alpha)(z)$$

$$= \varphi(z)\ (|\alpha + \rho|^2 - |\rho|^2)^\ell\ f(\alpha)\ \Delta_\alpha(z) = \varphi(z)\ (|\alpha + \rho|^2 - |\rho|^2)^\ell\ \Delta_\alpha(z).$$

Here ρ is the half-sum of positive roots of the Riemannian symmetric pair (K,L), and we may choose f so that $f(\alpha) = 1$ for almost all α since α tends to infinity in the interior of F relative to its affine span. It follows that

$$(|\alpha + \rho|^2 - |\rho|^2)^\ell \int_S \overline{\Delta_\alpha(z)\varphi(z)}\ d\mu(z)$$

$$= \int_S \overline{(P_\ell \Delta_\alpha)(z)}\ d\mu(z) = \int_S \overline{\Delta_\alpha(z)}\ (P_\ell^* \mu)(z)\ dz$$

where P_ℓ^* is the adjoint. Since $|\Delta_\alpha(z)| \leq 1$ on S and $P_\ell^* \mu$ is smooth (hence bounded) it follows that

$$\int_S \overline{\Delta_\alpha(z)\varphi(z)}\ d\mu(z) \lesssim (|\alpha + \rho|^2 - |\rho|^2)^{-\ell} \to 0$$

as $\alpha_k \to \infty$. This proves the assertion in case $\varphi \in C_c^\infty(S \backslash S_F)$. Now assume only $\varphi|_{S_F} = 0$. We will show that there exists a sequence $\varphi_j \in C_c^\infty(S \backslash S_F)$ such that

(3.6.34) $$\tilde{\varphi}_j \to \tilde{\varphi} \quad \text{in} \quad A(K) \quad \text{(Fourier algebra)}$$

where $\tilde{\varphi}(s) := \varphi(e \cdot s)$ for all $s \in K$. In order to prove (3.6.34) let W be a 0-neighborhood in $i\mathfrak{m}$, where $\mathfrak{k} = \mathfrak{l} \oplus i\mathfrak{m}$, and let $Z \mapsto \gamma(Z)$ be a diffeomorphism from W onto a neighborhood of $e \in S$. Then there exists a continuous function δ on W such that

$$\int_S f(z)\, dz = \int_W f(\gamma(Z))\, \delta(Z)\, dZ$$

for all f with support in $\gamma(W)$. Since $A(K)$ is invariant under translations (by elements in K_F) we may assume that $\operatorname{Supp} \varphi \subset\subset \gamma(W)$. Since S_F is a submanifold of S, we may choose γ such that $W = U \times V$, where U and V are bounded convex 0-neighborhoods in complementary vector subspaces of $i\mathfrak{m}$, and

(3.6.35) $$S_F \cap \gamma(W) = \gamma(\{0\} \times V).$$

Now choose $\chi \in C_0^\infty(W)$ such that $\chi = 1$ on $(\{0\} \times V) \cap \operatorname{Supp}(\varphi \circ \gamma)$. Define $\chi_j \in C_0^\infty(\gamma(W))$, for $j \geq 1$, by putting

(3.6.36) $$(\chi_j \circ \gamma)(X,Y) := \chi(jX, Y)$$

for all $(X,Y) \in \frac{1}{j} U \times V \subset W$. Since $k < r$ by assumption, we have $m := \dim V = \dim S - \dim S_F > 0$. Then

$$\int_S |\chi_j(z)\varphi(z)|^2 = \int_W |(\chi_j \circ \gamma)(Z)|^2\, |\varphi(\gamma(Z))|^2\, \delta(Z)\, dZ$$

$$= \int_V \int_U |\chi(jX,Y)|^2\, |\varphi(\gamma(X,Y))|^2\, \delta(X,Y)\, dX\, dY$$

$$= j^{-m} \int_V \int_U |\chi(\xi,Y)|^2\, |\varphi(\gamma(\tfrac{\xi}{j}, Y))|^2\, \delta(\tfrac{\xi}{j}, Y)\, d\xi\, dY \lesssim j^{-m} \to 0$$

since χ has compact support in W and $|\varphi \circ \gamma|^2 \cdot \delta$ is bounded in W. Thus $\|\chi_j\varphi\|_2 \to 0$ as $j \to \infty$, and Plancherel's Theorem yields

$$\sum_{\alpha \in K^{\#}} \left\| (\chi_j\varphi)^{\#}_{\alpha} \right\|^2_{HS} \to 0 \tag{3.6.37}$$

where HS is the Hilbert-Schmidt norm. Every A in the Lie algebra $\mathfrak{k}$ of K induces a vector field on S such that $(A\chi_j)(z) = d\chi_j(z)A_z$ for every $z \in S$, where $d\chi_j$ is the derivative and $A_z \in T_z(S)$ is the tangent vector. Using the chain rule it follows that

$$(A\chi_j)\gamma(Z) = d(\chi_j \circ \gamma)(Z)d\gamma(Z)^{-1}A_{\gamma(Z)}. \tag{3.6.38}$$

Write

$$d\gamma(X,Y)^{-1}A_{\gamma(X,Y)} = (B(X,Y),C(X,Y))$$

as a tangent vector on $U \times V$. Then (3.6.38) implies

$$d(\chi_j \circ \gamma)(X,Y)d\gamma(X,Y)^{-1}A_{\gamma(X,Y)}$$
$$= j(D_1\chi)(jX,Y)B(X,Y) + (D_2\chi)(jX,Y)C(X,Y)$$

where D_1 and D_2 denote the partial derivatives. It follows that

$$\int_S |(A\chi_j)(z)|^2\, |\varphi(z)|^2\, dz = \int_W |(A\chi_j)(\gamma(Z))|^2\, |\varphi(\gamma(Z))|^2\, \delta(Z)\ dZ$$

$$= \int_V \int_U |j(D_1\chi)(jX,Y)B(X,Y) + (D_2\chi)(jX,Y)C(X,Y)|^2\, |\varphi(\gamma(X,Y))|^2\, \delta(X,Y)\ dX\, dY$$

$$= j^{-m}\int_V \int_U |j(D_1\chi)(\xi,Y)B(\tfrac{\xi}{j}, Y) + (D_2\chi)(\xi,Y)C(\tfrac{\xi}{j}, Y)|^2\, (D_1\chi)(\xi,Y)\ B(\tfrac{\xi}{j}, Y)\ d\xi\, dY.$$

Since $\varphi \circ \gamma$ is smooth and vanishes on $\{0\} \times V$ we have $|\varphi(\gamma(\tfrac{\xi}{j}, Y))| \lesssim j^{-1}$ by Taylor's formula, so that the above integral is again dominated by j^{-m} and we obtain $\|A\chi_j\|_2 \to 0$ as $j \to \infty$. Since $A(\chi_j\varphi) = (A\chi_j) \cdot \varphi + \chi_j \cdot A\varphi$

and $\mathrm{Supp}(A\varphi) \subset\subset \gamma(W)$, this implies $\|A(\chi_j\varphi)\|_2 \to 0$. For every $\alpha \in K^\#$ we have

$$(A(\chi_j\varphi))^\#_\alpha = \int_K \alpha(s)^* A(\chi_j\varphi)(s)\, ds = \int_K \alpha(s)^* \frac{d}{d\vartheta}\Big|_{\vartheta=0} (\chi_j\varphi)(\exp(\vartheta A)s)\, ds$$

$$= \frac{d}{d\vartheta} \int_K \alpha(\exp(-\vartheta A)t)^* (\chi_j\varphi)(t)\, dt$$

$$= \int_K \alpha(t)^* (\chi_j\varphi)(t)\, dt \; \frac{d}{d\vartheta}\, \alpha(\exp(\vartheta A)) = (\chi_j\varphi)^\#_\alpha\, d\alpha(A),$$

where $d\alpha : \mathfrak{k} \to \mathfrak{u}(H_\alpha)$ (skew-adjoint operators) is the infinitesimal generator of α. Again by Plancherel's Theorem,

$$\sum_{\alpha\in K^\#} \|(\chi_j\varphi)^\#_\alpha \cdot d\alpha(A)\|^2_{HS} \to 0. \tag{3.6.39}$$

Now consider the strictly positive K-invariant operator

$$B_\alpha := I + \sum_i d\alpha(A_i) d\alpha(A_i)^*$$

on H_α, where (A_i) is an orthonormal basis of $\mathfrak{k}$. For the trace norm on $\mathcal{L}(H_\alpha)$, we have

$$\sum_{\alpha\in K^\#} \|(\chi_j\varphi)^\#_\alpha\|_{tr} = \sum_{\alpha\in K^\#} \|(\chi_j\varphi)^\#_\alpha B_\alpha^{1/2} B_\alpha^{-1/2}\|_{tr}$$

$$\leq \left[\sum_{\alpha\in K^\#} \|B_\alpha^{-1/2}\|^2_{HS}\right]^{1/2} \left[\sum_{\alpha\in K^\#} \|(\chi_j\varphi)^\#_\alpha B_\alpha^{1/2}\|^2_{HS}\right]^{1/2}$$

$$= \left[\sum_{\alpha\in K^\#} \mathrm{tr}(B_\alpha^{-1})\right]^{1/2} \left[\sum_{\alpha\in K^\#} \mathrm{tr}((\chi_j\varphi)^\#_\alpha B_\alpha ((\chi_j\varphi)^\#_\alpha)^*)\right]^{1/2}.$$

The first factor is finite since $\sum \oplus B_\alpha^{-1}$ is of trace-class. The second factor gives

$$\sum_{\alpha\in K^\#}\left(\|(\chi_j\varphi)^\#_\alpha\|^2_{HS} + \sum_i \|[A_j(\chi_j\varphi)]^\#_\alpha\|^2_{HS}\right)$$

which tends to zero by (3.6.37) and (3.6.39). It follows that $\tilde{\chi}_j\tilde{\varphi} \to 0$ in $A(K)$, so that $(1 - \tilde{\chi}_j)\tilde{\varphi} \to \tilde{\varphi}$ in $A(K)$. Since $1 - \chi_j$ vanishes in a neighborhood of $\gamma(W) \cap S_F$, the assertion (3.6.34) follows. Writing

$$\int_S \overline{\Delta_\alpha\varphi}\, d\mu = \int_K \overline{\Delta_\alpha(\varphi - \varphi_j)}\, d\mu + \int_K \overline{\Delta_\alpha\varphi_j}\, d\mu = \langle\Delta_\alpha(\varphi - \varphi_j), \mu^\#\rangle + \int_K \overline{\Delta_\alpha\varphi_j}\, d\mu$$

we have, noting that $|\Delta_\alpha| \le 1$ on S,

$$\left|\int_S \overline{\Delta_\alpha\varphi}\, d\mu\right| \le \|\Delta_\alpha(\varphi - \varphi_j)\|_{A(K)} \cdot \|\mu^\#\|_{W*(K)} + \left|\int_K \overline{\Delta_\alpha\varphi_j}\, d\mu\right|$$

$$\le \|\varphi - \varphi_j\|_{A(K)} \cdot \|\mu^\#\|_{W*(K)} + \left|\int_K \overline{\Delta_\alpha\varphi_j}\, d\mu\right| \to 0$$

as $\alpha_k \to \infty$, by applying the first part of the proof to φ_j with j large enough. Q.E.D.

3.6.40. LEMMA. *Let* $p \in \mathcal{P}(Z_1(c))$ and let $q \in \mathcal{P}^\beta(Z_0(c))$ *for some signature* $\beta = (\beta_{k+1},\dots,\beta_r) \in \vec{\mathbb{N}}^{r-k}$. *Let* $\ell \in \mathbb{Z}$ *be fixed. Consider a sequence in* $\vec{\mathbb{N}}^k$ *of signatures of the form* $\alpha = (\alpha_1,\dots,\alpha_k, 0,\dots,0)$ *with* $\alpha_k \to +\infty$. *Then there exists* $\varphi_\alpha \in \mathcal{C}^\infty(S)$ *having type* $(\vec{\mathbb{N}}^k, \beta - \ell)$ *such that*

$$(3.6.41)\qquad \int_S \Delta_{\alpha_1,\dots,\alpha_k,0,\dots,0}(z)\ p(z)\ q(z)\ \Delta_r(z)^{-\ell}\, d\mu(z) \sim \int_S \varphi_{\alpha_1,\dots,\alpha_k}(z)\, d\mu(z)$$

for every distribution μ *on* S. *Here* $\sim$ *means that the difference tends to* 0 *as* $\alpha_k \to \infty$.

Proof. We may assume $q(w) = \delta_\beta(\sigma w)$ for all $w \in Z_0(c)$, where $\sigma \in K'_c$ (cf. (3.6.32)) and δ_β is the conical polynomial on $Z_0(c)$ of type β.

Choose $s \in K'$ such that $s|_{Z_0(c)} = \sigma$ and $s|_{Z_1(c)} = \text{id}$. Then the right translations give

$$\rho_s[\Delta_{\alpha_1,\ldots,\alpha_k,0,\ldots,0}\ \Delta_r^{-\ell}\ p\ \delta_\beta] = \Delta_{\alpha_1,\ldots,\alpha_k,0,\ldots,0}\ \Delta_r^{-\ell} p q.$$

Since the assertion is invariant under ρ_σ, we may assume $\sigma = \text{id}$ and $q = \delta_\beta$. Let

$$\Delta_\beta(z) := \Delta_{k+1}(z)^{\beta_{k+1}-\beta_{k+2}} \ldots \Delta_r(z)^{\beta_r}$$

be the conical polynomial on Z of signature $(\beta_{k+1},\ldots,\beta_{k+1},\beta) \in \vec{\mathbb{N}}^r$. Then we have

$$\begin{aligned} \Delta_\beta(u + w) &= \Delta_{k+1}(u + w)^{\beta_{k+1}-\beta_{k+2}} \ldots \Delta_r(u + w)^{\beta_r} \\ &= \Delta_k(u)^{\beta_{k+1}-\beta_{k+2}}\ \Delta_k(u)^{\beta_{k+2}-\beta_{k+3}} \ldots \Delta_k(u)^{\beta_r}\ \Delta_c^\beta(w) = \Delta_k(u)^{\beta_{k+1}} \delta_\beta(w) \end{aligned} \tag{3.6.42}$$

for all $u \in Z_1(c)$, $w \in Z_0(c)$. Define $\gamma := (\alpha_1 - \beta_{k+1},\ldots,\alpha_k - \beta_{k+1},0,\ldots,0)$. Putting $z = u + v + w \in Z_1(c) \oplus Z_{1/2}(c) \oplus Z_0(c)$ it is clear that $\Delta_\beta(z) - \Delta_\beta(u + w)$ vanishes on S_F. By Lemma 3.6.33, this implies

$$\int_S \Delta_{\alpha_1,\ldots,\alpha_k,0,\ldots,0}(z)\ \delta_\beta(w)\ d\mu(z) = \int_S \Delta_\gamma(z)\ \Delta_k(u)^{\beta_{k+1}}\ \delta_\beta(w)\ d\mu(z)$$

$$= \int_S \Delta_\gamma(z)\ \Delta_\beta(u + w)\ d\mu(z) \sim \int_S \Delta_\gamma(z) . \Delta_\beta(z)\ d\mu(z)$$

as $\alpha_k \to \infty$. Assume $\alpha_k \ge |\ell|$ and define $\varphi_{\alpha_1,\ldots,\alpha_k}(z) := p(u)\Delta_\gamma(u)\Delta_\beta(u)\Delta_r(z)^{-1}$. Since $p \cdot \Delta_\gamma$ belongs to $\mathcal{P}(Z_1(c))$ we may assume

$$(p \cdot \Delta_\gamma)(u) = (\Delta_1^{\ell_1-\ell_2}\ \Delta_2^{\ell_2-\ell_3} \ldots \Delta_k^{\ell_k})(\tau u)$$

for all $u \in Z_1(c)$, where $\ell_1 \ge \ldots \ge \ell_k \ge |\ell| - \beta_{k+1}$ and $\tau \in \text{Aut}(Z_1(c))'$ (commutator subgroup). Choose $t \in K$ such that $t|_{Z_1(c)} = \tau$ and ρ_t leaves $\Delta_{k+1},\ldots,\Delta_r$ invariant. Then

$$\rho_t^{-1}\varphi_{\alpha_1,\ldots,\alpha_k} = \rho_\tau^{-\ell}(p\Delta_\gamma) \cdot \Delta_\beta\ \Delta_r^{-\ell} = \Delta_1^{\ell_1-\ell_2} \ldots \Delta_k^{\ell_k}\ \Delta_\beta \Delta_r^{-\ell}$$

has signature $(\ell_1 + \beta_{k+1} - \ell, \ldots, \ell_k + \beta_{k+1} - \ell, \beta_{k+1} - \ell, \ldots, \beta_r - \ell)$ with $\ell_k + \beta_{k+1} - \ell \geq 0$. Q.E.D.

3.6.43. PROPOSITION. *For every* $f \in \mathcal{C}^\infty(S)$ *we have*

$$\int_S \overline{\Delta_{\alpha_1,\ldots,\alpha_k,0,\ldots,0}(z)\, f(z)}\, dE_e(z) \to \int_{S_c} \overline{f_c(w)}\, dE_c(w) \tag{3.6.44}$$

whenever $\alpha_k \to +\infty$. *Here* E_c *is the characteristic convolutor of the* K_c*-circular domain* $\Omega_c := \Omega \cap Z_0(c)$ *of rank* $r - k$, *with Shilov boundary* S_c, *and* $f_c(w) := f(c + w)$ *is the restriction of* f *to* S_c.

Proof. Using density arguments we may assume that there exists $\ell \in \mathbb{Z}$ such that $\Delta(z)^\ell \cdot \overline{f(z)} \in \mathcal{P}(Z)$. Write $z = u + v + w$ with $u \in Z_1(c)$, $v \in Z_{1/2}(c)$ and $w \in Z_0(c)$. Since

$$\mathcal{P}(Z) = \mathcal{P}(Z_1(c)) \otimes \mathcal{P}(Z_{1/2}(c)) \otimes \mathcal{P}(Z_0(c))$$

we may assume $\overline{f(z)} = \Delta(z)^{-1} p(u) g(v) q(w)$ where $p \in \mathcal{P}(Z_1(c))$, $g \in \mathcal{P}(Z_{1/2}(c))$ and $q \in \mathcal{P}(Z_0(c))$. Assume first that $g(v)$ has no constant term, i.e., $g(0) = 0$. Since $v = 0$ for all $z = u + v + w \in S_F$, it follows that f vanishes on S_F. By Lemma 3.6.33

$$\int_S \overline{\Delta_{\alpha_1,\ldots,\alpha_k,0,\ldots,0}(z)\, f(z)}\, dE_e(z) \to 0.$$

On the other hand we have for all $w \in S_c$

$$\overline{f_c(w)} = \overline{f(c + w)} = \Delta_c(w)^{-\ell} p(c) g(0) q(w) = 0$$

showing that $\int_{S_c} \overline{f_c(w)}\, dE_c(w) = 0$. Hence the assertion is true in case $g(0) = 0$. Now assume that $g(v)$ is constant, say, $g(v) = 1$. Then $\overline{f(z)} =$

$p(u)q(w)\Delta(z)^{-\ell}$. We may assume that $q \in \mathcal{P}^{\beta}(Z_0(c))$ for $\beta = (\beta_{k+1},\ldots,\beta_r) \in \vec{\mathbb{N}}^{r-k}$. Then

$$\overline{f_c(w)} = \Delta_c(w)^{-\ell} p(c) q(w)$$

is pure of type $\beta - \ell$. Put $\alpha = (\alpha_1,\ldots,\alpha_k,0,\ldots,0)$. By Lemma 3.6.40 there exists $\varphi_\alpha \in \mathcal{C}^\infty(S)$ of type $(\vec{\mathbb{N}}^k, \beta - \ell)$ such that

$$\int_S (\Delta_\alpha(z) \cdot \overline{f(z)} - \varphi_\alpha(z))\, d\mu(z) \to 0 \tag{3.6.45}$$

for every distribution μ on S. Putting $\mu = \delta_e$, (3.6.45) implies $\varphi_\alpha(e) \to \overline{f(e)}$ since $\Delta_\alpha(e) = 1$. Putting $\mu = E_e$ we obtain

$$\int_S \overline{\Delta_\alpha(z)}\ f(z)\, dE_e(z) \sim \int_S \varphi_\alpha(z)\, dE_e(z) = \overline{E_e^{\#}(\varphi_\alpha)(e)}$$

where $\sim$ means that the difference tends to 0 as $\alpha_k \to \infty$. In case $\beta_r \geq \ell$, $\varphi_\alpha \in H^2(S)$ and $\bar{f}_c \in H^2(S_c)$. Thus

$$\int_{S_c} f_c(w)\, dE_c(w) = \overline{E_c^{\#}(\bar{f}_c)(e - c)} = f_c(e - c) = f(e)$$

$$= \lim \overline{\varphi_\alpha(e)} = \lim E_e^{\#}(\varphi_\alpha)(e) = \lim \int_S \overline{\Delta_\alpha(z)}\ f(z)\, dE_e(z).$$

In case $\beta_r < \ell$, $\varphi_\alpha \in H^2(S)^\perp$. Thus

$$\int_{S_c} f_c(w)\, dE_c(w) = \overline{E_c^{\#}(\bar{f}_c)(e - c)} = 0$$

$$= \lim E_e^{\#}(\varphi_\alpha)(e) = \lim \int_S \overline{\Delta_\alpha(z)}\ f(z)\, dE_e(z).$$

Thus the assertion holds in both cases. Q.E.D.

3.6.46. COROLLARY. *For every L-biinvariant function* $g \in \mathcal{C}^\infty(S)$ *and each* $\beta = (\beta_{k+1},\ldots,\beta_r) \in \vec{\mathbb{Z}}^{r-k}$, *we have*

$$\lim_{\alpha} (E_e g)^\#(\alpha) = (E_c g_c)^\#(\beta) \tag{3.6.47}$$

whenever $\alpha = (\alpha_1,\ldots,\alpha_r) \in \vec{\mathbb{Z}}^r$ *satisfies* $\alpha_k \to +\infty$ *and* $\alpha_{k+1} \to \beta_{k+1}, \ldots, \alpha_r \to \beta_r$.

Proof. We may assume $\alpha_{k+1} = \beta_{k+1},\ldots,\alpha_r = \beta_r$. By integrating (3.6.44) over L, we obtain

$$(E_e g)^\#(\alpha) = \int_S \overline{\phi_\alpha(z)}\; g(z)\; dE_e(z) = \int_S \overline{\Delta_{\alpha_1,\ldots,\alpha_r}(z)}\; g(z)\; dE_e(z)$$

$$= \int_S \overline{\Delta_{\alpha_1,\ldots,\alpha_k,0,\ldots,0}(z)}\; \overline{\Delta_k(z)}^{-\beta_{k+1}}\; \overline{\Delta_{k+1}(z)}^{\beta_{k+1}-\beta_{k+2}} \ldots \overline{\Delta_r(z)}^{\beta_r}\, g(z)\; dE_e(z)$$

$$\to \int_{S_c} \overline{\delta_\beta(w)}\; g_c(w)\, dE_c(w) = \int_{S_c} \overline{\phi_\beta(w)}\; g_c(w)\; dE_c(w) = (E_c g_c)^\#(\beta).$$

Q.E.D.

Since (3.6.47) agrees with (3.6.29) and $\mathcal{D}^L(\vec{\mathbb{Z}}^r)$ is abelian, the proof of Theorem 3.6.26 is complete. As a consequence of Theorem 3.6.26, there exists a C*-representation

$$\pi_c^L : \mathcal{D}^L(S) \to \mathcal{D}^{L_c}(S_c) \subset \mathcal{L}(L^2(S_c)) \tag{3.6.48}$$

such that (cf. (3.6.47))

$$\pi_c^L((E_e g)^\#) = (E_c g_c)^\# \tag{3.6.49}$$

for every L-biinvariant $g \in \mathcal{C}^\infty(S)$. Here we use the fact that $\mathcal{D}^L(S)$ is abelian. Using K-covariance, we define (3.6.48) for every tripotent $c \in S_k$, not just $c = e_1 + \ldots + e_k$.

Using the notation (3.6.29) we define for any $0 \le k \le r$

$$\mathrm{Spec}_k\, \mathcal{D}^L(\vec{\mathbb{Z}}^r) := \{\beta_k : \beta \in \vec{\mathbb{N}}^{r-k}\}. \tag{3.6.50}$$

In particular

$$\mathrm{Spec}_0\ \mathcal{D}^L(\vec{\mathbb{Z}}^r) = \{\alpha_0 : \alpha \in \vec{\mathbb{N}}^r\}. \tag{3.6.51}$$

Combining Theorem 3.6.26 with a geometric realization of $\mathrm{Spec}\ \mathcal{D}^L(\vec{\mathbb{Z}}^r)$ similar to the proof of Proposition 3.1.33, we obtain

3.6.52. THEOREM. *The character sets (3.6.50) are pairwise disjoint. Each such set is discrete (hence open) in its closure*

$$\mathrm{Spec}_k\ \mathcal{D}^L(\vec{\mathbb{Z}}^r)^{c\ell} = \dot{\bigcup_{\ell\geq k}}\ \mathrm{Spec}_\ell\ \mathcal{D}^L(\vec{\mathbb{Z}}^r) \tag{3.6.53}$$

which is compact. In particular,

$$\mathrm{Spec}_+\ \mathcal{D}^L(\vec{\mathbb{Z}}^r) := \mathrm{Spec}_0\ \mathcal{D}^L(\vec{\mathbb{Z}}^r)^{c\ell} = \dot{\bigcup_{\ell\geq k}}\ \mathrm{Spec}_\ell\ \mathcal{D}^L(\vec{\mathbb{Z}}^r) \tag{3.6.54}$$

is compact and contains $\mathrm{Spec}_0\ \mathcal{D}^L(\vec{\mathbb{Z}}^r)$ *as a discrete subset.*

In abreviated form we have

$$\mathrm{Spec}_+\ \mathcal{D}^L(\vec{\mathbb{Z}}^r)^{c\ell} = \dot{\bigcup_{0\leq\ell\leq k}}\ \vec{\mathbb{N}}^{r-\ell}, \tag{3.6.55}$$

$$\mathrm{Spec}\ \mathcal{D}^L(\vec{\mathbb{Z}}^r) = \dot{\bigcup_{0\leq\ell\leq k}}\ \vec{\mathbb{Z}}^{r-\ell}. \tag{3.6.56}$$

3.7 Hardy Multipliers Over S-bicircular Domains

In this section we introduce a commutative C^*-algebra whose spectrum plays a crucial role in the analysis of Hardy-Toeplitz operators over an S-bicircular domain $\Omega = S\exp(\Lambda)S \subset S^{\mathbb{C}}$ for a compact connected Lie group S. We assume that Ω is log-conical, i.e. Λ is a convex cone. The harmonic analysis of the Hardy space $H^2(S)$ is discussed in Section 2.11.

3.7.1. DEFINITION. For any integrable function $u \in L^1(S)$, the *convolution operator* with *symbol* u is the bounded operator $u^\# : L^2(S) \to L^2(S)$ defined by

$$(u^\# h)(z) := \int_S h(w^{-1}z)\ u(w)\ dw \tag{3.7.2}$$

for all $h \in L^2(S)$ and $z \in S$. We have $u^\# v^\# = (u^\# v)^\#$ for the convolution product

$$(u^\# v)(z) := \int_S v(w^{-1}z)\ u(w)\ dw$$

of functions. Generalizing (3.7.2), we define a convolution operator $u^\# : \mathcal{C}^\infty(S) \to \mathcal{C}^\infty(S)$ for any *distribution* u on S by putting

$$(u^\# h)(z) := \int_S h(w^{-1}z)\ du(w). \tag{3.7.3}$$

Then $u^\# v^\# = (u^\# v)^\#$ for the convolution product

$$\int_S h(z)\ d(u^\# v)(z) = \int_S \int_S h(zw)\ du(z)\ dv(w) \tag{3.7.4}$$

of distributions on S. The definition (3.7.3) applies in particular to complex bounded *measures* u on S.

3.7.5. DEFINITION. The *spatial group C^*-algebra* of S is the C^*-algebra

$$C^*(S) := C^*(u^\# : u \in L^1(S)) \tag{3.7.6}$$

generated by all convolution operators (3.7.2) on $L^2(S)$.

3.7.7. DEFINITION. The *spatial group von Neumann algebra* of S is the W^*-algebra

$$W^*(S) := W^*(u^\# : u \in \mathcal{M}(S))$$

generated by all convolution operators (3.7.3) with measure symbol u.

A measure (resp., a distribution) u on S is called *central* if

$$\int_S h(z)\ du(z) = \int_S h(wzw^{-1})\ du(z) \tag{3.7.9}$$

for all $w \in S$ and $h \in \mathcal{C}^\infty(S)$. The convolution product (3.7.4) of central measures (or distributions) u and v on S is again central.

3.7.10. PROPOSITION. *There exists a central distribution* E_e *on* S, *called the "characteristic convolutor" of* Ω, *such that*

$$\int_S h(s)\ dE_e(z) = \lim_{\substack{a\in\Lambda\\ a\to 0}} \int_S E_e(\exp(a)z)\ h(z)\ dz \tag{3.7.11}$$

for all test functions $h \in \mathcal{C}^\infty(S)$. *Here* $E_e(\exp(a)z)$ *is the Szegö characteristic function (2.11.23) on* Ω.

Proof. Taking the distribution limit in (2.11.23), define for $z \in S$

$$dE_e(z) = \sum_{\alpha\in S^\#\cap\Lambda^\#} d_\alpha\ \text{trace}\ \dot{\alpha}(z)\ dz. \qquad \text{Q.E.D.}$$

3.7.12. PROPOSITION. *The convolution operator* $E_e^\#$ *with symbol* E_e *coincides with the Szegö projection* $E_e^\# : L^2(S) \to H^2(S)$.

Proof. The Szegö projection E satisfies

$$\begin{aligned}(Eh)(z) = (E_z|h)_S = \int_S \overline{E(w,z)}\ h(w)\ dw &= \int_S E(z,w)\ h(w)\ dw \\ &= \int_S E_e(zw^{-1})\ h(w)\ dw\end{aligned}$$

for all $h \in L^2(S)$ and $z \in \Omega$. Here we use Proposition 2.11.19. Now fix $z \in S$. Then we obtain for all $h \in \mathcal{C}^\infty(S)$

$$(Eh)(z) = \lim_{\substack{a\in\Lambda\\ a\to 0}} (Eh)(\exp(a)z) = \lim_{\substack{a\in\Lambda\\ a\to 0}} \int_S E_e(\exp(a)zs^{-1})\ h(s)\ ds$$

$$= \lim_{\substack{a \in \Lambda \\ a \to 0}} \int_S E_e(\exp(a)w)\ h(w^{-1}z)\ dw \ = \int_S h(w^{-1}z)\ dE_e^{\#}(w). \quad \text{Q.E.D.}$$

3.7.13. DEFINITION. Denote by F_α the representation space of $\alpha \in S^{\#}$. For any bounded family $(B_\alpha)_{\alpha \in S^{\#}}$ of endomorphisms $B_\alpha \in \mathcal{L}(F_\alpha)$, the associated *multiplication operator* is the bounded operator

$$\sum_{\alpha \in S^{\#}}^{\oplus} \mathcal{L}^2(F_\alpha) \xrightarrow{(B_\alpha)} \sum_{\alpha \in S^{\#}}^{\oplus} \mathcal{L}^2(F_\alpha) \tag{3.7.14}$$

defined as the componentwise *right* multiplication $(A_\alpha) \mapsto (A_\alpha B_\alpha)$ by B_α.

For every measure (or distribution) u on S and $\alpha \in S^{\#}$, define the α-th *Fourier coefficient* of u to be the linear endomorphism

$$u_\alpha^{\#} := \int_S \alpha(z)^* \ du(z) \in \mathcal{L}(F_\alpha). \tag{3.7.15}$$

In particular for $u \in L^1(S)$, we obtain the α-th Fourier coefficient

$$u_\alpha^{\#} := \int_S \alpha(z)^* \ u(z)\ dz. \tag{3.7.16}$$

For $u \in L^2(S) \subset L^1(S)$ this agrees with (2.11.7).

3.7.17. PROPOSITION. *For every* $u \in \mathcal{M}(S)$, *the Fourier transform (2.11.9) induces a commuting diagram*

$$\begin{array}{ccc} L^2(S) & \xrightarrow{\ ()^{\#}\ } & \sum\limits_{\alpha \in S^{\#}}^{\oplus} \mathcal{L}^2(F_\alpha) \\ {\scriptstyle u^{\#}} \downarrow & & \downarrow {\scriptstyle (u_\alpha^{\#})} \\ L^2(S) & \xrightarrow[\ ()^{\#}\ ]{} & \sum\limits_{\alpha \in S^{\#}}^{\oplus} \mathcal{L}^2(F_\alpha) \end{array}$$

of convolution and (right) multiplication operators, resp. If u *is a distribution, a similar diagram exists when restricting to smooth functions.*

Proof. As in the proof of Proposition 3.5.21, one shows $h^{\#}_{\alpha} u^{\#}_{\alpha} = (u^{\#}h)^{\#}_{\alpha}$ for all $\alpha \in S^{\#}$.

Q.E.D.

3.7.18. PROPOSITION. *There exists an anti-isomorphism*

$$\Phi: W^*(S) \to \sum_{\alpha \in S^{\#}}^{\oplus} \mathcal{L}(F_\alpha)$$

of W^**-algebras such that*

$$\Phi(u) = (u^{\#}_{\alpha})_{\alpha \in S^{\#}} \tag{3.7.19}$$

for every measure u. *Via* Φ *we may identify*

$$C^*(S) = \{(A_\alpha)_{\alpha \in S^{\#}} : \alpha \mapsto \|A_\alpha\| \text{ vanishes at } \infty\},$$

$$W^*(S) = \{(A_\alpha)_{\alpha \in S^{\#}} : \alpha \mapsto \|A_\alpha\| \text{ bounded}\}$$

and obtain $C^*(S) = W^*(S) \cap \mathcal{K}(L^2(S)) \lhd W^*(S)$ *and* $W^*(S) = C^*(S)^{\#\#}$ *(double dual).*

3.7.20. DEFINITION. For any bounded function $\varphi \in L^\infty(S^{\#})$, the *multiplication operator* with *symbol* φ is the bounded operator

$$\sum_{\alpha \in S^{\#}}^{\oplus} \mathcal{L}^2(F_\alpha) \xrightarrow{(\varphi(\alpha))} \sum_{\alpha \in S^{\#}}^{\oplus} \mathcal{L}^2(F_\alpha) \tag{3.7.21}$$

given by $(A_\alpha) \mapsto (\varphi(\alpha)A_\alpha)$.

For any central measure (or distribution) u on S and $\alpha \in S^{\#}$, define the α-th *Fourier coefficient* of u as the scalar

$$u^{\#}(\alpha) := \frac{1}{d_\alpha} \int_S \overline{\text{trace } \alpha(z)} \, du(z) \tag{3.7.22}$$

where $d_\alpha := \dim F_\alpha$.

3.7.23. PROPOSITION. *For every central measure* u *on* S *the Fourier transform (2.11.9) induces a commuting diagram*

$$\begin{array}{ccc} L^2(S) & \xrightarrow{(\,)^\#} & \sum^{\oplus}_{\alpha\in S^\#} \mathcal{Z}^2(F_\alpha) \\ \big\downarrow u^\# & & \big\downarrow (u^\#(\alpha)) \\ L^2(S) & \xrightarrow[(\,)^\#]{} & \sum^{\oplus}_{\alpha\in S^\#} \mathcal{Z}^2(F_\alpha) \end{array}$$

If u *is a distribution, a similar diagram exists when restricting to smooth functions.*

Proof. Since u is central, the α-th Fourier coefficient $u^\#_\alpha \in \mathcal{Z}(F_\alpha)$ commutes with the representation α. By Schur's Lemma

$$u^\#_\alpha = c \cdot \mathrm{Id}_{F_\alpha}$$

for some constant c. Taking the trace, we obtain $c = u^\#(\alpha)$. Q.E.D.

Let T be a maximal torus in S, with Lie algebra *t*. Then $\Lambda \subset it$ and we can consider the polar cone $\Lambda^\# \subset (it)^\#$. Identify $S^\#$ with a subset of $(it)^\#$ via the highest weight functionals.

3.7.24. DEFINITION. The *characteristic multiplier* of Ω is the bounded function $\chi \in L^\infty(S^\#)$ given by

$$\chi(\alpha) := \begin{cases} 1 & \text{if } \alpha \in S^\# \cap \Lambda^\# \\ 0 & \text{if } \alpha \in S^\# \setminus \Lambda^\#. \end{cases}$$

3.7.25. PROPOSITION. *The multiplication operator (3.7.21) with symbol* χ *coincides with the orthogonal projection*

$$\sum^{\oplus}_{\alpha\in S^\#} \mathcal{Z}^2(F_\alpha) \xrightarrow{(\chi(\alpha))} \sum^{\oplus}_{\alpha\in S^\#\cap\Lambda^\#} \mathcal{Z}^2(F_\alpha).$$

3.7.26. PROPOSITION. *The Fourier transform (2.11.9) induces a commuting diagram*

$$\begin{array}{ccc} L^2(S) & \xrightarrow{\ ()^{\#}\ } & \sum\limits_{\alpha \in S^{\#}}^{\oplus} \mathcal{L}^2(F_\alpha) \\ {\scriptstyle E}\downarrow & & \downarrow{\scriptstyle (\chi(\alpha))} \\ H^2(S) & \xrightarrow[\ ()^{\#}\ ]{} & \sum\limits_{\alpha \in S^{\#} \cap \Lambda^{\#}}^{\oplus} \mathcal{L}^2(F_\alpha) \end{array}$$

As in Proposition 3.5.49, we can introduce for every $g \in A(S)$ (Fourier algebra) a bounded operator

(3.7.27) $$(E_e g)^{\#} : L^2(S) \to L^2(S)$$

satisfying

(3.7.28) $$(E_e g)^{\#} h(z) = \int_S h(w^{-1}z)\ g(w)\ dE_e(w)$$

for all $h \in \mathcal{C}^\infty(S)$ and $z \in S$. The operator (3.9.27) belongs to $W^*(S)$ and satisfies

$$\Phi((E_e g)^{\#}) = ((E_e g)_\alpha^{\#})_{\alpha \in S^{\#}}$$

where

(3.7.29) $$(E_e g)_\alpha^{\#} = \int_S \alpha(z)^*\ g(z)\ dE_e(z).$$

3.7.30. DEFINITION. The *Hardy block multiplier algebra* associated with Ω is the non-unital C^*-algebra

(3.7.31) $$\mathcal{D}(S) := C^*(((E_e g)_\alpha^{\#})_{\alpha \in S^{\#}} : g \in A(S))$$

generated by the block multiplication operators (3.7.29).

Via the anti-isomorphism Φ, $\mathcal{D}(S)$ can be identified with the C^*-algebra generated by all (left) convolution operators (3.7.28). Since these operators are bounded and commute with right translations of S, we have

(3.7.32) $$\mathcal{D}(S) \subset W^*(S).$$

A function g on S is called *central* if

(3.7.33) $$g(wzw^{-1}) = g(z)$$

for all $z,w \in S$. For any central $g \in A(S)$ the distribution $E_e g$ on S is central, and we can consider the convolution operator $(E_e g)^{\#} : L^2(S) \to L^2(S)$ defined by

(3.7.34) $$(E_e g)^{\#} h(z) := \int_S h(w^{-1}z)\ g(w)\ dE_e(w)$$

for all $h \in L^2(S)$ and $z \in S$. By Proposition 3.7.23 we obtain the corresponding bounded function

(3.7.35) $$(E_e g)^{\#}(\alpha) := \frac{1}{d_\alpha} \int_S \overline{\text{trace}\ \alpha(z)}\ g(z)\ dE_e(z)$$

on $S^{\#}$.

3.7.36. DEFINITION. The *Hardy multiplier algebra* associated with Ω is the non-unital abelian C^*-algebra

(3.7.37) $$\mathcal{D}^L(S) := C^*(((E_e g)^{\#}(\alpha)) : g \in A(S) \text{ central}\}$$

generated by the multiplication operators (3.7.35).

Via Proposition 3.7.23, we may identify $\mathcal{D}^L(S)$ with the C^*-algebra generated by the convolution operators (3.7.34).

3.7.38. PROPOSITION. *The Szegö projection* $E_e^{\#}$ *satisfies*

$$E_e^{\#}\ \mathcal{D}(S)\ E_e^{\#} = E_e^{\#}\ \mathcal{D}^L(S)\ E_e^{\#}.$$

Proof. For every $g \in A(S)$ we have $E_e^{\#}\ (E_e g)^{\#}\ E_e^{\#} = E_e^{\#}\ (E_e f)^{\#}\ E_e^{\#}$ where

(3.7.39) $$f(z) := \int_S g(w^{-1}zw)\ dw \in A(S)$$

is central. Q.E.D.

The *spectrum* (= character space) Spec $\mathcal{D}^L(S)$ of the abelian Banach algebra (3.7.37) is a locally compact Hausdorff space which is not compact since $\mathcal{D}^L(S)$ has no unit. Its structure can be analyzed in a similar way as for symmetric or K-circular domains.

4. Toeplitz Operators and Toeplitz C^*-Algebras

4.0. Introduction

In this chapter we develop a structure theory for multi-variable Toeplitz operators, using the Toeplitz C^*-algebra generated by these operators and its representation theory.

The first two Sections 4.1 and 4.2 study Toeplitz operators over strictly pseudoconvex domains, in the Bergman and Hardy space setting. Since these domains have a smooth boundary, the principal methods come from differential analysis. We construct the basic "Toeplitz C^*-extensions" so important in modern index theory and express commutation properties of Toeplitz operators in terms of the boundary behavior of their symbols. The existence of a smooth family of peaking functions is essential here.

Before treating domains with non-smooth, stratified boundary it is necessary to introduce another important algebraic concept: groupoids and groupoid C^*-algebras. This is done in Section 4.3. Using the theory of groupoids, one can analyze Toeplitz C^*-algebras for domains having a polar decomposition under the action of an abelian Lie group. The Sections 4.4 and 4.5 treat the tubular case (translation group action), whereas Sections 4.6 and 4.7 treat the polycircular domains (rotation group action). Under the Fourier transform, Toeplitz operators correspond to generalized *Wiener-Hopf integral operators* (in several variables) and it is in this setting that the analysis is actually implemented. However, throughout the book the emphasis is on the dual "Toeplitz" setting which is much more natural in case of a non-commutative group action. In Section 4.6 we briefly discuss the important generalization to Siegel domains where the standard groupoid approach does not apply any more (the group action is nilpotent but not abelian).

The theory of Hopf C^*-algebras and (co)crossed products described in Sections 4.8 and 4.9 can be regarded as the non-commutative analogue of groupoid C^*-theory, in the setting where standard Fourier analysis methods don't apply. The basic types of Hopf C^*-algebras (group C^*-algebras, group function algebras) are introduced along with their dual algebras. The well-known Fourier-Stieltjes algebra of a locally compact group fits naturally into this framework.

In Section 4.10, the relationship with Toeplitz operators is then established, in the general setting of K-circular domains, by realizing the Toeplitz C^*-algebra as a (subalgebra of a) co-crossed product under a suitable Hopf C^*-algebra coaction. The advantage of this approach is that the representation theory of co-crossed products is basically understood in terms of its C^*-factors, in our case the "multiplier C^*-algebras" studied in Chapter 3 and the Fourier-Stieltjes algebra. For the important special case of symmetric domains, a complete account of Toeplitz C^*-algebras and their representations is developed in Sections 4.11 (Hardy space) and 4.12 (weighted Bergman spaces). We also discuss additional results such as the relationship between Toeplitz operators and singular integral operators of Calderon-Zygmund type.

4.1 Bergman-Toeplitz Operators Over Bounded Domains

In this section we introduce Toeplitz operators and their associated C^*-algebras, acting on the Bergman space over a bounded domain $\Omega \subset \mathbb{C}^n$. A complete structure theory is then obtained in the special case of strictly pseudoconvex domains with smooth boundary. For the necessary background ($\bar{\partial}$-Neumann problem, etc.), cf. Section 2.1.

4.1.1. DEFINITION. For any bounded function $f \in L^\infty(\Omega)$, the *multiplication operator* with *symbol* f is the bounded operator $f : L^2(\Omega) \to L^2(\Omega)$ defined by

$$(fh)(z) := f(z)h(z) \tag{4.1.2}$$

for all $h \in L^2(\Omega)$ and $z \in \Omega$.

Identifying the operator (4.1.2) with its associated symbol yields an injective C^*-algebra homomorphism from $L^\infty(\Omega)$ onto an abelian C^*-subalgebra of $\mathcal{L}(L^2(\Omega))$, the C^*-algebra of all bounded operators on $L^2(\Omega)$. Now consider the Bergman space $H^2(\Omega)$, with Bergman projection $E_\Omega : L^2(\Omega) \to H^2(\Omega)$.

4.1.3. DEFINITION. The *Bergman-Toeplitz operator* $T_\Omega(f)$ with *symbol* $f \in L^\infty(\Omega)$ is defined as the compression

$$T_\Omega(f) := E_\Omega \circ f|_{H^2(\Omega)} \tag{4.1.4}$$

of the multiplication operator (4.1.2). Thus

$$T_\Omega(f)h = E_\Omega(fh) \tag{4.1.5}$$

for every $h \in H^2(\Omega)$.

4.1.6. PROPOSITION. *For every* $f \in L^\infty(\Omega)$, $T_\Omega(f)$ *is a bounded operator on* $L^2(\Omega)$ *satisfying*

$$\|T_\Omega(f)\| \le \|f\|_\infty, \tag{4.1.7}$$

$$T_\Omega(f)^* = T_\Omega(\bar{f}). \tag{4.1.8}$$

Moreover, if $\varphi \in H^\infty(\Omega) := \mathcal{O}(\Omega) \cap L^\infty(\Omega)$, *then*

$$T_\Omega(f)\, T_\Omega(\varphi) = T_\Omega(f\varphi)\,, \tag{4.1.9}$$

$$T_\Omega(\bar{\varphi})\, T_\Omega(f) = T_\Omega(\bar{\varphi}f). \tag{4.1.10}$$

Proof. Viewing E_Ω as a projection operator in $\mathcal{L}(L^2(\Omega))$ we may write

$$T_\Omega(f) = E_\Omega f E_\Omega. \tag{4.1.11}$$

Then the first two assertions are obvious. For (4.1.9), note that $E_\Omega \varphi E_\Omega = \varphi E_\Omega$ since φ is holomorphic. Now (4.1.10) follows from (4.1.9) and (4.1.8). Q.E.D.

Let $\bar{\Omega}$ be the closure of a bounded domain Ω in $\mathbb{C}^n$. Then the algebra $\mathcal{C}(\bar{\Omega})$ of all continuous functions on $\bar{\Omega}$ becomes a subalgebra of $L^\infty(\Omega)$ via the (injective) restriction mapping $f \mapsto f|_\Omega$.

4.1.12. DEFINITION. The *Bergman-Toeplitz* C^**-algebra* over Ω is defined as the unital C^*-algebra

$$\mathcal{T}(\Omega) := C^*(T_\Omega(f) : f \in \mathcal{C}(\bar{\Omega})\,) \tag{4.1.13}$$

generated by all Bergman-Toeplitz operators (4.1.5) with continuous symbol $f \in \mathcal{C}(\bar{\Omega})$.

4.1.14. PROPOSITION. *Let Ω be a bounded domain in a complex vector space Z. Let $\mathcal{P}(Z)$ denote the algebra of all complex-valued holomorphic polynomials on Z. Then the Toeplitz C^*-algebra satisfies*

$$\mathcal{T}(\Omega) = C^*(T_\Omega(p) : p \in \mathcal{P}(Z)).$$

Proof. Let $\bar{Z}$ denote the complex conjugate of Z and let $Z_{\mathbb{R}} := \{(z,w) \in Z \oplus \bar{Z} : z = w\}$ be the real vector space underlying Z. Since $\bar{\Omega}$ is compact, the Stone-Weierstrass theorem implies that

$$\mathcal{C}(\bar{\Omega}) = \overline{\mathcal{P}(Z_{\mathbb{R}})} \qquad \text{(uniform closure)}.$$

Here $\mathcal{P}(Z_{\mathbb{R}})$ denotes the set of all real-analytic complex-valued polynomials on Z. Since $\mathcal{P}(Z_{\mathbb{R}}) \cong \mathcal{P}(Z \oplus \bar{Z}) \cong \mathcal{P}(Z) \otimes \mathcal{P}(\bar{Z})$, it follows that every $f \in \mathcal{C}(\bar{\Omega})$ is uniformly approximated by finite sums $\sum_i \overline{p_i(z)}\, q_i(z)$ with $p_i, q_i \in \mathcal{P}(Z)$. Applying (4.1.11), we get

$$T_\Omega(f) = \lim \sum_i T_\Omega(p_i)^* \, T_\Omega(q_i)$$

in the sense of uniform convergence. Q.E.D.

4.1.15. PROPOSITION. *For every bounded domain Ω, the Bergman-Toeplitz C^*-algebra $\mathcal{T}(\Omega)$ acts irreducibly (i.e., without proper closed invariant subspaces) on $H^2(\Omega)$.*

Proof. Suppose Q is an orthogonal projection on $H^2(\Omega)$ commuting with $\mathcal{T}(\Omega)$. Then $QT_\Omega(f) = T_\Omega(f)Q$ for all $f \in \mathcal{C}(\bar{\Omega})$. Since $1 \in H^2(\Omega)$, we have $g := Q1 \in H^2(\Omega)$. For all $h,k \in \mathcal{A}(\Omega)$ (cf. (1...)), we have

$$\begin{aligned}(g|\bar{h}k)_\Omega &= (hg|k)_\Omega = (T_\Omega(h)g|k)_\Omega = (T_\Omega(h)Q1|k)_\Omega \\ &= (QT_\Omega(h)1|k)_\Omega = (Qh|k)_\Omega = (h|Qk)_\Omega = (h|kg)_\Omega = (\bar{g}|\bar{h}k)_\Omega.\end{aligned} \tag{4.1.16}$$

Hence $g - \bar{g}$ is orthogonal to the linear span of $k\bar{h}$ (for $h,k \in \mathcal{P}(Z)$), i.e. to all real-analytic complex-valued polynomials on $\bar{\Omega}$. Since $\mathcal{P}(Z_{\mathbb{R}})$ is uniformly dense in $\mathcal{C}(\bar{\Omega})$ by the Stone-Weierstrass Theorem, $\mathcal{P}(Z_{\mathbb{R}})$ is dense in $L^2(\Omega)$. Therefore $g = \bar{g}$. Since g is holomorphic, g is constant. Since $\mathcal{A}(\Omega)$ is dense in $H^2(\Omega)$, (4.1.16) implies $Qh = g \cdot h$ for all $h \in H^2(\Omega)$. Since $Q^2 = Q$, we get $g = 0$ or $g = 1$, and hence $Q = 0$ or $Q = \mathrm{id}$.

Q.E.D.

4.1.17. PROPOSITION. *Let Ω be a bounded domain and let $f \in \mathcal{C}(\bar{\Omega})$ satisfy $f|_{\partial\Omega} = 0$. Then the Toeplitz operator $T_\Omega(f)$ on $H^2(\Omega)$ is compact.*

Proof. Suppose first that $f \in L^\infty(\Omega)$ has support contained in a compact subset K of Ω. Choose a compact subset L of Ω satisfying $d := \mathrm{dist}(K,\partial L) > 0$. By Proposition 2.1.2, there exists $c > 0$ such that

$$\sup |h(L)| \leq c \cdot \|h\|_2$$

for all $h \in H^2(\Omega)$. Now let $z,w \in K$ satisfy $|z - w| \leq d/2$. Then the line segment $[z,w]$ is contained in L, and the mean value theorem together with Cauchy's inequality imply

$$|h(z) - h(w)| \leq |z - w| \cdot \sup_{\xi \in [z,w]} |h'(\xi)| \leq |z - w| \frac{2}{d} \cdot \sup |h(L)| \leq \frac{2c}{d} |z - w| \cdot \|h\|_2,$$

since $\mathrm{dist}(\xi,\partial L) \geq \frac{d}{2}$ for all $\xi \in [z,w]$. This shows that the subset

$$\mathcal{F} := \{h|_K : h \in H^2(\Omega), \|h\|_2 \leq 1\}$$

of $\mathcal{C}(K)$ is bounded and equicontinuous. By Ascoli's Theorem, $\mathcal{F}$ is relatively compact. Thus the restriction mapping

$$\rho_K : H^2(\Omega) \to \mathcal{C}(K), \quad h \mapsto h|_K$$

is a compact operator. Since the canonical inclusion $i_K : \mathcal{C}(K) \to L^2(\Omega)$ defined by

$$i_K(\varphi)(z) := \begin{cases} \varphi(z) & z \in K \\ 0 & z \in \Omega \setminus K \end{cases}$$

is continuous, it follows that the multiplication operator $\chi_K|_{H^2(\Omega)} = i_K \circ \rho_K$ by the characteristic function χ_K of K is a compact operator from $H^2(\Omega)$ into $L^2(\Omega)$. Since $\mathrm{Supp}(f) \subset K$, if follows that

$$f|_{H^2(\Omega)} = f\chi_K|_{H^2(\Omega)} : H^2(\Omega) \to L^2(\Omega)$$

is a compact operator. Therefore $T_\Omega(f) = E_\Omega \circ f|_{H^2(\Omega)}$ is compact in case $f \in L^\infty(\Omega)$ has compact support. Now suppose $f \in \mathcal{C}(\bar{\Omega})$ satisfies $f|_{\partial\Omega} = 0$. Let (K_n) be a sequence of compact subsets of Ω satisfying $K_n \subset K^o_{n+1}$ for all n and $\Omega = \bigcup_n K_n$. Given $\varepsilon > 0$, there exists $\delta > 0$ such that

$$\|z - w\| \le \delta \Rightarrow |f(z) - f(w)| \le \varepsilon$$

for all $z,w \in \bar{\Omega}$, since f is uniformly continuous. Choose $m \in \mathbb{N}$ large enough such that K_m contains the set $\{z \in \Omega : \mathrm{dist}(z,\partial\Omega) \ge \delta\}$. Then $|f(z) - (f \cdot \chi_{K_n})(z)| \le \varepsilon$ for all $z \in \bar{\Omega}$ and $n \ge m$, since in case $z \in K_n$ we have $f(z) = (f \cdot \chi_{K_n})(z)$ whereas in case $z \in \bar{\Omega}\setminus K_n$ there exists $w \in \partial\Omega$ such that $\|z - w\| \le \delta$ which implies $|f(z) - (f \cdot \chi_{K_n})(z)| = |f(z)| = |f(z) - f(w)| \le \varepsilon$. It follows that $f \cdot \chi_{K_n} \to f$ in $L^\infty(\Omega)$. Therefore $\|T_\Omega(f) - T_\Omega(f \cdot \chi_{K_n})\| \to 0$ by (4.1.7.). Since the operators $T_\Omega(f \cdot \chi_{K_n})$ are compact by the first part of the proof, the assertion follows. Q.E.D.

4.1.18. THEOREM. *Let Ω be a strictly pseudoconvex domain. Then for every continuous $f \in \mathcal{C}(\bar{\Omega})$, the restriction $(I - E_\Omega)f|_{H^2(\Omega)}$ is a compact operator from $H^2(\Omega)$ into $L^2(\Omega)$.*

Proof. Since f can be uniformly approximated by smooth functions we may assume that f is smooth in a neighborhood of $\bar{\Omega}$. For every $h \in H^2(\Omega)$ we have $fh \in \mathrm{Dom}(\bar{\partial}_0)$, since

(4.1.19) $$\bar{\partial}_0(fh) = (\bar{\partial} f) \cdot h$$

and $\bar{\partial} f$ is bounded on $\bar{\Omega}$. Let

(4.1.20) $$\bar{\partial} f : L^2_0(\Omega) \to L^2_1(\Omega)$$

denote the operator of multiplication by $\bar{\partial} f$. Then (4.1.19) can be written as

$$\bar{\partial}_0 f|_{H^2(\Omega)} = \bar{\partial} f|_{H^2(\Omega)}.$$

Lemma 2.1.22, applied to $f\varphi$, gives

$$(I - E_\Omega) f|_{H^2(\Omega)} = \bar{\partial}^*_1 N^\Omega_1 \bar{\partial}_0 f|_{H^2(\Omega)} = \bar{\partial}^*_1 N^\Omega_1 \cdot \bar{\partial} f|_{H^2(\Omega)}.$$

Since $\bar{\partial}^*_1 N^\Omega_1$ is compact by Lemma 2.1.24 and (4.1.20) is bounded, the assertion follows.

Q.E.D.

4.1.21. COROLLARY. *Let Ω be strictly pseudoconvex. Then the "semi-commutator"*

(4.1.22) $$T_\Omega(\varphi)T_\Omega(\psi) - T_\Omega(\varphi\psi)$$

of Bergman-Toeplitz operators is compact for all $\varphi, \psi \in \mathcal{C}(\bar{\Omega})$.

Proof. By definition and (4.1.12), we have

$$T_\Omega(\varphi)T_\Omega(\psi) - T_\Omega(\varphi\psi) = (E_\Omega\varphi E_\Omega\psi - E_\Omega\varphi\psi)|_{H^2(\Omega)} = E_\Omega\varphi(E_\Omega - I)\psi|_{H^2(\Omega)}.$$

Since $(E_\Omega - I)\psi|_{H^2(\Omega)}$ is a compact operator by Theorem 4.1.18, the assertion follows.

Q.E.D.

4.1.23. THEOREM. *Let Ω be a strictly pseudoconvex domain. Let* p *be a polynomial in* k *non-commuting variables. Then we have for all*

$f_1, \ldots, f_k \in \mathcal{C}(\bar{\Omega})$

$$\|p(T_\Omega(f_1), \ldots, T_\Omega(f_k))\| \geq \|p(f_1|_{\partial\Omega}, \ldots, f_k|_{\partial\Omega})\|_\infty .$$

Proof. For each $s \in \partial\Omega$, there exists a peaking function $h_s \in \mathcal{A}(\Omega)$ at $\{s\}$ [FK4]. Consider the powers $h_s^n(z) := h_s(z)^n$ for all n. As in the proof of Theorem 4.11.16 below this implies for all $f \in \mathcal{C}(\bar{\Omega})$

$$\frac{(fh_s^n|h_s^n)_\Omega}{(h_s^n|h_s^n)_\Omega} \to f(s).$$

In particular

$$\inf_{\partial\Omega} |f| \geq \inf\{\frac{\|fh\|_\Omega}{\|h\|_\Omega} : 0 \neq h \in H^2(\Omega)\}. \tag{4.1.24}$$

Now consider k-tuples $(\lambda_1, \ldots, \lambda_k) \in \sigma(f_1|_{\partial\Omega}, \ldots, f_k|_{\partial\Omega})$ in the joint spectrum of $f_1|_{\partial\Omega}, \ldots, f_k|_{\partial\Omega} \in \mathcal{C}(\partial\Omega)$. Then the function

$$f := \sum_{j=1}^{k} |f_j - \lambda_j|^2 \in \mathcal{C}(\bar{\Omega})$$

has a zero on $\partial\Omega$. By (4.1.24), it follows that for each $\varepsilon > 0$ there exists a unit vector $h \in H^2(\Omega)$ such that $\|fh\|_\Omega \leq \varepsilon$. Since

$$\sum_j \|T_\Omega(f_j)h - \lambda_j h\|_\Omega^2 \leq \sum_j \|f_j h - \lambda_j h\|_\Omega^2 = \|fh\|_\Omega^2 \leq \varepsilon^2,$$

it follows that $\|T_\Omega(f_j)h - \lambda_j h\|_\Omega \leq \varepsilon$ for every $1 \leq j \leq k$. Taking products, we see that for every $\delta > 0$ there exists a unit vector $h \in H^2(\Omega)$ satisfying $\|p(T_\Omega(f_1), \ldots, T_\Omega(f_k))h - p(\lambda_1, \ldots, \lambda_k)h\|_\Omega \leq \delta$. Therefore

$$\|p(T_\Omega(f_1), \ldots, T_\Omega(f_k))\| \geq \|p(T_\Omega(f_1), \ldots, T_\Omega(f_k))h\|_\Omega \geq |p(\lambda_1, \ldots, \lambda_k)| - \delta.$$

For $\delta \to 0$, this implies

$$\|p(T_\Omega(f_1), \ldots, T_\Omega(f_k))\| \geq \sup |p(\lambda_1, \ldots, \lambda_k)| = \|p(f_1|_{\partial\Omega}, \ldots, f_k|_{\partial\Omega})\|_\infty.$$

Q.E.D.

4.1.25. THEOREM. *Let* Ω *be a strictly pseudoconvex bounded domain with smooth boundary* $\partial\Omega$. *Then the Bergman-Toeplitz* C^**-algebra* $\mathcal{T}(\Omega)$ *has the commutator ideal* $\mathcal{K}(H^2(\Omega))$ *(compact operators), and there exists a* C^**-algebra isomorphism*

$$\mathcal{T}(\Omega)/\mathcal{K}(H^2(\Omega)) \xrightarrow[\approx]{\sigma} \mathcal{C}(\partial\Omega) \tag{4.1.26}$$

such that for every $f \in \mathcal{C}(\bar{\Omega})$,

$$\sigma(T_f + \mathcal{K}(H^2(\Omega))) = f|_{\partial\Omega}. \tag{4.1.27}$$

Proof. By Corollary 4.1.21, the commutator

$$\begin{aligned}[T_\Omega(\varphi),T_\Omega(\psi)] &:= T_\Omega(\varphi)T_\Omega(\psi) - T_\Omega(\psi)T_\Omega(\varphi)\\ &= (T_\Omega(\varphi)T_\Omega(\psi) - T_\Omega(\varphi\psi)) - (T_\Omega(\psi)\, T_\Omega(\varphi) - T_\Omega(\psi\varphi))\end{aligned} \tag{4.1.28}$$

is a compact operator on $H^2(\Omega)$. Hence the commutator ideal $\mathcal{T}(\Omega)'$, generated by these commutators, is contained in $\mathcal{K}(H^2(\Omega))$. Now suppose $\mathcal{T}(\Omega)' = \{0\}$, i.e., $\mathcal{T}(\Omega)$ is commutative. Then $T_\Omega(p)$ is a normal operator for every polynomial $p \in \mathcal{P}(\mathbb{C}^n)$. By [R1; Lemma 2.1], this implies that $H^2(\Omega)$ is invariant under the adjoint multiplication operator $\bar{p}$. Therefore $\bar{p} = \bar{p} \cdot 1 \in H^2(\Omega)$ for every $p \in \mathcal{P}(\mathbb{C}^n)$, a contradiction. It follows that $\mathcal{T}(\Omega)' \neq \{0\}$. By Proposition 4.1.15 and [D1], $\mathcal{T}(\Omega)'$ contains $\mathcal{K}(H^2(\Omega))$ and hence

$$\mathcal{T}(\Omega)' = \mathcal{K}(H^2(\Omega)). \tag{4.1.29}$$

Therefore the mapping

$$\mathcal{C}(\bar{\Omega}) \xrightarrow{\tau} \mathcal{T}(\Omega)/\mathcal{K}(H^2(\Omega))$$

given by $f \mapsto T_\Omega(f) + \mathcal{K}(H^2(\Omega))$ is a C^*-homomorphism which is surjective by (4.1.14). The restriction mapping

$$\mathcal{C}(\bar{\Omega}) \xrightarrow{\rho} \mathcal{C}(\partial\Omega),\ f \mapsto f|_{\partial\Omega}$$

is surjective by Tietze's extension theorem, and every $f \in \mathrm{Ker}(\rho)$ gives rise to a compact operator $T_\Omega(f)$ by Proposition 4.1.17. Thus there exists a surjective C^*-homomorphism

$$\mathcal{C}(\partial\Omega) \xrightarrow{\bar{\tau}} \mathcal{T}(\Omega)/\mathcal{K}(H^2(\Omega))$$

such that $\bar{\tau} \circ \rho = \tau$. In order to show that $\bar{\tau}$ is injective, let $A \in \mathcal{K}(H^2(\Omega))$ be arbitrary. By (4.1.28) and (4.1.29), A belongs to the C^*-ideal $\mathcal{J}$ generated by all semi-commutators (4.1.22). Thus $A = \lim A_n$, where each A_n is a sum of operators of the form

$$T_\Omega(\varphi_1) \cdots T_\Omega(\varphi_k)(T_\Omega(\varphi_0)T_\Omega(\psi_0) - T_\Omega(\varphi_0\psi_0))\, T_\Omega(\psi_1) \cdots T_\Omega(\psi_\ell)$$

where $\varphi_0, \ldots, \varphi_k, \psi_0, \ldots, \psi_\ell \in \mathcal{C}(\bar{\Omega})$. Since

$$\varphi_1|_{\partial\Omega} \cdots \varphi_k|_{\partial\Omega}\, (\varphi_0|_{\partial\Omega}\, \psi_0|_{\partial\Omega} - \varphi_0\psi_0|_{\partial\Omega})\, \psi_1|_{\partial\Omega} \cdots \psi_\ell|_{\partial\Omega} = 0,$$

Theorem 4.1.23 implies $\|T_\Omega(f) + A\| \geq \|f|_{\partial\Omega}\|_\infty$ for every $f \in \mathcal{C}(\bar{\Omega})$. Thus $\bar{\tau}$ is injective. Put $\sigma := \bar{\tau}^{-1}$. Q.E.D.

4.1.30. COROLLARY. *For every* $f \in \mathcal{C}(\bar{\Omega})$, *the operator* $T_\Omega(f)$ *is essentially normal, i.e.,*

$$[T_\Omega(f)^*, T_\Omega(f)] \in \mathcal{K}(H^2(\Omega)),$$

and we have $\|T_\Omega(f)\| = \|f\|_\infty$ *and* $\text{ess - Spec}\, T_\Omega(f) = f(\partial\Omega)$. *In particular,* $T_\Omega(f)$ *is a Fredholm operator if and only if* f *has no zeros on* $\partial\Omega$.

4.2 Hardy-Toeplitz Operators Over Strictly Pseudoconvex Domains

In this section we study Toeplitz operators and their associated C^*-algebras, acting on the Hardy space over a strictly pseudoconvex domain $\Omega \subset \mathbb{C}^n$ with smooth boundary $\partial\Omega$, endowed with the normalized surface measure.

For the necessary background (tangential $\bar{\partial}$-Neumann problem, etc.), cf. Section 2.2.

4.2.1. DEFINITION. For any bounded function $f \in L^\infty(\partial\Omega)$, the *multiplication operator* with *symbol* f is the bounded operator $f : L^2(\partial\Omega) \to L^2(\partial\Omega)$ defined by

$$(fh)(z) := f(z)h(z) \tag{4.2.2}$$

for all $h \in L^2(\partial\Omega)$ and $z \in \partial\Omega$.

Identifying a symbol f with its associated multiplication operator (4.2.2) yields an injective C^*-algebra homomorphism from $L^\infty(\partial\Omega)$ onto an abelian C^*-subalgebra of $\mathcal{L}(L^2(\partial\Omega))$, the C^*-algebra of all bounded operators on $L^2(\partial\Omega)$. Now consider the Hardy space $H^2(\partial\Omega)$ over Ω, with Szegö projection $E : L^2(\partial\Omega) \to H^2(\partial\Omega)$.

4.2.3. DEFINITION. The *Hardy-Toeplitz operator* $T_{\partial\Omega}(f)$ with *symbol* $f \in L^\infty(\partial\Omega)$ is defined as the compression

$$T_{\partial\Omega}(f) := E \circ f|_{H^2(\partial\Omega)} \tag{4.2.4}$$

of the multiplication operator (4.2.2). Thus

$$T_{\partial\Omega}(f)h = E(fh) \tag{4.2.5}$$

for every $h \in H^2(\partial\Omega)$.

4.2.6. PROPOSITION. *For every* $f \in L^\infty(\partial\Omega)$, $T_{\partial\Omega}(f)$ *is a bounded operator on* $H^2(\partial\Omega)$ *satisfying*

$$\|T_{\partial\Omega}(f)\| \le \|f\|_\infty, \tag{4.2.7}$$

$$T_{\partial\Omega}(f)^* = T_{\partial\Omega}(\bar{f}). \tag{4.2.8}$$

Moreover, if $\varphi \in H^\infty(\partial\Omega) := H^2(\partial\Omega) \cap L^\infty(\partial\Omega)$, *then*

$$T_{\partial\Omega}(f)\, T_{\partial\Omega}(\varphi) = T_{\partial\Omega}(f\varphi), \tag{4.2.9}$$

$$T_{\partial\Omega}(\bar{\varphi})\, T_{\partial\Omega}(f) = T_{\partial\Omega}(\bar{\varphi}f). \tag{4.2.10}$$

Proof. Viewing E as a projection operator in $\mathcal{L}(L^2(\partial\Omega))$ we may write

$$T_{\partial\Omega}(f) = E\, f\, E. \tag{4.2.11}$$

Then the first two assertions are obvious. For (4.2.9), note that $E \varphi E = \varphi E$ since φ is holomorphic. Now (4.2.10) follows from (4.2.9) and (4.2.8).
Q.E.D.

Let $\mathcal{C}(\partial\Omega)$ denote the subalgebra of $L^\infty(\partial\Omega)$ consisting of all continuous functions.

4.2.12. DEFINITION. The *Hardy-Toeplitz C^*-algebra* over $\partial\Omega$ is defined as the unital C^*-algebra

$$(4.2.13) \qquad \mathcal{T}(\partial\Omega) := C^*(T_{\partial\Omega}(f) : f \in \mathcal{C}(\partial\Omega))$$

generated by all Hardy-Toeplitz operators (4.2.4) on $H^2(\partial\Omega)$ with continuous symbol $f \in \mathcal{C}(\partial\Omega)$.

Via the restriction to $\partial\Omega$, $\mathcal{C}(\partial\Omega)$ contains $\mathcal{A}(\Omega)$ and the polynomial algebra $\mathcal{P}(\mathbb{C}^n)$ as subalgebras.

4.2.14. PROPOSITION. *$\mathcal{T}(\partial\Omega)$ is generated by the operators $T_{\partial\Omega}(p)$ with polynomial symbol $p \in \mathcal{P}(\mathbb{C}^n)$.*

Proof. By the Stone-Weierstrass Theorem, $\mathcal{C}(\partial\Omega)$ is the C^*-algebra generated by $\mathcal{P}(\mathbb{C}^n)$. Now apply Proposition 4.2.6. Q.E.D.

4.2.15. PROPOSITION. *For every strictly pseudoconvex domain Ω with smooth boundary $\partial\Omega$, the Hardy-Toeplitz C^*-algebra $\mathcal{T}(\partial\Omega)$ acts irreducibly on $H^2(\partial\Omega)$.*

Proof. Suppose Q is an orthogonal projection on $H^2(\partial\Omega)$ commuting with $\mathcal{T}(\partial\Omega)$. Then $QT_{\partial\Omega}(f) = T_{\partial\Omega}(f)Q$ for all $f \in \mathcal{C}(\partial\Omega)$. Since $1 \in H^2(\partial\Omega)$, we have $g := Q1 \in H^2(\partial\Omega)$. For all $h,k \in \mathcal{A}(\Omega)$, we get

$$(4.2.16) \qquad (g|\bar{h}k)_{\partial\Omega} = (Qh|k)_{\partial\Omega} = (\bar{g}|\bar{h}k)_{\partial\Omega}$$

by a computation similar to (4.1.16). This holds in particular for $h,k \in \mathcal{P}(\mathbb{C}^n)$. By a density argument, it follows that $g - \bar{g} = 0$ on $\partial\Omega$. Let $\mathcal{P} : \Omega \times \partial\Omega \to \mathbb{R}$ denote the Poisson kernel of Ω [S7]. Since $g \in H^2(\partial\Omega)$,

$$g(z) := \int_{\partial\Omega} \mathcal{P}(z,w)\ g(w)\ d\sigma(w)$$

defines a holomorphic function in Ω. Since g is real on $\partial\Omega$, it follows that g is real and therefore constant on Ω. Since $\mathcal{A}(\Omega)$ is dense in $H^2(\partial\Omega)$ (4.2.16) implies $Qh = gh$ for all $h \in H^2(\partial\Omega)$. Since $Q^2 = Q$, we get $g = 0$ or $g = 1$ and therefore $Q = 0$ or $Q = \text{id}$. Q.E.D.

4.2.17. THEOREM. *Let Ω be a strictly pseudoconvex domain. Then for every continuous* $f \in \mathcal{C}(\partial\Omega)$, the operator $(I - E) \circ f|_{H^2(\partial\Omega)}$ *from* $H^2(\partial\Omega)$ *into* $L^2(\partial\Omega)$ *is compact.*

Proof. Since f can be uniformly approximated by smooth functions, we may assume that f is smooth in a neighborhood of $\partial\Omega$. For every $h \in H^2(\partial\Omega)$ we have $fh \in \text{Dom}(\bar\partial_0)$ since

$$\bar\partial_0(fh) = [\bar\partial f] \cdot h \tag{4.2.18}$$

and $\bar\partial f$ is bounded on $\partial\Omega$. Here $[\bar\partial f]$ is the equivalence class of $\bar\partial f$ for the equivalence defining $L_1^2(\partial\Omega)$ (cf. Definition 2.2.6). Let

$$[\bar\partial f] : L^2(\partial\Omega) \to L_1^2(\partial\Omega) \tag{4.2.19}$$

denote the corresponding multiplication operator which is bounded. As in the proof of Theorem 4.1.18 one shows

$$(I - E)f|_{H^2(\partial\Omega)} = \bar\partial_1^* N_1^S [\bar\partial f] |_{H^2(\partial\Omega)}$$

using Lemma 2.2.18. Since $\bar\partial_1^* N_1^S$ is compact by Lemma 2.2.19 and (4.2.19) is bounded, the assertion follows. Q.E.D.

As in Section 4.1, Theorem 4.2.17 has the following consequence:

4.2.20. COROLLARY. *Let Ω be strictly pseudoconvex. Then the "semi-commutator"*

$$T_{\partial\Omega}(\varphi)\, T_{\partial\Omega}(\psi) - T_{\partial\Omega}(\varphi\psi) \tag{4.2.21}$$

of Hardy-Toeplitz operators is compact for all $\varphi, \psi \in \mathcal{C}(\partial\Omega)$.

4.2.22. THEOREM. *Let* p *be a polynomial in* k *non-commuting variables. Then we have for all* $f_1, \ldots, f_k \in \mathcal{C}(\partial\Omega)$

$$\|p(T_{\partial\Omega}(f_1), \ldots, T_{\partial\Omega}(f_k))\| \geq \|p(f_1, \ldots, f_k)\|_\infty.$$

Proof. For each $s \in \partial\Omega$, there exists a peaking function $h_s \in \mathcal{A}(\Omega)$ at $\{s\}$ [FK4]. Consider the powers $h_s^n(z) := h_s(z)^n$ for all n. As in the proof of Theorem 4.11.16 below this implies for $f \in \mathcal{C}(\partial\Omega)$

$$\frac{(fh_s^n | h_s^n)_{\partial\Omega}}{(h_s^n | h_s^n)_{\partial\Omega}} \to f(s).$$

In particular,

$$\inf_{\partial\Omega} |f| \geq \inf\{\frac{\|fh\|_{\partial\Omega}}{\|h\|_{\partial\Omega}} : 0 \neq h \in H^2(\partial\Omega)\}. \tag{4.2.23}$$

Now consider k-tuples $(\lambda_1, \ldots, \lambda_k) \in \sigma(f_1, \ldots, f_k)$ in the joint spectrum of $f_1, \ldots, f_k \in \mathcal{C}(\partial\Omega)$. Then the function

$$f := \sum_{j=1}^{k} |f_j - \lambda_j|^2 \in \mathcal{C}(\partial\Omega)$$

has a zero $s \in \partial\Omega$. By (4.2.23) it follows that for each $\varepsilon > 0$ there exists a unit vector $h \in H^2(\partial\Omega)$ such that $\|fh\|_{\partial\Omega} \leq \varepsilon$. Since

$$\sum_j \|T_{\partial\Omega}(f_j)h - \lambda_j h\|_{\partial\Omega}^2 \leq \sum_j \|f_j h - \lambda_j h\|_{\partial\Omega}^2 = \|fh\|_{\partial\Omega}^2 \leq \varepsilon^2,$$

it follows that $\|T_{\partial\Omega}(f_j)h - \lambda_j h\|_{\partial\Omega} \leq \varepsilon$ for every $1 \leq j \leq k$. Taking products of the form

$$T_{\partial\Omega}(f_1) \cdots T_{\partial\Omega}(f_k) - \lambda_1 \cdots \lambda_k = \sum_{\ell=1}^{k} T_{\partial\Omega}(f_1) \cdots T_{\partial\Omega}(f_{\ell-1})(T_{\partial\Omega}(f_\ell) - \lambda_\ell)\lambda_{\ell+1} \cdots \lambda_k$$

we see that for every $\delta > 0$ there exists a unit vector $h \in H^2(\partial\Omega)$ satisfying $\|p(T_{\partial\Omega}(f_1), \ldots, T_{\partial\Omega}(f_k))h - p(\lambda_1, \ldots, \lambda_k)h\|_{\partial\Omega} \leq \delta$. Therefore

$$\|p(T_{\partial\Omega}(f_1), \ldots, T_{\partial\Omega}(f_k))\| \geq \|p(T_{\partial\Omega}(f_1), \ldots, T_{\partial\Omega}(f_k))h\|_{\partial\Omega} \geq |p(\lambda_1, \ldots, \lambda_k)| - \delta.$$

For $\delta \to 0$, we obtain

$$\|p(T_{\partial\Omega}(f_1), \ldots, T_{\partial\Omega}(f_k))\| \geq \sup |p(\lambda_1, \ldots, \lambda_k)| = \|p(f_1, \ldots, f_k)\|_\infty.$$

Q.E.D.

4.2.24. THEOREM. *Let Ω be a strictly pseudoconvex bounded domain with smooth boundary. Then the Hardy-Toeplitz C^*-algebra $\mathcal{T}(\partial\Omega)$ has the commutator ideal $\mathcal{K}(H^2(\partial\Omega))$ (compact operators), and there exists a C^*-isomorphism*

$$\mathcal{T}(\partial\Omega)/\mathcal{K}(H^2(\partial\Omega)) \xrightarrow[\approx]{\sigma} \mathcal{C}(\partial\Omega) \tag{4.2.25}$$

such that for every $f \in \mathcal{C}(\partial\Omega)$,

$$\sigma(T_{\partial\Omega}(f) + \mathcal{K}(H^2(\partial\Omega)) = f. \tag{4.2.26}$$

Proof. By Corollary 4.2.20, the commutator

$$\begin{aligned}[T_{\partial\Omega}(\varphi), T_{\partial\Omega}(\psi)] &:= T_{\partial\Omega}(\varphi)T_{\partial\Omega}(\psi) - T_{\partial\Omega}(\psi)T_{\partial\Omega}(\varphi) \\ &= (T_{\partial\Omega}(\varphi)T_{\partial\Omega}(\psi) - T_{\partial\Omega}(\varphi\psi)) - (T_{\partial\Omega}(\psi)T_{\partial\Omega}(\varphi) - T_{\partial\Omega}(\psi\varphi))\end{aligned} \tag{4.2.27}$$

is a compact operator on $H^2(\partial\Omega)$. Hence the commutator ideal $\mathcal{T}(\partial\Omega)'$, generated by these commutators, is contained in $\mathcal{K}(H^2(\partial\Omega))$. Now suppose $\mathcal{T}(\partial\Omega)' = \{0\}$, i.e., $\mathcal{T}(\partial\Omega)$ is commutative. Then $T_{\partial\Omega}(p)$ is a normal operator for every $p \in \mathcal{P}(\mathbb{C}^n)$. By [R1; Lemma 2.1], $H^2(\partial\Omega)$ is invariant under the adjoint multiplication operator $\bar{p}$. Therefore $\bar{p} = \bar{p} \cdot 1 \in H^2(\partial\Omega)$ has a holomorphic extension

$$h(z) = \int_{\partial\Omega} \mathcal{P}(z,w)\overline{p(w)}\, d\sigma(w)$$

to Ω, which has to agree with $\overline{p(z)}$. This is a contradiction showing that $\mathcal{T}(\partial\Omega)' \neq \{0\}$. By Proposition 4.2.15 and [D1], $\mathcal{T}(\partial\Omega)'$ contains $\mathcal{K}(H^2(\partial\Omega))$, so that

(4.2.28) $$\mathcal{T}(\partial\Omega)' = \mathcal{K}(H^2(\partial\Omega)).$$

Therefore the mapping

$$\mathcal{C}(\partial\Omega) \xrightarrow{\tau} \mathcal{T}(\partial\Omega)/\mathcal{K}(H^2(\partial\Omega))$$

given by $f \mapsto T_{\partial\Omega}(f) + \mathcal{K}(H^2(\partial\Omega))$ is a C^*-homomorphism which is surjective by (4.2.13). In order to show that τ is injective, let $A \in \mathcal{K}(H^2(\partial\Omega))$ be arbitrary. By (4.2.28) and (4.2.27), A belongs to the C^*-ideal $\mathcal{J}$ generated by all semi-commutators (4.2.21). Thus $A = \lim A_n$, where each A_n is a sum of operators of the form

$$T_{\partial\Omega}(\varphi_1) \cdots T_{\partial\Omega}(\varphi_k)\,(T_{\partial\Omega}(\varphi_0)T_{\partial\Omega}(\psi_0) - T_{\partial\Omega}(\varphi_0\psi_0))\,T_{\partial\Omega}(\psi_1) \cdots T_{\partial\Omega}(\psi_\ell)$$

where $\varphi_0, \ldots, \varphi_k, \psi_0, \ldots, \psi_\ell \in \mathcal{C}(\partial\Omega)$. Since

$$\varphi_1 \cdots \varphi_k\,(\varphi_0\psi_0 - \varphi_0\psi_0)\,\psi_1 \cdots \psi_\ell = 0$$

on $\partial\Omega$, Theorem 4.2.22 implies $\|T_{\partial\Omega}(f) + A_n\| \geq \|f\|_\infty$ for every $f \in \mathcal{C}(\partial\Omega)$. For $n \to \infty$, we obtain $\|T_{\partial\Omega}(f) + A\| \geq \|f\|_\infty$, showing that τ is injective. Put $\sigma := \tau^{-1}$. Q.E.D.

4.2.29. COROLLARY. *For every* $f \in \mathcal{C}(\partial\Omega)$, *the operator* $T_{\partial\Omega}(f)$ *is essentially normal, i.e.,*

$$[T_{\partial\Omega}(f)^*, T_{\partial\Omega}(f)] \in \mathcal{K}(H^2(\partial\Omega)),$$

and we have $\|T_{\partial\Omega}(f)\| = \|f\|_\infty$ *and* $\text{ess-Spec}\ T_{\partial\Omega}(f) = f(\partial\Omega)$. *In particular,* $T_{\partial\Omega}(f)$ *is a Fredholm operator if and only if* f *has no zeros on* $\partial\Omega$.

4.3 Groupoid C^*-Algebras

For the study of Toeplitz operators one needs convolution operators not only on groups, as treated in Chapter 3, but also on more general objects called groupoids.

4.3.1. DEFINITION. A locally compact Hausdorff space $\mathcal{G}$ is called a *groupoid* if it is endowed with a continuous involution

$$\mathcal{G} \ni x \mapsto x^{-1} \in \mathcal{G}$$

and a continuous (partial) product

$$\mathcal{G} \times \mathcal{G} \supset \mathcal{G}^2 \to \mathcal{G}, \quad (x,y) \mapsto xy$$

such that $\mathcal{G}^2$ contains (x,x^{-1}) and (x^{-1},x) for all $x \in \mathcal{G}$, and the following axioms hold:

(4.3.2) $(x,y), (y,z) \in \mathcal{G}^2 \Rightarrow (xy,z), (x,yz) \in \mathcal{G}^2$ and $(xy)z = x(yz)$,

(4.3.3) $$(x,y) \in \mathcal{G}^2 \Rightarrow (xy)y^{-1} = x \text{ and } x^{-1}(xy) = y.$$

Note that (xy,y^{-1}) and (x^{-1},xy) belong to $\mathcal{G}^2$ since (y,y^{-1}) and (x^{-1},x) are in $\mathcal{G}^2$.

4.3.4. DEFINITION. Let $\mathcal{G}$ be a locally compact groupoid. For every $x \in \mathcal{G}$, the elements

(4.3.5) $$\vec{x} := x^{-1}x,$$

(4.3.6) $$\overleftarrow{x} := xx^{-1}$$

of $\mathcal{G}$ are called the *domain* and *range* of x, respectively. We have

(4.3.7) $$\mathcal{G}^2 = \{(x,y) \in \mathcal{G} \times \mathcal{G} : \vec{x} = \overleftarrow{y}\}.$$

The *unit space* of $\mathcal{G}$ is defined as

(4.3.8) $$\mathcal{G}^0 := \{\vec{x} : x \in \mathcal{G}\} = \{\overleftarrow{y} : y \in \mathcal{G}\}.$$

Since the mappings $x \mapsto \vec{x}$, $x \mapsto \overleftarrow{x}$ on $\mathcal{G}$ are continuous, it follows from (4.3.7) and (4.3.8) that $\mathcal{G}^2 \subset \mathcal{G} \times \mathcal{G}$ and $\mathcal{G}^0 \subset \mathcal{G}$ are closed subspaces.

4.3.9. DEFINITION. Let $\mathcal{G}$ be a locally compact groupoid with unit space $\mathcal{G}^0$. For every $\sigma \in \mathcal{G}^0$, the closed subspace

$$\mathcal{G}_\sigma := \{x \in \mathcal{G} : \vec{x} = \sigma = \overleftarrow{x}\}$$

of $\mathcal{G}$ has the structure of a locally compact group called the *stabilizer group* at σ. The subset

$$\mathcal{G} \cdot \sigma := \{\tau \in \mathcal{G}^0 : \exists x \in \mathcal{G}, \vec{x} = \sigma, \overleftarrow{x} = \tau\}$$

of $\mathcal{G}^0$ is called the *orbit* of σ under $\mathcal{G}$. These orbits form a partition of $\mathcal{G}^0$ (i.e., different orbits are disjoint).

4.3.10. EXAMPLE. Every locally compact group Γ becomes a locally compact groupoid under its usual product and inverse. The unit space consists of the unit element ε of Γ. We have $\Gamma_\varepsilon = \Gamma$ and $\Gamma \cdot \varepsilon = \{\varepsilon\}$.

4.3.11. EXAMPLE. Let Γ be a locally compact group, acting on a locally compact space Σ via a continuous action

$$\Sigma \leftarrow \Gamma \ltimes \Sigma \tag{4.3.12}$$

denoted by

$$\alpha \ltimes \sigma \leftarrow\!\shortmid (\alpha,\sigma). \tag{4.3.13}$$

Then the product space

$$\mathcal{G} := \Gamma \times \Sigma \tag{4.3.14}$$

becomes a locally compact groupoid with partial product

$$(\alpha, \beta \ltimes \sigma)(\beta,\sigma) := (\alpha\beta, \sigma) \tag{4.3.15}$$

and inverse

$$(\alpha,\sigma)^{-1} := (\alpha^{-1}, \alpha \ltimes \sigma) \tag{4.3.16}$$

for all $\alpha, \beta \in \Gamma$ and $\sigma \in \Sigma$. This groupoid is called the *transformation groupoid* associated with the action (4.3.12). Let ε be the unit element of Γ. Since

$$\overrightarrow{(\alpha,\sigma)} = (\varepsilon,\sigma) \equiv \sigma,$$

$$\overleftarrow{(\alpha,\sigma)} = (\varepsilon, \alpha \ltimes \sigma) \equiv \alpha \ltimes \sigma,$$

we may identify the unit space $\mathcal{G}^0 = \{\varepsilon\} \times \Sigma$ with Σ. For transformation groupoids, the notions of stabilizer subgroup and orbit reduce to the analogous concepts for group actions. More precisely

$$\mathcal{G}_\sigma = \{(\alpha,\tau) \in \mathcal{G} : \sigma = \tau, \alpha \ltimes \sigma = \sigma\} = \Gamma_\sigma \times \{\sigma\}$$

can be identified with the stabilizer subgroup Γ_σ of Γ at σ, whereas

$$\mathcal{G} \cdot \sigma = \{(\varepsilon, \alpha \ltimes \sigma) : \alpha \in \Gamma\} = \{\varepsilon\} \times \Gamma \cdot \sigma$$

can be identified with the orbit of $\sigma \in \Sigma$ under Γ. In case (4.3.12) is the trivial action of Γ on a point $\Sigma = \{pt\}$, we obtain Example 4.3.10.

4.3.17. EXAMPLE. Let Σ be a locally compact space. The product space

$$\mathcal{G} := \Sigma \times \Sigma \tag{4.3.18}$$

becomes a locally compact groupoid with operations

$$(\rho,\sigma)(\sigma,\tau) := (\rho,\tau), \quad (\sigma,\tau)^{-1} := (\tau,\sigma)$$

for all $\rho,\sigma,\tau \in \Sigma$. This groupoid is called the *matrix groupoid* over Σ. Since

$$\overleftarrow{(\sigma,\tau)} = (\sigma,\sigma) \equiv \sigma,$$

$$\overrightarrow{(\sigma,\tau)} = (\tau,\tau) \equiv \tau,$$

we may identify the unit space $\mathcal{G}^0 = \{(\sigma,\sigma) : \sigma \in \Sigma\}$ with Σ via the diagonal embedding. We have $\mathcal{G}_\sigma = \{\sigma\}$ and $\mathcal{G} \cdot \sigma = \mathcal{G}$ for all $\sigma \in \Sigma$.

If $\mathcal{G}$ is a groupoid and S is a locally closed subset of its unit space $\mathcal{G}^0$, the set

$$\mathcal{G}|_S := \{x \in \mathcal{G} : \overrightarrow{x} \in S, \overleftarrow{x} \in S\} \tag{4.3.19}$$

is a groupoid with unit space S, for the restricted partial product and inverse. This groupoid is called the *reduction* of $\mathcal{G}$ to S [R3; Definition 1.4.].

4.3.20. EXAMPLE. For the transformation groupoid $\mathcal{G} = \Gamma \times \Sigma$ associated with an action of Γ on Σ, we have

$$\Gamma \times \Sigma|_S = \{(\alpha, \sigma) \in \Gamma \times S : \alpha \ltimes \sigma \in S\} \tag{4.3.21}$$

whenever S is a locally closed subspace of Σ.

4.3.22. EXAMPLE. For the matrix groupoid $\mathcal{G} = \Sigma \times \Sigma$ over Σ, the reduction to $S \subset \Sigma$ coincides with the matrix groupoid over S:

$$\Sigma \times \Sigma|_S = S \times S.$$

Given a locally compact groupoid $\mathcal{G}$, let $\mathcal{C}_c(\mathcal{G})$ denote the topological vector space of all compactly supported continuous functions $\varphi : \mathcal{G} \to \mathbb{C}$, with the inductive limit topology. The dual space $\mathcal{M}(\mathcal{G})$ of all (Radon) measures on $\mathcal{G}$ will be endowed with the weak topology. Let $\mathcal{M}_+(\mathcal{G})$ denote the space of all positive measures.

4.3.23. DEFINITION. A weakly continuous mapping

$$\mathcal{G}^0 \ni \sigma \mapsto \overleftarrow{d}\sigma \in \mathcal{M}_+(\mathcal{G})$$

is called a *left Haar system* if it satisfies $\mathrm{Supp}(\overleftarrow{d}\sigma) = \{x \in \mathcal{G} : \overleftarrow{x} = \sigma\}$ and

$$\int_{\mathcal{G}} F(xy)\, \overleftarrow{d}\overrightarrow{x}(y) = \int_{\mathcal{G}} F(z)\, \overleftarrow{d}\overleftarrow{x}(z) \tag{4.3.24}$$

for all $x \in \mathcal{G}, \sigma \in \mathcal{G}^0$ and $F \in \mathcal{C}_c(\mathcal{G})$. By putting

$$\int_{\mathcal{G}} F(x)\, \overrightarrow{d}\sigma(x) := \int_{\mathcal{G}} F(x^{-1})\, \overleftarrow{d}\sigma(x) \tag{4.3.25}$$

for all $F \in \mathcal{C}_c(\mathcal{G})$ and $\sigma \in \Sigma$, we obtain analogously a *right Haar system*, satisfying $\operatorname{Supp}(\vec{d}\sigma) = \{x \in \mathcal{G} : \vec{x} = \sigma\}$ and

$$\int_{\mathcal{G}} F(xy)\ \overset{\rightarrow\leftarrow}{dy}(x) = \int_{\mathcal{G}} F(z)\ \overset{\rightarrow\rightarrow}{dy}(z) \tag{4.3.26}$$

for all $y \in \mathcal{G}$. If S is a locally closed subset of $\mathcal{G}^0$, we obtain left (resp., right) Haar systems $\overleftarrow{d}\sigma(x) \cdot \chi(x)$ and $\vec{d}\sigma(x) \cdot \chi(x)$ on the reduction of $\mathcal{G}$ to S. Here $\sigma \in S$ and χ denotes the characteristic function of $\mathcal{G}|_S \subset \mathcal{G}$.

4.3.27. EXAMPLE. Let Γ be a locally compact group with left Haar measure $\overleftarrow{d}\alpha$ and right Haar measure

$$\vec{d}\alpha := \overleftarrow{d}(\alpha^{-1}).$$

Since the groupoid associated with Γ has unit space $\{\varepsilon\}$, we may define

$$\overleftarrow{d}\varepsilon(\alpha) := \overleftarrow{d}\alpha,$$

$$\vec{d}\varepsilon(\alpha) := \vec{d}\alpha$$

as a left (resp., right) Haar system on Γ.

4.3.28. EXAMPLE. Generalizing Example 4.3.27, let Γ act on a locally compact space Σ and consider the associated transformation groupoid $\mathcal{G} := \Gamma \times \Sigma$ with unit space Σ. Let $d\sigma$ denote the Dirac measure at $\sigma \in \Sigma$, and put

$$\overleftarrow{d}\sigma(\alpha,\tau) := \overleftarrow{d}\alpha \cdot d\sigma(\alpha \ltimes \tau), \tag{4.3.29}$$

$$\vec{d}\sigma(\alpha,\tau) := \vec{d}\alpha \cdot d\sigma(\tau) \tag{4.3.30}$$

for all $(\alpha,\tau) \in \mathcal{G}$. Then we have $\operatorname{Supp} \overleftarrow{d}\sigma = \{x \in \mathcal{G} : \overleftarrow{x} = \sigma\}$ and $\operatorname{Supp} \vec{d}\sigma = \Gamma \times \{\sigma\} = \{x \in \mathcal{G} : \vec{x} = \sigma\}$. Now let $x = (\alpha,\sigma) \in \mathcal{G}$ be fixed. Then

$$\int F(xy)\ \overset{\leftarrow\rightarrow}{dx}(y) = \int F((\alpha,\sigma)(\beta, \beta^{-1} \ltimes \sigma))\ \overleftarrow{d}\sigma(\beta, \beta^{-1} \ltimes \sigma)$$

$$= \int F(\alpha\beta, \beta^{-1} \ltimes \sigma)\, \overleftarrow{d}\beta = \int F(\gamma, \gamma^{-1}\alpha \ltimes \sigma)\, \overleftarrow{d}\gamma$$

$$= \int F(z)\ \overleftarrow{d}(\alpha \ltimes \sigma)(z) = \int F(z)\ \overleftarrow{d}\overleftarrow{x}\,(z)$$

for all $F \in \mathcal{C}_c(\mathcal{G})$. This shows that (4.3.29) is a left Haar system on $\mathcal{G}$. Similarly, let $y = (\beta, \tau) \in \mathcal{G}$ be fixed. Then

$$\int F(xy)\ \overrightarrow{d}\overleftarrow{y}\,(x) = \int F((\alpha, \beta \ltimes \tau)(\beta,t))\ \overrightarrow{d}(\beta \ltimes \tau)(\alpha, \beta \ltimes \tau)$$

$$= \int F(\alpha\beta, \tau)\ \overrightarrow{d}\alpha = \int F(\gamma, \tau)\ \overrightarrow{d}\gamma$$
$$= \int F(z)\ \overrightarrow{d}\tau(z) = \int F(z)\ \overrightarrow{d}\overrightarrow{y}\,(z).$$

This shows that (4.3.30) is a right Haar system.

4.3.31. EXAMPLE. Let Σ be a locally compact space endowed with a strictly positive measure μ, and consider the associated matrix groupoid $\mathcal{G} := \Sigma \times \Sigma$ with unit space Σ. Let $d\rho$ denote the Dirac measure at $\rho \in \Sigma$, and put

(4.3.32) $$\overleftarrow{d}\rho(\sigma,\tau) = d\rho(\sigma)\ d\mu(\tau),$$

(4.3.33) $$\overrightarrow{d}\rho(\sigma,\tau) = d\mu(\sigma)\ d\rho(\tau)$$

for all $(\sigma,\tau) \in \mathcal{G}$. Then we have $\mathrm{Supp}\ \overleftarrow{d}\rho = \{\rho\} \times \Sigma = \{x \in \mathcal{G} : \overleftarrow{x} = \rho\}$ and $\mathrm{Supp}\ \overrightarrow{d}\rho = \Sigma \times \{\rho\} = \{x \in \mathcal{G} : \overrightarrow{x} = \rho\}$. Now let $x = (\sigma,\rho) \in \mathcal{G}$ be fixed. Then

$$\int F(xy)\ \overleftarrow{d}\overrightarrow{x}\,(y) = \int F((\sigma,\rho)(\rho,\tau))\ \overleftarrow{d}\rho(\rho,\tau)$$

$$= \int F(\sigma,\tau)\ d\mu(\tau) = \int F(\sigma,\tau)\ \overleftarrow{d}\sigma(\sigma,\tau) = \int F(z)\ \overleftarrow{d}\overleftarrow{x}\,(z)$$

for all $F \in \mathcal{C}_c(\mathcal{G})$. This shows that (4.3.32) is a left Haar system on $\mathcal{G}$. Similarly, let $y = (\rho,\tau) \in \mathcal{G}$ be fixed. Then

$$\int F(xy)\ \overrightarrow{d}\overleftarrow{y}\,(x) = \int F((\sigma,\rho)(\rho,\tau))\ \overrightarrow{d}\rho(\sigma,\rho)$$

$$= \int F(\sigma,\tau)\, d\mu(\sigma) = \int F(\sigma,\tau)\, \overrightarrow{d}\,\tau(\sigma,\tau) = \int F(z)\, \overrightarrow{d}\,\overrightarrow{y}\,(z).$$

This shows that (4.3.33) is a right Haar system.

Let $\mathcal{G}$ be a locally compact groupoid, with left Haar system $\{\overleftarrow{d}\,\sigma : \sigma \in \mathcal{G}^0\}$. Define a *convolution product* on $\mathcal{C}_c(\mathcal{G})$ by putting

(4.3.34) $$(F_\# G)(x) := \int_{\mathcal{G}} F(xy)\; G(y^{-1})\; \overleftarrow{d}\,\overrightarrow{x}\,(y) = \int_{\mathcal{G}} F(xy^{-1})\; G(y)\; \overrightarrow{d}\,\overrightarrow{x}\,(y).$$

This product is associative, i.e., we have

(4.3.35) $$(F_\# G)_\# H = F_\#(G_\# H)$$

whenever $F,G,H \in \mathcal{C}_c(\mathcal{G})$. In fact,

$$(F_\# G)_\# H(x) = \int (F_\# G)(xy)\; H(y^{-1})\; \overleftarrow{d}\,\overrightarrow{x}\,(y)$$

$$= \int \int F(xyz)\; G(z^{-1})\; H(y^{-1})\; \overleftarrow{d}\,\overrightarrow{y}\,(z)\; \overleftarrow{d}\,\overrightarrow{x}\,(y)$$

$$= \int \int F(xw)\; G(w^{-1}y)\; H(y^{-1})\; \overleftarrow{d}\,\overleftarrow{y}\,(w)\; \overleftarrow{d}\,\overrightarrow{x}\,(y)$$

by putting $w = yz$ whenever $\overrightarrow{y} = \overleftarrow{z}$. On the other hand,

$$(F_\#(G_\# H))(x) = \int F(xw)\; (G_\# H)(w^{-1})\; \overleftarrow{d}\,\overrightarrow{x}\,(w)$$

$$= \int \int F(xw)\; G(w^{-1}y)\; H(y^{-1})\; \overleftarrow{d}\,\overleftarrow{w}\,(y)\; \overleftarrow{d}\,\overrightarrow{x}\,(w).$$

Now (4.3.35) follows from the fact that $\overrightarrow{x} = \overleftarrow{y} = \overleftarrow{w}$ on the support of integration. Putting

(4.3.36) $$F^*(x) := \overline{F(x^{-1})}$$

for all $F \in \mathcal{C}_c(\mathcal{G})$ and $x \in \mathcal{G}$, we obtain

$$(F_\# G)^*(x) = \overline{(F_\# G)(x^{-1})} = \int \overline{F(x^{-1}y)}\ \overline{G(y^{-1})}\ \overleftarrow{\overleftarrow{d}x}(y)$$

$$= \int \overline{F(z)}\ \overline{G(z^{-1}x^{-1})}\ \overleftrightarrow{dx}(z) = \int G^*(xz)\ F^*(z^{-1})\ \overleftrightarrow{dx}(z) = (G^*_\# F^*)(x)$$

whenever $G \in \mathcal{C}_c(\mathcal{G})$, so that $(F_\# G)^* = (G^*)_\# F^*$ and $\mathcal{C}_c(\mathcal{G})$ becomes a *-algebra. It is a normed *-algebra under the norm

$$\|F\| := \max\left(\sup_{\sigma\in\mathcal{G}^0} \int |F|\ \overleftarrow{d}\sigma,\ \sup_{\sigma\in\mathcal{G}^0} \int |F|\ \overrightarrow{d}\sigma\right).$$

Now let μ be a positive measure on $\mathcal{G}^0$. Define measures $\overleftarrow{d}\mu$ and $\overrightarrow{d}\mu$ on $\mathcal{G}$ by putting

$$\int_{\mathcal{G}} F(y)\ \overleftarrow{d}\mu(y) := \int_{\mathcal{G}^0} \int_{\mathcal{G}} F(y)\ \overleftarrow{d}\sigma(y)\ d\mu(\sigma), \tag{4.3.37}$$

$$\int_{\mathcal{G}} F(y)\ \overrightarrow{d}\mu(y) := \int_{\mathcal{G}^0} \int_{\mathcal{G}} F(y)\ \overrightarrow{d}\sigma(y)\ d\mu(\sigma), \tag{4.3.38}$$

respectively. In the special case when $\mu = \sigma$ is the Dirac measure at $\sigma \in \mathcal{G}^0$, we recover the measures $\overleftarrow{d}\sigma$ and $\overrightarrow{d}\sigma$, respectively. Consider the Lebesgue spaces

$$L^2(\overleftarrow{\mathcal{G}}) := L^2(\mathcal{G}, \overleftarrow{d}\mu),\quad L^2(\overrightarrow{\mathcal{G}}) := L^2(\mathcal{G}, \overrightarrow{d\mu}).$$

4.3.39. DEFINITION. Let $F \in \mathcal{C}_c(\mathcal{G})$. The *right convolution operator* with symbol F is the bounded operator $R(F) : L^2(\overleftarrow{\mathcal{G}}) \longrightarrow L^2(\overleftarrow{\mathcal{G}})$ defined by

$$(R(F)\Phi)(x) := (\Phi_\# F)(x) = \int_{\mathcal{G}} \Phi(xy)\ F(y^{-1})\ \overleftrightarrow{dx}(y) \tag{4.3.40}$$

for all $\Phi \in L^2(\overrightarrow{\mathcal{G}})$ and $x \in \mathcal{G}$. Since $\mathcal{C}_c(\mathcal{G})$ is a Hilbert algebra with respect to $\overrightarrow{\mu}$ [R3; Proposition 1.10], it follows that (4.3.40) defines an anti-representation of $\mathcal{C}_c(\mathcal{G})$ on $L^2(\overleftarrow{\mathcal{G}})$. The C^*-algebra

$$C^*_\mu(\mathcal{G}) := C^*(R(F) : F \in \mathcal{C}_c(\mathcal{G})) \tag{4.3.41}$$

generated by these operators is called the *spatial groupoid C^*-algebra* of $\mathcal{G}$ induced by the measure μ on $\mathcal{G}^0$.

4.3.42. EXAMPLE. Let $\mathcal{G} = \Gamma \times \Sigma$ be the transformation groupoid associated with an action of Γ on Σ, endowed with the Haar system (4.3.39). Then $\mathcal{C}_c(\mathcal{G})$ has the convolution

$$(F_\# G)(\alpha,\sigma) = \int F((\alpha,\sigma)(\beta,\tau))\ G(\beta^{-1}, \beta \ltimes \tau)\ \overleftarrow{d}\sigma(\beta,\tau)$$

$$= \int \int F((\alpha,\sigma)(\beta,\tau))\ G(\beta^{-1}, \beta \ltimes \tau)\ \overleftarrow{d}\beta\ d\sigma(\beta \ltimes \tau)$$

$$= \int F((\alpha,\sigma)(\beta, \beta^{-1} \ltimes \sigma))\ G(\beta^{-1}, \sigma)\ \overleftarrow{d}\beta$$

$$= \int F(\alpha\beta, \beta^{-1} \ltimes \sigma)\ G(\beta^{-1}, \sigma)\ \overleftarrow{d}\beta = \int F(\alpha\beta^{-1}, \beta \ltimes \sigma)\ G(\beta,\sigma)\ \overrightarrow{d}\beta$$

for all $\alpha \in \Gamma$ and $\sigma \in \Sigma$. The involution is given by

$$F^*(\alpha,\sigma) := \overline{F(\alpha^{-1}, \alpha \ltimes \alpha)}.$$

In case $S \subset \Sigma$ is a locally closed subset, the reduction $\mathcal{G}|_S$ has the convolution product

$$(F_\# G)(\alpha,\sigma) = \int F(\alpha\beta^{-1}, \beta \ltimes \sigma)\ \chi(\beta \ltimes \sigma)\ G(\beta,\sigma)\ \overrightarrow{d}\beta$$

for all $(\alpha,\sigma) \in \mathcal{G}|_S$. Here χ is the characteristic function of S. Now let μ be a measure on Σ and consider the associated measures

(4.3.43) $$\int F(x)\ \overleftarrow{d}\mu(x) = \int_\Sigma \int_\Gamma F(\alpha, \alpha^{-1} \ltimes \sigma)\ \overleftarrow{d}\alpha\ d\mu(\sigma),$$

(4.3.44) $$\int F(x)\ \overrightarrow{d}\mu(x) = \int_\Sigma \int_\Gamma F(\alpha,\sigma)\ \overrightarrow{d}\alpha\ d\mu(\sigma)$$

on $\mathcal{G}$. By (4.3.40), the convolution operator has the form

(4.3.45) $$(R(F)\Phi)(\beta,\tau) = \int_\Gamma \Phi(\beta\alpha^{-1}, \alpha \ltimes \tau)\ F(\alpha, \tau)\ \overrightarrow{d}\alpha$$

for all $(\beta, \tau) \in \mathcal{G}$. The C^*-algebra $C^*_\mu(\mathcal{G})$ generated by these operators is called the *spatial transformation group C^*-algebra* associated with the action (4.3.12) and the measure μ.

4.3.46. EXAMPLE. Let $\mathcal{G} = \Sigma \times \Sigma$ be the matrix groupoid over a locally compact space Σ. Consider the Haar system (4.3.32) on $\mathcal{G}$ induced by a strictly positive measure μ on Σ. Then $\mathcal{C}_c(\mathcal{G})$ has the convolution product

$$(F_\# G)(\rho,\tau) = \int_\Sigma F(\rho, \sigma)\ G(\sigma, \tau)\ d\mu(\sigma)$$

which generalizes the usual matrix multiplication. The involution $F^*(\sigma,\tau) = \overline{F(\tau,\sigma)}$ generalizes the matrix adjoint. Now fix a point $o \in \Sigma$ and consider the associated Dirac measure on $\mathcal{G}^0 \equiv \Sigma$. Then there are isomorphisms

$$L^2(\overleftarrow{\mathcal{G}}) \approx L^2(\{o\} \times \Sigma),$$

$$L^2(\overrightarrow{\mathcal{G}}) \approx L^2(\Sigma \times \{o\})$$

where Σ carries the measure μ. For $F \in \mathcal{C}_c(\mathcal{G})$, the associated convolution operator on $L^2(\overleftarrow{\mathcal{G}}) \approx L^2(\Sigma)$ is given by

$$(R(F)\varphi)(\tau) = \int \varphi(\sigma)\ F(\sigma, \tau)\ d\mu(\sigma)$$

for all $\varphi \in L^2(\Sigma)$ and $\tau \in \Sigma$, i.e. $F_\#$ is an integral operator with kernel F. These operators are of trace-class, and it follows that the spatial groupoid C^*-algebra

$$C^*_o(\mathcal{G}) = \mathcal{K}(L^2(\Sigma)) \tag{4.3.47}$$

induced by o consists of all compact operators on $L^2(\Sigma)$.

4.4 Hardy-Toeplitz Operators Over Tubular Domains

In this section we study Toeplitz operators and their associated C^*-algebras, acting on the Hardy space $H^2(iX)$ over a tubular domain $\Pi = \Lambda \times iX$ whose base Λ is a symmetric cone in a real Jordan algebra X. We assume that Λ is irreducible. The Hardy space and the associated C^*-algebra of Hardy multipliers are studied in Sections 2.3 and 3.1.

4.4.1. DEFINITION. For any bounded function $f \in L^\infty(iX)$, the *multiplication operator* with *symbol* f is the bounded operator $f : L^2(iX) \to L^2(iX)$ defined by

$$(fh)(z) := f(z)h(z) \tag{4.4.2}$$

for all $h \in L^2(iX)$ and $z \in iX$.

Identifying the operator (4.4.2) with its associated symbol yields an injective C^*-algebra homomorphism from $L^\infty(iX)$ onto an abelian C^*-subalgebra of $\mathcal{L}(L^2(iX))$, the C^*-algebra of all bounded operators on $L^2(iX)$. The translation action (2.3.5) of iX on $L^2(iX)$ induces an adjoint action of iX on $\mathcal{L}(L^2(iX))$ which satisfies for every $z \in iX$

$$Ad(z^\#)f = z^\# f \quad \text{(multiplication operator)}$$

where $(z^\# f)(w) := f(w - z)$ belongs to $L^\infty(iX)$. Now consider the Hardy space $H^2(iX)$ over Π, with Szegö projection $E : L^2(iX) \to H^2(iX)$.

4.4.3. DEFINITION. The *Hardy-Toeplitz operator* $T_{iX}(f)$ with *symbol* $f \in L^\infty(iX)$ is defined as the compression

$$T_{iX}(f) = E \circ f|_{H^2(iX)} \tag{4.4.4}$$

of the multiplication operator (4.4.2). Thus

$$T_{iX}(f)h := E(f \cdot h) \tag{4.4.5}$$

for every $h \in H^2(iX)$.

The translation action (2.3.5) of iX on $L^2(iX)$ leaves $H^2(iX)$ invariant and thus induces an adjoint action of iX on $\mathcal{L}(H^2(iX))$ which satisfies

(4.4.6) $$\mathrm{Ad}(z^{\#})T_{iX}(f) = T_{iX}(z^{\#}f)$$

for all $z \in iX$ and $f \in L^\infty(iX)$.

4.4.7. PROPOSITION. *For every* $f \in L^\infty(iX)$, $T_{iX}(f)$ *is a bounded operator on* $H^2(iX)$ *satisfying*

(4.4.8) $$\|T_{iX}(f)\| \le \|f\|_\infty,$$

(4.4.9) $$T_{iX}(f)^* = T_{iX}(\bar{f}).$$

Moreover, if $\varphi \in H^\infty(iX) := H^2(iX) \cap L^\infty(iX)$, *then*

(4.4.10) $$T_{iX}(f)\, T_{iX}(\varphi) = T_{iX}(f\varphi),$$

(4.4.11) $$T_{iX}(\bar{\varphi})\, T_{iX}(f) = T_{iX}(\bar{\varphi}f).$$

Proof. As an operator in $L^2(iX)$, we have

(4.4.12) $$T_{iX}(f) = E\, f\, E.$$ Q.E.D.

For every $\mu \in L^1(X)$ consider the inverse Fourier transform $\mu_{\#}$ defined in (3.1.15).

4.4.13. DEFINITION. The *Hardy-Toeplitz* C^**-algebra* over iX is defined as the non-unital C^*-algebra

(4.4.14) $$\mathcal{T}(iX) := C^*(T_{iX}(\mu_{\#}) : \mu \in L^1(X))$$

generated by all Hardy-Toeplitz operators (4.4.4) on $H^2(iX)$ with symbols of the form (3.1.15). Since $z^{\#}\mu_{\#} = ((-z)^{\#}\mu)_{\#}$ for all $\mu \in L^1(X)$, it follows that $\mathcal{T}(iX)$ is invariant under the adjoint action (4.4.6) of iX.

Now consider the Hardy multiplier C^*-algebra $\mathcal{D}(X)$ on $L^2(X)$ defined in (3.1.18).

4.4.15. PROPOSITION. *The translation action*

$$(\alpha_{\#}\varphi)(\beta) := \varphi(\beta + \alpha)$$

of X *on* $L^\infty(X)$ *leaves* $\mathcal{D}(X)$ *invariant and induces a* C^**-action*

(4.4.16) $$X \xrightarrow{d} \text{Aut } \mathcal{D}(X)$$

of X *on* $\mathcal{D}(X)$.

Proof. By definition, $\mathcal{D}(X)$ is translation invariant. Thus $\alpha_\#$ is a C^*-algebra automorphism of $\mathcal{D}(X)$ for every $\alpha \in X$. We have to show that the homomorphism (4.4.16) defined by $d(\alpha) := \alpha_\#$ is pointwise norm-continuous, i.e. for every $\varphi \in \mathcal{D}(X)$ we have

(4.4.17) $$\forall \varepsilon > 0, \exists \delta > 0: |\alpha| \leq \delta \Rightarrow ||\alpha_\#\varphi - \varphi|| \leq \varepsilon.$$

This is equivalent to saying that φ is uniformly continuous on X. In order to prove (4.4.17), we may assume that

$$\varphi(\alpha) = (\mu_\#\chi)(\alpha) = \int_{\alpha-\Lambda^\#} \mu$$

where $\mu \in L^1(X)$ is positive and $\Lambda^\#$ denotes the polar cone of Λ. Put $B_r := \{x \in X : |x| \leq r\}$. For any $\varepsilon > 0$, there exists $r > 0$ such that

$$\int_{X \setminus B_r} \mu \leq \varepsilon/2.$$

Now let $\alpha, \beta \in X$ and consider the symmetric difference $C_{\alpha,\beta} := (\alpha - \Lambda^\#) \oplus (\beta - \Lambda^\#)$ of $\alpha - \Lambda^\#$ and $\beta - \Lambda^\#$. By [R6] there exists $\eta > 0$ such that every measurable set E of measure $m(E) \leq \eta$ satisfies

$$\int_E \mu \leq \varepsilon/2.$$

Since B_r is compact, there exists $\delta > 0$ such that

$$|\alpha - \beta| \leq \delta \Rightarrow m(C_{\alpha,\beta} \cap B_r) \leq \eta.$$

It follows that

$$|\varphi(\alpha) - \varphi(\beta)| \leq \int_{C_{\alpha,\beta}} \mu = \int_{C_{\alpha,\beta} \cap B_r} \mu + \int_{C_{\alpha,\beta} \setminus B_r} \mu \leq \frac{\varepsilon}{2} + \frac{\varepsilon}{2} = \varepsilon.$$

This proves that φ is uniformly continuous on X. Q.E.D.

Consider the (non-compact) spectrum Spec $\mathcal{D}(X)$. The translation action (4.4.16) of X on $\mathcal{D}(X)$ induces a natural action

(4.4.18) $$\text{Spec } \mathcal{D}(X) \leftarrow X \times \text{Spec } \mathcal{D}(X), \ \alpha \ltimes \sigma \leftarrow\!\shortmid (\alpha, \sigma)$$

defined by

(4.4.19) $$(\alpha \ltimes \sigma)\varphi := \sigma(\alpha_\# \varphi)$$

for all $\varphi \in \mathcal{D}(X) \subset L^\infty(X)$. For the characters β_A $(\beta \in X)$ defined in (3.1.19), we have

(4.4.20) $$\alpha \ltimes \beta_A = (\alpha + \beta)_A.$$

Here we put $A := \bar{\Lambda}$. By Proposition 3.1.33, the subset $\text{Spec}_+ \mathcal{D}(X)$ of Spec $\mathcal{D}(X)$ is compact.

4.4.21. DEFINITION. Consider the transformation groupoid $X \times \text{Spec } \mathcal{D}(X)$ associated with the action (4.4.18). The reduced groupoid

(4.4.22) $$\mathcal{G}_S(X) := X \times \text{Spec } \mathcal{D}(X)|_{\text{Spec}_+ \mathcal{D}(X)}$$

with unit space $\text{Spec}_+ \mathcal{D}(X)$ is called the *Hardy groupoid* over Λ. Let

(4.4.23) $$0_A \cdot \varphi = \varphi(0) \qquad (\varphi \in \mathcal{D}(X))$$

denote the "base point" of $\text{Spec}_+ \mathcal{D}(X)$, and consider the corresponding *spatial groupoid C^*-algebra*

(4.4.24) $$C^*_{0_A}(\mathcal{G}_S(X)) \subset \mathcal{L}(L^2(\mathcal{G}_S(X)))$$

defined via (4.3.41) using the Dirac measure at 0_A.

4.4.25. THEOREM. *The Hardy-Toeplitz C^*-algebra $\mathcal{T}(iX)$ is unitarily equivalent to the Hardy groupoid C^*-algebra $\mathcal{C}^*_{0_A}(\mathcal{G}_S(X))$.*

Proof. For every $\mu \in L^1(X)$, define the convolution operator $\mu_\# : L^2(X) \to L^2(X)$ by

$$(\mu_\# \varphi)(\alpha) = \int_X \varphi(\alpha - \beta)\, \mu(\beta)\, d\beta.$$

The compression

$$W_\mu := \chi\, \mu_\#\, \chi \tag{4.4.26}$$

onto the subspace $L^2(\Lambda^\#)$ is called the (continuous) *Wiener-Hopf operator* with symbol μ. By definition

$$W_\mu \varphi(\alpha) = \int_{\Lambda^\#} \varphi(\alpha - \beta)\, \mu(\beta)\, d\beta \tag{4.4.27}$$

for all $\varphi \in L^2(\Lambda^\#)$ and $\alpha \in \Lambda^\#$. Now consider the Fourier transform (2.3.8). By standard Fourier theory, there exists a commuting diagram

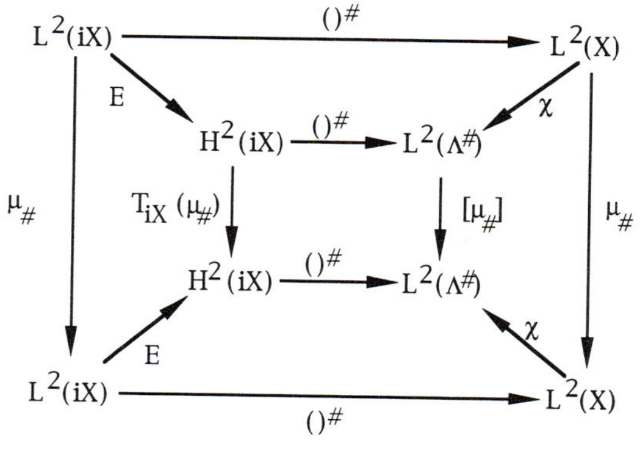

for every $\mu \in L^1(X)$. Here $\mu_\#$ on the left denotes multiplication by the inverse Fourier transform $\mu_\#$. Since the Toeplitz operators $T_{iX}(\mu_\#)$ generate $\mathcal{T}(iX)$ by (4.4.14), the restriction $\mathcal{F}$ of $()^\#$ to $H^2(iX)$ yields a C^*-isomorphism

(4.4.28) $$\mathrm{Ad}(\mathcal{F}) : \mathcal{T}(iX) \xrightarrow[\approx]{} \mathcal{W}(\Lambda^{\#})$$

onto the (non-unital) *Wiener-Hopf* C^**-algebra* $\mathcal{W}(\Lambda^{\#})$, generated by all Wiener-Hopf operators (4.4.27). Now consider the groupoid $\mathcal{G}_S(X)$ and the "base point" 0_A of its unit space $\mathrm{Spec}_+ \mathcal{D}(X)$. By (4.3.29), we have

$$\int_{\mathcal{G}_S(X)} \Phi(\alpha,\sigma)\, \overleftarrow{d}\, 0_A(\alpha,\sigma) = \int_{\mathrm{Spec}_+\mathcal{D}(X)} \int_X \Phi(\alpha, -\alpha \ltimes \sigma)\, d\alpha\, d0_A(\sigma)$$

$$= \int_X \Phi(\alpha, -\alpha \ltimes 0_A)\, d\alpha = \int_{\Lambda^{\#}} \Phi(-\alpha, \alpha_A)\, d\alpha$$

since F has support in $\mathcal{G}_S(X)$. It follows that

(4.4.29) $$(V\Phi)(\alpha) := \Phi(-\alpha, \alpha_A) \qquad (\alpha \in \Lambda^{\#})$$

defines a Hilbert space isomorphism $V : L^2(\mathcal{G}_S(X)) \xrightarrow[\approx]{} L^2(\Lambda^{\#})$. Under this isomorphism, the right convolution operator $R(F)$ induced by $F \in \mathcal{C}_c(\mathcal{G}_S(X))$ has the form

$$(\mathrm{Ad}(V)R(F))\varphi(\alpha) = R(F)(V^{-1}\varphi)(-\alpha, \alpha_A)$$

(4.4.30) $$= \int_X (V^{-1}\varphi)(-\alpha - \beta, \beta \ltimes \alpha_A)\, F(\beta, \alpha_A)\, d\alpha$$

$$= \int_X \varphi(\alpha + \beta)\, F(\beta,\alpha_A)\, d\alpha = \int_{\Lambda^{\#}} \varphi(\gamma)\, F(\gamma - \alpha, \alpha_A)\, d\gamma$$

for all $\varphi \in L^2(\Lambda^{\#})$ and $\alpha \in \Lambda^{\#}$. Every $\mu \in \mathcal{C}_c(X)$ defines a function

(4.4.31) $$F(\alpha, \sigma) := \mu(-\alpha)$$

in $\mathcal{C}_c(\mathcal{G}_S(X))$ since $\mathrm{Spec}_+ \mathcal{D}(X)$ is compact. By (4.4.30), we have

$$(\mathrm{Ad}(V)R(F)\varphi)(\alpha) = \int_{\Lambda^{\#}} \varphi(\beta)\, \mu(\alpha - \beta)\, d\beta = (W_\mu\varphi)(\alpha).$$

By [MR; Proposition 3.5], the C^*-algebra $C^*_{0_A}(\mathcal{G}_S(X))$ is generated by all convolution operators $R(F)$ with F given by (4.4.31). It follows that (4.4.29) induces a C^*-isomorphism

$$\mathrm{Ad}(V) : C^*_{0_A}(\mathcal{G}_S(X)) \underset{\approx}{\longrightarrow} \mathcal{W}(\Lambda^\#).$$

Now apply (4.4.28). Q.E.D.

In order to realize $\mathcal{G}_S(X)$ explicitly, we use the model (3.1.38) of Spec $\mathcal{D}(X)$, and the identification (3.1.37) of its compact subset $\mathrm{Spec}_+ \mathcal{D}(X)$. In order to describe the action of X on Spec $\mathcal{D}(X)$ note that, for any $\gamma \in X$, we have (in the notation of Theorem 3.1.21)

$$P_B(\gamma + \alpha_n) = P_B\gamma + P_B\alpha_n \to P_B\gamma + \beta$$

for $n \to \infty$. By weak* continuity of translations, this implies for $\alpha = \alpha_n$,

$$(4.4.32) \quad \gamma \ltimes \beta_B = w^* - \lim_n \gamma \ltimes \alpha_A = w^* - \lim_n (\gamma + \alpha)_A = (P_B\gamma + \beta)_B$$

so that the action of γ on the model (3.1.38) has the form $\gamma \ltimes (c,\beta) = (c, \gamma_0 + \beta)$, where $\gamma_0 = P_B\gamma \in X_0(c)$ is the Peirce 0-component. Hence we may identify

$$(4.4.33) \quad \mathcal{G}_S(X) = \{(\gamma,c,\beta) : c = c^2 \in X, \beta \in X_0^+(c), \gamma \in X, \gamma_0 + \beta \in X_0^+(c)\}.$$

4.4.34. THEOREM. *For every idempotent* $c \in X$ *and every* $a \in iX_0(c)^\perp = i(X_1(c) \oplus X_{1/2}(c))$ *there exists an irreducible representation*

$$(4.4.35) \qquad \tau_c^a : \mathcal{W}(\Lambda^\#) \to \mathcal{L}(L^2(\Lambda_c^\#))$$

of $\mathcal{W}(\Lambda^\#)$ *on the* L^2*-space of the (self-dual) homogeneous cone* $\Lambda_c = \pi_c(\Lambda) \subset X_0(c)$ *which is uniquely determined by the property*

$$(4.4.36) \qquad \tau_c^a(W_{\mu\nu}) = \mu_\#(a)\, W_\nu$$

for all continuous functions $\mu : X_0(c)^\perp \to \mathbb{C}$ *and* $\nu : X_0(c) \to \mathbb{C}$ *with compact support. The representations (4.4.35) are pairwise inequivalent.*

Proof. Define a $*$-representation

$$\tau_c^a : C_c(\mathcal{G}_S(X)) \to \mathcal{L}(L^2(\Lambda_c^\#))$$

by putting

$$(\tau_c^a(F)\xi)(\beta) := \int_{\{\beta \geq x_0\}} F(-x,c,\beta)\, e^{(x_1 + x_{1/2}|a)}\, \xi(\beta - x_0)\, dx$$

for all $\xi \in L^2(\Lambda_c^\#)$ and $\beta \in \Lambda_c^\#$ Here $x = x_1 + x_{1/2} + x_0$ is the Peirce decomposition of $x \in X$ relative to c. Then τ_c^a has an extension to a C*-representation on $C^*(\mathcal{G}_S(X))$. Now let $\mu \in C_c(X_0(c)^\perp)$ and $\nu \in C_c(X_0(c))$. Using (4.4.31), the function $F \in C_c(\mathcal{G}_S(X))$ defining the Wiener-Hopf operator $W_{\mu\nu}$ is given by

$$F(-x,c,\beta) = \mu(x)\, \nu(x) = \mu(x_1 + x_{1/2})\, \nu(x_0).$$

It follows that

$$(\tau_c^a(F)\xi)(\beta) = \int_{\{\beta \geq x_0\}} \mu(x_1 + x_{1/2})\, e^{(x_1 + x_{1/2}|a)}\, \nu(x_0)\, \xi(\beta - x_0)\, dx$$

$$= \int_{X_1 \oplus X_{1/2}} \mu(x_1 + x_{1/2})\, e^{(x_1 + x_{1/2}|a)} \int_{\Lambda_c^\#} \nu(\beta - y_0)\, \xi(y_0)\, dy_0$$

$$= \mu_\#(a)\, W_\nu \xi(\beta).$$

This proves (4.4.36) and shows that the representations (4.4.35) are irreducible. Using (4.4.36) it follows easily that, for different pairs $(c,a) \neq (c',a')$, the corresponding representations (4.4.35) have different null-spaces and are therefore inequivalent.

Q.E.D.

4.4.37. THEOREM. *For every symmetric cone* $\Lambda \subset X$ *of rank* r, *the Wiener-Hopf* C*-*algebra* $\mathcal{W}(\Lambda^\#)$ *admits a* C*-*filtration*

(4.4.38) $$\mathcal{J}_k := \bigcap_{p \in P_k} \bigcap_{a \in iX_0(p)^\perp} \operatorname{Ker} \tau_p^a$$

with essentially commutative graduation

(4.4.39) $$\mathcal{J}_{k+1}/\mathcal{J}_k \approx C_0(\Sigma_k) \otimes \mathcal{K}$$

where P_k *is the space of all rank k idempotents and*

(4.4.40) $$\Sigma_k := \bigcup_{p \in P_k} \{p\} \times iX_0(p)^\perp \subset P_k \times iX$$

is a vector bundle over P_k $(0 \le k \le r)$. (For $k = r$, $\mathcal{K}$ is missing).

4.4.41. COROLLARY. *The* C^**-representations* τ_c^a *defined in Theorem* 4.4.34 *constitute all irreducible representations of* $\mathcal{W}(\Lambda^\#)$ *up to unitary equivalence.*

The *proof* of Theorem 4.4.37 can be obtained using the explicit structure of the groupoid $\mathcal{G}_S(X)$ (cf. [MR]). Since $\mathcal{W}(\Lambda^\#)$ is C^*-isomorphic to the Toeplitz C^*-algebra $\mathcal{T}(iX)$ via (4.4.28), the preceding theorems can of course be reformulated in "holomorphic terms," using the Hardy space $H^2(iX)$ instead of $L^2(\Lambda^\#)$. Thus Theorem 4.4.37 can also be deduced from the more general Theorem 4.11.113 concerning bounded symmetric domains (cf. [U5]).

The Toeplitz C^*-algebra makes sense in greater generality, namely for the (symmetric) Siegel domains

$$\Pi = \{(u,v) \in U \times V : u + u^* + \Phi(v,v) \in \Lambda\}$$

introduced in (1.3.68). Here $U = X \oplus iX$ and $\Phi : V \times V \to U$ is a "Λ-positive" hermitian mapping. Consider the Hardy space $H^2(\Sigma)$ over the extreme boundary

$$\Sigma = \{(u,v) \in U \times V : u + u^* = -\Phi(v,v)\} = \{(a - \frac{\Phi(b,b)}{2}, b) : a \in iX, b \in V\}$$

of Π. Let $C_0(\Sigma)$ be the C^*-algebra of all continuous functions on Σ vanishing at infinity. For $f \in C_0(\Sigma)$, the multiplication operator

(4.4.42) $$f : L^2(\Sigma) \to L^2(\Sigma), \ h \mapsto fh$$

is bounded, and we define the *Hardy-Toeplitz operator* as the compression

(4.4.43) $$T_\Sigma(f) := E_\Sigma \, f \, E_\Sigma$$

of (4.4.42) along the orthogonal projection $E_\Sigma : L^2(\Sigma) \to H^2(\Sigma)$. Thus

$$T_\Sigma(f)h := E_\Sigma(fh)$$

for all $h \in H^2(\Sigma)$. Consider the *Toeplitz* C^*-*algebra*

$$(4.4.44) \qquad \mathcal{T}(\Sigma) := C^*(T_\Sigma(f) : f \in \mathcal{C}_0(\Sigma))$$

generated by the operators (4.4.43). In the special case $V = \{0\}$ and $\Phi = 0$, we obtain the tubular domains $\Pi = \Lambda \times iX$ with extreme boundary $\Sigma = iX$. One can show [U5; Proposition 2.4] that $\mathcal{T}(\Sigma)$ acts irreducibly on $H^2(\Sigma)$. By Theorem 1.3.82, the boundary components of Π have the form $h_{a,b}(\Pi_p)$ where $p = p^2 \in X$ is a non-zero idempotent and

$$(a,b) \in iX_0(p)^\perp \times V_0(p)^\perp$$

belongs to a vector space defined in terms of the Peirce decomposition (1.3.79) of $Z := U \oplus V$. Here

$$\Pi_p = \{(u,v) \in Z_0(p) : u + u^* + \Phi(v,v) \in \Lambda_p\}$$

is a symmetric Siegel domain contained in $Z_0(p)$, with respect to the open negative cone Λ_p of $X_0(p)$. Its extreme boundary is

$$\Sigma_p = \{(u,v) \in Z_0(p) : u + u^* = -\Phi(v,v)\} = \Sigma \cap Z_0(p).$$

4.4.45. THEOREM. *For every idempotent* $p \in X$ *and every* $(a,b) \in iX_0(p)^\perp \times V_0(p)$ *there exists an irreducible* C^*-*representation*

$$(4.4.46) \qquad \rho_{p,a,b} : \mathcal{T}(\Sigma) \to \mathcal{L}(H^2(\Sigma_p))$$

of $\mathcal{T}(\Sigma)$ *on the Hardy space* $H^2(\Sigma_p)$ *associated with the symmetric Siegel domain* Π_p *in* $Z_0(p)$ *and its extreme boundary* Σ_p. *This representation is uniquely determined by the property*

$$(4.4.47) \qquad \rho_{p,a,b}(T_\Sigma(f)) = T_{\Sigma_p}(f_p^{a,b})$$

for all $f \in \mathcal{C}_0(\Sigma)$, *where*

for all $f \in C_0(\Sigma)$, *where*

$$f_p^{a,b}(w) := f(h_{a,b}(w)) \tag{4.4.48}$$

for all $w \in \Sigma_p \subset \Sigma$. *The representations* (4.4.46) *are pairwise inequivalent.*

We define the "k-th extreme boundary"

$$\Sigma_k := \bigcup_{p \in P_k} \{p\} \times iX_0(p)^\perp \times V_0(p)^\perp \tag{4.4.49}$$

as a vector bundle over the compact space P_k of all rank k idempotents $p \in X$. Here $0 \le k \le r :=$ rank (Λ). By Theorem 1.3.82,

$$\partial_k \Pi = \bigcup_{(p,a,b) \in \Sigma_k} h_{a,b}(\Pi_p) \tag{4.4.50}$$

is the k-th "partial boundary" of Π, so that

$$\partial \Pi = \dot{\bigcup_{1 \le k \le r}} \partial_k \Pi \qquad \text{(disjoint union)}.$$

4.4.51. THEOREM. *For every symmetric Siegel domain* Π *of rank* r, *with extreme boundary* Σ, *the Hardy-Toeplitz* C^*-*algebra* $\mathcal{T}(\Sigma)$ *admits a* C^*-*filtration*

$$\mathcal{J}_k := \bigcap_{(p,a,b) \in \Sigma_k} \text{Ker } \rho_{p,a,b}$$

with essentially commutative graduation

$$\mathcal{J}_{k+1}/\mathcal{J}_k \approx C_0(\Sigma_k) \otimes \mathcal{K} \qquad (0 \le k < r),$$

$$\mathcal{J}_{r+1}/\mathcal{J}_r \approx C_0(\Sigma_r) = C_0(\Sigma).$$

Here we put $\mathcal{J}_{r+1} := \mathcal{T}(\Sigma)$ *and* $\mathcal{J}_0 := \{0\}$. *In particular, the representations* (4.4.46) *constitute all irreducible representations of* $\mathcal{T}(\Sigma)$, *up to unitary equivalence.*

This theorem follows also from the corresponding Theorem 4.11.113 for bounded symmetric domains. For details, cf. [U5].

4.5 Bergman-Toeplitz Operators Over Tubular Domains

In this section we study Toeplitz operators and their associated C^*-algebras, acting on (weighted) Bergman spaces $H^2_\lambda(\Pi)$ over a tubular domain $\Pi = \Lambda \times iX$, whose base Λ is a symmetric cone in a real Jordan algebra X. The weighted Bergman spaces and the associated multiplier C^*-algebras are introduced in Sections 2.4 and 3.2. We assume that Λ is irreducible. Let p be the genus (2.4.1). Let $\lambda > p - 1$ and consider the associated Lebesgue space $L^2_\lambda(\Pi)$ defined in (2.4.19).

4.5.1. DEFINITION. For any bounded function $f \in L^\infty(\Pi)$, the *multiplication operator* with *symbol* f is the bounded operator $f : L^2_\lambda(\Pi) \to L^2_\lambda(\Pi)$ defined for all $h \in L^2_\lambda(\Pi)$ and $z \in \Pi$ by

(4.5.2) $$(fh)(z) := f(z)h(z) .$$

Identifying the operator (4.5.2) with its symbol, we obtain an injective C^*-algebra homomorphism from $L^\infty(\Pi)$ onto an abelian C^*-subalgebra of $\mathcal{L}(L^2_\lambda(\Pi))$, the C^*-algebra of all bounded operators on $L^2_\lambda(\Pi)$. The translation action (2.4.6) of iX on $L^2_\lambda(\Pi)$ induces an adjoint action of iX on $\mathcal{L}(L^2_\lambda(\Pi))$ which satisfies for every $z \in iX$

$$\mathrm{Ad}(z^\#)f = z^\# f \qquad \text{(multiplication operator)}$$

where $(z^\# f)(w) := f(w - z)$ belongs to $L^\infty(\Pi)$. Consider the λ-Bergman space $H^2_\lambda(\Pi)$ over Π, with λ-Bergman projection $E_\lambda : L^2_\lambda(\Pi) \to H^2_\lambda(\Pi)$.

4.5.3. DEFINITION. The *λ-Bergman Toeplitz operator* $T_\lambda(f)$ with symbol $f \in L^\infty(\Pi)$ is defined as the compression

(4.5.4) $$T_\lambda(f) := E_\lambda \circ f|_{H^2_\lambda(\Pi)}$$

of the multiplication operator (4.5.2). Thus

(4.5.5) $$T_\lambda(f)h = E_\lambda(fh)$$

for every $h \in H^2_\lambda(\Pi)$.

The action (2.4.6) leaves $H^2_\lambda(\Pi)$ invariant and thus induces an adjoint action of iX on $\mathcal{L}(H^2_\lambda(\Pi))$ satisfying

(4.5.6) $$Ad(z^\#)T_\lambda(f) = T_\lambda(z^\# f)$$

for all $z \in iX$ and $f \in L^\infty(\Pi)$.

4.5.7. PROPOSITION. *For any* $f \in L^\infty(\Pi)$, $T_\lambda(f)$ *is a bounded operator on* $H^2_\lambda(\Pi)$ *satisfying*

(4.5.8) $$\|T_\lambda(f)\| \leq \|f\|_\infty,$$

(4.5.9) $$T_\lambda(f)^* = T_\lambda(\bar{f}).$$

Moreover, if $\varphi \in H^\infty_\lambda(\Pi) := H^2_\lambda(\Pi) \cap L^\infty(\Pi)$, *we have*

(4.5.10) $$T_\lambda(f)\ T_\lambda(\varphi) = T_\lambda(f\varphi),$$

(4.5.11) $$T_\lambda(\bar{\varphi})\ T_\lambda(f) = T_\lambda(\bar{\varphi} f).$$

Proof. As an operator in $L^2_\lambda(\Pi)$, we have

(4.5.12) $$T_\lambda(f) = E_\lambda\ f\ E_\lambda.$$ Q.E.D.

For every $\alpha \in \Lambda^\#$ consider the bounded function on Π given by

(4.5.13) $$\alpha_\#(z) = e^{\alpha \cdot z}.$$

4.5.14. DEFINITION. The *λ-Bergman-Toeplitz C^*-algebra* over Π is defined as the non-unital C^*-algebra

(4.5.15) $$\mathcal{T}_\lambda(\Pi) := C^*(T_\lambda(e^{z \cdot \alpha}) : \alpha \in \Lambda^\#)$$

generated by all λ-Bergman Toeplitz operators (4.5.5) on $H^2_\lambda(\Pi)$ with symbols of the form (4.5.13). Since $w^\#(e^{z\cdot\alpha}) = e^{w\cdot\alpha}e^{z\cdot\alpha}$ for all $\alpha \in \Lambda^\#$, it follows that $\mathcal{T}_\lambda(\Pi)$ is invariant under the adjoint action (4.5.6) of iX.

For $\lambda > p - 1$ let $\mathcal{D}_\lambda(X)$ be the λ-Bergman multiplier C^*-algebra on $L^2(X)$ defined in (3.2.4) and consider its spectrum Spec $\mathcal{D}_\lambda(X)$. The translation action (4.4.16) of X on $\mathcal{D}_\lambda(X)$ induces a natural action

(4.5.16) $$\text{Spec } \mathcal{D}_\lambda(X) \leftarrow X \times \text{Spec } \mathcal{D}_\lambda(X), \quad \alpha \ltimes \sigma \leftarrow\!\shortmid (\alpha,\sigma)$$

defined by

(4.5.17) $$(\alpha \ltimes \sigma)\varphi := \sigma(\alpha_\#\varphi) \, .$$

for all $\varphi \in \mathcal{D}_\lambda(X) \subset L^\infty(X)$. For the characters β_A $(\beta \in X)$ defined in (3.2.5) we have

(4.5.18) $$\alpha \ltimes \beta_A = (\alpha + \beta)_A$$

for all $\beta,\alpha \in X$. Consider the polar cone $\Lambda^\#$ of Λ. By Proposition 3.2.11, the closure $\text{Spec}_+ \mathcal{D}_\lambda(X)$ is compact.

4.5.19. DEFINITION. Consider the transformation groupoid $X \ltimes \text{Spec } \mathcal{D}_\lambda(X)$ associated with the action (4.4.16). The reduced groupoid

(4.5.20) $$\mathcal{G}_\lambda(X) := X \times \text{Spec } \mathcal{D}_\lambda(X)|_{\text{Spec}_+\mathcal{D}_\lambda(X)}$$

with unit space $\text{Spec}_+ \mathcal{D}_\lambda(X)$ is called the *λ-Bergman groupoid* over Λ.

Since $0 \in \Lambda^\#$, we may consider the Dirac measure 0_A on $\text{Spec}_+ \mathcal{D}_\lambda(X)$ and obtain the associated spatial groupoid C^*-algebra

(4.5.21) $$C^*_{0_A}(\mathcal{G}_\lambda(X)) \subset \mathcal{L}(L^2(\mathcal{G}_\lambda(X)))$$

defined in (4.3.41).

4.5.22. THEOREM. *The Bergman-Toeplitz C^*-algebra $\mathcal{T}_\lambda(\Pi)$ is spatially equivalent to the Bergman groupoid C^*-algebra* $C^*_{0_\Lambda}(\mathcal{G}_\lambda(X))$.

Proof. For every $\alpha \in \Lambda^\#$, define the "unilateral shift"

$$[\alpha_\#] : L^2(\Lambda^\#) \to L^2(\Lambda^\#)$$

be putting

$$[\alpha_\#]\varphi(\beta) := \begin{cases} \varphi(\beta-\alpha) & \text{if } \beta - \alpha \in \Lambda^\# \\ 0 & \text{if } \beta - \alpha \notin \Lambda^\# \end{cases} \tag{4.5.23}$$

for all $\varphi \in L^2(\Lambda^\#)$ and $\beta \in \Lambda^\#$. Consider the multiplication operator $\chi_\gamma : L^2(\Lambda^\#) \to L^2(\Lambda^\#)$ by the bounded function

$$\chi_\gamma(\alpha) := \left(\frac{\Delta(\alpha)}{\Delta(\alpha + \gamma)}\right)^{\lambda/2-p/4} \tag{4.5.24}$$

on $\Lambda^\#$. The composition $[\alpha_\#] \cdot \chi_\alpha$ is called a *weighted shift operator.* Now consider the transform (2.4.27). Then there exists a commuting diagram

$$\begin{array}{ccc} H^2_\lambda(\Pi) & \xrightarrow{\ ()^\#\ } & L^2(\Lambda^\#) \\ {\scriptstyle T_\lambda(e^{z\cdot\alpha})}\downarrow & & \downarrow{\scriptstyle [\alpha_\#]\cdot\chi_\alpha} \\ H^2_\lambda(\Pi) & \xrightarrow[\ ()^\#\ ]{} & L^2(\Lambda^\#) \end{array}$$

for every $\alpha \in \Lambda^\#$. In fact, we have for all $\varphi \in L^2(\Lambda^\#)$

$$\sqrt{\Gamma_\Lambda(\lambda)}\ ([\alpha_\#]\chi_\alpha\varphi)_\#(z) = \int_{\Lambda^\#} e^{z\cdot\gamma}\ ([\alpha_\#]\chi_\alpha\varphi)(\gamma)\ \Delta(\gamma)^{\lambda/2-p/4}\ d\gamma$$

$$= \int_{\alpha+\Lambda^\#} e^{z\cdot\gamma}\,(\chi_\alpha\varphi)(\gamma - \alpha)\ \Delta(\gamma)^{\lambda/2-p/4}\ d\gamma = \int_{\alpha+\Lambda^\#} e^{z\cdot\gamma}\ \varphi(\gamma - \alpha)\ \Delta(\gamma - \alpha)^{\lambda/2-p/4}\ d\gamma$$

$$= \int_{\Lambda^\#} e^{z\cdot(\alpha+\beta)}\ \varphi(\beta)\ \Delta(\beta)^{\lambda/2-p/4}\ d\beta = \sqrt{\Gamma_\Lambda(\lambda)}\ e^{z\cdot\alpha}\ \varphi_\#(z).$$

Since the operators $T_\lambda(e^{z\cdot\alpha})$ generate $\mathcal{T}_\lambda(\Pi)$ by (4.5.15), it follows that $\mathcal{F} := ()^\#$ realizes $\mathcal{T}_\lambda(\Pi)$ as a C^*-subalgebra of the C^*-algebra $\mathcal{W}_\lambda(\Lambda^\#)$ generated by the operators (4.5.23) and (4.5.24). For $\alpha, \beta \in \Lambda^\#$ we have

$$\Delta(\alpha + \beta) = \Delta(P_\beta^{1/2}(P_\beta^{-1/2}\alpha + e)) = \Delta(\beta)\, \Delta(P_\beta^{-1/2}\alpha + e).$$

Since $P_\beta^{-1/2}\alpha \to 0$ as $\alpha \to \infty$ (in the Λ-ordering) it follows that

$$\lim_{\beta\to\infty} \chi_\alpha(\beta) = 1$$

for every $\alpha \in \Lambda^\#$. Thus $\chi_\alpha \geq \varepsilon > 0$ for every α which shows that

$$\chi_\alpha = (T_\lambda(e^{z\cdot\alpha})^* T_\lambda(e^{z\cdot\alpha}))^{1/2} \in \mathcal{T}_\lambda(\Pi)$$

is invertible and $[\alpha_\#] = T_\lambda(e^{z\cdot\alpha}) \cdot \chi_\alpha^{-1} \in \mathcal{T}_\lambda(\Pi)$. It follows that

(4.5.25) $$\mathrm{Ad}(\mathcal{F}) : \mathcal{T}_\lambda(\Pi) \xrightarrow[\approx]{} \mathcal{W}_\lambda(\Lambda^\#)$$

is a C^*-isomorphism. Now consider the groupoid $\mathcal{G}_\lambda(X)$. As in the proof of Theorem 4.4.25 one shows that

(4.5.26) $$(V\varphi)(\alpha) := \varphi(-\alpha, \alpha_A) \qquad (\alpha \in \Lambda^\#)$$

defines a Hilbert space isomorphism $V : L^2(\mathcal{G}_\lambda(X)) \xrightarrow[\approx]{} L^2(\Lambda^\#)$ such that the convolution operator $R(F)$ induced by $F \in \mathcal{C}_c(\mathcal{G}_\lambda(X))$ has the form

(4.5.27) $$(\mathrm{Ad}(V)R(F))\varphi(\alpha) = \int_{\Lambda^\#} \varphi(\beta)\, F(\beta - \alpha, \alpha_A)\, d\beta$$

for all $\varphi \in L^2(\Lambda^\#)$ and $\alpha \in \Lambda^\#$. Every $\alpha \in \Lambda^\#$ defines a function

(4.5.28) $$F_\alpha(\beta,\sigma) := \delta_{\alpha,-\beta},$$

which belongs to $\mathcal{C}_c(\mathcal{G}_\lambda(X))$ since $\mathrm{Spec}_+\, \mathcal{D}_\lambda(X)$ is compact. By (4.5.27),

$$\mathrm{Ad}(V)R(F_\alpha) = [\alpha_\#]$$

is the unilateral shift. For every $\mu \in L^1(X)$, we have $\mu_\# \chi_\alpha \in \mathcal{D}_\lambda(X)$ by (3.2.4). Therefore there exists a function $G_{\mu,\alpha} \in \mathcal{C}_c(\mathcal{G}_\lambda(X))$ with

$$G_{\mu,\alpha}(\beta,\sigma) = \sigma(\mu_\# \chi_\alpha) \cdot \delta_{\beta,0} \tag{4.5.29}$$

for all $(\beta,\sigma) \in \mathcal{G}_\lambda(X)$. In particular, $G_{\mu,\alpha}(\beta, \gamma_A) = (\mu_\# \chi_\alpha)(\gamma) \cdot \delta_{\beta,0}$ for all $\gamma \in \Lambda^\#$, and (4.5.27) implies

$$\mathrm{Ad}(G_{\mu,\alpha})_\# \varphi = (\mu_\# \chi_\alpha)\varphi$$

for all $\varphi \in L^2(\Lambda^\#)$. For all $\alpha, \beta \in \Lambda^\#$ and $\mu \in L^1(X)$, we have the convolution formulas

$$(F_\alpha)_\#(G_{\mu,\beta})_\#(F_\alpha^*) = \widehat{\alpha_\#(\mu_\# \chi_\beta)}, \tag{4.5.30}$$

$$(F_\alpha^*)_\#(G_{\mu,\beta})_\#(F_\alpha) = \widehat{(-\alpha)_\#(\mu_\# \chi_\beta)} \tag{4.5.31}$$

as functions supported on $\{0\} \times \mathrm{Spec}_+ \mathcal{D}_\lambda(X) \subset \mathcal{G}_\lambda(X)$. Here $\hat{\varphi}$ denotes the Gelfand transform of $\varphi \in \mathcal{D}_\lambda(X)$ on the spectrum. Since $\mathcal{D}_\lambda(X)$ is generated by the functions $\alpha_\#(\mu_\# \chi_\beta)$ and $(-\alpha)_\#(\mu_\# \chi_\beta)$, it follows that

$$\mathcal{C}(\{0\} \times \mathrm{Spec}_+ \mathcal{D}_\lambda(X)) \subset \mathcal{C}_c(\mathcal{G}_\lambda(X))$$

is generated by the functions (4.5.30) and (4.5.31). Taking translations, one shows that $\mathcal{C}_c(\mathcal{G}_\lambda(X))$ is generated by the functions (4.5.30) and (4.5.31). Thus (4.5.27) yields a C^*-isomorphism

$$\mathrm{Ad}(V) : C^*_{0_A}(\mathcal{G}_\lambda(X)) \xrightarrow[\approx]{} \mathcal{W}_\lambda(\Lambda^\#). \tag{4.5.32}$$

Now combine (4.5.25) and (4.5.32). Q.E.D.

We will now, following Section 3.2, give an explicit realization of $\mathcal{G}_\lambda(X)$. By Theorem 3.2.6 every sequence $\alpha = \alpha_n \in \Lambda^\#$ gives rise, after passing to a subsequence, to a character

$$\beta_B = w^* - \lim_{n \to \infty} \alpha_A \in \mathcal{D}_\lambda(X),$$

where $\beta = \lim P_B\alpha \in X_0(c)$ and P_B is the orthogonal projection onto the tangent space $T(B) = X_0(c)$ for a face $B \subset A := \bar{\Lambda}$ determined by the idempotent $c \in X$. It follows that we may identify

$$\text{(4.5.33)} \qquad \mathrm{Spec}_+ \mathcal{D}_\lambda(X) \approx \{(c,\beta) : c = c^2 \in X, \beta \in X_0^+(c)\},$$

where $X_0^+(c) = P_B\Lambda^\#$ is the closed positive cone of $X_0(c)$. Comparing with (4.4.33), we see that $\mathrm{Spec}_+ \mathcal{D}_\lambda(X)$ can be identified with $\mathrm{Spec}_+ \mathcal{D}(X)$, although the characters β_B associated with $\beta \in X_0^+(c)$ act differently on $\mathcal{D}(X)$ and $\mathcal{D}_\lambda(X)$. Applying (4.5.18) and (4.4.32), it follows that the action of $\gamma \in X$ is still given by $\gamma \ltimes (c,\beta) = (c, \gamma_0 + \beta)$ where $\gamma_0 \in X_0(c)$ is the Peirce 0-component. Thus

$$\mathcal{G}_\lambda(X) \approx \{(\gamma,c,\beta) \in X \times X \times X : c = c^2, \beta \in X_0^+(c), \gamma_0 + \beta \in X_0^+(c)\}.$$

The analysis of the Toeplitz C*-algebra $\mathcal{T}_\lambda(\Pi)$ and its representations could be carried out similarly as in Section 4.4. For an alternative approach applying to more general situations, cf. [U11].

4.6 Hardy-Toeplitz Operators Over Polycircular Domains

In this section we study Toeplitz operators and their associated C*-algebras, acting on the Hardy space $H^2(\mathbb{T}^r)$ over a polycircular domain $\Omega = e^\Lambda \cdot \mathbb{T}^r$ in $(\mathbb{C}^\times)^r$. We assume that Ω is bounded and log-conical, i.e., the logarithmic base Λ is a convex cone in $\mathbb{R}^r_<$. Then $S = \mathbb{T}^r$ is the Shilov boundary of Ω. The Hardy space and its associated multiplier C*-algebra are described in Sections 2.5 and 3.3.

4.6.1. DEFINITION. For any bounded function $f \in L^\infty(\mathbb{T}^r)$, the *multiplication operator* with *symbol* f is the bounded operator $f : L^2(\mathbb{T}^r) \to L^2(\mathbb{T}^r)$ defined for all $h \in L^2(\mathbb{T}^r)$ and $z \in \mathbb{T}^r$ by

$$\text{(4.6.2)} \qquad (fh)(z) := f(z)h(z) .$$

Identifying the operator (4.6.2) with its symbol yields an injective C*-algebra homomorphism from $L^\infty(\mathbb{T}^r)$ onto an abelian C*-subalgebra of $\mathcal{L}(L^2(\mathbb{T}^r))$, the C*-algebra of all bounded operators on $L^2(\mathbb{T}^r)$. The translation action (2.5.2) of $\mathbb{T}^r$ on $L^2(\mathbb{T}^r)$ induces an adjoint action of $\mathbb{T}^r$ on $\mathcal{L}(L^2(\mathbb{T}^r))$ which satisfies for every $z \in \mathbb{T}^r$

$$\mathrm{Ad}(z^\#)f = z^\# f \quad \text{(multiplication operator)}$$

where $(z^\# f)(w) := f(\bar{z}w)$ belongs to $L^\infty(\mathbb{T}^r)$. Now consider the Hardy space $H^2(\mathbb{T}^r)$ over Ω, with Szegö projection $E : L^2(\mathbb{T}^r) \to H^2(\mathbb{T}^r)$.

4.6.3. DEFINITION. The *Hardy-Toeplitz operator* $T_S(f)$ with *symbol* $f \in L^\infty(\mathbb{T}^r)$ is defined as the compression

(4.6.4) $$T_S(f) := E \circ f|_{H^2(\mathbb{T}^r)}$$

of the multiplication operator (4.6.2). Thus

(4.6.5) $$T_S(f)h = E(f\, h)$$

for every $h \in H^2(\mathbb{T}^r)$.

The translation action (2.5.2) of $\mathbb{T}^r$ on $L^2(\mathbb{T}^r)$ leaves $H^2(\mathbb{T}^r)$ invariant and thus induces an adjoint action of $\mathbb{T}^r$ on $\mathcal{L}(H^2(\mathbb{T}^r))$ which satisfies

(4.6.6) $$\mathrm{Ad}(z^\#)T_S(f) = T_S(z^\# f)$$

for all $z \in \mathbb{T}^r$ and $f \in L^\infty(\mathbb{T}^r)$.

4.6.7. PROPOSITION. *For every* $f \in L^\infty(\mathbb{T}^r)$, $T_S(f)$ *is a bounded operator on* $H^2(\mathbb{T}^r)$ *satisfying*

(4.6.8) $$\|T_S(f)\| \le \|f\|_\infty,$$

(4.6.9) $$T_S(f)^* = T_S(\bar{f}).$$

Moreover, if $\varphi \in H^\infty(\mathbb{T}^r) := H^2(\mathbb{T}^r) \cap L^\infty(\mathbb{T}^r)$, *we have*

(4.6.10) $$T_S(f)\, T_S(\varphi) = T_S(f\varphi),$$

(4.6.11) $$T_S(\bar{\varphi})\, T_S(f) = T_S(\bar{\varphi} f).$$

Proof. As an operator on $L^2(\mathbb{T}^r)$ we have

$$T_S(f) = E\, f\, E. \tag{4.6.12}$$

Q.E.D.

Consider the subalgebra $\mathcal{C}(\mathbb{T}^r)$ of $L^\infty(\mathbb{T}^r)$ consisting of all continuous functions.

4.6.13. DEFINITION. The *Hardy-Toeplitz C^*-algebra* over Ω is defined as the unital C^*-algebra

$$\mathcal{T}_\Omega(\mathbb{T}^r) := C^*(T_S(f) : f \in \mathcal{C}(\mathbb{T}^r)) \tag{4.6.14}$$

generated by all Hardy-Toeplitz operators (4.6.4) on $H^2(\mathbb{T}^r)$ with continuous symbol $f \in \mathcal{C}(\mathbb{T}^r)$.

Since $z^\# f \in \mathcal{C}(\mathbb{T}^r)$ for all $z \in \mathbb{T}^r$ and $f \in \mathcal{C}(\mathbb{T}^r)$, it follows that $\mathcal{T}_\Omega(\mathbb{T}^r)$ is invariant under the adjoint action (4.6.6) of $\mathbb{T}^r$. Putting

$$\alpha_\#(z) := z^\alpha = z_1^{\alpha_1} \cdots z_r^{\alpha_r} \tag{4.6.15}$$

for all $z \in \mathbb{T}^r$ and $\alpha \in \mathbb{Z}^r$, we have

$$\mathcal{T}_\Omega(\mathbb{T}^r) := C^*(T_S(\alpha_\#) : \alpha \in \mathbb{Z}^r), \tag{4.6.16}$$

since the functions (4.6.15) are total in $\mathcal{C}(\mathbb{T}^r)$ by the Stone-Weierstrass Theorem.

Let $\mathcal{D}(\mathbb{Z}^r)$ be the Hardy multiplier C^*-algebra on $L^2(\mathbb{Z}^r)$ defined in (3.3.18) and consider its spectrum Spec $\mathcal{D}(\mathbb{Z}^r)$. The translation action (3.3.10) of $\mathbb{Z}^r$ on $\mathcal{D}(\mathbb{Z}^r)$ induces a natural action

$$\text{Spec}\, \mathcal{D}(\mathbb{Z}^r) \leftarrow \mathbb{Z}^r \times \text{Spec}\, \mathcal{D}(\mathbb{Z}^r),\ \alpha \ltimes \sigma \leftarrow\!\shortmid (\alpha, \sigma) \tag{4.6.17}$$

defined for all $\varphi \in \mathcal{D}(\mathbb{Z}^r) \subset L^\infty(\mathbb{Z}^r)$ by

$$(\alpha \ltimes \sigma)\varphi := \sigma(\alpha_\# \varphi) \tag{4.6.18}$$

For the characters β_A $(\beta \in \mathbb{Z}^r)$ defined in (3.3.19), we have

(4.6.19) $$\alpha \ltimes \beta_A = (\alpha + \beta)_A.$$

Let $\Lambda^\#$ be the polar cone of Λ. By Proposition 3.3.31, the subset $\mathrm{Spec}_+ \mathcal{D}(\mathbb{Z}^r)$ of $\mathrm{Spec}\, \mathcal{D}(\mathbb{Z}^r)$ is compact.

4.6.20. DEFINITION. Consider the transformation groupoid $\mathbb{Z}^r \times \mathrm{Spec}\, \mathcal{D}(\mathbb{Z}^r)$ associated with the action (4.5.17). The reduced groupoid

(4.6.21) $$\mathcal{G}_S(\mathbb{Z}^r) := \mathbb{Z}^r \times \mathrm{Spec}\, \mathcal{D}(\mathbb{Z}^r)|_{\mathrm{Spec}_+ \mathcal{D}(\mathbb{Z}^r)}$$

with unit space $\mathrm{Spec}_+ \mathcal{D}(\mathbb{Z}^r)$ is called the *Hardy groupoid* for Ω.

Since $0 \in \Lambda^\# \cap \mathbb{Z}^r$ we may consider the Dirac measure 0_A on $\mathrm{Spec}_+ \mathcal{D}(\mathbb{Z}^r)$, and obtain the associated spatial groupoid C^*-algebra

(4.6.22) $$C^*_{0_A}(\mathcal{G}_S(\mathbb{Z}^r)) \subset \mathcal{L}(L^2(\mathcal{G}_S(\mathbb{Z}^r))$$

defined in (4.3.41).

4.6.23. THEOREM. *The Hardy-Toeplitz C^*-algebra is spatially equivalent to the Hardy groupoid C^*-algebra* $C^*_{0_A}(\mathcal{G}_S(\mathbb{Z}^r))$.

Proof. For every $\mu \in L^1(\mathbb{Z}^r)$, define the convolution operator $\mu_\#: L^2(\mathbb{Z}^r) \to L^2(\mathbb{Z}^r)$ by

(4.6.24) $$(\mu_\# \varphi)(\beta) := \sum_{\alpha \in \mathbb{Z}^r} \varphi(\beta - \alpha)\, \mu(\alpha).$$

The compression

$$W_\mu := \chi\, \mu_\#\, \chi$$

of (4.6.24) onto the subspace $L^2(\Lambda^\# \cap \mathbb{Z}^r)$ is called the *discrete Wiener-Hopf operator* with symbol μ. By definition,

(4.6.25) $$W_\mu \varphi(\beta) = \sum_{\alpha \in \Lambda^\# \cap \mathbb{Z}^r} \mu(\beta - \alpha)\, \varphi(\alpha)$$

for all $\varphi \in L^2(\Lambda^\# \cap \mathbb{Z}^r)$ and $\beta \in \Lambda^\# \cap \mathbb{Z}^r$. For the function $\alpha(\beta) := \delta_{\alpha,\beta}$ (Kronecker delta) with $\alpha \in \mathbb{Z}^r$,

$$\alpha_\# \varphi(\beta) := \varphi(\beta - \alpha)$$

is the bilateral shift, and W_α becomes the "unilateral" shift determined by $\Lambda^\# \cap \mathbb{Z}^r$. For $\alpha = 0$, we obtain the identity. Now consider the Fourier transform (2.5.8). By standard Fourier theory, there exists a commuting diagram

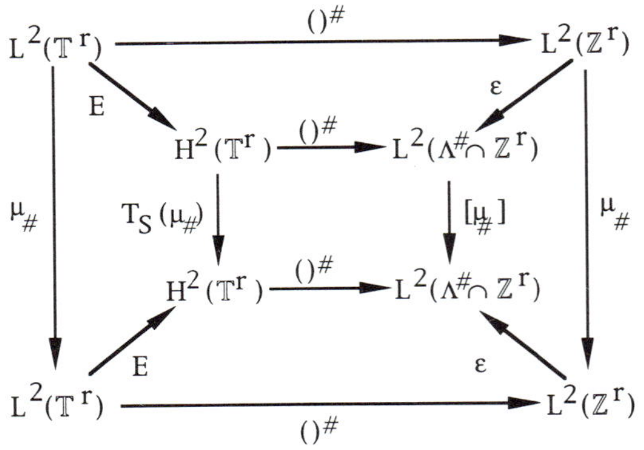

for every $\mu \in L^1(\mathbb{Z}^r)$. Here $\mu_\#$ on the left denotes multiplication by the inverse Fourier transform $\mu_\#$, and $T_S(\mu_\#)$ is the corresponding Toeplitz operator. Since these operators generate $\mathcal{T}_\Omega(\mathbb{T}^r)$ by (4.5.16), the restriction $\mathcal{F}$ of ()# to $H^2(\mathbb{T}^2)$ induces a C^*-isomorphism

$$\text{(4.6.26)} \qquad \mathrm{Ad}(\mathcal{F}) : \mathcal{T}_\Omega(\mathbb{T}^r) \xrightarrow[\approx]{} \mathcal{W}(\Lambda^\# \cap \mathbb{Z}^r)$$

onto the *Wiener-Hopf* C^**-algebra* $\mathcal{W}(\Lambda^\# \cap \mathbb{Z}^r)$, generated by all Wiener-Hopf operators (4.6.25). Now consider the groupoid $\mathcal{G}_S(\mathbb{Z}^r)$ and the "base point" 0_A of its unit space $\mathrm{Spec}_+ \mathcal{D}(\mathbb{Z}^r)$. By (4.3.29) we have

$$\int_{\mathcal{G}_S(\mathbb{Z}^r)} \Phi(\alpha, \sigma)\, \overleftarrow{d}\, 0_A(\alpha, \sigma) = \int_{\mathrm{Spec}_+ \mathcal{D}(\mathbb{Z}^r)} \sum_{\alpha \in \mathbb{Z}^r} \Phi(\alpha, -\alpha \ltimes \sigma)\, d0_A(\sigma)$$

$$= \sum_{\alpha \in \mathbb{Z}^r} \Phi(\alpha, -\alpha \ltimes 0_A) = \sum_{\alpha \in \Lambda^\# \cap \mathbb{Z}^r} \Phi(-\alpha, \alpha_A)$$

since Φ has support in $\mathcal{G}_S(\mathbb{Z}^r)$. It follows that

$$(V\Phi)(\alpha) := \Phi(-\alpha,\alpha_A) \qquad (\alpha \in \Lambda^\# \cap \mathbb{Z}^r) \tag{4.6.27}$$

defines a Hilbert space isomorphism $V : L^2(\mathcal{G}_S(\mathbb{Z}^r)) \xrightarrow[\approx]{} L^2(\Lambda^\# \cap \mathbb{Z}^r)$. Under this isomorphism, the convolution operator $R(F)$ induced by $F \in \mathcal{C}_c(\mathcal{G}_S(\mathbb{Z}^r))$ has the form

$$(\mathrm{Ad}(V)R(F))\varphi(\alpha) = R(F)(V^{-1}\varphi)(-\alpha, \alpha_A)$$

$$= \sum_{\beta\in\mathbb{Z}^r} (V^{-1}\varphi)(-\alpha - \beta, \beta \ltimes \alpha_A)\, F(\beta, \alpha_A) \tag{4.6.28}$$

$$= \sum_{\beta\in\mathbb{Z}^r} \varphi(\alpha + \beta)\, F(\beta, \alpha_A) = \sum_{\gamma\in\Lambda^\#\cap\mathbb{Z}^r} \varphi(\gamma)\, F(\gamma - \alpha, \alpha_A)$$

for all $\varphi \in L^2(\Lambda^\# \cap \mathbb{Z}^r)$ and $\alpha \in \Lambda^\# \cap \mathbb{Z}^r$. Every $\mu \in \mathcal{C}_c(\mathbb{Z}^r)$ defines a function

$$F(\beta,\sigma) := \mu(-\beta) \tag{4.6.29}$$

in $\mathcal{C}_c(\mathcal{G}_S(\mathbb{Z}^r))$ since $\mathrm{Spec}_+\, \mathcal{D}(\mathbb{Z}^r)$ is compact. By (4.6.28), we have

$$(\mathrm{Ad}(V)R(F)\varphi)(\beta) = \sum_{\gamma\in\Lambda^\#\cap\mathbb{Z}^r} \varphi(\gamma)\, \mu(\beta - \gamma) = W_\mu\varphi(\beta).$$

In the special case $F(\beta,\sigma) = \delta_{\alpha,-\beta}$ for $\alpha \in \mathbb{Z}^r$, we obtain the unilateral shift W_α. By [MR; Proposition 3.5], the C^*-algebra $C^*_{0_A}(\mathcal{G}_S(\mathbb{Z}^r))$ is generated by all convolution operators $R(F)$ with F given by (4.6.29). It follows that (4.6.27) induces a C^*-isomorphism

$$\mathrm{Ad}(V) : C^*_{0_A}(\mathcal{G}_S(\mathbb{Z}^r)) \xrightarrow[\approx]{} \mathcal{W}(\Lambda^\# \cap \mathbb{Z}^r). \tag{4.6.30}$$

Now combine (4.6.26) and (4.6.30). Q.E.D.

We will now, following Section 3.3, give an explicit realization of $\mathcal{G}_S(\mathbb{Z}^r)$. By Theorem 3.3.23, every sequence $\alpha = \alpha_n \in \Lambda^\#$ gives rise, after passing to a subsequence, to a character

$$\beta_B = w^* - \lim_{n\to\infty} \alpha_A \in \text{Spec } \mathcal{D}(\mathbb{Z}^r)$$

where $\beta = \lim P_B\alpha \in T(B)$ and P_B is the orthogonal projection onto the tangent space $T(B)$ for a face $B \subset A := \bar{\Lambda}$. It follows that we may identify

$$(4.6.31) \qquad \text{Spec}_+ \mathcal{D}(\mathbb{Z}^r) \approx \{(B,\beta) : B \text{ face of } \bar{\Lambda},\ \beta \in T(B)^+ := P_B\Lambda^{\#}\}.$$

For any fixed $\gamma \in \mathbb{Z}^r$, we have $P_B(\gamma + \alpha_n) = P_B\gamma + P_B\alpha_n \to P_B\gamma + \beta$ as $n \to \infty$, so that (4.6.19) implies, for $\alpha = \alpha_n$,

$$\gamma \ltimes \beta_B = w^* - \lim \gamma \ltimes \alpha_A = w^* - \lim(\gamma + \alpha)_A = (P_B\gamma + \beta)_B.$$

Hence

$$(4.6.32) \qquad \gamma \ltimes (B,\beta) = (B,\ P_B\gamma + \beta)$$

is the action of $\mathbb{Z}^r$. Combining with (4.6.31), we may identify

$$(4.6.33)\ \mathcal{G}_S(\mathbb{Z}^r) \approx \{(\gamma,B,\beta): \gamma \in \mathbb{Z}^r,\ B \text{ face of } \bar{\Lambda},\ \beta \in T(B)^+,\ P_B\gamma + \beta \in T(B)^+\}.$$

A complete analysis of the resulting Toeplitz C*-algebra is carried out in Section 4.7 in the setting of Bergman spaces.

4.7 Bergman-Toeplitz Operators Over Polycircular Domains

In this section we study Toeplitz operators and their associated C*-algebras acting on the Bergman space $H^2(\Omega)$ over a polycircular domain $\Omega = e^{\Lambda} \cdot \mathbb{T}^r$ whose logarithmic base Λ is a convex domain in $\mathbb{R}^r_<$. The Bergman space and its associated multiplier C*-algebra are discussed in Sections 2.6 and 3.4. We assume that Ω contains the origin.

Since Ω is a bounded domain in $\mathbb{C}^r$, we define the *multiplication operators*

$$(4.7.1) \qquad f : L^2(\Omega) \to L^2(\Omega)$$

for $f \in L^\infty(\Omega)$, and the associated *Bergman-Toeplitz operators*

$$(4.7.2) \qquad T_\Omega(f) := E_\Omega\, f\, E_\Omega$$

on $H^2(\Omega)$ as in Section 4.1. The translation action (2.6.2) of $\mathbb{T}^r$ on $L^2(\Omega)$ induces an adjoint action of $\mathbb{T}^r$ on $\mathcal{L}(L^2(\Omega))$ such that for $z \in \mathbb{T}^r$

$$\mathrm{Ad}(z^\#)f = z^\# f \quad \text{(multiplication operator)}$$

where $(z^\# f)(w) := f(\bar{z}w)$ belongs to $L^\infty(\Omega)$. The action (2.6.2) leaves $H^2(\Omega)$ invariant and thus induces an adjoint action of $\mathbb{T}^r$ on $H^2(\Omega)$ satisfying

$$\text{(4.7.3)} \qquad \mathrm{Ad}(z^\#)T_\Omega(f) = T_\Omega(z^\# f)$$

for all $z \in \mathbb{T}^r$ and $f \in L^\infty(\Omega)$. As in Definition 4.1.13 we define the *Bergman-Toeplitz C^*-algebra* over Ω,

$$\text{(4.7.4)} \qquad \mathcal{T}(\Omega) := C^*(T_\Omega(f) : f \in \mathcal{C}(\bar{\Omega})) = C^*(T_\Omega(z^\alpha) : \alpha \in \mathbb{N}^r),$$

where $z^\alpha := z_1^{\alpha_1} \cdots z_r^{\alpha_r}$. The realization (4.7.4) of $\mathcal{T}(\Omega)$ is a special case of Proposition 4.1.14. Since $w^\# f \in \mathcal{C}(\bar{\Omega})$ whenever $w \in \mathbb{T}^r$ and $f \in \mathcal{C}(\bar{\Omega})$, it follows that $\mathcal{T}(\Omega)$ is invariant under the adjoint action (4.7.3) of $\mathbb{T}^r$. Equivalently, we have $w^\# z^\alpha = \bar{w}^\alpha z^\alpha$ for all $\alpha \in \mathbb{N}^r$.

Let $\mathcal{D}_\Omega(\mathbb{Z}^r)$ be the Bergman multiplier C^*-algebra on $L^2(\mathbb{Z}^r)$ defined in (3.4.4) and consider its spectrum $\mathrm{Spec}\ \mathcal{D}_\Omega(\mathbb{Z}^r)$. The translation action of $\mathbb{Z}^r$ on $\mathcal{D}_\Omega(\mathbb{Z}^r)$ induces a natural action

$$\text{(4.7.5)} \qquad \mathrm{Spec}\ \mathcal{D}_\Omega(\mathbb{Z}^r) \leftarrow \mathbb{Z}^r \times \mathrm{Spec}\ \mathcal{D}_\Omega(\mathbb{Z}^r), \quad \alpha \ltimes \sigma \leftarrow\!\shortmid (\alpha, \sigma)$$

defined by

$$\text{(4.7.6)} \qquad (\alpha \ltimes \sigma)\varphi := \sigma(\alpha_\# \varphi)$$

for all $\varphi \in \mathcal{D}_\Omega(\mathbb{Z}^r) \subset L^\infty(\mathbb{Z}^r)$. For the characters β_A defined in (3.4.5) we have

$$\text{(4.7.7)} \qquad \alpha \ltimes \beta_A = (\alpha + \beta)_A.$$

By Proposition 3.4.27, the closure $\mathrm{Spec}_+\ \mathcal{D}_\Omega(\mathbb{Z}^r)$ is compact.

4.7.8. DEFINITION. Consider the transformation groupoid $\mathbb{Z}^r \times \text{Spec } \mathcal{D}_\Omega(\mathbb{Z}^r)$ associated with the action (4.7.5). The reduced groupoid

$$(4.7.9) \qquad \mathcal{G}_\Omega(\mathbb{Z}^r) := \mathbb{Z}^r \times \text{Spec } \mathcal{D}_\Omega(\mathbb{Z}^r)|_{\text{Spec}_+ \mathcal{D}_\Omega(\mathbb{Z}^r)}$$

with unit space $\text{Spec}_+ \mathcal{D}_\Omega(\mathbb{Z}^r)$ is called the *Bergman groupoid* for Ω. Since $0 \in \mathbb{N}^r$, we may consider the Dirac measure 0_A on $\text{Spec}_+ \mathcal{D}_\Omega(\mathbb{Z}^r)$ and obtain the associated spatial groupoid C^*-algebra

$$(4.7.10) \qquad C^*_{0_A}(\mathcal{G}_\Omega(\mathbb{Z}^r)) \subset \mathcal{L}(L^2(\mathcal{G}_\Omega(\mathbb{Z}^r))$$

defined in (4.3.41).

4.7.11. THEOREM. *The Bergman-Toeplitz C^*-algebra $\mathcal{T}(\Omega)$ is spatially equivalent to a C^*-subalgebra of the Bergman groupoid C^*-algebra*

$C^*_{0_A}(\mathcal{G}_\Omega(\mathbb{Z}^r))$, which agrees with $C^*_{0_A}(\mathcal{G}_\Omega(\mathbb{Z}^r))$ in case Ω has no "virtual faces".

Proof. For every $\alpha \in \mathbb{N}^r$, define the "unilateral" shift $[\alpha_\#] : L^2(\mathbb{N}^r) \to L^2(\mathbb{N}^r)$ by putting

$$(4.7.12) \qquad [\alpha_\#]\varphi(\beta) := \begin{cases} \varphi(\beta-\alpha) & \text{if } \beta - \alpha \in \mathbb{N}^r \\ 0 & \text{if } \beta - \alpha \notin \mathbb{N}^r \end{cases}$$

for all $\varphi \in L^2(\mathbb{N}^r)$ and $\beta \in \mathbb{N}^r$. Define also the multiplication operator $\chi_\alpha : L^2(\mathbb{N}^r) \to L^2(\mathbb{N}^r)$ by the (bounded) function

$$(4.7.13) \qquad \chi_\alpha(\beta) := \frac{\|z^{\alpha+\beta}\|_\Omega}{\|z^\beta\|_\Omega} \qquad (\beta \in \mathbb{N}^r).$$

The composition $[\alpha_\#]\chi_\alpha$ is called a *weighted shift operator*. For $\alpha = 0$, we obtain the identity.

Now consider the transform (2.6.7). Then there exists a commuting diagram

$$\begin{array}{ccc} H^2(\Omega) & \xrightarrow{\ ()^\#\ } & L^2(\mathbb{N}^r) \\ {\scriptstyle T_\Omega(z^\alpha)}\downarrow & & \downarrow{\scriptstyle [\alpha_\#]\chi_\alpha} \\ H^2(\Omega) & \xrightarrow[\ ()^\#\ ]{} & L^2(\mathbb{N}^r) \end{array}$$

for every $\alpha \in \mathbb{N}^r$. In fact, we have for all $\alpha \in \mathbb{N}^r$ and the corresponding δ-functions, $([\alpha_\#]\chi_\alpha)\beta = \chi_\alpha(\beta) \cdot (\alpha + \beta)$ whereas

$$T_\Omega(z^\alpha)\beta_\# = z^\alpha \frac{z^\beta}{\|z^\beta\|_\Omega} = \frac{z^{\alpha+\beta}}{\|z^\beta\|_\Omega} = \frac{\|z^{\alpha+\beta}\|_\Omega}{\|z^\beta\|_\Omega}(\alpha + \beta)_\# = \chi_\alpha(\beta) \cdot (\alpha + \beta)_\#.$$

Since the operators $T_\Omega(z^\alpha)$ generate $\mathcal{T}(\Omega)$ by (4.7.4), it follows that $\mathcal{F} := ()\#$ induces a C^*-embedding

(4.7.14) $$\mathrm{Ad}(\mathcal{F}) : \mathcal{T}(\Omega) \to \mathcal{W}_\Omega(\mathbb{N}^r)$$

into the C^*-algebra $\mathcal{W}_\Omega(\mathbb{N}^r)$ generated by the operators (4.7.12) and (4.7.13). Now consider the groupoid $\mathcal{G}_\Omega(\mathbb{Z}^r)$. As in the proof of Theorem 4.6.23 one shows that

(4.7.15) $$(V\varphi)(\alpha) := \varphi(-\alpha, \alpha_A) \qquad (\alpha \in \mathbb{N}^r)$$

defines a Hilbert space isomorphism $V : L^2(\mathcal{G}_\Omega(\mathbb{Z}^r)) \xrightarrow[\approx]{} L^2(\mathbb{N}^r)$ such that the convolution operator $R(F)$ induced by $F \in \mathcal{C}_c(\mathcal{G}_\Omega(\mathbb{Z}^r))$ has the form

(4.7.16) $$(\mathrm{Ad}(V)R(F)\varphi)(\alpha) = \sum_{\beta \in \mathbb{N}^r} \varphi(\beta)\, F(\beta - \alpha, \alpha_A)$$

for all $\varphi \in L^2(\mathbb{N}^r)$ and $\alpha \in \mathbb{N}^r$. Every $\alpha \in \mathbb{N}^r$ defines a function

(4.7.17) $$F_\alpha(\beta, \sigma) := \delta_{\alpha,-\beta}$$

which belongs to $\mathcal{C}_c(\mathcal{G}_\Omega(\mathbb{Z}^r))$ since $\mathrm{Spec}_+ \mathcal{D}_\Omega(\mathbb{Z}^r)$ is compact. By (4.7.16), $\mathrm{Ad}(V)R(F_\alpha) = [\alpha_\#]$ is the unilateral shift. Since

$$\chi_\alpha = 0_\# \chi_\alpha \in \mathcal{D}_\Omega(\mathbb{Z}^r)$$

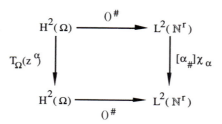

there is a continuous function $G_\alpha \in \mathcal{C}_c(\mathcal{G}_\Omega(\mathbb{Z}^r))$ such that

$$G_\alpha(\gamma,\sigma) = \sigma(\chi_\alpha) \cdot \delta_{\gamma,0} \tag{4.7.18}$$

for all $(\gamma,\sigma) \in \mathcal{G}_\Omega(\mathbb{Z}^r)$. In particular, $G_\alpha(\gamma, \beta_A) = \chi_\alpha(\beta) \cdot \delta_{\gamma,0}$ for all $\beta \in \mathbb{N}^r$. By (4.7.16), we have $\mathrm{Ad}(V)R(G_\alpha)\varphi = \chi_\alpha\varphi$ for all $\varphi \in L^2(\mathbb{N}^r)$. For all $\alpha, \beta \in \mathbb{N}^r$, we have the convolution formulas

$$F_\alpha \# G_\beta \# F_\alpha^* = \widehat{\alpha_\# \chi_\beta} , \tag{4.7.19}$$

$$F_\alpha^* \# G_\beta \# F_\alpha = \widehat{(-\alpha)_\# \chi_\beta} \tag{4.7.20}$$

as functions on $\{0\} \times \mathrm{Spec}_+ \mathcal{D}_\Omega(\mathbb{Z}^r) \subset \mathcal{G}_\Omega(\mathbb{Z}^r)$. Here $\hat{\varphi}$ denotes the Gelfand transform of $\varphi \in \mathcal{D}_\Omega(\mathbb{Z}^r)$ on the spectrum. Since $\mathcal{D}_\Omega(\mathbb{Z}^r)$ is generated by the functions $\alpha_\#\chi_\beta$ and $(-\alpha)_\#\chi_\beta$, it follows that

$$\mathcal{C}(\{0\} \times \mathrm{Spec}_+ \mathcal{D}_\Omega(\mathbb{Z}^r)) \subset \mathcal{C}_c(\mathcal{G}_\Omega(\mathbb{Z}^r))$$

is generated by the functions (4.7.19) and (4.7.20). Taking translations, one shows that $\mathcal{C}_c(\mathcal{G}_\Omega(\mathbb{Z}^r))$ is generated by the functions (4.7.19) and (4.7.20). Thus (4.7.15) induces a C^*-isomorphism

$$\mathrm{Ad}(V) : C^*_{0_A}(\mathcal{G}_\Omega(\mathbb{Z}^r)) \xrightarrow[\approx]{} \mathcal{W}_\Omega(\mathbb{N}^r). \tag{4.7.21}$$

Now combine (4.7.14) and (4.7.21) to obtain the first assertion. Now suppose Ω has no virtual faces (for details, cf. [SSU]). Then there exists $\delta > 0$ such that

$$\Omega_\delta := \bigcup_{1\le j\le r} \{z \in \mathbb{B}^r : |z_j| < \delta\} \subset \Omega.$$

Since

$$\pi^{-r} \int_{\Omega_\delta} |z^\alpha|^2 \, dV(z) = \frac{\delta^{2|\alpha|+r}}{(\alpha_1 + 1) \cdots (\alpha_r + 1)}$$

and $|z^{\alpha+\beta}|^2 \ge \delta^{2|\alpha|}|z^\beta|^2$ for all $z \in \Omega\backslash\Omega_\delta$, it follows that $\chi_\alpha(\beta) \ge \varepsilon > 0$ for all $\alpha,\beta \in \mathbb{N}^r$. Therefore the operators

$$\chi_\alpha = (T_\Omega(z^\alpha)^* \, T_\Omega(z^\alpha))^{1/2} \in \mathcal{T}(\Omega)$$

are invertible which implies $U_\alpha := T_\Omega(z^\alpha)\chi_\alpha^{-1} \in \mathcal{T}(\Omega)$ for all $\alpha \in \mathbb{N}^r$. It follows that

(4.7.22) $$\mathrm{Ad}(\mathcal{F}) : \mathcal{T}(\Omega) \xrightarrow[\approx]{} \mathcal{W}_\Omega(\mathbb{N}^r)$$

is a C^*-isomorphism. Q.E.D.

We will now, following Section 3.4, give an explicit realization of $\mathcal{G}_\Omega(\mathbb{Z}^r)$. By Theorem 3.4.9, every sequence $\alpha = \alpha_n \in \Lambda^\#$ gives rise, after passing to a subsequence, to a character

$$\beta_B = w^* - \lim_{n\to\infty} \alpha_A \in \mathrm{Spec}\, \mathcal{D}_\Omega(\mathbb{Z}^r)$$

where $\beta = \lim P_B\alpha \in T(B)$ and P_B is the orthogonal projection onto the tangent space $T(B)$ for a face $B \subset A := \bar{\Lambda}$. It follows that we may identify

(4.7.23) $$\mathrm{Spec}_+\, \mathcal{D}_\Omega(\mathbb{Z}^r) \approx \{(B,\beta) : B \text{ face of } \bar{\Lambda},\ \beta \in T(B)^+ = P_B\Lambda^\#\}.$$

For any fixed $\gamma \in \mathbb{Z}^r$, we have $P_B(\gamma + \alpha_n) = P_B\gamma + P_B\alpha_n \to P_B\gamma + \beta$ as $n \to \infty$, so that (4.7.7) implies, for $\alpha = \alpha_n$,

(4.7.24) $$\gamma \ltimes \beta_B = w^* - \lim \gamma \ltimes \alpha_A = w^* - \lim (\gamma + \alpha)_A = (P_B\gamma + \beta)_B.$$

Hence the action of $\mathbb{Z}^r$ is given by

(4.7.25) $$\gamma \ltimes (B,\beta) = (B, P_B\gamma + \beta),$$

giving rise to the groupoid

(4.7.26) $$\mathcal{G}_\Omega(\mathbb{Z}^r) \approx \{(\gamma,B,\beta) : \gamma \in \mathbb{Z}^r,\ B \text{ face of } \bar{\Lambda},\ \beta \in T(B)^+,\ P_B\gamma + \beta \in T(B)^+\}.$$

Consider now the case $r = 2$ [SSU]:

4.7.27. THEOREM. *Let $\Omega \subset \mathbb{C}^2$ be a bounded bicircular domain, with Bergman-Toeplitz C^*-algebra $\mathcal{T}(\Omega)$. Assume that Ω has no virtual faces. Then $\mathcal{T}(\Omega)$ has a filtration*

(4.7.28) $$\mathcal{K}(H^2(\Omega)) = I_1 \subset I_2 \subset \mathcal{T}(\Omega)$$

such that for $0 \le k \le 2$ *(putting* $I_0 := \{0\}$ *and* $I_3 := \mathcal{T}(\Omega)$*) we have*

$$I_{k+1}/I_k \cong \int_B^{\oplus} C^*(\mathcal{F}_B) \tag{4.7.29}$$

(C^**-algebraic sum or integral) where* B *runs over all faces of* $\bar{\Lambda}$ *of codimension* k (i.e., dim B = 2 - k) *and* $C^*(\mathcal{F}_B)$ *is the* C^**-algebra of the corresponding foliation* $\mathcal{F}_B$ of $\mathbb{T}^2$ (cf. [C4]).

Proof. For $0 \le k \le 2$, put

$$X_k := \dot{\bigcup_B} \operatorname{Spec}_B \mathcal{D}_\Omega(\mathbb{Z}^2) \qquad \text{(disjoint union)}$$

where B runs over all faces of $\bar{\Lambda}$ of dimension 2 - k. By Proposition 3.4.27, we have

$$X_+ := \operatorname{Spec}_A \mathcal{D}_\Omega(\mathbb{Z}^2)^{cl} = X_0 \,\dot{\cup}\, X_1 \,\dot{\cup}\, X_2.$$

For $k = 0$, i.e., $B = A = \bar{\Lambda}$ we have $T(B) = \mathbb{R}^2$ and $P_B = \text{id}$. Using (4.7.25) it follows that $X_0 = \operatorname{Spec}_A \mathcal{D}_\Omega(\mathbb{Z}^2)$ is an open groupoid-invariant subset of the unit space X_+ of $\mathcal{G} := \mathcal{G}_\Omega(\mathbb{Z}^2)$. Here invariant means a union of orbits (cf. [MR]). The reduced groupoid

$$\mathcal{G}|_{X_0} = \mathbb{Z}^2 \ltimes \mathbb{Z}_+^2 \mid \mathbb{Z}_+^2 \approx \mathbb{Z}_+^2 \times \mathbb{Z}_+^2$$

is isomorphic to the trivial groupoid. Thus

$$I_1 := C^*(\mathcal{G}|_{X_0}) \approx \mathcal{K}(L^2(\mathbb{Z}_+^2)) \tag{4.7.30}$$

is the C^*-algebra of compact operators. Now consider the "boundary" $\partial X_+ := X_1 \cup X_2$. Then X_1 is an open invariant subset of ∂X_+. In general, if $Y \subset Z$ are closed invariant subsets of X_+, there is an exact sequence

$$0 \to C^*(\mathcal{G}|_{Z \setminus Y}) \to C^*(\mathcal{G}|_Z) \xrightarrow{\pi(Y,Z)} C^*(\mathcal{G}|_Y) \to 0$$

with quotient mapping $\pi(Y,Z)$. By (4.7.30), we have $I_1 = \text{Ker}\ \pi(\partial X_+, X_+)$. Put

$$I_2 := \text{Ker}\ \pi(X_2, \partial X_+) = \pi(\partial X_+, X_+)^{-1}\ C^*(\mathcal{G}|_{X_1}).$$

Then we have C*-algebra isomorphisms

$$\pi(\partial X_+, X_+) : I_2/I_1 \underset{\approx}{\longrightarrow} C^*(\mathcal{G}|_{X_1}), \tag{4.7.31}$$

$$\pi(X_2, \partial X_+) : C^*(\mathcal{G})/I_2 \underset{\approx}{\longrightarrow} C^*(\mathcal{G}|_{X_2}). \tag{4.7.32}$$

For the proof of Theorem 4.7.27 it suffices to analyze the quotient C*-algebras $C^*(\mathcal{G}|_{X_k})$, $k = 1,2$. Consider first the case $k = 2$. Let $\partial_2\bar{\Lambda}$ denote the extreme boundary (singleton faces) of $\bar{\Lambda}$. Then

$$\mathcal{G}|_{X_2} \approx \mathbb{Z}^2 \ltimes \partial_2\bar{\Lambda} \qquad \text{(trivial action)} \tag{4.7.33}$$

and hence

$$C^*(\mathcal{G}|_{X_2}) \approx C^*(\mathbb{Z}^2 \ltimes \partial_2\bar{\Lambda}) = C(\mathbb{T}^2) \otimes C_0(\partial_2\bar{\Lambda}) = C_0(\mathbb{T}^2 \times \partial_2\bar{\Lambda}). \tag{4.7.34}$$

In order to study $C^*(\mathcal{G}|_{X_1})$, let $B \subset \bar{\Lambda}$ be a 1-dimensional face. By Proposition 3.4.27, there is a homeomorphism

$$\chi_B: \overline{P_B\Lambda^\#} \to \text{Spec}_B\ \mathcal{D}_\Omega(\mathbb{Z}^2) =: X_0(B)$$

given by $\chi_B\beta = \beta_B$ (cf. 3.4.12)) for all $\beta \in \overline{P_B\Lambda^\#}$. Since B is exposed,

$$B = \{x \in \bar{\Lambda} : x \cdot u = \sup_{x \in \bar{\Lambda}} x \cdot u\}$$

for some unit vector $u = (u_1,u_2) \in \mathbb{R}^2_+$. Then $T(B) = \mathbb{R}u^\perp$ and $P_Bx = x \cdot u^\perp$. Suppose first that $u_2 = 0$, i.e., $u = (1,0)$. Then $\overline{P_B\Lambda^\#} = \mathbb{Z}_+$ and χ_B becomes an equivariant map for the (restricted) action $\gamma \ltimes \beta := \beta - \gamma_2$ on $\mathbb{Z}^2$. Hence

$$C^*(\mathcal{G}|_{X_0(B)}) \approx C^*(\mathbb{Z}^2 \ltimes X_0(B)|_{X_0(B)}) \approx C^*(\mathbb{Z}^2 \ltimes \mathbb{Z}_+|_{\mathbb{Z}_+})$$

(4.7.35)
$$= \mathcal{C}(\mathbb{T}) \otimes C^*(\mathbb{Z}_+ \times \mathbb{Z}_+) \approx \mathcal{C}(\mathbb{T}) \otimes \mathcal{K}(L^2(\mathbb{Z}_+)) \approx C^*(\mathcal{F}_B).$$

The case $u = (0,1)$ is analogous. Now suppose $u_1 > 0$, $u_2 > 0$. Then $X_0(B)$ is invariant under the $\mathbb{Z}^2$-action and χ_B is equivariant for the action

(4.7.36)
$$\gamma \ltimes \beta := \beta - \gamma \cdot u^{\perp}$$

of $\mathbb{Z}^2$ on the subgroup $\overline{P_B \Lambda^\#} = \overline{\mathbb{Z}_+^2 \cdot u^{\perp}} \cap \mathbb{R}$ of $\mathbb{R}$. Therefore

(4.7.37)
$$C^*(\mathcal{G}|_{X_0(B)}) = \mathbb{Z}^2 \ltimes \mathcal{C}_0(X_0(B)) \approx \mathbb{Z}^2 \ltimes \mathcal{C}_0(\overline{P_B \Lambda^\#})$$

is a crossed product [P1]. In case $\theta = u_2/u_1$ is rational, write $\theta = p/q$ for relatively prime integers $p,q > 0$. By [SSU, Lemma 3.1]

$$\overline{P_B \Lambda^\#} = \|(p,q)\|^{-1} \cdot \mathbb{Z} \approx \mathbb{Z}$$

via the mapping $\beta \mapsto -\|(p,q)\|\beta$. Via this isomorphism, the action (4.7.36) has the form

(4.7.38)
$$\gamma \ltimes c = c + \gamma_2 q - \gamma_1 p$$

for all $c \in \mathbb{Z}, \gamma \in \mathbb{Z}^2$. Choose $a,b \in \mathbb{Z}_>$ with $bq - ap = 1$. Then (q,p) and (a,b) form a basis of $\mathbb{Z}^2$ and $(q,p) \ltimes c = c$ while $(a,b) \ltimes c = c + 1$. Therefore

(4.7.39)
$$\mathbb{Z}^2 \ltimes \mathcal{C}_0(\overline{P_B \Lambda^\#}) \approx \mathbb{Z}^2 \ltimes \mathcal{C}_0(\mathbb{Z})$$
$$\approx (\mathbb{Z} \ltimes \mathcal{C}_0(\mathbb{Z})) \otimes \mathcal{C}(\mathbb{T}) \approx \mathcal{K}(L^2(\mathbb{Z})) \otimes \mathcal{C}(\mathbb{T}) \approx C^*(\mathcal{F}_B).$$

In case $\theta = u_2/u_1$ is irrational, the mapping $\beta \mapsto c = u_1^{-1}\beta$ gives an isomorphism $\overline{P_B \Lambda^\#} \approx \mathbb{R}$ such that the action (4.7.36) becomes

(4.7.40)
$$\gamma \ltimes c = c + \gamma \cdot (\theta, -1)$$

for all $c \in \mathbb{R}$ and $\gamma \in \mathbb{Z}^2$. Applying Proposition 5.6.26 below we obtain

$$(4.7.41) \qquad \mathbb{Z}^2 \ltimes \mathcal{C}_0(\overline{P_B \Lambda^\#}) \approx \mathbb{Z}^2 \underset{\theta}{\ltimes} \mathcal{C}_0(\mathbb{R}) \approx C^*(\mathcal{F}_\theta) = C^*(\mathcal{F}_B)$$

since $T(B) = \mathbb{R}u^\perp = \mathbb{R}(\theta,-1)$ implies $\mathcal{F}_\theta = \mathcal{F}_B$. Since $C^*(\mathcal{G}|_{X_1})$ is the C^*-algebraic sum of the C^*-algebras $C^*(X_0(B))$ for all 1-dimensional faces $B \subset \bar{\Lambda}$, the assertion follows. Q.E.D.

4.8 Hopf C^*-Algebras

In this section, we present the basic facts concerning Hopf C^*-algebras, following [LPRS] and [V1]. For a Hilbert space H, let $\mathcal{L}(H)$ be the C^*-algebra of all bounded operators on H, and denote by $\mathcal{K}(H)$ the C^*-subalgebra of all compact operators. A C^*-subalgebra $\mathcal{A} \subset \mathcal{L}(H)$ is called *full* (or non-degenerate) if $\{a \cdot \xi : a \in \mathcal{A}, \xi \in H\}$ is dense in H [D1; Proposition 2.2.6]. Equivalently, for every non-zero $\eta \in H$ there exists $a \in A$ with $a \cdot \eta \neq 0$ [P1; 2.2.4].

4.8.1. DEFINITION. Let $\mathcal{A}$ be a full C^*-subalgebra of $\mathcal{L}(H)$. The *multiplier algebra*

$$(4.8.2) \qquad \bar{\mathcal{A}} := \{x \in \mathcal{L}(H) : x\mathcal{A} + \mathcal{A}x \subset \mathcal{A}\}$$

is a unital C^*-algebra containing $\mathcal{A}$ as a C^*-ideal. The *strict topology* on $\bar{\mathcal{A}}$ is generated by the family of semi-norms $x \mapsto ||xa|| + ||bx||$, where $a, b \in \mathcal{A}$ are arbitrary.

One can show that $\bar{\mathcal{A}}$ is independent of the choice of full embedding $\mathcal{A} \subset \mathcal{L}(H)$ and coincides with the completion of $\mathcal{A}$ with respect to the strict topology (which is weaker than the norm topology).

4.8.3. EXAMPLE. For a locally compact space S, the abelian C^*-algebra

$$(4.8.4) \qquad \mathcal{C}_0(S) := \{S \xrightarrow{f} \mathbb{C} : f \text{ continuous, vanishing at } \infty\}$$

with pointwise operations

$$(f_1 \cdot f_2)(s) := f_1(s) \cdot f_2(s), \; f^*(s) := f(s)^*$$

and norm

$$\|f\|_\infty := \sup_{s \in S} |f(s)|$$

has the multiplier algebra

$$\overline{\mathcal{C}_0(S)} = \mathcal{C}_b(S) = \{S \xrightarrow{f} \mathbb{C} : f \text{ continuous, bounded}\} \tag{4.8.5}$$

[V1; Example 0.2.2]. Moreover, on norm-bounded subsets of $\mathcal{C}_b(S)$, the strict topology agrees with the topology of *compact convergence* [V1; Lemma 0.2.3]. Here we realize $\mathcal{C}_0(S)$ as a full C^*-algebra $\mathcal{C}_0(S) \subset \mathcal{L}(L^2(S))$ of multiplication operators

$$(f \cdot \varphi)(s) := f(s)\varphi(s)$$

on the Hilbert space

$$L^2(S) := \{S \xrightarrow{\varphi} \mathbb{C} : \varphi \ \mu\text{-measurable}, \int_S |\varphi|^2 \, d\mu < \infty\}$$

of complex functions, where μ is a measure with full support on S.

4.8.6. EXAMPLE. Let G be a locally compact unimodular group, with Haar measure ds. For $u \in L^1(G)$, consider the left convolution operators $u^\#$ on $L^2(G)$ defined by

$$(u^\# h)(t) := \int_G h(s^{-1}t) \; u(s) \; ds$$

for all $h \in L^2(G)$ and $t \in G$. The norm-closure

$$C^*(G) := C^*(u^\# : u \in L^1(G)) \subset \mathcal{L}(L^2(G)) \tag{4.8.7}$$

is a full C^*-subalgebra [D1; Proposition 13.3.1] called the *spatial group C^*-algebra* of G. Its multiplier algebra

$$\overline{C^*(G)} \tag{4.8.8}$$

is a C^*-subalgebra of the spatial group von Neumann algebra

$$W^*(G) = W^*(s^\# : s \in G) \subset \mathcal{L}(L^2(G)) \tag{4.8.9}$$

generated by the left-regular representation defined by

$$(s^\# h)(t) := h(s^{-1}t) \tag{4.8.10}$$

for all $s, t \in G$ and $h \in L^2(G)$. If G is compact, then the C^*-algebras (4.8.8) and (4.8.9) coincide. Now suppose G is abelian. Let

$$G^\# := \{G \xrightarrow{\alpha} U(\mathbb{C}) : \alpha \quad \text{continuous homomorphism}\}$$

denote its character group. Choosing compatible Haar measures on G and $G^\#$, respectively, we have a Hilbert space isomorphism

$$L^2(G) \underset{\approx}{\xrightarrow{()^\#}} L^2(G^\#), \ h \mapsto h^\# \tag{4.8.11}$$

given by the Fourier transform

$$h^\#(\alpha) := \int_G h(s)\ \alpha(s)^*\ ds$$

for all $h \in L^2(G)$ and $\alpha \in G^\#$. By basic Fourier theory there is a commuting diagram

$$\begin{array}{ccc} L^2(G) & \xleftarrow{\ u^\#\ } & L^2(G) \\ {\scriptstyle ()^\#}\downarrow & & \downarrow{\scriptstyle ()^\#} \\ L^2(G^\#) & \xleftarrow[(u^\# \alpha))]{} & L^2(G^\#) \end{array}$$

for all $u \in \mathcal{C}_c(G) \subset L^1(G)$. Here $(u^\#(\alpha))$ is the multiplication operator by the function

$$u^\#(\alpha) := \int_G u(s)\ \alpha(s)^*\ ds \qquad (\alpha \in G^\#)$$

on $G^\#$. It follows that (4.8.10) induces a C^*-isomorphism

$$\mathcal{L}(L^2(G)) \xrightarrow[\approx]{} \mathcal{L}(L^2(G^\#))$$

by which the spatial group C^*-algebra $C^*(G)$ is isomorphic to the C^*-algebra $\mathcal{C}_0(G^\#)$, realized by multiplication operators on $L^2(G^\#)$.

Let $\mathcal{A}$ and $\mathcal{B}$ be C^*-algebras, realized as full C^*-subalgebras $\mathcal{A} \subset \mathcal{L}(H)$, $\mathcal{B} \subset \mathcal{L}(K)$ for some Hilbert spaces H and K, respectively. Let $H \otimes K$ be the Hilbert space tensor product. The norm closure

$$\mathcal{A} \otimes \mathcal{B} \subset \mathcal{L}(H \otimes K) \tag{4.8.12}$$

of the algebraic tensor product of $\mathcal{A}$ and $\mathcal{B}$, acting on $H \otimes K$ in the natural way, is called the *spatial tensor* product of $\mathcal{A}$ and $\mathcal{B}$ [V1; Définition 0.1.1]. The C^*-algebra $\mathcal{A} \otimes \mathcal{B}$ is independent of the choice of full embeddings of $\mathcal{A}$ and $\mathcal{B}$, and (4.8.12) is a full C^*-embedding of $\mathcal{A} \otimes \mathcal{B}$. Let $\overline{\mathcal{A} \otimes \mathcal{B}}$ be the multiplier algebra, and define C^*-subalgebras

$$\overleftarrow{\mathcal{A} \otimes \mathcal{B}} := \{x \in \overline{\mathcal{A} \otimes \mathcal{B}} : x(i_H \otimes \mathcal{B}) + (i_H \otimes \mathcal{B})x \subset \mathcal{A} \otimes \mathcal{B}\}, \tag{4.8.13}$$

$$\overrightarrow{\mathcal{A} \otimes \mathcal{B}} := \{x \in \overline{\mathcal{A} \otimes \mathcal{B}} : x(\mathcal{A} \otimes i_K) + (\mathcal{A} \otimes i_K)x \subset \mathcal{A} \otimes \mathcal{B}\}. \tag{4.8.14}$$

Here i_H and i_K denote the identity operators on H and K, respectively.

4.8.15. EXAMPLE. For a locally compact space S and a C^*-algebra $\mathcal{A}$, the C^*-algebra

$$\mathcal{C}_0(S,\mathcal{A}) := \{S \xrightarrow{F} \mathcal{A} : F \text{ norm-continuous, } \|F\| \text{ vanishing at } \infty\} \tag{4.8.16}$$

with operations

$$(F_1 \cdot F_2)(s) := F_1(s)F_2(s), \; F^*(s) := F(s)^*$$

and norm

$$\|F\|_\infty := \sup_{s \in S} \|F(s)\|$$

has the multiplier algebra

$$\mathcal{C}_b(S,\overline{\mathcal{A}}) := \{S \xrightarrow{F} \overline{\mathcal{A}} : F \text{ strictly continuous, } \|F\| \text{ bounded}\} \tag{4.8.17}$$

[V1; Example 0.2.2]. Here we realize $\mathcal{C}(S,\mathcal{A})$ as a full C^*-subalgebra $\mathcal{C}_0(S,\mathcal{A}) \subset \mathcal{L}(L^2(S,H))$ of multiplication operators

$$(F \cdot \Phi)(s) := F(s)\Phi(s) \tag{4.8.18}$$

on the Hilbert space

$$L^2(S,H) := \{S \xrightarrow{\Phi} H : \Phi \text{ strongly } \mu\text{-measurable}, \int_S \|\Phi\|^2 \, d\mu < \infty\}$$

of H-valued mappings, where μ is a measure with full support on S and $\mathcal{A}$ is realized as a full C^*-subalgebra of $\mathcal{L}(H)$ for some Hilbert space H. We may identify

$$H \otimes L^2(S) = L^2(S,H) \tag{4.8.19}$$

by putting $(h \otimes \varphi)(s) := h \cdot \varphi(s)$ for all $\varphi \in L^2(S)$, $h \in H$ and $s \in S$. Using the multiplication representation (4.8.18) we may identify

$$\mathcal{A} \otimes \mathcal{C}_0(S) = \mathcal{C}_0(S, \mathcal{A}) \tag{4.8.20}$$

by putting $(a \otimes f)(s) = a \cdot f(s)$ for all $f \in \mathcal{C}_0(S)$, $a \in \mathcal{A}$ and $s \in S$. Combining (4.8.20) and (4.8.17), it follows that

$$\overline{\mathcal{A} \otimes \mathcal{C}_0(S)} = \mathcal{C}_b(S,\overline{\mathcal{A}}) = \{S \xrightarrow{F} \overline{\overline{\mathcal{A}}} : F \text{ strictly continuous}, \|F\| \text{ bounded}\}. \tag{4.8.21}$$

For the "reduced" multiplier algebras defined in (4.8.13) and (4.8.14) we obtain by [V1; Example 0.2.14]

$$\begin{aligned} \overleftarrow{\mathcal{A} \otimes \mathcal{C}_0(S)} &:= \{x \in \mathcal{C}_b(S,\overline{\overline{\mathcal{A}}}) : x(i_H \otimes \mathcal{C}_0(S)) + (i_H \otimes \mathcal{C}_0(S))x \subset \mathcal{A} \otimes \mathcal{C}_0(S)\} \\ &= \mathcal{C}_b(S,\mathcal{A}) = \{S \xrightarrow{F} \mathcal{A} : F \text{ norm-continuous}, \|F\| \text{ bounded}\} \end{aligned} \tag{4.8.22}$$

and

$$\begin{aligned} \overrightarrow{\mathcal{A} \otimes \mathcal{C}_0(S)} &:= \{x \in \mathcal{C}_b(S,\overline{\overline{\mathcal{A}}}) : x(\mathcal{A} \otimes 1_S) + (\mathcal{A} \otimes 1_S)x \subset \mathcal{A} \otimes \mathcal{C}_0(S)\} \\ &= \mathcal{C}_0(S,\overline{\overline{\mathcal{A}}}) = \{S \xrightarrow{F} \overline{\overline{\mathcal{A}}} : F \text{ strictly continuous}, \|F\| \text{ vanishing at } \infty\}. \end{aligned} \tag{4.8.23}$$

Here 1_S is the constant function 1 on S.

4.8.24. EXAMPLE. Let S and T be locally compact spaces and consider full measures μ and ν on S and T, respectively. Let $\mu \times \nu$ be the (full) product measure on $S \times T$. We may identify

$$L^2(T) \otimes L^2(S) = L^2(T \times S) \tag{4.8.25}$$

by putting $(\psi \otimes \varphi)(t,s) := \psi(t)\varphi(s)$ for all $\varphi \in L^2(S)$, $\psi \in L^2(T)$, $s \in S$ and $t \in T$. Using the multiplication representation (4.8.18) we may identify

$$\mathcal{C}_0(T) \otimes \mathcal{C}_0(S) = \mathcal{C}_0(T \times S) \tag{4.8.26}$$

by putting $(g \otimes f)(t,s) := g(t)f(s)$ for all $f \in \mathcal{C}_0(S)$, $s \in S$, $g \in \mathcal{C}_0(T)$, and $t \in T$. For the multiplier algebras, we obtain by Example 4.8.15

$$\overline{\overline{\mathcal{C}_0(T \times S)}} = \mathcal{C}_b(T \times S) = \mathcal{C}_b(S, \mathcal{C}_b(T)), \tag{4.8.27}$$

$$\overrightarrow{\mathcal{C}_0(T) \otimes \mathcal{C}_0(S)} = \mathcal{C}_0(S, \mathcal{C}_b(T)), \tag{4.8.28}$$

$$\overleftarrow{\mathcal{C}_0(T) \otimes \mathcal{C}_0(S)} = \mathcal{C}_b(S, \mathcal{C}_0(T)). \tag{4.8.29}$$

4.8.30. EXAMPLE. Let G_1 and G_2 be locally compact groups and consider the direct product group $G_1 \times G_2$, with the product Haar measure. Identifying $L^2(G_1) \otimes L^2(G_2) = L^2(G_1 \times G_2)$ and using the respective left-regular representations, we obtain for the spatial tensor product

$$C^*(G_1) \otimes C^*(G_2) = C^*(G_1 \times G_2). \tag{4.8.31}$$

4.8.32. DEFINITION. Let $\mathcal{A}$ and $\mathcal{B}$ be C^*-algebras. A C^*-homomorphism $\rho : \mathcal{A} \to \overline{\overline{\mathcal{B}}}$ into the multiplier algebra is called *strict* if ρ has a unique extension to a unital C^*-homomorphism

$$\bar{\rho} : \overline{\overline{\mathcal{A}}} \to \overline{\overline{\mathcal{B}}} \tag{4.8.33}$$

which is strictly continuous on bounded subsets of $\overline{\overline{\mathcal{A}}}$ [V1; Lemma 0.2.6]. The homomorphism $\bar{\rho}$ is called the *strict extension* of ρ.

4.8.34. DEFINITION. A *Hopf* C^**-algebra* is a C^*-algebra $\mathcal{B}$ together with an injective strict morphism

(4.8.35) $$\mathcal{B} \xrightarrow{\ \delta\ } \overleftarrow{\mathcal{B} \otimes \mathcal{B}}$$

such that there exists a commuting diagram

(4.8.36)

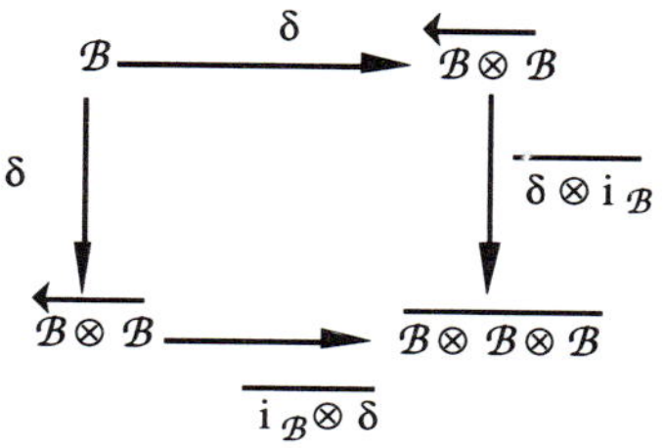

where $i_{\mathcal{B}}$ is the identity mapping on $\mathcal{B}$ and $^-$ denotes strict extension. $(\mathcal{B}, \delta)$ is called *abelian* if $\mathcal{B}$ is abelian, and *co-abelian* (or symmetric) if the flip automorphism $\sigma(b_1 \otimes b_2) := b_2 \otimes b_1$ of $\mathcal{B} \otimes \mathcal{B}$ satisfies $\bar{\sigma}\delta = \delta$. A non-zero C^*-homomorphism $\mathcal{B} \xrightarrow{\ \varepsilon\ } \mathbb{C}$ is called a *co-unit* of $(\mathcal{B}, \delta)$ if the diagram

(4.8.37)

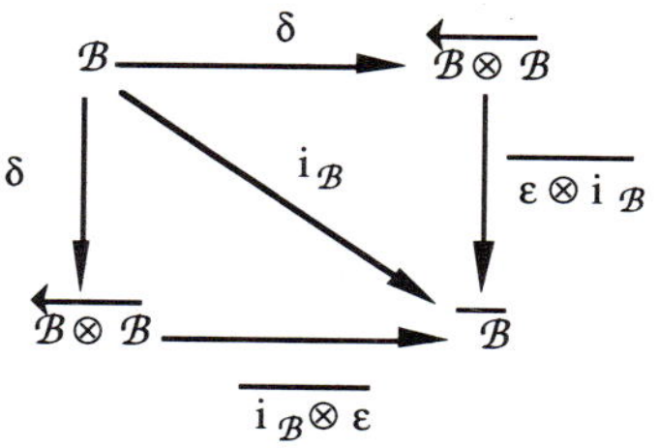

commutes. An involutive C^*-antiautomorphism $\mathcal{B} \xrightarrow{\ \iota\ } \mathcal{B}$ is called a *co-involution* of $(\mathcal{B}, \delta)$ if the diagram

(4.8.38)

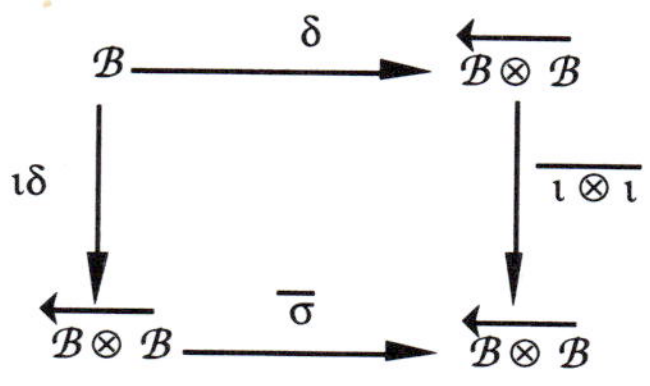

commutes.

4.8.39. PROPOSITION. *Let* G *be a locally compact unimodular group. Then the spatial group* C^**-algebra* $C^*(G)$ *becomes a co-abelian Hopf* C^**-algebra with coproduct*

$$C^*(G) \xrightarrow{\delta_G} \overleftarrow{\overline{C^*(G) \otimes C^*(G)}} \subset \overline{C^*(G \times G)} \tag{4.8.40}$$

defined by

$$\delta_G(u^\#) := (\delta_G u)^\# \quad \textit{(left convolution on } G \times G) \tag{4.8.41}$$

for all $u \in L^1(G)$. *Here* $\delta_G : G \to G \times G$ *is the diagonal mapping and* $\delta_G u$ *is the image measure of* $u(s)ds$. *The weak extension of (4.8.40) satisfies*

$$\delta_G(s^\#) = s^\# \otimes s^\# \tag{4.8.42}$$

for all $s \in G$ *and the associated left translation operators. The Hopf algebra* $(C^*(G), \delta_G)$ *has the co-involution*

$$C^*(G) \xrightarrow{\iota_G} C^*(G) \ , \quad \iota_G u^\# := ((\bar{u})^\#)^* \tag{4.8.43}$$

for $u \in L^1(G)$, *with* $\bar{u}(s) := \overline{u(s)}$. *If (and only if)* G *is amenable, there exists a co-unit*

$$C^*(G) \xrightarrow{\varepsilon_G} \mathbb{C} \ , \quad \varepsilon_G u^\# := \int_G u(s)ds. \tag{4.8.44}$$

For any Hopf C^*-algebra (B, δ), the dual Banach space $B^\#$ becomes a Banach algebra under the product

$$(fg)(b) := \overline{f \otimes g}\ (\delta b) \tag{4.8.45}$$

defined for all $f,g \in B^\#$ and $b \in B$. Here $\overline{f \otimes g}$ is the strict extension of $f \otimes g : B \otimes B \to \mathbb{C}$. This Banach algebra, denoted by $(B, \delta)^\#$, is abelian if and only if (B, δ) is co-abelian. If ι is a co-involution of (B,δ), then

$$f^*(b) := f(\iota(b^*))^* \tag{4.8.46}$$

defines an involution of $(B,\delta)^{\#}$.

4.8.47. EXAMPLE. For the co-abelian Hopf C^*-algebra $(C^*(G), \delta_G)$ associated with a locally compact unimodular group G, the Banach dual space

$$B(G) := C^*(G)^{\#}$$

consists of all "coefficient functions"

(4.8.48) $$f(s) = (\xi|\pi(s)\eta) \qquad (s \in G)$$

on G. Here

(4.8.49) $$\pi: G \to U(H) \qquad \text{(unitary group)}$$

is a continuous unitary representation of G on a Hilbert space H, weakly contained in the left-regular representation (4.8.10), and $\xi, \eta \in H$. By [E1; Proposition 2.1 and 2.1.6], $C^*(G)^{\#}$ has the norm

(4.8.50) $$\|f\| := \sup_{u \in L^1(G), \|u^{\#}\| \le 1} \langle u,f\rangle$$

where

(4.8.51) $$\langle u,f\rangle := \int_G u(s)\ f(s)\ ds.$$

Writing f in the form (4.8.48), we also have $\langle u,f\rangle = (\xi|\pi(u)\eta)$ where

(4.8.52) $$\pi(u) := \int_G u(s)\ \pi(s)\ ds$$

is the representation of $L^1(G)$ on H associated with (4.8.59). One can show [V1] that $(C^*(G), \delta_G)^{\#}$ has the product $(f \cdot g)(s) = f(s) \cdot g(s)$ and the involution $f^*(s) = f(s)^*$ for all $f,g \in C^*(G)^{\#}$ and $s \in G$. In other words, $(C^*(G), \delta_G)^{\#}$ becomes an (abelian) *-subalgebra of $\mathcal{C}_b(G)$.

In case G is compact, $C^*(G)^{\#} = A(G)$ is the *Fourier algebra* of G whose Banach space dual

(4.8.53) $$A(G)^{\#} = W^*(G)$$

coincides with the (reduced) *group von Neumann algebra* of G, generated by the left translation operators (4.8.10) on $L^2(G)$. It follows that A(G) becomes a left Banach module over $W^*(G)$ via the pairing

$$A(G) \leftarrow W^*(G) \times A(G), \quad a \ltimes f \leftarrow\!\shortmid (a,f)$$

defined by

(4.8.54) $$\langle b|a \ltimes f\rangle := \langle ba|f\rangle$$

for all $b \in W^*(G)$. Similarly, $W^*(G)$ becomes a right Banach module over A(G) via the pairing

$$W^*(G) \times A(G) \rightarrow W^*(G), \quad (a,f) \mapsto a \rtimes f$$

defined by

(4.8.55) $$\langle a \rtimes f|g\rangle := \langle a|fg\rangle$$

for all $g \in A(G)$.

4.8.56. PROPOSITION. *Let* G *be a locally compact group with unit element* e. *Then the* C^**-algebra* $\mathcal{C}_0(G)$ *becomes an abelian Hopf* C^**-algebra with coproduct*

(4.8.57) $$d_G : \mathcal{C}_0(G) \rightarrow \overleftarrow{\mathcal{C}_0(G) \otimes \mathcal{C}_0(G)} \subset \mathcal{C}_b(G \times G)$$

defined by

(4.8.58) $$(d_G f)(s,t) := f(st)$$

for all $f \in \mathcal{C}_0(G)$ *and* $s,t \in G$. *This Hopf algebra has the co-unit*

(4.8.59) $$\mathbb{C} \xleftarrow{e_G} \mathcal{C}_0(G), \quad e_G f := f(e)$$

and the co-involution

(4.8.60) $$\mathcal{C}_0(G) \xleftarrow{j_G} \mathcal{C}_0(G), \quad (j_G f)(s) := f(s^{-1}).$$

Proof. Let $f,g \in \mathcal{C}_0(G)$ be arbitrary and put $F := f \otimes g \in \mathcal{C}(G \times G)$ (cf. (4.8.26)). Then (4.8.58) implies for all $r, s, t \in G$

$$((d_G \otimes i_G)F)(r,s,t) = ((d_G \otimes i_G)(f \otimes g))(r,s,t)$$

$$= (d_G f \otimes g)(r,s,t) = (d_G f)(r,s) \cdot g(t) = f(rs)g(t) = F(rs,t)$$

and

$$((i_G \otimes d_G)F)(r,s,t) = ((i_G \otimes d_G)(f \otimes g))(r,s,t)$$

$$= (f \otimes d_G g)(r,s,t) = f(r)(d_G g)(s,t) = f(r)g(st) = F(r,st).$$

By linearity, these relations hold for all $F \in \mathcal{C}_0(G) \otimes \mathcal{C}_0(G)$. Applying strict continuity, we obtain for all $f \in \mathcal{C}_0(G)$

$$\overline{d_G \otimes i_G}\ (d_G f)(r,s,t) = (d_G f)(rs,t) = f((rs)t)$$

$$= f(r(st)) = (d_G f)(r,st) = \overline{i_G \otimes d_G}\ (d_G f)(r,s,t).$$

The remaining assertions are proved in a similar way. Q.E.D.

For a Hopf C^*-algebra $(\mathcal{A}, d)$, the dual Banach space $\mathcal{A}^\#$ becomes a Banach algebra under the product

$$(4.8.61) \qquad (\varphi^\# \psi)(a) := \overline{\varphi \otimes \psi}\ (da)$$

defined for all $\varphi, \psi \in \mathcal{A}^\#$ and $a \in \mathcal{A}$. Here $\overline{\varphi \otimes \psi}$ is the strict extension of $\varphi \otimes \psi : \mathcal{A} \otimes \mathcal{A} \to \mathbb{C}$. This Banach algebra, denoted by $(\mathcal{A}, d)^\#$, has a unit element $e \in \mathcal{A}^\#$ if and only if e is a counit of $(\mathcal{A}, d)$. If j is a co-involution of $(\mathcal{A}, d)$, then

$$(4.8.62) \qquad \varphi^\vee(a) := \varphi(j(a^*))^* \qquad (\varphi \in \mathcal{A}^\#, a \in \mathcal{A})$$

defines an involution of $(\mathcal{A}, d)^\#$. Note that (4.8.61) and (4.8.62) are obtained from (4.8.45) and (4.8.46) after a change of notation.

4.8.63. EXAMPLE. For the Hopf C^*-algebra $(\mathcal{C}_0(G), d_G)$ associated with a locally compact unimodular group G with unit element e, the Banach dual space

$$\mathcal{M}(G) := \mathcal{C}_0(G)^\#$$

consists of all (complex, bounded) *measures* u on G, with norm

$$\|u\|_1 := \int_G d|u|(s).$$

In this case, $(\mathcal{C}_0(G), d_G)^\#$ has the convolution product

$$(u \# v)f = \int_G \int_G f(st) \ du(s) \ dv(t),$$

the involution $d\check{u}(x) = du(x^{-1})^*$ and the unit element e_G = Dirac measure at $e \in G$. There is a pairing

$$\mathcal{M}(G) \times \mathcal{C}_b(G) \to \mathbb{C} \tag{4.8.64}$$

given by

$$(u,f) \mapsto \langle u,f \rangle := \int_G f(s) \ du(s).$$

4.8.65. EXAMPLE. In case G is an abelian locally compact group, the Fourier transform (4.8.11) induces an isomorphism

$$(C^*(G), \delta_G, \iota_G) \xrightarrow[\approx]{} (\mathcal{C}_0(G^\#), d_{G^\#}, j_{G^\#})$$

of involutive Hopf C^*-algebras [V1; Proposition 4.5]. Thus the co-abelian Hopf C^*-algebra of G is isomorphic to the abelian Hopf C^*-algebra of $G^\#$.

4.9 Actions and Coactions on C^*-Algebras

In order to study actions and crossed products of C^*-algebras in a setting involving duality, it is useful to work in a Hopf C^*-algebraic framework.

4.9.1. DEFINITION. Let $(\mathcal{B}, d_{\mathcal{B}})$ be a Hopf C^*-algebra and let $\mathcal{A}$ be a C^*-algebra. An injective strict C^*-homomorphism

$$\overline{\mathcal{A} \otimes \mathcal{B}} \supset \overleftarrow{\mathcal{A} \otimes \mathcal{B}} \xleftarrow{\;d\;} \mathcal{A} \tag{4.9.2}$$

defines an *action* of $(\mathcal{B}, d_{\mathcal{B}})$ on $\mathcal{A}$ if the diagram

$$\begin{array}{ccc} \overleftarrow{\mathcal{A} \otimes \mathcal{B}} & \xleftarrow{\quad d \quad} & \mathcal{A} \\ {\scriptstyle \overline{d \otimes i_{\mathcal{B}}}}\Big\downarrow & & \Big\downarrow{\scriptstyle d} \\ \overline{\mathcal{A} \otimes \mathcal{B} \otimes \mathcal{B}} & \xleftarrow[\overline{i_{\mathcal{A}} \otimes d_{\mathcal{B}}}]{} & \overleftarrow{\mathcal{A} \otimes \mathcal{B}} \end{array}$$

commutes. Here $i_{\mathcal{A}}$ and $i_{\mathcal{B}}$ are the respective identity mappings.

4.9.3. PROPOSITION. *Let G be a unimodular locally compact group, and consider the abelian Hopf C^*-algebra $(\mathcal{C}_0(G), d_G)$. Let*

$$\mathcal{C}_b(G,\mathcal{A}) = \overleftarrow{\mathcal{A} \otimes \mathcal{C}_0(G)} \xleftarrow{\;d\;} \mathcal{A}$$

be an action of $(\mathcal{C}_0(G), d_G)$ on a C^*-algebra $\mathcal{A}$. Then

$$d_s(a) := (da)(s) \qquad (s \in G,\ a \in \mathcal{A}) \tag{4.9.4}$$

defines a C^*-action d *on $\mathcal{A}$, and every C^*-action arises this way. If $\mathcal{A} \subset \mathcal{L}(H)$ is a full C^*-subalgebra for some Hilbert space, the corresponding spatial crossed product is defined by*

$$\mathcal{A} \underset{d}{\otimes} C^*(G) = C^*((da)(i_H \otimes \rho_u) : a \in \mathcal{A},\ u \in L^1(G)), \tag{4.9.5}$$

where ρ_u is the right convolution operator on $L^2(G)$.

Proof. Let $f \in \mathcal{C}_0(G)$, $a \in \mathcal{A}$ be arbitrary and put $F := a \otimes f \in \mathcal{C}(G, \mathcal{A})$ (cf. (4.8.20)). Then (4.8.37) implies for all $s,t \in G$

$$(i_{\mathcal{A}} \otimes d_G)F(s,t) = (i_{\mathcal{A}} \otimes d_G)(a \otimes f)(s,t)$$

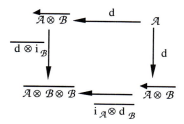

$$= (a \otimes d_G f)(s,t) = a \cdot f(st) = F(st)$$

and

$$(d \otimes i_G)F(s,t) = (d \otimes i_G)(a \otimes f)(s,t) = (da \otimes f)(s,t)$$

$$= da(s)f(t) = (d_s a)f(t) = d_s(a \cdot f(t)) = d_s F(t).$$

By linearity, these relations hold for all $F \in \mathcal{C}_0(G,\mathcal{A})$. Applying strict continuity, we obtain

$$\overline{i_{\mathcal{A}} \otimes d_G}\ (da)(s,t) = da(st) = d_{st}a,$$

$$\overline{d \otimes i_G}\ (da)(s,t) = d_s(da)(t) = d_s d_t a.$$

It follows that $d : G \to \mathrm{Aut}(\mathcal{A})$ is a group homomorphism which is continuous with respect to pointwise norm-convergence in $\mathcal{A}$ and thus defines a C^*-action of G on $\mathcal{A}$ [V1; Proposition 5.1.5]. In order to identify the (reduced) crossed product, note that the space $\mathcal{C}_c(G,\mathcal{A})$ of all compactly supported continuous mappings $F : G \to \mathcal{A}$ becomes a normed *-algebra with convolution product

(4.9.6) $$F_1^{\#}F_2(t) := \int_G F_1(s)\ d_s(F_2(s^{-1}t))\ ds,$$

involution $F^*(t) := d_t(F(t^{-1})^*)$ (since G is unimodular) and norm

$$\|F\|_1 := \int_G \|F(s)\|\ ds$$

[P1; 7.6.1]. Now let $\mathcal{A} \subset \mathcal{L}(H)$ be a full C^*-subalgebra for some Hilbert space H. For every $F \in \mathcal{C}_c(G,\mathcal{A})$ define the right convolution operator

(4.9.7) $$(F^{\#}\Phi)(t) := \int_G d_t(F(s))\ \Phi(ts)\ ds$$

for all $\Phi \in L^2(G,H)$. Then $F^{\#}$ is a bounded operator and we have for all $F_1, F_2 \in \mathcal{C}_c(G,\mathcal{A})$:

$$F_1^{\#}(F_2^{\#}\Phi)(t) = \int_G d_t(F_1(s))\ (F_2^{\#}\Phi)(ts)\ ds$$

$$= \int_G \int_G d_t(F_1(s))\ d_{ts}(F_2(x))\ \Phi(tsx)\ dx\ ds$$

$$= \int_G \int_G d_t(F_1(s))\ d_{ts}(F_2(s^{-1}y))\ \Phi(ty)\ dy\ ds$$

$$= \int_G d_t\Big(\int_G F_1(s)\ d_s(F_2(s^{-1}y))\ ds\Big)\ \Phi(ty)\ dy$$

$$= \int_G d_t((F_1^{\#}F_2)(y))\ \Phi(ty)\ dy = (F_1^{\#}F_2)^{\#}\Phi(t).$$

This shows $F_1^{\#}F_2^{\#} = (F_1^{\#}F_2)^{\#}$ for the convolution product (4.9.6). Since we also have $(F^{\#})^* = (F^*)^{\#}$, the mapping $F \mapsto F^{\#}$ is a *-representation of $\mathcal{C}_c(G,\mathcal{A})$ on $L^2(G,H)$. The norm closure

(4.9.8) $$\mathcal{A} \underset{d}{\otimes} C^*(G) := C^*(F^{\#} : F \in \mathcal{C}_c(G,\mathcal{A}))$$

in $\mathcal{L}(L^2(G,H))$ is called the *spatial crossed product* for the action d [P1; 7.7.4]. Now consider the multiplication representation (4.8.18) of $\mathcal{C}_b(G,\mathcal{A})$ on $L^2(G,H)$. Then

$$((da)\Phi)(t) = (da)(t)\ \Phi(t) = (d_t a)\ \Phi(t)$$

for all $a \in \mathcal{A}$, $\Phi \in L^2(G,H)$ and $t \in G$. Identifying $L^2(G,H) = H \otimes L^2(G)$ we obtain for $\varphi \in L^2(G)$, $h \in H$ and $u \in \mathcal{C}_c(G)$:

$$(da)(i_H \otimes \rho_u)(h \otimes \varphi)(t) = (da)(h \otimes \rho_u\varphi)(t) = (d_t a)(h \otimes \rho_u\varphi)(t)$$

$$= (d_t a)h \cdot (\rho_u\varphi)(t) = (d_t a)h \cdot \int_G \varphi(ts)\ u(s)\ ds.$$

On the other hand, the element $a \otimes u \in \mathcal{C}_c(G,\mathcal{A})$ has the generalized convolution operator (cf. (4.9.7))

$$(a \otimes u)^{\#}(h \otimes \varphi)(t) = \int d_t((a \otimes u)(s))\ (h \otimes \varphi)(ts)\ ds$$

$$= \int d_t(a \cdot u(s))\ h\ \varphi(ts)\ ds = (d_t a) \cdot h \cdot \int_G u(s)\ \varphi(ts)\ ds.$$

It follows that for all $a \in \mathcal{A}$ and $u \in \mathcal{C}_c(G)$

$$(a \otimes u)^{\#} = (da)(i_H \otimes \rho_u) \tag{4.9.9}$$

thus proving (4.9.5). Q.E.D.

4.9.10. EXAMPLE. For the trivial action of G on $\mathcal{A}$, the spatial crossed product

$$\mathcal{A} \underset{\text{triv}}{\otimes} C^*(G) = \mathcal{A} \otimes C^*(G)$$

is the (untwisted) spatial tensor product, since in this case we have $da = a \otimes i_G$ for all $a \in \mathcal{A}$, which shows that the crossed product has the generators

$$(da)(i_H \otimes \rho_u) = (a \otimes i_G)(i_H \otimes \rho_u) = a \otimes \rho_u.$$

4.9.11. DEFINITION. Let G be a locally compact group, with coabelian Hopf C^*-algebra $(C^*(G), \delta_G)$. A *coaction* of G on a C^*-algebra $\mathcal{A}$ is defined as an action

$$\mathcal{A} \xrightarrow{\delta} \overleftarrow{\mathcal{A} \otimes C^*(G)} \tag{4.9.12}$$

of $C^*(G)$ on $\mathcal{A}$, in the sense of Definition 4.9.1. If $\mathcal{A} \subset \mathcal{L}(H)$ is a full C^*-subalgebra for some Hilbert space H, we define the spatial *co-crossed product*

$$\mathcal{A} \underset{\delta}{\otimes} \mathcal{C}_0(G) := C^*((\delta a)(i_H \otimes f) : a \in \mathcal{A}, f \in \mathcal{C}_0(G)), \tag{4.9.13}$$

where f is the multiplication operator on $L^2(G)$.

The notions of action and coaction of a group G satisfy a duality theory generalizing the well-known Takai duality theory for abelian groups [V1, LPRS]. More precisely, let G be a locally compact group, which for simplicity we assume to be unimodular (for example, G may be abelian or compact or a semi-simple Lie group). Let δ be a coaction of G

on a C^*-algebra $\mathcal{A}$, realized as a full C^*-subalgebra of $\mathcal{L}(H)$ for some Hilbert space H. Then the cocrossed product

$$\mathcal{A} \underset{\delta}{\otimes} \mathcal{C}_0(G) \subset \mathcal{L}(H \otimes L^2(G))$$

is a full C^*-subalgebra. Now consider the *right regular representation* $\rho : G \to U(L^2(G))$ of G on $L^2(G)$ defined by

(4.9.14) $$(\rho_s\varphi)(t) := \varphi(ts)$$

for all $\varphi \in L^2(G)$ and $s,t \in G$. Since $\rho(G)$ lies in the commutant of $C^*(G)$, every operator of the form $i_H \otimes \rho_s$ commutes with $\mathcal{A} \otimes C^*(G)$ and hence with $\delta(A)$. Therefore the C^*-automorphism

(4.9.15) $$d_s := \mathrm{Ad}(i_H \otimes \rho_s)$$

of $\mathcal{L}(H \otimes L^2(G))$ satisfies

$$d_s((\delta a)(i_H \otimes f)) = d_s(\delta a) \cdot d_s(i_H \otimes f) = \delta a \cdot (i_H \otimes \rho_s f)$$

for all $a \in \mathcal{A}$ and $f \in \mathcal{C}_0(G)$. It follows that d_s leaves $\mathcal{A} \underset{\delta}{\otimes} \mathcal{C}_0(G)$ invariant, and we obtain an action

(4.9.16) $$G \xrightarrow{d} \mathrm{Aut}(\mathcal{A} \underset{\delta}{\otimes} \mathcal{C}_0(G))$$

called the *dual action* of the coaction δ. By Proposition 4.9.3, we may realize (4.9.16) as a C^*-monomorphism

$$\mathcal{A} \underset{\delta}{\otimes} \mathcal{C}_0(G) \xrightarrow{d} \overleftarrow{(\mathcal{A} \underset{\delta}{\otimes} \mathcal{C}_0(G)) \otimes \mathcal{C}_0(G)} = \mathcal{C}_b(G, \mathcal{A} \underset{\delta}{\otimes} \mathcal{C}_0(G))$$

determined by

$$d((\delta a)(i_H \otimes f))(t) = d_t((\delta a)(i_H \otimes f)) = (\delta a)(i_H \otimes \rho_t f)$$

for all $a \in \mathcal{A}$, $f \in \mathcal{C}_0(G)$ and $t \in G$. The corresponding spatial crossed product

$$(\mathcal{A} \underset{\delta}{\otimes} \mathcal{C}_0(G)) \underset{d}{\otimes} C^*(G) \subset \mathcal{L}(H \otimes L^2(G) \otimes L^2(G))$$

is generated by the operators $d((\delta a)i_H \otimes f)(i_H \otimes i_G \otimes \rho_u)$, where $a \in \mathcal{A}$, $f \in \mathcal{C}_0(G)$ and ρ_u is the right convolution operator with symbol $u \in L^1(G)$. The important *duality theorem* [NT, LPRS] asserts that there exists a C^*-isomorphism

$$\Phi : \mathcal{A} \otimes \mathcal{K}(L^2(G)) \xrightarrow[\approx]{} (\mathcal{A} \underset{\delta}{\otimes} \mathcal{C}_0(G)) \underset{d}{\otimes} C^*(G)$$

satisfying

$$\Phi((\delta a)(i_H \otimes f\rho_u)) = d((\delta a)(i_H \otimes f)) \cdot (i_H \otimes i_G \otimes u^\#), \tag{4.9.17}$$

where $u^\#$ is the left convolution operator associated with u.

4.10 Hardy-Toeplitz Operators Over K-circular Domains

In this section we study Toeplitz operators and their associated C^*-algebras acting on the Hardy space $H^2(S)$ over a K-circular domain

$$\Omega = e \cdot \exp(A) \cdot K$$

in the complexification $S^{\mathbb{C}}$ of $S := L\backslash K$. We assume that Ω is log-conical. The Hardy space and its associated multiplier C^*-algebra are introduced in Sections 2.10 and 3.5. Note that K acts on the right.

4.10.1. DEFINITION. For any bounded function $f \in L^\infty(K)$, the *multiplication operator* with *symbol* f is the bounded operator $f : L^2(K) \to L^2(K)$ defined for all $h \in L^2(K)$ and $s \in K$ by

$$(fh)(s) := f(s)h(s). \tag{4.10.2}$$

Identifying the operator (4.10.2) with its symbol yields an injective C^*-algebra homomorphism from $L^\infty(K)$ onto an abelian C^*-subalgebra of $\mathcal{L}(L^2(K))$, the C^*-algebra of all bounded operators on $L^2(K)$.

The right translation action (2.10.3) of K on $L^2(K)$ induces an adjoint action of K on $\mathcal{L}(L^2(K))$ which satisfies for every $s \in K$

$$\mathrm{Ad}(\rho_s)f = \rho_s f \qquad \text{(multiplication operator)}$$

where $(\rho_s f)(t) = f(ts)$ belongs to $L^\infty(K)$.

4.10.3. DEFINITION. For any bounded function $f \in L^\infty(S)$, the *multiplication operator* with *symbol* f is the bounded operator $f : L^2(S) \to L^2(S)$ defined for all $h \in L^2(S)$ and $z \in S$ by

$$(fh)(z) := f(z)h(z). \tag{4.10.4}$$

Identifying the operator (4.10.4) with its symbol yields an injective C^*-algebra homomorphism from $L^\infty(S)$ onto an abelian C^*-subalgebra of $\mathcal{L}(L^2(S))$, the C^*-algebra of all bounded operators on $L^2(S)$. The right translation action (2.10.3) of K on $L^2(S)$ induces an adjoint action of K on $\mathcal{L}(L^2(S))$ which satisfies for every $s \in K$

$$\mathrm{Ad}(\rho_s)f = \rho_s f \qquad \text{(multiplication operator)}$$

where $(\rho_s f)(z) := f(zs)$ belongs to $L^\infty(S)$.

4.10.5. LEMMA. *The orthogonal projection* $P : L^2(K) \to L^2(S)$ *satisfies* $PfP = \tilde{f}$ (multiplication operator) *for all* $f \in L^\infty(K)$, *where*

$$\tilde{f}(t) = \int_L f(\ell t)\, d\ell \tag{4.10.6}$$

belongs to $L^\infty(S)$. *If* f *is continuous, then* $\tilde{f}$ *is also continuous.*

Proof. Let $h \in L^2(S) \subset L^2(K)$. Since h is left L-invariant,

$$P(fh)(t) = \int_L (fh)(\ell t)\, d\ell = \int_L f(\ell t)\, h(t)\, d\ell = \int_L f(\ell t)\, d\ell \cdot h(t) = \tilde{f}(t)\, h(t).$$

Q.E.D.

Now consider the Hardy space $H^2(S)$ over Ω, with Szegö projection $E : L^2(S) \to H^2(S)$.

4.10.7. DEFINITION. The *Hardy-Toeplitz operator* $T_S(f)$ with symbol $f \in L^\infty(S)$ is defined as the compression

$$T_S(f) = E \circ f|_{H^2(S)} \tag{4.10.8}$$

of the multiplication operator (4.10.4). Thus

(4.10.9) $$T_S(f)h = E(fh)$$

for every $h \in H^2(S)$.

4.10.10. PROPOSITION. *For every* $f \in L^\infty(S)$, $T_S(f)$ *is a bounded operator on* $H^2(S)$ *satisfying*

(4.10.11) $$\|T_S(f)\| \le \|f\|_\infty ,$$

(4.10.12) $$T_S(f)^* = T_S(\bar{f}).$$

If $\varphi \in H^\infty(S) := H^2(S) \cap L^\infty(S)$, *we have*

(4.10.13) $$T_S(f)T_S(\varphi) = T_S(f\varphi),$$

(4.10.14) $$T_S(\bar{\varphi})T_S(f) = T_S(\bar{\varphi}f).$$

Proof. As an operator on $L^2(S)$ we have

(4.10.15) $$T_S(f) = E\, f\, E.$$ Q.E.D.

Let $\mathcal{C}(S)$ denote the subalgebra of $L^\infty(S)$ consisting of all continuous functions.

4.10.16. DEFINITION. The *Hardy-Toeplitz* C^**-algebra* is defined as the unital C^*-algebra

(4.10.17) $$\mathcal{T}(S) := C^*(T_S(f) : f \in \mathcal{C}(S))$$

generated by all Hardy-Toeplitz operators (4.10.8) on $H^2(S)$ with continuous symbol $f \in \mathcal{C}(S)$.

Our first goal is to construct a coaction of K (cf. Section 4.9) on the Hardy block multiplier algebra $\mathcal{D}(K)$ introduced in (3.5.55). Consider the C^*-monomorphism

(4.10.18) $$\delta_K : C^*(K) \to \overleftarrow{C^*(K) \otimes C^*(K)}$$

defining the Hopf C^*-algebra structure on the (spatial) group C^*-algebra $C^*(K)$ of K (cf. (4.8.44)). The weak closure $W^*(K)$ is the group von Neumann algebra of K, and δ_K has an extension to a W^*-monomorphism

(4.10.19) $$\delta_K : W^*(K) \to W^*(K) \bar{\otimes} W^*(K)$$

determined by

(4.10.20) $$\delta_K s^\# := s^\# \otimes s^\# \qquad (s \in K)$$

for the left translation operators. Thus there is a commuting diagram

$$\begin{array}{ccc} W^*(K) & \xrightarrow{\delta_K} & W^*(K) \bar{\otimes} W^*(K) \\ \downarrow{\scriptstyle \delta_K} & & \downarrow{\scriptstyle i \bar{\otimes} \delta_K} \\ W^*(K) \bar{\otimes} W^*(K) & \xrightarrow[\delta_K \bar{\otimes} i]{} & W^*(K) \bar{\otimes} W^*(K) \bar{\otimes} W^*(K) \end{array}$$

of W^*-homomorphisms.

4.10.21. THEOREM. *The restriction of* (4.10.19) *defines a* C^*-*coaction*

(4.10.22) $$\delta_K : \mathcal{D}(K) \to \overleftarrow{\mathcal{D}(K) \otimes C^*(K)}$$

of K *on* $\mathcal{D}(K)$.

Proof. It suffices to show that (4.10.19) maps the C^*-subalgebra $\mathcal{D}(K)$ of $W^*(K)$ into the correct multiplier algebra. Consider the right action of $A(K)$ on $W^*(K)$ determined by

(4.10.23) $$\langle T \rtimes f, g \rangle := \langle T, fg \rangle$$

for all $T \in W^*(K)$ and $f,g \in A(K)$ (cf. (3.5.52)). In order to show

(4.10.24) $$\delta(a)(i \otimes u^\#) \in \mathcal{D}(K) \otimes C^*(K)$$

for all $a \in \mathcal{D}(K)$ and $u \in L^1(K)$, we may assume that $u \in \mathcal{C}^\infty(K)$ and $a = E_e^\# \rtimes f$ for some $f \in \mathcal{C}^\infty(K)$, since $\mathcal{C}^\infty(K)$ is dense in $A(K)$ by [E1; p. 219].

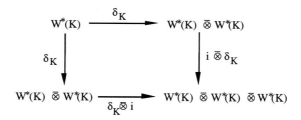

Then $F(s,t) := f(s)u(s^{-1}t)$ belongs to $\mathcal{C}^\infty(K \times K) \subset A(K \times K)$. As the predual of

$$W^*(K \times K) = W^*(K) \bar{\otimes} W^*(K)$$

(von Neumann algebra tensor product), $A(K \times K)$ is a completion (of L^1-type) of $A(K) \odot A(K)$ (algebraic tensor product) [T1]. It follows that

$$F(s,t) = \lim_n \sum_{i \in I_n} \phi_i^n(s)\psi_i^n(t) \tag{4.10.25}$$

in $A(K \times K)$, where I_n is finite and $\phi_i^n, \psi_i^n \in \mathcal{C}^\infty(K)$ for each n and $i \in I_n$. By [LPRS; p. 754] we have $\delta(a)(i \otimes u^\#) = \rho^\# \in W^*(K \times K)$ (left convolution), where

$$\rho(s,t) = E_e(s)f(s)u(s^{-1}t) = E_e(s)F(s,t). \tag{4.10.26}$$

It follows that

$$\rho^\# = (E_e^\# \otimes i) \rtimes F = \lim_n \sum_{i \in I_n} (E_e^\# \rtimes \phi_i^n) \otimes (\psi_i^n)^\# \tag{4.10.27}$$

in $W^*(K \times K)$. Since $E_e^\# \rtimes \phi_i^n \in \mathcal{D}(K)$ and $\psi_i^n \in L^1(K)$, we obtain $\rho^\# \in \mathcal{D}(K) \otimes C^*(K)$.

Q.E.D.

Suppose that M is a von Neumann algebra and $\delta : M \to M \bar{\otimes} W^*(K)$ is a W^*-monomorphism defining a coaction of K on M, i.e., giving rise to a commuting diagram

$$\begin{array}{ccc} M & \xrightarrow{\quad\delta\quad} & M \otimes W^*(K) \\ \delta \downarrow & & \downarrow \delta \otimes i \\ M \otimes W^*(K) & \xrightarrow[i \otimes \delta_K]{} & M \otimes W^*(K) \otimes W^*(K) \end{array}$$

.

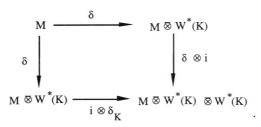

As in the C^*-algebra theory (cf. Section 4.9) one defines the W^*-cocrossed product

(4.10.28) $$M \underset{\delta}{\otimes} L^\infty(K) := W^*((\delta m)(i \otimes f) : m \in M, f \in L^\infty(K)).$$

This concept applies in particular to the case $M := W^*(K)$ and $\delta := \delta_K$.

4.10.29. PROPOSITION. *There exists a W^*-isomorphism*

$$\nu : W^*(K) \underset{\delta_K}{\otimes} L^\infty(K) \xrightarrow[\approx]{} \mathcal{L}(L^2(K))$$

determined by

(4.10.30) $$\nu((\delta_K u^\#) \cdot (i \otimes f)) = u^\# \cdot f$$

for all $u \in \mathcal{M}(K)$ *and* $f \in L^\infty(K)$.

Proof. The unitary operator W on $L^2(K \times K)$ defined by

$$W\xi(s,t) := \xi(s,s^{-1}t)$$

satisfies

(4.10.31) $$\delta_K m = W(m \otimes i)W^*$$

for all $m \in W^*(K)$ since for $s \in K$ and $h,k \in L^2(K)$ we have $\delta_K s^\# = s^\# \otimes s^\#$ (left convolutions) and therefore

$$(\delta_K s^\#)W(h \otimes k)(x,y) = W(h \otimes k)(s^{-1}x, s^{-1}y) = h(s^{-1}x)k(x^{-1}y)$$

$$= W(s^\# h \otimes k)(x,y) = W(s^\# \otimes i)(h \otimes k)(x,y)$$

for all $x,y \in K$. It follows [NT; (2.6)] that δ_K is the coaction of K which is dual to the trivial action of K on $\mathbb{C}$. By [NT; (2.13)] there exists a W^*-isomorphism

$$\pi : \mathcal{L}(L^2(K)) \xrightarrow[\approx]{} W^*(K) \underset{\delta_K}{\otimes} L^\infty(K)$$

satisfying

(4.10.32) $$\pi(s^\#) = s^\# \otimes s^\# \qquad (s \in K),$$

(4.10.33) $$\pi(f) = i \otimes f \qquad (f \in L^\infty(K)).$$

Integrating (4.10.32) we see that

(4.10.34) $$\pi(u^\#) = \delta_K u^\#$$

for all $u \in \mathcal{M}(K)$. Now put $\nu := \pi^{-1}$. Q.E.D.

4.10.35. PROPOSITION. *There exists an injective C^*-homomorphism*

$$\mathcal{T}(L^2(K)) \xleftarrow{\ \nu\ } \mathcal{D}(K) \underset{\delta_K}{\otimes} \mathcal{C}(K)$$

on the co-crossed product, satisfying

(4.10.36) $$\nu((\delta_K a) \cdot (i \otimes f)) = a \cdot f$$

for all $a \in \mathcal{D}(K)$ *and* $f \in \mathcal{C}(K)$. *For every* $s \in K$, *there is a commuting diagram*

(4.10.37) $$\begin{array}{ccc} \mathcal{T}(L^2(K)) & \xleftarrow{\ \nu\ } & \mathcal{D}(K) \underset{\delta_K}{\otimes} \mathcal{C}(K) \\ \Big\downarrow {\scriptstyle Ad(\rho_s)} & & \Big\downarrow {\scriptstyle d_s} \\ \mathcal{T}(L^2(K)) & \xleftarrow[\ \nu\ ]{} & \mathcal{D}(K) \underset{\delta_K}{\otimes} \mathcal{C}(K) \end{array}$$

where $d_s := Ad(i \otimes \rho_s)$.

Proof. For every $s \in K$, $a \in \mathcal{D}(K)$ and $f \in \mathcal{C}(K)$ we have

$$d_s((\delta_K a)(i \otimes f)) = (\delta_K a)(i \otimes \rho_s f)$$

since $\delta_K a$ commutes with $i \otimes \rho_s$. Since $a \in W^*(K)$ commutes with ρ_s we obtain

$$\nu(d_s((\delta_K a)\ (i \otimes f))) = a \cdot \rho_s f = Ad(\rho_s)(af) = Ad(\rho_s)\ \nu((\delta_K a)\ (i \otimes f)).$$

Q.E.D.

According to Proposition 4.10.35, we may realize the co-crossed product as a C^*-subalgebra of $\mathcal{L}(L^2(K))$.

4.10.38. THEOREM. *As* C^*-*subalgebras of* $\mathcal{L}(L^2(K))$ *we have*

$$\mathcal{T}(S) = E_e^{\#} \, (\mathcal{D}(K) \underset{\delta_K}{\otimes} \mathcal{C}(K)) \, E_e^{\#}.$$

Proof. By Proposition 3.5.13, there is a commuting diagram

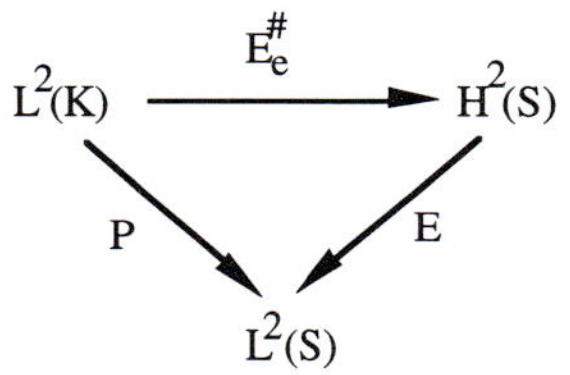

where

$$(Pf)(s) = \int_L f(\ell s) \, d\ell$$

and E is the Szegö projection. For every $f \in \mathcal{C}(S)$, the function $\tilde{f}(s) :=$ $f(e \cdot s)$ on K is left L-invariant and we have $f = P \tilde{f} P$ for the corresponding multiplication operators. The identity

$$T_S(f) = E f E = EP \tilde{f} PE = E_e^{\#} \tilde{f} E_e^{\#} = E_e^{\#} (E_e^{\#}\tilde{f}) E_e^{\#}$$

gives the inclusion

(4.10.39) $$\mathcal{T}(S) \subset E_e^{\#} \, (\mathcal{D}(K) \underset{\delta_K}{\otimes} \mathcal{C}(K)) \, E_e^{\#}.$$

For the converse inclusion it suffices to consider finite products of the form

$$(E_e f_1)^{\#} g_1 \, (E_e f_2)^{\#} g_2 \cdots (E_e f_n)^{\#} g_n$$

where $f_1, \ldots, f_n \in \mathcal{C}^{\infty}(K)$ and $g_1, \ldots, g_n \in \mathcal{C}(K)$. Since $\mathcal{C}(K \times \cdots \times K) \cong$ $\mathcal{C}(K) \otimes \cdots \otimes \mathcal{C}(K)$ is a C^*-algebra tensor product, we may assume that the continuous function

$$F(t_0, t_1, \ldots, t_n) := \prod_{j=1}^{n} f_j(t_{j-1}\, t_j^{-1})\, g_j(t_j) \tag{4.10.40}$$

on $K \times \cdots \times K$ $(n+1$ copies) is a product

$$F(t_0, t_1, \ldots, t_n) = \prod_{i=0}^{n} \varphi_i(t_i) \tag{4.10.41}$$

where $\varphi_0, \ldots, \varphi_n \in \mathcal{C}(K)$. Now we have for all $h,k \in H^2(S)$

$$(k \mid T_S(\varphi_0) \cdots T_S(\varphi_n)h)_S = (k \mid \varphi_0\, E\, \varphi_1\, E \cdots E\, \varphi_n\, h)_S =$$

$$\int_K \overline{k(t_0)}\, \varphi_0(t_0)\, (E\, \varphi_1\, E \cdots E\, \varphi_n\, h)(t_0)\, dt_0$$

$$= \int_K \int_K \overline{k(t_0)}\, \varphi_0(t_0)\, E(t_0, t_1)\, \varphi_1(t_1)\, (E\, \varphi_2\, E \cdots E\, \varphi_n\, h)(t_1)\, dt_1\, dt_0$$

$$= \int_K \cdots \int_K \overline{k(t_0)}\, \varphi_0(t_0)\, E(t_0, t_1)\, \varphi_1(t_1)\, E(t_1, t_2)\, \varphi_2(t_2) \cdots$$

$$E(t_{n-1}, t_n)\, \varphi_n(t_n)\, h(t_n)\, dt_n \cdots dt_1\, dt_0 \tag{4.10.42}$$

$$= \int_K \cdots \int_K \overline{k(t_0)}\, \varphi_0(t_0)\, E(t_0 t_1^{-1}, e)\, \varphi_1(t_1)\, E(t_1 t_2^{-1}, e)\, \varphi_2(t_2) \cdots$$

$$E(t_{n-1} t_n^{-1}, e)\, \varphi_n(t_n)\, h(t_n)\, dt_n \cdots dt_0$$

$$= \int_K \cdots \int_K \overline{k(t_0)}\, \varphi_0(t_0)\, \varphi_1(s_1^{-1} t_0) \cdots \varphi_n(s_n^{-1} \cdots s_1^{-1}\, t_0) \cdot$$

$$h(s_n^{-1} \cdots s_1^{-1} t_0)\, dE_e(s_1) \cdots dE_e(s_n)\, dt_0.$$

Here we put $s_j := t_{j-1}\, t_j^{-1}$ for $1 \le j \le n$, so that $t_j = s_j^{-1} s_{j-1}^{-1} \cdots s_1^{-1} t_0$. On the other hand, we have

$$(k \mid (E_e f_1)^{\#} g_1 \cdots (E_e f_n)^{\#} g_n h)_S = \int_K \overline{k(t_0)}\, ((E_e f_1)^{\#} g_1 \cdots (E_e f_n)^{\#} g_n h)(t_0)\, dt_0$$

$$= \int_K \int_K \overline{k(t_0)}\, g_1(s_1^{-1}t_0)\, ((E_e f_2)^{\#} g_2 \cdots (E_e f_n)^{\#} g_n h)(s_1^{-1}t_0) \cdot f_1(s_1)\, dE_e(s_1)\, dt_0$$

$$= \int_K \int_K \int_K \overline{k(t_0)}\, g_1(s_1^{-1}t_0)\, g_2(s_2^{-1}s_1^{-1}t_0)\, ((E_e f_3)^{\#} g_3 \cdots (E_e f_n)^{\#} g_n h)\, (s_2^{-1}s_1^{-1}t_0)$$

$$\cdot f_2(s_2)\, dE_e(s_2)\, f_1(s_1)\, dE_e(s_1)\, dt_0$$

$$= \int_K \cdots \int_K \overline{k(t_0)}\, g_1(s_1^{-1}t_0)\, g_2(s_2^{-1}s_1^{-1}t_0) \cdots g_n(s_n^{-1} \cdots s_1^{-1}t_0)\, h(s_n^{-1} \cdots s_1^{-1}t_0) \cdot$$

$$\cdot f_1(s_1) \cdots f_n(s_n)\, dE_e(s_1) \cdots dE_e(s_n)\, dt_0$$

$$= \int_K \cdots \int_K \overline{k(t_0)}\, F(t_0, s_1^{-1}t_0, s_2^{-1}s_1^{-1}t_0, \ldots, s_n^{-1} \cdots s_1^{-1}t_0)\, h(s_n^{-1} \cdots s_1^{-1}t_0) \cdot$$

$$\cdot dE_e(s_1) \cdots dE_e(s_n)\, dt_0 .$$

Comparing with (4.10.42) we obtain

(4.10.43) $$E_e^{\#}\, (E_e f_1)^{\#}\, g_1 \cdots (E_e f_n)^{\#}\, g_n\, E_e^{\#} = T_S(\varphi_0) \cdots T_S(\varphi_n).$$

Therefore (4.10.39) is an equality. Q.E.D.

4.11 Hardy-Toeplitz Operators Over Symmetric Domains

In this chapter we study Toeplitz operators and their associated C^*-algebras acting on the Hardy space $H^2(S)$ over a symmetric domain $\Omega \subset Z$ with Shilov boundary S. The Hardy space and its associated multiplier C^*-algebra are discussed in detail in Sections 2.8 and 3.6.

4.11.1. DEFINITION. For any bounded function $f \in L^\infty(S)$, the *multiplication operator* with *symbol* f is the bounded operator $f : L^2(S) \to L^2(S)$ defined for all $h \in L^2(S)$ and $z \in S$ by

(4.11.2) $$(fh)(z) := f(z)h(z).$$

Identifying the operator (4.11.2) with its symbol yields an injective C^*-algebra homomorphism from $L^\infty(S)$ onto an abelian C^*-subalgebra of

$\mathcal{L}(L^2(S))$, the C^*-algebra of all bounded operators on $L^2(S)$. The right translation action (2.8.3) of K on $L^2(S)$ induces an adjoint action of K on $\mathcal{L}(L^2(S))$ which satisfies for every $s \in K$

$$Ad(\rho_s)f = \rho_s f$$

where $(\rho_s f)(z) := f(zs)$ belongs to $L^\infty(S)$. Now consider the Hardy space $H^2(S)$ over S associated with Ω, with Szegö projection $E : L^2(S) \to H^2(S)$.

4.11.3. DEFINITION. The *Hardy-Toeplitz operator* $T_S(f)$ with symbol $f \in L^\infty(S)$ is defined as the compression

$$T_S(f) := E \circ f|_{H^2(S)} \tag{4.11.4}$$

of the multiplication operator (4.11.2). Thus

$$T_S(f)h = E(fh) \tag{4.11.5}$$

for every $h \in H^2(S)$.

The right translation action (2.8.3) of K on $L^2(S)$ leaves $H^2(S)$ invariant and thus induces an adjoint action of K on $\mathcal{L}(H^2(S))$ which satisfies

$$Ad(\rho_s)T_S(f) = T_S(\rho_s f) \tag{4.11.6}$$

for all $s \in K$ and $f \in L^\infty(S)$.

4.11.7. PROPOSITION. *For every* $f \in L^\infty(S)$, $T_S(f)$ *is a bounded operator on* $H^2(S)$ *satisfying*

$$\|T_S(f)\| \le \|f\|_\infty , \tag{4.11.8}$$

$$T_S(f)^* = T_S(\bar{f}). \tag{4.11.9}$$

Moreover, if $\varphi \in H^\infty(S) := H^2(S) \cap L^\infty(S)$, we have

$$T_S(f)\, T_S(\varphi) = T_S(f\varphi), \tag{4.11.10}$$

(4.11.11) $$T_S(\bar{\varphi})\, T_S(f) = T_S(\bar{\varphi} f).$$

Proof. As an operator on $L^2(S)$ we have $T_S(f) = E\, f\, E$. Q.E.D.

Let $\mathcal{C}(S)$ denote the subalgebra of $L^\infty(S)$ consisting of all continuous functions.

4.11.12. DEFINITION. The *Hardy-Toeplitz C^*-algebra* over Ω, is defined as the unital C^*-algebra

$$\mathcal{T}(S) := C^*(T_S(f) : f \in \mathcal{C}(S))$$

generated by all Hardy-Toeplitz operators (4.11.4) with continuous symbol $f \in \mathcal{C}(S)$.

Since $\rho_s f \in \mathcal{C}(S)$ whenever $s \in K$ and $f \in \mathcal{C}(S)$, it follows that $\mathcal{T}(S)$ is invariant under the adjoint action (4.11.6) of K.

4.11.13. PROPOSITION. *$\mathcal{T}(S)$ is generated (as a C^*-algebra) by all operators $T_S(p)$ with polynomial symbols $p \in \mathcal{P}(Z)$.*

Since $T_S(p)\, T_S(q) = T_S(pq)$ for all $p,q \in \mathcal{P}(Z)$, it is in fact enough to consider linear polynomials.

4.11.14. PROPOSITION. *The Toeplitz C^*-algebra $\mathcal{T}(S)$ acts irreducibly on $H^2(S)$.*

Proof. Let P be a projection in $H^2(S)$ commuting with $\mathcal{T}(S)$. Put $f := P1 \in H^2(S)$. Then

(4.11.15) $$Pg = P(T_S(g)1) = T_S(g)(P1) = T_S(g)f = gf$$

for all $g \in \mathcal{P}(Z)$. For any $z \in \Omega$, the reproducing property of the Szegö kernel vector $E_z \in H^2(S)$ (cf. 2.8.9) implies

$$(PE_z \mid g)_S = (E_z \mid Pg)_S = (E_z \mid gf)_S = g(z)\, f(z) = (E_z \mid g)_S\, f(z).$$

Since $g \in \mathcal{P}(Z)$ is arbitrary, a density argument shows that $\overline{f(z)}$ is an eigenvalue of P. Since Ω is connected it follows that $f = 0$ or $f = 1$. Therefore (4.11.15) implies $P = 0$ or $P = \mathrm{id}$. Q.E.D.

4.11.16. THEOREM. *Let* p *be a polynomial in* k *non-commuting variables. Then we have for all* $f_1, \ldots, f_k \in L^\infty(S)$

$$\|p(T_S(f_1), \ldots, T_S(f_k))\| \geq \|p(f_1, \ldots, f_k)\|_\infty .$$

Proof. By [FK4] there exists a continuous mapping

$$S \ni w \mapsto h_w \in \mathcal{A}(\Omega)$$

such that h_w is a peaking function for $\{w\}$. Consider the powers $h_w^n(z) := h_w(z)^n$ for all n. Since the mapping $(z,w) \mapsto h_w(z)$ on $S \times S$ is jointly continuous and satisfies $|h_w(z)| < 1 = h_z(z)$ whenever $w \neq z$, it follows that for each open neighborhood U of $z \in S$ there exists an open neighborhood $V \subset\subset U$ of z such that

$$\sup_{w \in S \setminus U} |h_w(z)| < \inf_{w \in V} |h_w(z)|. \tag{4.11.17}$$

We claim for every $f \in \mathcal{C}(S)$ and every $z \in S$:

$$\int_S f(w)\ |h_w(z)|^{2n}\ dw \Big/ \int_S |h_w(z)|^{2n}\ dw \to f(z). \tag{4.11.18}$$

For the proof we may assume that f is real and satisfies $f(z) = 0$. For every $\varepsilon > 0$ there exists by continuity of f an open neighborhood U of $z \in S$ such that $\sup f(U) < \varepsilon$. For this U choose V according to (4.11.17). Then

$$\begin{aligned} \int_S f(w)\ |h_w(z)|^{2n}\ dw &= \int_U f(w)\ |h_w(z)|^{2n}\ dw + \int_{S\setminus U} f(w)\ |h_w(z)|^{2n}\ dw \\ &< \varepsilon \cdot \int_S |h_w(z)|^{2n}\ dw + \mathrm{Vol}(S\setminus U) \cdot \|f\|_\infty \sup_{w \in S\setminus U} |h_w(z)|^{2n}. \end{aligned} \tag{4.11.19}$$

On the other hand

(4.11.20) $$\int_S |h_w(z)|^{2n}\, dw \ge \int_V |h_w(z)|^{2n}\, dw \ge \mathrm{Vol}(V) \cdot \inf_{w\in V} |h_w(z)|^{2n}.$$

Dividing (4.11.19) by (4.11.20), we see that

$$\int_S f(w)\ |h_w(z)|^{2n}\, dw \Big/ \int_S |h_w(z)|^{2n}\, dw < \varepsilon + \frac{\mathrm{Vol}(S\backslash U)}{\mathrm{Vol}(V)} \cdot ||f||_\infty \cdot \left(\frac{\sup_{w\in S\backslash U} |h_w(z)|}{\inf_{w\in V} |h_w(z)|}\right)^{2n}.$$

By (4.11.17), the second term converges to 0. This proves (4.11.18). We show next that for every $f \in L^\infty(S)$

(4.11.21) $$\operatorname*{ess-inf}_S |f| \ge \inf\{\frac{||fh||_S}{||h||_S} : 0 \ne h \in H^2(S)\}.$$

For the proof we may assume that the right-hand side is 1. Since $h_w^n \in H^2(S)$ for all $w \in S$ and $n \ge 0$, we get

(4.11.22) $$\int_S |f(z)|^2\ |h_w(z)|^{2n}\, dz \ge \int_S |h_w(z)|^{2n}\, dz$$

for every $w \in S$. Now let $h \in \mathcal{C}(S, \mathbb{R}_+)$ be arbitrary. Since $w \mapsto h_w$ is continuous, we may integrate (4.11.22) again and obtain

(4.11.23) $$\int_S \int_S |f(z)|^2\ h(w)\ |h_w(z)|^{2n}\, dz\, dw \ge \int_S \int_S h(w)\ |h_w(z)|^{2n}\, dz\, dw.$$

Now observe that the integral

$$I_n := \int_S |h_w(z)|^{2n}\, dw$$

is independent of $z \in S$, since we may assume for every $s \in K$, $h_w(zs^{-1}) = h_{ws}(z)$. Dividing by I_n, it follows from (4.11.23) and the dominated convergence theorem (the quotients in (4.11.21) are bounded by $||h||_\infty$) that

$$\int_S |f(z)|^2\ h(z)\, dz \ge \int_S h(z)dz.$$

Since h is arbitrary, $|f| \geq 1$ a.e. on S, thus showing (4.11.21). Now suppose $\|p(f_1, \ldots, f_k)\|_\infty = 1$. Then there exists a k-tuple $(\lambda_1, \ldots, \lambda_k) \in \sigma(f_1, \ldots, f_k)$ in the joint spectrum of $f_1, \ldots, f_k \in L^\infty(S)$ [BD; §19, Def. 7] with $|p(\lambda_1, \ldots, \lambda_k)| = 1$. By [BD; p. 100], the function

$$f := \left(\sum_{j=1}^{k} |f_j - \lambda_j|^2\right)^{1/2} \in L^\infty(S)$$

is not bounded away from 0. By (4.11.21) it follows that for each $\varepsilon > 0$ there exists a unit vector $h \in H^2(S)$ such that $\|fh\|_S \leq \varepsilon$. Hence

$$\sum_j \|T_S(f_j)h - \lambda_j h\|_S^2 \leq \sum_j \|f_j h - \lambda_j h\|_S^2 = \|fh\|_S^2 \leq \varepsilon^2$$

showing that $\|T_S(f_j)h - \lambda_j h\|_S \leq \varepsilon$ for every $1 \leq j \leq k$. Taking products, we see that for every $\delta > 0$ there exists a unit vector $h \in H^2(S)$ satisfying

$$\|p(T_S(f_1), \ldots, T_S(f_k))h - p(\lambda_1, \ldots, \lambda_k)h\|_S \leq \delta.$$

Therefore

$$\|p(T_S(f_1), \ldots, T_S(f_k))\| \geq \|p(T_S(f_1), \ldots, T_S(f_k))h\|_S \geq |p(\lambda_1, \ldots \lambda)| - \delta_k = 1 - \delta.$$

For $\delta \to 0$, the assertion follows. Q.E.D.

4.11.24. THEOREM. *Let $\mathcal{T}^\infty(S)$ be the C^*-algebra generated by all Toeplitz operators* $T_S(f)$ *with symbol* $f \in L^\infty(S)$. *Let $\mathcal{J}^\infty$ denote the closed *-ideal generated by all semi-commutators*

(4.11.25) $$T_S(\varphi)\, T_S(\psi) - T_S(\varphi\psi)$$

with $\varphi, \psi \in L^\infty(S)$. *Then there exists a C^*-algebra isomorphism*

(4.11.26) $$\mathcal{T}^\infty(S)/\mathcal{J}^\infty \xrightarrow[\approx]{\sigma} L^\infty(S)$$

such that $\sigma(T_S(\varphi) + \mathcal{J}^\infty) = f$ *for every* $f \in L^\infty(S)$.

Proof. By definition of $\mathcal{J}^\infty$, the *-linear mapping

$$L^\infty(S) \xrightarrow{\tau} \mathcal{T}^\infty(S)/\mathcal{J}^\infty, \quad f \mapsto T_S(f) + \mathcal{J}^\infty$$

is a homomorphism. Since $\mathcal{T}^\infty(S)$ is generated by all operators $T_S(f)$, $f \in L^\infty(S)$, it follows that τ is surjective. In order to show that τ is also injective, let $A \in \mathcal{J}^\infty$ be arbitrary. Then $A = \lim A_n$, where each A_n is a sum of terms

$$T_S(\varphi_1) \cdots T_S(\varphi_m)\,(T_S(\varphi_0)T_S(\psi_0) - T_S(\varphi_0\psi_0))\,T_S(\psi_1) \cdots T_S(\psi_n),$$

with $\varphi_0, ..., \varphi_m, \psi_0, ..., \psi_n \in L^\infty(S)$. Since $\varphi_1 \cdots \varphi_m(\varphi_0\psi_0 - \varphi_0\psi_0)\psi_1 \cdots \psi_n$ vanishes on S, Theorem 4.11.16 implies $\|T_S(f) + A_n\| \geq \|f\|_\infty$. For $n \to \infty$, we get $\|T_S(f) + A\| \geq \|f\|_\infty$. Thus τ is also injective. Q.E.D.

4.11.27. COROLLARY. *For* $f \in L^\infty(S)$ *we have*

(4.11.28) $$\|T_S(f)\| = \|f\|_\infty,$$

(4.11.29) $$\mathrm{Spec}(T_S(f)) \supset \mathrm{Spec}(f) \ (= \text{essential range of } f).$$

Proof. (4.11.28) follows from

$$\|f\|_\infty = \|f\| \geq \|T_S(f)\| \geq \|T_S(f) + \mathcal{J}^\infty\| = \|f\|_\infty.$$

If $T_S(f)$ is invertible, then $T_S(f) + \mathcal{J}^\infty \in \mathcal{T}^\infty(S)/\mathcal{J}^\infty$ is also invertible and, by Theorem 4.11.24, f is invertible in $L^\infty(S)$. Replacing f by $f - \lambda$, we obtain (4.11.29). Q.E.D.

Since $\mathcal{J}^\infty$ contains the commutator ideal $\mathcal{T}^\infty(S)'$, it follows that the compact operators $\mathcal{K}(H^2(S)) = \mathcal{K}(H^2(S))' \subset \mathcal{T}^\infty(S)'$ are also contained in $\mathcal{J}^\infty$. Therefore the preceding argument can be sharpened to show that $T_S(f)$ being Fredholm implies that f is invertible in $L^\infty(S)$. Thus we have the same inclusion (4.11.29) for the *essential* spectrum of $T_S(f)$. Restricting to the case of continuous symbols, we obtain in a similar way:

4.11.30. THEOREM. *Let* $\mathcal{T}(S)$ *be the Hardy-Toeplitz* C^**-algebra* (4.11.14) *and let* $\mathcal{J}$ *denote the closed* $*$*-ideal generated by all semi-commutators* (4.11.25) *with* $\varphi, \psi \in \mathcal{C}(S)$. *Then there exists a* C^**-algebra isomorphism*

(4.11.31) $$\mathcal{T}(S)/\mathcal{J} \xrightarrow[\approx]{\sigma} \mathcal{C}(S)$$

such that $\sigma(T_S(f) + \mathcal{J}) = f$ *for all* $f \in \mathcal{C}(S)$.

4.11.32. COROLLARY. *For* $f \in \mathcal{C}(S)$ *we have*

$$\|T_S(f)\| = \|f\|_\infty, \tag{4.11.33}$$

$$\text{ess-Spec}(T_S(f)) \supset f(S). \tag{4.11.34}$$

The Hardy space $H^2(S)$ of a symmetric ball $\Omega \subset Z$ contains the polynomial algebra $\mathcal{P}(Z)$ as a dense subspace. For $f \in \mathcal{P}(Z)$ the Toeplitz operator $T_S(f)h := fh$ leaves $\mathcal{P}(Z)$ invariant. We are interested in the "adjoint" of this operator. Consider also the "differential" scalar product (2.7.10) on $\mathcal{P}(Z)$. Let $C : \mathcal{P}(Z) \to \mathcal{P}(Z)$ denote the "diagonal" operator defined by

$$Cp = ((n/r))_\alpha p \tag{4.11.35}$$

for all $p \in \mathcal{P}^\alpha(Z)$ and $\alpha \in \vec{\mathbb{N}}^r$.

4.11.36. PROPOSITION. *For every* $p,q,f \in \mathcal{P}(Z)$, *we have*

$$(\partial_f p \mid q)_Z = (p \mid fq)_Z. \tag{4.11.37}$$

Proof. We may assume that $f(z) = (z|u)$ is linear. By orthogonality, we may also assume that p and q are homogeneous of degree m and m-1, respectively. Write $p(z) = (z|v)^m$ for some $v \in Z$ (these functions span $\mathcal{P}^m(Z)$). Then

$$\partial_f p = m \cdot (z|v)^{m-1} \cdot (u|v)$$

and hence

$$(\partial_f p \mid q)_Z = \overline{(u|v)}\ ((z|v)^{m-1} \mid q)_Z = m(v|u)(m-1)!\ q(v). \tag{4.11.38}$$

On the other hand,

$$(p|fq)_Z = ((z|v)^m \mid fq)_Z = m!\ f(v)q(v). \tag{4.11.39}$$

Since (4.11.38) and (4.11.39) agree, the assertion is proved. Q.E.D.

4.11.40. PROPOSITION. *For* $f \in \mathcal{P}(Z)$ *the adjoint* $T_S(f)^*$ *(with respect to* $H^2(S)$*) satisfies*

$$T_S(f)^*|_{\mathcal{P}(Z)} = C\,\partial_f\,C^{-1}$$

where ∂_f *is the constant coefficient differential operator given by* f.

Proof. For $p \in \mathcal{P}^\alpha(Z)$, $q \in \mathcal{P}^\beta(Z)$ and $\alpha,\beta \in \vec{\mathbb{N}}^r$, we apply (2.8.24) and Proposition 4.11.36 and obtain

$$(p \mid T_S(f)^* Cq)_S = (fp \mid Cq)_S = ((n/r))_\beta (fp \mid q)_S = (fp \mid q)_Z$$

$$= (p \mid \partial_f q)_Z = ((n/r))_\alpha (p \mid \partial_f q)_S = (p \mid C\partial_f q)_S.$$

It follows that $T_S(f)^* C = C\,\partial_f$, as asserted. Q.E.D.

Specializing to linear polynomials

(4.11.41) $$\ell(z) = (z|v) \qquad (v \in Z \text{ fixed})$$

we consider the directional derivative

(4.11.42) $$(\partial_v p)(z) = (\partial_\ell p)(z) = p'(z)v$$

and its adjoint $\partial_\ell^* : \mathcal{P}(Z) \to \mathcal{P}(Z)$ with respect to $H^2(S)$. Since the operator C is self-adjoint on $\mathcal{P}(Z)$, it follows from Proposition 4.11.40 that

(4.11.43) $$\partial_\ell^* = C\,T_S(\ell)\,C^{-1}.$$

We now begin a deeper study of Hardy-Toeplitz operators over Ω. Assume first that Ω is of tube type. In case S is the Shilov boundary of a symmetric ball Ω of tube type, one can use the harmonic decomposition

(4.11.44) $$H^2(S) \cong H^2(\mathbb{T}) \otimes L^2(S')$$

proved in (2.8.66) to obtain a more detailed description of some basic Hardy-Toeplitz operators. Recall that in this case Ω is the open unit ball of a Jordan algebra Z which has a determinant $\Delta : Z \to \mathbb{C}$. Moreover, $S' := \{z \in S : \Delta(z) = 1\}$ is the reduced Shilov boundary of S.

4.11.45. PROPOSITION. *Let Ω be a symmetric ball of tube type, with determinant Δ. Then the operator $T_S(\Delta)$ with symbol Δ is an isometry:*

(4.11.46) $$T_S(\Delta)^* T_S(\Delta) = id_{H^2(S)}.$$

Proof. By Proposition 1.5.75, the group K' acts transitively on S'. Since Δ is K'-invariant (by (2.7.29)) and homogeneous, it follows from $S = \mathbb{T} \cdot S'$ that $|\Delta(z)| = 1$ for all $z \in S$. This means that

(4.11.47) $$\bar{\Delta}\,\Delta = 1$$

as functions on S. Now apply (4.11.9) and (4.11.11). Q.E.D.

4.11.48. PROPOSITION. *Let Ω be a symmetric ball of tube type. Let $\ell \in \mathcal{P}^1(Z)$ be linear. Then*

(4.11.49) $$T_S(\Delta)^* \, T_S(\partial_\ell \Delta) = T_S(\ell)^*.$$

Proof. For every invertible element $z \in Z$, the determinant satisfies "Cramer's rule"

$$z^{-1} = \frac{1}{\Delta(z)} \operatorname{grad}_z \Delta,$$

where $\operatorname{grad}_z \Delta \in Z$ is the "gradient" vector characterized by the duality

$$\Delta'(z)v = \langle \operatorname{grad}_z \Delta | v \rangle$$

for all $v \in Z$, where $\langle u|v \rangle := (u|v^*)$ is the "standard bilinear form" of Z [S4]. Now let $z \in S$. Then z is invertible and $z^{-1} = z^*$ [L9]. It follows that

$$\Delta(z)^{-1}\Delta'(z)v = \Delta(z)^{-1}\langle \operatorname{grad}_z \Delta | v \rangle = \langle z^{-1} | v \rangle = \langle z^* | v \rangle = \langle v | z^* \rangle = (v|z) = \overline{(z|v)}.$$

Since $|\Delta| = 1$ on S by (4.11.47), it follows that $\ell(z) := (z|v)$ satisfies

(4.11.50) $$\bar{\Delta} \cdot \partial_{\ell}\Delta = \bar{\ell}$$

as functions on S. Now apply (4.11.9) and (4.11.11). Q.E.D.

The isometry $T_S(\Delta)$ is not surjective (i.e., a Hilbert space isomorphism) but has a cokernel described in "geometric" terms as follows:

4.11.51. PROPOSITION. *Let Ω be a symmetric ball of tube type. Then* $\mathrm{Ker}(T_S(\Delta)^*)$ *is the closure (in* $H^2(S)$*) of the space of K'-harmonic polynomials*

$$\mathcal{H}(Z) = \sum_{\alpha_r=0} \mathcal{P}^{\alpha}(Z).$$

Proof. By definition, we have

$$\mathcal{H}(Z) = \{q \in \mathcal{P}(Z) : \partial_{\Delta}q = 0\}.$$

The multiplication operator $h \mapsto \Delta \cdot h$ maps $\mathcal{P}^{\alpha}(Z)$ into $\mathcal{P}^{\alpha+\mathbb{1}}(Z)$, where $\alpha + \mathbb{1} := (\alpha_1 + 1, ..., \alpha_r + 1)$. It follows that the adjoint operators ∂_{Δ} (in the differential scalar product, cf. (4.11.37)) and $T_S(\Delta)^*$ (in $H^2(S)$) map $\mathcal{P}^{\alpha+\mathbb{1}}(Z)$ into $\mathcal{P}^{\alpha}(Z)$ and differ only by a factor

$$T_S(\Delta)^*p = c_{\alpha} \cdot \partial_{\Delta}p$$

for all $p \in \mathcal{P}^{\alpha}(Z)$, where $c_{\alpha} > 0$. The assertion follows. Q.E.D.

4.11.52. THEOREM. *Let Ω be a symmetric ball of tube type and consider the tensor product decomposition* (4.11.44) *of the Hardy space* $H^2(S)$. *For any* $u \in Z$ *put* $\ell(z) := (z|u)$. *Then there exist bounded operators* A_u *and* B_u *on* $L^2(S')$ *such that*

(4.11.53) $$T_S(\Delta) = T_{\mathbb{T}}(\zeta) \otimes \mathrm{id},$$

(4.11.54) $$T_S(\ell) = \mathrm{id} \otimes B_u^* + T_{\mathbb{T}}(\zeta) \otimes A_u^*,$$

(4.11.55) $$T_S(\partial_{\ell}\Delta) = \mathrm{id} \otimes A_u + T_{\mathbb{T}}(\zeta) \otimes B_u.$$

Here ζ *denotes the variable of the* 1*-torus* $\mathbb{T}$, *with associated (classical) Toeplitz operator* $T_{\mathbb{T}}(\zeta)$ *acting on* $H^2(\mathbb{T})$.

Proof. For any $p \in \mathcal{P}(Z)$, $T_S(p)^*$ leaves the $H^2(S)$-closure

$$\overline{\mathcal{H}(Z)} = \operatorname{Ker}(T_S(\Delta)^*) \tag{4.11.56}$$

invariant, since (4.11.10) implies

$$[T_S(p)^*, T_S(\Delta)^*] = [T_S(\Delta), T_S(p)]^* = 0.$$

Now let $q \in \mathcal{H}(Z)$. By (2.8.28), we can write

$$\partial_\ell \Delta \cdot q = \sum_{k \geq 0} \Delta^k q_k \qquad \text{(finite sum)} \tag{4.11.57}$$

where $q_k \in \mathcal{H}(Z)$ for all k. By (4.11.49) and (4.11.56), we get

$$T_S(\ell)^* q = T_S(\Delta)^* \partial_\ell \Delta \cdot q = \sum_{k \geq 0} T_S(\Delta)^* \Delta^k q_k$$

$$= T_S(\Delta)^* q_0 + \sum_{k \geq 1} \Delta^{k-1} q_k = \sum_{k \geq 1} \Delta^{k-1} q_k \in \mathcal{H}(Z).$$

By the uniqueness of the decomposition (4.11.57) it follows that $q_k = 0$ for all $k \geq 2$, i.e.

$$\partial_\ell \Delta \cdot q = A_u q + \Delta \cdot B_u q \tag{4.11.58}$$

for certain bounded operators on $\mathcal{H}(Z)$. This gives (4.11.55). Now (4.11.55) follows from (4.11.49) and (4.11.46). Q.E.D.

The operators A_u, B_u have the following properties.

4.11.59. PROPOSITION. *Let* S' *be the reduced Shilov boundary of a symmetric ball* Ω *of tube type. Then*

$$B_u = T_S(\ell)^* |_{L^2(S')} , \tag{4.11.60}$$

(4.11.61) $$A_u^* = T_S(\partial_\ell \Delta)^* |_{L^2(S')} .$$

Moreover, we have the commutation relations for $u, v \in Z$

(4.11.62) $$[A_u, A_v] = 0 = [B_u, B_v],$$

(4.11.63) $$[A_u, B_v^*] = 0 = [B_u, A_v^*],$$

(4.11.64) $$[A_u, B_v] = [A_v, B_u],$$

(4.11.65) $$[B_u^*, B_v] = [A_v, A_u^*].$$

Proof. These relations follow by straightforward computation from the definitions. Q.E.D.

4.11.66. DEFINITION. The *reduced* Toeplitz C^*-algebra over S' is defined as the unital C^*-algebra

(4.11.67) $$\Psi(S') := C^*(A_u, B_u : u \in Z)$$

defined by all operators (4.11.60) and (4.11.61) on $L^2(S')$.

4.11.68. EXAMPLE. Let Ω be the "Lie ball" in $Z = \mathbb{C}^n$, $n \geq 3$. By Example 1.5.77, the reduced Shilov boundary of Ω is the sphere $S' = \mathbb{S}^{n-1}$ in $\mathbb{R}^n$. Since $K' = SO(d)$, we can identify the harmonic polynomials

$$\mathcal{H}^m(Z) \cong \mathcal{H}^m(\mathbb{S}^{n-1})$$

with the space of m-homogeneous harmonic polynomials restricted to $\mathbb{S}^{n-1}$. Further,

$$L^2(\mathbb{S}^{n-1}) = \sum_{m \geq 0}^{\oplus} \mathcal{H}^m(\mathbb{S}^{n-1})$$

is the orthogonal decomposition into "spherical harmonics". Now let $u \in Z$ and put $\ell(z) = (z|u) = 2\, z \cdot \bar{u}$. Since $\Delta(z) = z \cdot z$ we obtain $\partial_\ell \Delta(z) = \Delta'(z)u = 2\, z \cdot u = (z|\bar{u})$. For any $q \in \mathcal{H}^m(Z)$, (2.7.41) implies for $a = n - 2$

$$(z|\bar{u}) \cdot q = ((z|\bar{u})\, q - \frac{\Delta \cdot \partial_u q}{m + a/2}) + \Delta \cdot \frac{\partial_u q}{m + a/2}.$$

Comparing with (4.11.58) we get

$$(4.11.69) \qquad A_u q = (z|\bar{u})\, q - \frac{\Delta \cdot \partial_u q}{m + a/2} = 2(z \cdot u\, q - \frac{\Delta \cdot \partial_u q}{2m + a}),$$

$$(4.11.70) \qquad B_u q = \frac{\partial_u q}{m + a/2} = 2\,\frac{\partial_u q}{2m + a}.$$

Replacing u by $\bar{u} \in Z$, we obtain similarly, using (4.11.54)

$$(4.11.71) \qquad B_u^* q = (z|u)\, q - \frac{\Delta \cdot \partial_{\bar{u}} q}{m + a/2} = A_{\bar{u}} q,$$

$$(4.11.72) \qquad A_u^* q = \frac{\partial_{\bar{u}} q}{m + a/2} = B_{\bar{u}} q.$$

(This simple relationship between B_u^* and $A_{\bar{u}}$ holds only for Jordan algebras of rank 2, in fact there is no "natural" conjugation $u \mapsto \bar{u}$ in the higher rank case.) Now suppose that $u = \bar{u}$ is real, and consider the restriction of q to $\mathbb{S}^{n-1}$. Since $\Delta = 1$ on $\mathbb{S}^{n-1}$, we obtain from (4.11.69) and (4.11.70)

$$\frac{1}{2} A_u q = x \cdot u\ q - \frac{\partial_u q}{2m + a}, \quad \frac{1}{2} B_u q = \frac{\partial_u q}{2m + a}$$

for all $q \in \mathcal{H}^m(\mathbb{S}^{n-1})$ and $x \in \mathbb{S}^{n-1}$. For any fixed vector $u \in Z$, the holomorphic vector field

$$D_u = (u - \{zu^* z\}) \frac{\partial}{\partial z} = (u - 2\, z \cdot \bar{u}\ z + z \cdot z\ \bar{u}) \frac{\partial}{\partial z}$$

is tangential to the Shilov boundary S. If u is real, D_u is also tangential to S' and reduces to

$$D_u = 2(u - x \cdot u\ x) \frac{\partial}{\partial x}$$

since $x \cdot x = 1$ for $x \in S'$. Applying D_u to any $q \in \mathcal{H}^m(S')$ we get by Euler's relation

$$\frac{1}{2} D_u q = \partial_u q - m(x \cdot u)q = |x| \, \partial_u q(\frac{x}{|x|}).$$

Here q is identified with its m-homogeneous extension to $Z^{\mathbb{R}}$ (or to Z). It follows that $\frac{1}{2} D_u$ is the *gradient* (with respect to $\mathbb{S}^{n-1}$) in direction u.

Now define the *Riesz operator* [L5; (4.5)]

$$R_u q(x) = \frac{-i}{m+1}(\partial_u q - m(x \cdot u)q) = i \frac{D_u}{2} \Lambda^{-1},$$

where

$$\Lambda^{-1} q := \frac{-q}{m+1} \qquad (q \in \mathcal{H}^m(Z))$$

is a convolution operator on $S' = K'/L'$ [L6; (3.6)]. Also define the multiplication operator $M_u q(x) := u \cdot x \, q(x)$. One can show [BCK] that M_u and R_u are bounded operators on $L^2(\mathbb{S}^{n-1})$ which generate the *Calderon-Zygmund C^*-algebra*

$$\Psi(\mathbb{S}^{n-1}) = C^*(M_u, R_u : u \in \mathbb{R}^n) \tag{4.11.73}$$

acting on $L^2(\mathbb{S}^{n-1})$. Moreover these operators have compact commutators and the commutator ideal

$$\Psi(\mathbb{S}^{n-1})' = \mathcal{K}(L^2(\mathbb{S}^{n-1}))$$

coincides with the C^*-algebra of all compact operators on $L^2(\mathbb{S}^{n-1})$. This follows from the fact that $\Psi(\mathbb{S}^{n-1})$ acts irreducibly, i.e. without proper invariant subspace, on $L^2(\mathbb{S}^{n-1})$ [D1]. In order to relate the Calderon-Zygmund C^*-algebra (4.11.73) to the reduced Toeplitz C^*-algebra as defined in (4.11.67), we compute for $q \in \mathcal{H}^m(Z)$

$$[A_u - (M_u - iR_u)]q = 2(x \cdot u)\, q - \frac{\partial_u q}{m + a/2} - ((1 + \frac{m}{m+1})x \cdot u \, q - \frac{\partial_u q}{m+1})$$

$$= \frac{a/2 - 1}{a/2 + m}(iR_u q + \frac{m}{m + 1} M_u q).$$

Since R_u and M_u are bounded, it follows that $A_u - (M_u - iR_u)$ is *compact.* Hence

(4.11.74) $$A_u \equiv M_u - iR_u$$

where $\equiv$ means equivalence modulo compact operators. Similarly, we have

(4.11.75) $$B_u \equiv M_u + iR_u.$$

It follows from (4.11.74) and (4.11.75), that the Calderon-Zygmund C^*-algebra is also generated by the operators A_u, B_u, i.e. coincides with the reduced Toeplitz C^*-algebra (4.11.67). This close relation to classical pseudo-differential operators does not hold for domains of rank ≥ 3.

4.11.76. THEOREM. *With respect to the tensor product decomposition (4.11.44) of* $H^2(S)$, *the commutator ideal* $\mathcal{T}(S)'$ *of the Hardy-Toeplitz* C^**-algebra* $\mathcal{T}(S)$ *over the Shilov boundary* S *of a symmetric ball of tube type has the form*

$$\mathcal{T}(S)' = \mathcal{K}(H^2(\mathbb{T})) \otimes \Psi(S').$$

Proof. Let

$$P = [T_{\mathbb{T}}(\zeta)^*, T_{\mathbb{T}}(\zeta)] \in \mathcal{K}(H^2(\mathbb{T}))$$

be the projection onto the constant functions on $\mathbb{T}$. Using (4.11.54) and (4.11.63), one shows

(4.11.77) $$[T_S(\ell_1)^*, T_S(\ell_2)] = P \otimes A^*_{u_2} A_{u_1}.$$

Therefore $\mathcal{T}(S)' \subset \mathcal{K}(H^2(\mathbb{T})) \otimes \Psi(S')$. For the converse note first that

$$[T_S(\Delta)^*, T_S(\Delta)] = P \otimes \mathrm{id}.$$

More generally, we have for all $m,n \geq 0$

$$T_S(\Delta)^m\,[T_S(\Delta)^*,\,T_S(\Delta)]\,T_S(\bar{\Delta})^n = T_{\mathbb{T}}(\zeta)^m\,P\,T_{\mathbb{T}}(\bar{\zeta})^n \otimes \mathrm{id}$$

The operator $T_{\mathbb{T}}(\zeta)^m\,P\,T_{\mathbb{T}}(\bar{\zeta})^n$ on $H^2(\mathbb{T})$ is a rank 1 operator having the matrix entry 1 only at the (m,n)-th place. Taking linear combinations of such operators we obtain all finite rank operators. It follows that

$$\mathcal{K}(H^2(\mathbb{T})) \otimes \mathrm{id} \subset \mathcal{T}(S)'.$$

Since $\Psi(S')$ is unital, it follows that the set

$$\mathcal{J} := \{K \in \mathcal{K}(H^2(\mathbb{T})) : K \otimes \Psi(S') \subset \mathcal{T}(S)'\}$$

is an ideal in $\mathcal{K}(H^2(\mathbb{T}))$. Now we have

(4.11.78)
$$[T_S(\Delta)^*, T_S(\ell)] = P \otimes A_u^*\,, \quad [T_S(\Delta)^*, T_S(\partial_\ell \Delta)] = P \otimes B_u,$$
$$[T_S(\Delta)^*, T_S(\Delta)]\,T_S(\ell) = P \otimes B_u^*\,, \quad [T_S(\Delta)^*, T_S(\Delta)]\,T_S(\partial_\ell \Delta) = P \otimes A_u.$$

These formulas imply $P \in \mathcal{J}$. Since $\mathcal{K}(H^2(\mathbb{T}))$ is a simple C^*-algebra, we obtain $\mathcal{J} = \mathcal{K}(H^2(\mathbb{T}))$. Q.E.D.

4.11.79. LEMMA. *Let* Z *be an irreducible Jordan algebra. For* $q \in \mathcal{H}(Z)$ *and* $k \in \mathbb{N}$, *we have*

$$\partial_v^*(\Delta^k q) = \Delta^k q_0 + (k+1)\Delta^{k+1}(A_v^* q)\,.$$

Proof. By (4.11.43), we have $h := \partial_v^*(\Delta^k q) = C\,T_S(\ell)\,C^{-1}\Delta^k q$. Since C is a diagonal operator, (4.11.54) implies $h = \Delta^k q_0 + \Delta^{k+1} q_1$ where $q_0, q_1 \in \mathcal{H}(Z)$. In order to compute q_1, let $p \in \mathcal{H}(Z)$ be arbitrary. Since

$$\partial_v(\Delta^{k+1}p) = (k+1)\Delta^k \cdot \partial_v\Delta \cdot p + \Delta^{k+1}\partial_v p$$

and $\partial_v p \in \mathcal{H}(Z)$ it follows from (4.11.47) that

$$(q_1 \mid p)_S = (\Delta^{k+1}q_1 \mid \Delta^{k+1}p)_S = (h \mid \Delta^{k+1}p)_S = (\Delta^k q \mid \partial_v(\Delta^{k+1}p))_S$$
$$= (k+1)(\Delta^k q \mid \Delta^k \cdot \partial_v\Delta \cdot p)_S = (k+1)(q \mid \partial_v\Delta \cdot p)_S$$

$$= (k+1)(q \mid A_v p)_S = (k+1)(A_v^* q \mid p)_S. \qquad \text{Q.E.D.}$$

4.11.80. LEMMA. *We have*

$$A_v \mathcal{P}^{(\alpha_1,\dots,\alpha_{r-1},0)}(Z) \subset \mathcal{P}^{(\alpha_1+1,\dots,\alpha_{r-1}+1,0)}(Z),$$

$$A_v^* \mathcal{P}^{(\beta_1,\dots,\beta_{r-1},0)}(Z) \subset \mathcal{P}^{(\beta_1-1,\dots,\beta_{r-1}-1,0)}(Z).$$

Proof. Put $\alpha = (\alpha_1, \dots, \alpha_{r-1}, 0)$, $\beta = (\beta_1, \dots, \beta_{r-1}, 0)$ and suppose $(q \mid A_v p)_S \neq 0$ for some $p \in \mathcal{P}^\alpha(Z)$ and $q \in \mathcal{P}^\beta(Z)$. Applying Proposition 4.11.59 and Lemma 4.11.79 we obtain for every $k \in \mathbb{N}$

$$(k+1)(A_v^* q \mid p)_S = (k+1)(\Delta^{k+1} A_v^* q \mid \Delta^{k+1} p)_S$$

$$= (\partial_v^* \Delta^k q \mid \Delta^{k+1} p)_S = (C\, T_S(\ell)\, C^{-1} \Delta^k q \mid \Delta^{k+1} p)_S$$

$$= c \cdot (\ell \Delta^k q \mid \Delta^{k+1} p)_S = c \cdot (\ell q \mid \Delta p)_S = c \cdot (A_v^* q \mid p)_S.$$

It follows that

$$(4.11.81) \qquad k+1 = c = \frac{((n/r))_{\alpha+k+1}}{((n/r))_{\beta+k}}.$$

Applying (4.11.81) to k and $k+1$ and dividing, we obtain

$$\frac{k+2}{k+1} = \prod_{j=1}^{r} \frac{(\frac{n}{r} - \frac{a}{2}(j-1))_{\alpha_j+k+2}}{(\frac{n}{r} - \frac{a}{2}(j-1))_{\beta_j+k+1}} \; \frac{(\frac{n}{r} - \frac{a}{2}(j-1))_{\beta_j+k}}{(\frac{n}{r} - \frac{a}{2}(j-1))_{\alpha_j+k+1}}$$

$$= \prod_{j=1}^{r} \frac{\frac{n}{r} - \frac{a}{2}(j-1) + \alpha_j + k + 1}{\frac{n}{r} - \frac{a}{2}(j-1) + \beta_j + k}.$$

Since $\alpha_r = \beta_r = 0$ and $\frac{n}{r} - \frac{a}{2}(j-1) = 1$, it follows that

(4.11.82) $$\prod_{j=1}^{r-1}\left(\frac{n}{r} - \frac{a}{2}(j-1) + \alpha_j + k + 1\right) = \prod_{j=1}^{r-1}\left(\frac{n}{r} - \frac{a}{2}(j-1) + \beta_j + k\right)$$

for every $k \in \mathbb{N}$. Therefore we have

$$\prod_{j=1}^{r-1}\left(x - \frac{a}{2}(j-1) + \alpha_j + 1\right) = \prod_{j=1}^{r-1}\left(x - \frac{a}{2}(j-1) + \beta_j\right)$$

as polynomials of degree $r - 1$ in x, and the set of roots

$$\{\frac{a}{2}(j-1) - \alpha_j - 1\} = \{\frac{a}{2}(j-1) - \beta_j\}$$

agrees up to permutation. Since both sets are written in strictly increasing order we have $\alpha_j + 1 = \beta_j$ for all $1 \le j \le r - 1$. Q.E.D.

4.11.83. PROPOSITION. *Let Z be an irreducible Jordan algebra with Peirce decomposition*

$$Z = \sum_{1\le i\le j\le r}^{\oplus} Z_{ij}.$$

Let $k \ge 0$ *and* $v \in Z_{ij}$, *where* $k < i \le j \le r$. *Then we have for all* $\alpha \in \vec{\mathbb{N}}^r$:

(4.11.84) $$\partial_v \Delta_\alpha \in \sum_{k<\ell\le r} \mathcal{P}^{\alpha-\varepsilon_\ell}(Z).$$

Here we put $\alpha - \varepsilon_\ell := (\alpha_1, \ldots, \alpha_{\ell-1}, \alpha_\ell - 1, \alpha_{\ell+1}, \ldots, \alpha_r)$.

Proof. We first prove (4.11.84) in case $v = e_i$ for some $k < i \le r$. We have for $\beta = (\alpha_1 - \alpha_r, \ldots, \alpha_{r-1} - \alpha_r, 0)$

(4.11.85) $$\partial_v \Delta_\alpha = \partial_v(\Delta_\beta \Delta^{\alpha_r}) = (\partial_v \Delta_\beta)\cdot \Delta^{\alpha_r} + \Delta_\beta \alpha_r \Delta^{\alpha_r - 1}\partial_v \Delta.$$

In case $i = r$, Lemma 4.11.80 implies $\partial_v \Delta = \Delta_{r-1}$, $\partial_v \Delta_\beta = 0$ and hence

$$\partial_v \Delta_\alpha = \alpha_r \Delta_\beta \Delta^{\alpha_r - 1} \Delta_{r-1} = \alpha_r \Delta_\gamma$$

where $\gamma = (\beta_1 + \alpha_r, \ldots, \beta_{r-1} + \alpha_r, \alpha_{r-1}) = \alpha - \varepsilon_r$. In case $i < r$, v belongs to the irreducible Jordan algebra

$$Z' := \sum_{1 \le i \le j < r}^{\oplus} Z_{ij}$$

of rank $r - 1$. Using induction on the rank, we obtain

$$\partial_v \Delta_\beta \in \sum_{k<\ell\le r-1} \mathcal{P}^{\beta-\varepsilon_\ell}(Z') \subset \sum_{k<\ell\le r-1} \mathcal{P}^{\beta-\varepsilon_\ell}(Z).$$

Therefore the first summand in (4.11.85) gives

$$\Delta^{\alpha_r} \cdot \partial_v \Delta_\beta \in \sum_{k<\ell\le r-1} \mathcal{P}^{\alpha-\varepsilon_\ell}(Z).$$

For the second summand note that (4.11.58) implies $\partial_v \Delta \cdot \Delta_\beta = A_v \Delta_\beta + \Delta \cdot B_v \Delta_\beta$ By Lemma 4.11.80, $A_v \Delta_\beta$ has type $(\beta_1 + 1, \ldots, \beta_{r-1} + 1, 0)$ and we obtain

$$\Delta^{\alpha_r - 1} \cdot A_v \Delta_\beta \in \mathcal{P}^{\alpha-\varepsilon_r}(Z).$$

Using Proposition 4.11.59 and (4.11.40) we have by induction

$$B_v \Delta_\beta = C\, \partial_v\, C^{-1} \Delta_\beta \in \sum_{k<\ell\le r-1} \mathcal{P}^{\alpha-\varepsilon_\ell}(Z') \subset \sum_{k<\ell\le r-1} \mathcal{P}^{\beta-\varepsilon_\ell}(Z)$$

showing that

$$\Delta^{\alpha_r} \cdot B_v \Delta_\beta \in \sum_{k<\ell\le r-1} \mathcal{P}^{\beta-\varepsilon_\ell}(Z).$$

This completes the first part of the proof. Now assume $v \in Z_{ij}$ for $k < i < j \le r$. Then the vector field

$$A := \{z e_j^* v\} \frac{\partial}{\partial z} \in \mathcal{K}^{\mathbb{C}}$$

belongs to the nilpotent subalgebra n_+ of $\mathcal{K}^{\mathbb{C}}$ generated by the positive root spaces. The Peirce composition rules [L8, L9] imply

$$u := e_j \cdot \exp(A) = e_j + \frac{v}{2} + c e_i$$

for some $c \in \mathbb{C}$. Now for any $s \in K^{\mathbb{C}}$ with right translation ρ_s we have

$$\partial_v(\rho_s\Delta_\alpha)(z) = \frac{\partial}{\partial t}\Big|_{t=0} (\rho_s\Delta_\alpha)(z + tv) = \frac{\partial}{\partial t}\Big|_{t=0} \Delta_\alpha(zs + t \cdot vs) = (\partial_{vs}\Delta_\alpha)(zs).$$

Since $\Delta\alpha$ is n_+-invariant, this implies

$$\rho_{\exp(-A)}\partial_{e_j}\Delta_\alpha = \rho_{\exp(-A)}\partial_{u\cdot\exp(-A)}\Delta_\alpha$$

$$= \partial_u(\rho_{\exp(-A)}\Delta_\alpha) = \partial_u\Delta_\alpha = \partial_{e_j}\Delta_\alpha + \frac{1}{2}\partial_v\Delta_\alpha + c \cdot \partial_{e_j}\Delta_\alpha.$$

Applying the first part of the proof to e_i and e_j, the assertion follows.
Q.E.D.

4.11.86. THEOREM. *Let* Z *be an irreducible Jordan triple of rank* r. *Then we have for every* $v \in Z$ and $\alpha \in \vec{\mathbb{N}}^r$

(4.11.87)
$$\partial_v\mathcal{P}^\alpha(Z) \subset \sum_{1\le\ell\le r} \mathcal{P}^{\alpha-\varepsilon_\ell}(Z),$$

(4.11.88)
$$(z|v) \cdot \mathcal{P}^\alpha(Z) \subset \sum_{1\le\ell\le r} \mathcal{P}^{\alpha+\varepsilon_\ell}(Z).$$

Proof. Let

$$Z = \sum_{0\le i\le j\le r}^{\oplus} Z_{ij}$$

be a Peirce decomposition of Z. We may assume that $v \in Z_{ij}$ for some $0 \le i \le j \le r$. In case $i = 0$ we have $\partial_v\Delta_\alpha = 0$. In case $i \ge 1$, v belongs to the Jordan algebra

$$Z' := \sum_{1\le i\le j\le r}^{\oplus} Z_{ij}$$

of rank r. Applying Proposition 4.11.83 to Z', we obtain

$$\partial_v\Delta_\alpha \in \sum_{1\le\ell\le r} \mathcal{P}^{\alpha-\varepsilon_\ell}(Z') \subset \sum_{1\le\ell\le r} \mathcal{P}^{\alpha-\varepsilon_\ell}(Z).$$

Now the first assertion follows with (4.11.84). For the second assertion, use Proposition 4.11.36. Q.E.D.

Now let $1 \leq k \leq r$ be fixed, and embed

$$\vec{\mathbb{N}}^{r-k} \subset \vec{\mathbb{N}}^r$$

by identifying $\beta := (\beta_{k+1}, ..., \beta_r) \in \vec{\mathbb{N}}^{r-k}$ with the signature $(\beta_{k+1},...,\beta_{k+1}, \beta_r) \in \vec{\mathbb{N}}^r$. Then the conical polynomial

$$\Delta_\beta(z) = \Delta_{k+1}(z)^{\beta_{k+1}-\beta_{k+2}} \dots \Delta_r(z)^{\beta_r}$$

on Z has the restriction

$$(4.11.89)\quad (\Delta_\beta)_c\,(w) = \Delta_\beta(c + w) = \Delta_{k+1}(c + w)^{\beta_{k+1}-\beta_{k+2}} \dots \Delta_r(c + w)^{\beta_r}$$

$$= \delta_1(w)^{\beta_{k+1}-\beta_{k+2}} \dots \delta_{r-k}(w)^{\beta_r} = \delta_\beta(w) \in \mathcal{P}^\beta(Z_0(c))$$

which agrees with the conical polynomial of type β relative to the Jordan triple $Z_0(c)$ of rank $r - k$. For fixed $\beta \in \vec{\mathbb{N}}^{r-k}$ consider the orthogonal projection

$$(4.11.90)\qquad \pi_\beta : \mathcal{P}(Z) \to \sum_{\alpha_1 \geq \cdots \geq \alpha_k \geq \beta_{k+1}} \mathcal{P}^{\alpha_1,\dots,\alpha_k,\beta}(Z).$$

4.11.91. LEMMA. *Let* $p \in \mathcal{P}(Z_1(c))$. *Then* $p\Delta_\beta \in \pi_\beta(\mathcal{P}(Z))$.

Proof. Every commutator γ in $\mathrm{Aut}(Z_1(c))^0$ has an extension $g \in K$ satisfying $g|_{Z_0(c)} = \mathrm{id}$ and $\mathcal{S}_g \ltimes \Delta_\beta = \Delta_\beta$. We may therefore assume

$$(4.11.92)\qquad p = \Delta_1^{\ell_1} \cdots \Delta_k^{\ell_k}$$

since $\mathcal{P}(Z_1(c))$ is spanned by polynomials of the form $\mathcal{S}_\gamma p$. But then

$$p\Delta_\beta = \Delta_1^{\ell_1} \cdots \Delta_k^{\ell_k}\Delta_\beta \in \pi_\beta(\mathcal{P}(Z)).$$

Q.E.D.

4.11.93. LEMMA. *Let* $p \in \mathcal{P}(Z_1(c))$ *and* $v \in Z_0(c)$. *Then* $\ell(z) := (z|v)$ *satisfies*

(4.11.94) $$T_S(\ell)^*(p\Delta_\beta) = \sum_{k<j\le r} (\beta_j + \frac{a}{2}(r - j) + b)^{-1} \cdot \pi_{\beta-\varepsilon_j}(p \cdot \partial_v\Delta_\beta).$$

Proof. As in the proof of Lemma 4.11.91, we may assume that (4.11.92) holds. Then $p\Delta_\beta = \Delta^\alpha$ for some $\alpha = (\alpha_1, ..., \alpha_k, \beta) \in \vec{\mathbb{N}}^r$. Applying Proposition 4.11.40 and (4.11.87), we obtain

(4.11.95) $$\begin{aligned} T_S(\ell)^*(p\Delta_\beta) = T_S(\ell)^*\Delta_\alpha &= \sum_{j=k+1}^{r} (\beta_j + \frac{a}{2}(r - j) + b)^{-1}(\partial_v\Delta_\alpha)_{\alpha-\varepsilon_j} \\ &= \sum_{j=k+1}^{r} (\beta_j + \frac{a}{2}(r - j) + b)^{-1}(p \cdot \partial_v\Delta_\beta)_{\alpha-\varepsilon_j}. \end{aligned}$$

Since $\mathcal{P}^{\alpha-\varepsilon_j}(Z) \subset \text{Ran } \pi_{\beta-\varepsilon_j}$ for all $j > k$, the assertion follows. Q.E.D.

Now consider the analytic function

$$H_c(z) = \exp\,(z|c) \in H^2(S)$$

and the sequence of unit vectors

(4.11.96) $$h_S^i(z) := H_c(z)^i/\|H_c^i\|_S.$$

4.11.97. LEMMA. *Let* $f \in \mathcal{C}(S, \mathbb{R}_+)$ *satisfy* $f_c = 0$. *Then*

$$\lim_{i\to\infty} \int_S f(z) \cdot |h_S^i(z)|^2 \, dz = 0.$$

Proof. For every $\varepsilon > 0$ there exists an open neighborhood $U \subset S$ of $c + S_c$ satisfying $\sup f(U) \le \varepsilon$. By [L9; 6.2] we have $\text{Re}\,(z|c) \le (c|c)$ on S and $\text{Re}\,(z|c) = (c|c)$ implies $z \in c + S_c$. Since $|H_c(z)| = \exp \text{Re}\,(z|c)$ it follows that there exists an open neighborhood $V \subset U$ of $c + S_c$ satisfying

$$q := \sup_{S\setminus U} |H_c| \,/\, \inf_V |H_c| < 1.$$

Therefore

$$\int_S f(z)\ |h_S^i(z)|^2\ dz = \int_U f(z)\ |h_S^i(z)|^2\ dz + \int_{S\setminus U} f(z)\ |h_S^i(z)|^2\ dz$$

$$\leq \varepsilon + \sup_S f \cdot \int_{S\setminus U} |H_c(z)|^{2i} dz \Big/ \int_V |H_c(z)|^{2i}\ dz$$

$$\leq \varepsilon + \sup_S f \cdot q^{2i}\ \mathrm{Vol}_S(S\setminus U)/\mathrm{Vol}_S(V).$$

Since $q^{2i} \to 0$, it follows that

$$\overline{\lim_{i\to\infty}} \int_S f(z)\ |h_S^i(z)|^2\ dz \leq \varepsilon. \qquad \text{Q.E.D.}$$

For two sequences (f_i), (g_i) in $L^2(S)$ we put

$$f_i \underset{S}{\sim} g_i \tag{4.11.98}$$

if $\lim_{i\to\infty} \|f_i - g_i\|_S = 0$.

4.11.99. LEMMA. *Let* $q \in \mathcal{P}(Z_0(c))$ *and* $\beta \in \vec{\mathbb{N}}^{r-k}$. *Then*

$$\pi_\beta(h_S^i q) \underset{S}{\sim} h_S^i q_\beta. \tag{4.11.100}$$

Proof. Every $\gamma \in \mathrm{Aut}\ Z_0(c)^0$ has an extension $g \in K$ satisfying $g(c) = c$. We may thus assume that $q = \delta_\alpha$ is the conical polynomial in $Z_0(c)$ of type $\alpha \in \vec{\mathbb{N}}^{r-k}$. By (4.11.89), $\Delta_\alpha - q$ vanishes on $c + S_c$. Therefore Lemma 4.11.97 implies

$$h_S^i q \underset{S}{\sim} h_S^i \Delta_\alpha$$

which gives

$$\pi_\beta(h_S^i q) \underset{S}{\sim} \pi_\beta(h_S^i \Delta_\alpha)$$

since π_β has a continuous extension to $H^2(S)$. Since h_S^i belongs to the closure of $\mathcal{P}(Z_1(c))$ in $H^2(S)$, Lemma 4.11.91 implies

$$\pi_\beta(h_S^i \Delta_\alpha) = \delta_{\alpha,\beta} h_S^i \Delta_\alpha \underset{S}{\sim} \delta_{\alpha,\beta} h_S^i q = h_S^i q_\beta. \qquad \text{Q.E.D.}$$

4.11.101. LEMMA. *Let* $p \in \mathcal{P}(Z)$. *Then*

(4.11.102) $$h_S^i p \underset{S}{\sim} h_S^i p_c, \quad h_S^i \bar{p} \underset{S}{\sim} h_S^i \bar{p}_c$$

where we embed $\mathcal{P}(Z_0(c)) \subset \mathcal{P}(Z)$ *via the Peirce projection.*

Proof. Since $p - p_c$ vanishes on $c + S_c$, Lemma 4.11.97 implies

$$\|h_S^i p - h_S^i p_c\|_S^2 = \int_S |(p - p_c)(z)|^2 \, |h_S^i(z)|^2 \, dz \to 0. \qquad \text{Q.E.D.}$$

4.11.103. PROPOSITION. *Let* $p \in \mathcal{P}(Z)$ *and* $q \in \mathcal{P}(Z_0(c)) \subset \mathcal{P}(Z)$. *Then*

(4.11.104) $$T_S(p)(h_S^i q) \underset{S}{\sim} h_S^i \cdot T_{S_c}(p_c) q,$$

(4.11.105) $$T_S(p)^*(h_S^i q) \underset{S}{\sim} h_S^i \cdot T_{S_c}(p_c)^* q$$

where S_c *is the Shilov boundary of* Ω_c.

Proof. By Lemma 4.11.101

$$T_S(p) h_S^i q = p h_S^i q \underset{S}{\sim} h_S^i p_c q = h_S^i \, T_{S_c}(p_c) q.$$

This proves (4.11.104). For (4.11.105) assume first that $p(z) = (z|v)$ is linear. In case $v \in Z_1(c) \oplus Z_{1/2}(c)$, p_c is constant and Lemma 4.11.101 implies

$$T_S(p)^*(h_S^i q) = E(\bar{p} h_S^i q) \underset{S}{\sim} E(\bar{p}_c h_S^i q) = \bar{p}_c h_S^i q = h_S^i T_{S_c}(p_c)^* q$$

since the Szegö projection E is continuous. In case $v \in Z_0(c)$ we may assume, as in the proof of Lemma 4.11.99, that $q = \delta_\beta$ is the conical polynomial of type $\beta \in \vec{\mathbb{N}}^{r-k}$ on $Z_0(c)$. Then $\Delta_\beta - q$ vanishes on $c + S_c$, and the same is true of $\partial_v(\Delta_\beta - q)$ since v is tangent to $Z_0(c)$. Applying Lemmas 4.11.93 and 4.11.99 we obtain

$$T_S(p)^*(h_S^i q) \underset{S}{\sim} T_S(p)^*(h_S^i \Delta_\beta) = \sum_{j>k} (\beta_j + \frac{a}{2}(r - j) + b)^{-1} \pi_{\beta-\varepsilon j}(h_S^i \, \partial_v \Delta_\beta)$$

$$\underset{S}{\sim} \sum_{j>k} (\beta_j + \frac{a}{2}(r - j) + b)^{-1} \pi_{\beta-\varepsilon_j}(h_S^i \cdot \partial_v q)$$

$$\underset{S}{\sim} \sum_{j>k} (\beta_j + \frac{a}{2}(r - j) + b)^{-1} h_S^i (\partial_v q)_{\beta-\varepsilon_j} = h_S^i \, T_{S_c}(p_c)^* q$$

where the last identity follows from (4.11.95), applied to S_c, and the fact that $p_c = p$. Now suppose (4.11.105) is true for polynomials $\varphi, \psi \in \mathcal{P}(Z)$. Applying (4.11.105) to q and to $T_{S_c}(\varphi_c)^* q \in \mathcal{P}(Z_0(c))$, we obtain

$$T_S(\varphi\psi)^*(h_S^i q) = T_S(\psi)^* T_S(\varphi)^* h_S^i q \underset{S}{\sim} T_S(\psi)^* \, h_S^i T_{S_c}(\varphi_c)^* q$$

$$\underset{S}{\sim} h_S^i T_{S_c}(\psi_c)^* T_{S_c}(\varphi_c)^* q = h_S^i T_{S_c}((\varphi\psi)_c)^* q.$$

Thus (4.11.105) holds for $p = \varphi\psi$. Since we proved (4.11.105) for linear p, the assertion follows. Q.E.D.

4.11.106. THEOREM. *For each tripotent* $c \in Z$ *of rank* k *there exists an irreducible representation*

(4.11.107) $$\sigma_c : \mathcal{T}(S) \to \mathcal{L}(H^2(S_c))$$

on the Hardy space $H^2(S_c)$ *over* Ω_c *which is uniquely determined by one of the following properties*

(4.11.108) $$\sigma_c(T_S(f)) = T_{S_c}(f_c)$$

for all $f \in C(S)$ *or*

(4.11.109) $$\lim_{i \to 0} \| A(h_S^i q) - h_S^i (\sigma_c A) q \|_S = 0 .$$

for all $q \in \mathcal{P}(Z_0(c)) \subset \mathcal{P}(Z)$ *and all operators* A *in the *-algebra* $\mathcal{T}_0$ *generated by Hardy-Toeplitz operators with polynomial symbols. The representations* σ_c *are pairwise inequivalent.*

Proof. For any $f \in \mathcal{C}(S)$ we have, for the normalized invariant measure dw on S_c,

$$\lim_{i\to\infty} \int_S |h_S^i|^2 f\, dz = \int_{S_c} f_c(w)\, dw. \tag{4.11.110}$$

In fact, Lemma 4.11.97 implies that every weak cluster point of the measures $|h_S^i|^2\, dz$ is supported on S_c and is obviously invariant under $K_c = \mathrm{Aut}(Z_0(c))^0$, since every $\gamma \in K_c$ has an extension $g \in K$ fixing c. By the uniqueness of the invariant measure, a compactness argument implies the assertion (4.11.110).

Now let $\mathcal{A}$ denote the set of all operators $A \in \mathcal{T}_0$ such that (4.11.109) holds for some operator $\sigma_c(A)$ acting on $\mathcal{P}(Z_0(c))$. By (4.11.110), $\sigma_c(A)$ is uniquely determined by A and

$$\|\sigma_c(A)\| \le \|A\| \tag{4.11.111}$$

for the respective operator norms. By definition, $\mathcal{A}$ is an algebra and (4.11.111) yields an extension $\sigma_c : \mathcal{A} \to \mathcal{L}(H^2(S_c))$ which is an algebra homomorphism. For every $p \in \mathcal{P}(Z)$, it follows from (4.11.104) that $T_S(p) \in \mathcal{A}$ and $\sigma_c(T_S(p)) = T_{S_c}(p_c)$. The corresponding statements $T_S(p)^* \in \mathcal{A}$ and $\sigma_c(T_S(p)^*) = T_{S_c}(p_c)^*$ for the adjoint are a consequence of the deeper fact (4.11.105). Hence $\mathcal{A} = \mathcal{T}_0$ and, by (4.11.111), σ_c has a unique C^*-extension, again denoted by σ_c, to the closure $\mathcal{T}(S)$. By continuity, (4.11.108) follows. As a consequence, we obtain a C^*-homomorphism

$$\sigma_c : \mathcal{T}(S) \to \mathcal{T}(S_c) \tag{4.11.112}$$

which is surjective. Applying Proposition 4.11.14 to the Jordan triple $Z_0(c)$ it follows that σ_c acts irreducibly on $H^2(S_c)$. If c and e are different tripotents, we have $c + S_c \neq e + S_e$ as subsets of S. This is clear if $\mathrm{rank}(c) \neq \mathrm{rank}(e)$ and follows from [L9; Lemma 6.2] if $\mathrm{rank}\,(c) = \mathrm{rank}\,(e)$. By Urysohn's Lemma there exists $f \in \mathcal{C}(S)$ vanishing on $c + S_c$ but not on $e + S_e$. By (4.11.108), $T_S(f)$ belongs to $\mathrm{Ker}(\sigma_c)$ but not to $\mathrm{Ker}(\sigma_e)$. Therefore σ_c and σ_e are inequivalent. Q.E.D.

4.11.113. LEMMA. *Let* $c, d \in Z$ *be orthogonal tripotents. Then* $d \in Z_0(c)$ *(Peirce 0-space) and we have*

$$Z_0(c + d) = (Z_0(c))_0(d), \; S_{c+d} = (S_c)_d$$

and

$$\sigma_{c+d} = \sigma_d \circ \sigma_c, \tag{4.11.114}$$

where $\sigma_d : \mathcal{T}(S_c) \to \mathcal{L}(H^2(S_{c+d}))$.

Proof. By (4.11.108) we have for all $f \in \mathcal{C}(S)$

$$\sigma_d \circ \sigma_c(T_S(f)) = \sigma_d(T_{S_c}(f_c))$$
$$= T_{(S_c)_d}((f_c)_d) = T_{S_{c+d}}(f_{c+d}) = \sigma_{c+d}(T_S(f))$$

since $(f_c)_d(w) = f_c(d + w) = f(c + (d + w)) = f((c + d) + w) = f_{c+d}(w)$ for all $w \in Z_0(c + d)$.

Q.E.D.

As a consequence of Lemma 4.11.113, the C^*-ideals

$$\mathcal{I}_k := \bigcap_{c \in S_k} \operatorname{Ker}(\sigma_c), \tag{4.11.115}$$

with S_k denoting the compact manifold of all rank k tripotents in Z (cf. Section 1.5), give rise to a natural filtration

$$\mathcal{I}_1 \subset \mathcal{I}_2 \subset \ldots \subset \mathcal{I}_r \subset \mathcal{T}(S) \tag{4.11.116}$$

of the Toeplitz C^*-algebra. Our goal is to determine the associated C^*-graduation $\mathcal{I}_{k+1}/\mathcal{I}_k$ $(0 \leq k \leq r)$. Here we put $\mathcal{I}_0 := \{0\}$ and $\mathcal{I}_{r+1} := \mathcal{T}(S)$.

4.11.117. PROPOSITION. $\mathcal{I}_1 = \mathcal{K}(H^2(S))$ *(compact operators).*

Proof. By Theorem 4.10.41, we have

$$E_e^\# \, C^*(K) \, E_e^\# \subset E_e^\# \, \mathcal{D}(K) \, E_e^\# \subset E_e^\# \, (\mathcal{D}(K) \underset{\delta_K}{\otimes} \mathcal{C}(K)) \, E_e^\# = \mathcal{T}(S). \tag{4.11.118}$$

It follows that $\mathcal{T}(S)$ contains a non-zero compact operator. Since $\mathcal{T}(S)$ is irreducible on $H^2(S)$ it follows [D1] that $\mathcal{K}(H^2(S)) \subset \mathcal{T}(S)$. Now let $c \in Z$ be a non-zero tripotent, and let $A \in \mathcal{K}(H^2(S))$. Since the peaking sequence (h_S^i) defined in (4.11.96) satisfies $h_S^i \to 0$ (weakly) it follows that $\|A(h_S^i q)\|_S \to 0$ for every $q \in \mathcal{P}(Z_c)$ which, by (4.11.109) implies $\sigma_c(A) = 0$. Thus

$$\mathcal{K}(H^2(S)) \subset I_1 := \bigcap_{c \in S_1} \operatorname{Ker} \sigma_c = \bigcap_{c \neq 0} \operatorname{Ker} \sigma_c .$$

Conversely, let $A \in I_1$. In order to show that A is compact we may assume that $A \geq 0$. Consider the action $(\rho_s h)(z) := h(zs)$ of K on $H^2(S)$, and the associated adjoint action $\operatorname{Ad}(\rho_s)$ of K on $\mathcal{T}(S)$. Then

$$B := \int_K \operatorname{Ad}(\rho_s) A \, ds \in \mathcal{T}(S) \tag{4.11.119}$$

is positive and K-invariant. Since

$$\sigma_c(\operatorname{Ad}(\rho_s)A) = \sigma_{cs}(A)$$

for $c \in S_1$ and $s \in K$ it follows that I_1 is invariant under the action of K so that $B \in I_1$. Since $\mathcal{T}(S)$ is a (non-unital) C*-subalgebra of the co-crossed product $\mathcal{D}(K) \underset{\delta_K}{\otimes} C(K)$ by (4.11.118) it follows [D1] that there exist a Hilbert space $H_c \supset H^2(S_c)$ and an irreducible representation

$$\nu_c : \mathcal{D}(K) \underset{\delta_K}{\otimes} C(K) \to \mathcal{L}(H_c) \tag{4.11.120}$$

such that

$$\nu_c(T_S(f)) = \begin{pmatrix} T_{S_c}(f_c) & 0 \\ 0 & 0 \end{pmatrix}$$

for all $f \in C(S)$. According to [LPRS; Theorem 3.7], there exist a C^*-representation

$$\pi_c : \mathcal{D}(K) \to \mathcal{L}(H_c) \tag{4.11.121}$$

and a Banach algebra representation

$$(4.11.122) \qquad \mu_c : A(K) \to \mathcal{L}(H_c)$$

of the Fourier algebra A(K) satisfying

$$(4.11.123) \qquad \nu_c((E_e f)^\# g) = \pi_c((E_e f)^\#)\, \mu_c(g)$$

for all $f, g \in A(K)$. Now consider the representation

$$(4.11.124) \qquad \pi_c^L : \mathcal{D}^L(S) \to \mathcal{L}(H^2(S_c))$$

of the abelian subalgebra $\mathcal{D}^L(S) \subset \mathcal{D}(K)$ constructed in (3.5.60). We claim that

$$(4.11.125) \qquad \pi_c(E_e^\# B E_e^\#) = \begin{pmatrix} \pi_c^L(E_e^\# B E_e^\#) & 0 \\ 0 & 0 \end{pmatrix}$$

for all $B \in \mathcal{D}^L(S)$. To prove this, we may assume that $B = (E_e f)^\#$ where $f \in \mathcal{C}^\infty(S)$ is L-biinvariant. Write

$$(4.11.126) \qquad f(st^{-1}) = \lim \sum_i \varphi^i(s)\psi^i(t)$$

for all $s, t \in K$, where $\varphi^i, \psi^i \in \mathcal{C}(K)$. Then (4.10.46) implies

$$(4.11.127) \qquad E_e^\#(E_e f)^\# E_e^\# = \lim \sum_i T_S(\varphi^i) T_S(\psi^i).$$

Consider the embedding $x \mapsto 1 \oplus x$ from K_c into K satisfying $e(1 \oplus x) = (c + c^\perp)(1 \oplus x) = c \oplus c^\perp x$. Then we have for all $x \in K_c$

$$f_c(x) \equiv f_c(xc^\perp) = f(c + xc^\perp) = f((1 \oplus x)e) \equiv f(1 \oplus x)$$

for all $f \in \mathcal{C}(K)$, with corresponding restriction $f_c \in \mathcal{C}(K_c)$. Using (4.11.126), this implies for all $x, y \in K_c$

$$f_c(xy^{-1}) = f(1 \oplus xy^{-1}) = f((1 \oplus x)(1 \oplus y)^{-1})$$

$$= \lim \sum_i \varphi^i(1 \oplus x)\psi^i(1 \oplus y) = \lim \sum_i \varphi_c^i(x)\psi_c^i(y).$$

Applying (4.11.127) to $S_c = L_c \backslash K_c$ we obtain

$$E_c^\#(E_c f_c)^\# E_c^\# = \lim \sum_i T_{S_c}(\varphi_c^i) T_{S_c}(\psi_c^i).$$

Therefore

$$\pi_c(E_e^\#(E_e f)^\# E_e^\#) = \nu_c(E_e^\#(E_e f)^\# E_e^\#)$$

$$= \lim \sum_i \nu_c(T_S(\varphi^i) T_S(\psi^i)) = \lim \sum_i \begin{pmatrix} T_{S_c}(\varphi_c^i) T_{S_c}(\psi_c^i) & 0 \\ 0 & 0 \end{pmatrix}$$

$$= \begin{pmatrix} E_c^\#(E_c f_c)^\# E_c^\# & 0 \\ 0 & 0 \end{pmatrix} = \begin{pmatrix} \pi_c^L(E_e^\#(E_e f)^\# E_e^\#) & 0 \\ 0 & 0 \end{pmatrix}.$$

This proves (4.11.125). The element $B \in \mathcal{T}(S)$ defined in (4.11.119) belongs to the fixed point algebra

$$B \in \mathcal{T}(S)^K \subset (\mathcal{D}(K) \underset{\delta_K}{\otimes} \mathcal{C}(K))^K = \mathcal{D}(K)$$

(cf. [L2]). Since $B \in \mathcal{T}(S)$ we have

$$B = E_e^\# B E_e^\# \in E_e^\# \mathcal{D}(K) E_e^\# = \mathcal{D}^L(S)$$

(cf. Lemma 3.5.61). Therefore (4.11.125) implies

$$\begin{pmatrix} \pi_c^L(B) & 0 \\ 0 & 0 \end{pmatrix} = \pi_c(B) = \nu_c(B) = \begin{pmatrix} \pi_c(B) & 0 \\ 0 & 0 \end{pmatrix} = \begin{pmatrix} 0 & 0 \\ 0 & 0 \end{pmatrix}$$

for all $c \in S_1$ since $B \in \mathcal{I}_1$. Applying Theorem 3.6.52, it follows that

$$B \in \bigcap_{c \in S_1} \operatorname{Ker} \pi_c^L = C^*(K)$$

is compact on $L^2(K)$ and thus on $H^2(S)$. Since $\operatorname{Ad}(\rho_s)A$ is positive for every $s \in K$, it follows that $\operatorname{Ad}(\rho_s)A$ is compact. In particular, A is compact showing that $\mathcal{I}_1 = \mathcal{K}(H^2(S))$. Q.E.D.

For any fixed $1 \leq j \leq r$, consider the bundle of Hilbert spaces

$$\mathcal{H}_j = (H^2(S_c))_{c \in S_j} \tag{4.11.128}$$

defined by the continuous cross-sections $(p_c)_{c \in S_j}$ for $p \in \mathcal{P}(Z)$. Here $p_c(w) := p(c + w)$ for all $w \in S_c$. We have $\dim H^2(S_c) = \infty$ if $j < r$ whereas $H^2(S_c) \approx \mathbb{C}$ if $j = r$. Let

$$\mathcal{K}(\mathcal{H}_j) = (\mathcal{K}(H^2(S_c))_{c \in S_j} \tag{4.11.129}$$

denote the corresponding C^*-bundle of elementary C^*-algebras. Since $\mathcal{H}_j$ is a trivial bundle of Hilbert spaces [D1], it follows that

$$\mathcal{K}_j \approx C(S_j) \otimes \mathcal{K} \quad (j < r), \tag{4.11.130}$$

$$\mathcal{K}_r \approx C(S). \tag{4.11.131}$$

For $A \in \mathcal{T}(S)$, put

$$\sigma_j(A) := (\sigma_c(A))_{c \in S_j} \tag{4.11.132}$$

as a field of operators acting on $\mathcal{H}_j$. Then $I_j = \text{Ker}\ \sigma_j$. Our main result is:

4.11.133. THEOREM. *The filtration* (4.11.116) *of the Hardy-Toeplitz* C^**-algebra* $\mathcal{T}(S)$ *has the graduation*

$$\sigma_j : I_{j+1}/I_j \underset{\equiv}{\rightarrow} \mathcal{K}_j. \tag{4.11.134}$$

Hence $\mathcal{T}(S)$ *is a "solvable"* C^**-algebra* [D3] *of length* r.

Proof. For every $A \in I_{j+1}$ and $c \in S_j$, the operator $\sigma_c(A)$ belongs to the Hardy-Toeplitz C^*-algebra $\mathcal{T}(S_c)$ over S_c. Now let $d \in Z_c$ be a rank 1 tripotent. Then $c + d \in S_{j+1}$ and $\sigma_d(\sigma_c(A)) = \sigma_{d+c}(A) = 0$ since $A \in I_{j+1}$. Since d is arbitrary, it follows from Proposition 4.11.117, applied to S_c, that $\sigma_c(A) \in \mathcal{K}(H^2(S_c))$. Since $\sigma_c(A)$ depends continuously on $c \in S_j$, we have $\sigma_j(A) \in \mathcal{K}_j$. Thus (4.11.134) is a well-defined C^*-homomorphism which is injective. Let

$$E_j : H^2(S) \to \sum_{\alpha \in \vec{N}^j}^{\oplus} \mathcal{P}^\alpha(Z) \qquad \text{(Hilbert sum)}$$

denote the orthogonal projection. Then $E_j \in \mathcal{I}_{j+1}$ [U2; Theorem 1.4] and we have

$$\sigma_c(T_S(p)E_jT_S(q)^*) = p_c \otimes q_c \qquad \text{(rank 1 operator)}$$

for all $p, q \in \mathcal{P}(Z)$. Therefore $\sigma_c(\mathcal{I}_{j+1}) = \mathcal{K}(H^2(S_c))$. Now suppose $a \in S_j$ is different from c. Then $c + S_c$ and $a + S_a$ are different subsets of S. By Urysohn's Theorem, there exists a function $f \in C(S)$ vanishing on $c + S_c$ but not on $a + S_a$. Hence $h := T_{S_a}(f_a)p \neq 0$ for a suitable $p \in \mathcal{P}(Z_a) \subset \mathcal{P}(Z)$. Therefore $A := T_S(f)T_S(p)E_j \in \mathcal{I}_{j+1}$ satisfies

$$\sigma_c(A) = T_{S_c}(f_c)T_{S_c}(p_c)(1_c \otimes 1_c) = 0$$

whereas

$$\sigma_a(A) = T_{S_a}(f_a)T_{S_a}(p)(1_a \otimes 1_a) = h \otimes 1_a \neq 0.$$

Thus the C^*-ideal $\sigma_a(\mathcal{I}_{j+1} \cap \text{Ker}\, \sigma_c)$ coincides with the simple C^*-algebra $\mathcal{K}_a$. Now [D1; Lemma 10.5.3] implies $\sigma_j(\mathcal{I}_{j+1}) = \mathcal{K}_j$. Q.E.D.

Let us illustrate Theorem 4.11.133 by considering symmetric domains of rank 1 or 2. The domains of rank 1 are the *Hilbert balls*

$$\Omega = \{z \in \mathbb{C}^n : z \cdot \bar{z} < 1\}.$$

Here $S = \mathbb{S}^{2n-1}$ is the sphere, and Theorem 4.11.133 gives the short exact sequence

$$0 \to \mathcal{K}(H^2(S)) \to \mathcal{T}(S) \overset{\sigma}{\to} C(S) \to 0 \qquad (4.11.135)$$

with σ determined by $\sigma(T_S(f)) = f$ for all $f \in C(S)$. This was proved, in the more general context of strongly pseudoconvex domains, in Theorem 4.2.24. The domains of rank 2 (and of tube type) are the *Lie balls*

$$\Omega_n = \{z \in \mathbb{C}^n : z \cdot \bar{z} < 1, \quad 1 + (z \cdot \bar{z})^2 - 2|z \cdot z|^2 > 0$$

studied in Example 1.5. Here we have $S_1 = S^*(\mathbb{S}^{n-1})$ (cosphere bundle), $S_2 = \mathbb{T} \cdot \mathbb{S}^{n-1}$ (Lie sphere). Thus we obtain an ideal $I_2 \lhd \mathcal{T}(S)$ and two short exact sequences

$$(4.11.136) \qquad 0 \to \mathcal{K}(H^2(S)) \to I_2 \xrightarrow{\sigma_1} C(S^*(\mathbb{S}^{n-1})) \otimes \mathcal{K} \to 0,$$

$$(4.11.137) \qquad 0 \to I_2 \to \mathcal{T}(S) \xrightarrow{\sigma_2} C(\mathbb{T} \cdot \mathbb{S}^{n-1}) \to 0.$$

Again, $\sigma_2(T_S(f)) = f$ for all $f \in C(S)$ but σ_1 is more interesting. In fact, we will show now that (4.11.136) is the standard pseudo-differential extension of the compact operators by classical matrix symbols of order 0. For any domain of tube type, the symbol homomorphism

$$\sigma_c : \mathcal{T}(S) \to \mathcal{T}(S_c)$$

for $c \in S_{r-1}$ can be described in terms of the reduced algebra $\Psi(S')$ and an associated "reduced" symbol homomorphism

$$\sigma_c' : \Psi(S') \to \mathbb{C}.$$

In order to describe σ_c', fix $c \in S_{r-1}$ and let $c^\perp \in S_1$ be the unique tripotent satisfying

$$(4.11.138) \qquad \Delta(c + c^\perp) = 1.$$

For example if $\{e_1, ..., e_r\}$ is a frame of orthogonal minimal projections in the Jordan algebra X and $c := e_1 + \cdots + e_{r-1}$, then $c^\perp = e_r$. This argument also shows that, in general, we have

$$(4.11.139) \qquad \Delta_c(\zeta c^\perp) = \Delta(c + \zeta c^\perp) = \zeta$$

for all $\zeta \in \mathbb{C}$. Since c has rank 1, we obtain $\Omega_c = \mathbb{B} \cdot c^\perp$ and $S_c = \mathbb{T} \cdot c^\perp$.

4.11.140. PROPOSITION. *The symbol homomorphism* σ_c *maps* $P \otimes \Psi(S')$ *onto* $\mathbb{C} \cdot P_c$, *and thus induces a homomorphism* $\sigma_c' : \Psi(S') \to \mathbb{C}$ *satisfying*

$$(4.11.141) \qquad \sigma_c(P \otimes A) = \sigma_c'(A) \cdot P_c$$

for all $A \in \Psi(S')$. *Here* P *and* P_c *denote the projection onto the constant functions in* $H^2(\mathbb{T})$ *and* $H^2(S_c)$ *respectively.*

Proof. Since rank $\Omega_c = 1$, the relation $\sigma_c(\mathcal{T}(S)) \subset \mathcal{T}(S_c)$ implies

$$\sigma_c(\mathcal{K}_{\mathbb{T}} \otimes \Psi(S')) = \sigma_c(\mathcal{T}(S)') \subset \mathcal{T}(S_c)' = \mathcal{K}(H^2(S_c)).$$

Now let $u \in Z$ be fixed and put $\ell(z) := (z|u)$. Then we have for all $\zeta \in \mathbb{C}$

$$\ell_c(\zeta c^\perp) = \ell(c + \zeta c^\perp) = (c + \zeta c^\perp|u) = (c|u) + \zeta(c^\perp|u).$$

The corresponding operator on $H^2(S_c)$ is

$$T_{S_c}(\ell_c) = (c|u) \cdot \mathrm{id} + (c^\perp|u)\ T_{\mathbb{T}}(\zeta).$$

Using (4.11.78), this implies

$$\sigma_c(P \otimes A_u^*) = \sigma_c[T_S(\Delta)^*, T_S(\ell)] = [T_{S_c}(\Delta_c)^*, T_{S_c}(\ell_c)]$$

(4.11.142)

$$= [T_{\mathbb{T}}(\zeta)^*, (c|u)\mathrm{id} + (c^\perp|u)\ T_{\mathbb{T}}(\zeta)] = (c^\perp|u)[T_{\mathbb{T}}(\zeta)^*, T_{\mathbb{T}}(\zeta)] = (c^\perp|u) \cdot P_c$$

and, similarly,

$$\sigma_c(P \otimes B_u^*) = \sigma_c([T_S(\Delta)^*, T_S(\Delta)]\ T_S(\ell_c)) = [T_{S_c}(\Delta_c)^*, T_{S_c}(\Delta_c)]\ T_{S_c}(\ell_c)$$

(4.11.143)

$$= [T_{\mathbb{T}}(\zeta)^*, T_{\mathbb{T}}(\zeta)]\ ((c|u) \cdot \mathrm{id} + (c^\perp|u)T_{\mathbb{T}}(\zeta)) = (c|u) \cdot P_c + (c^\perp|u)P_c T_{\mathbb{T}}(\zeta) = (c|u)P_c.$$

Since the C^*-algebra $P \otimes \Psi(S')$ is generated by operators of the form $P \otimes A_u^*$, $P \otimes B_u^*$ and their adjoints, the assertion follows. Q.E.D.

4.11.144. DEFINITION. The homomorphism

$$\sigma'_{r-1} : \Psi(S') \to \mathcal{C}(S_{r-1}),$$

defined by

$$\sigma'_{r-1}(A)(c) := \sigma'_c(A)$$

for all $c \in S_{r-1}$, is called the *reduced* $(r-1)$-*symbol homomorphism* of $\mathcal{T}(S)$.

4.11.145. EXAMPLE. For the Lie ball $\Omega \subset \mathbb{C}^n$ and its Shilov boundary $S = \mathbb{T} \cdot \mathbb{S}^{n-1}$, the reduced Toeplitz symbol

$$\sigma'_1 : \Psi(S') \to \mathcal{C}(S_1)$$

is the usual Calderon-Zygmund symbol of pseudo-differential operators of order ≤ 0 on $S' = \mathbb{S}^{n-1}$. To see this, identify $c \in S_1$ with an element $(x,\xi) \in \mathbb{S}^*(\mathbb{S}^{n-1})$ of the co-sphere bundle over $\mathbb{S}^{n-1}$ via the formula

$$c = \frac{x + i\xi}{2}$$

(cf. Example 1.5.52). Then

$$c^{\perp} = \bar{c} = \frac{x - i\xi}{2}.$$

Now let $u \in \mathbb{R}^n$, and consider the associated multiplication operator M_u and Riesz operator R_u, acting on $L^2(\mathbb{S}^{n-1})$. By [L6; (4.17) and (4.13)], the Calderon-Zygmund symbol of these operators at (x,ξ) is given by

$$\sigma_{(x,\xi)}(M_u) = x \cdot u, \tag{4.11.146}$$

$$\sigma_{(x,\xi)}(R_u) = \xi \cdot u. \tag{4.11.147}$$

Since the homomorphism

$$\sigma_{(x,\xi)} : \Psi(\mathbb{S}^{n-1}) \to \mathbb{C}$$

vanishes on the commutator ideal

$$\Psi(\mathbb{S}^{n-1})' = \mathcal{K}(L^2(\mathbb{S}^{n-1})),$$

it follows from (4.11.74) and (4.11.75) that

$$\sigma_{(x,\xi)}(A_u) = x \cdot u - i\xi \cdot u,$$

and

$$\sigma_{(x,\xi)}(B_u) = x \cdot u + i\xi \cdot u.$$

On the other hand, (4.11.78) implies

$$\sigma_c(P \otimes B_u) = \sigma_c(P \otimes A_u^*) = (c^{\perp}|u)P_c = 2c^{\perp} \cdot u\, P_c = (x - i\xi) \cdot u\, P_c,$$

$$\sigma_c(P \otimes A_u) = \sigma_c(P \otimes B_u^*) = (c|u)\, P_c = 2\, c \cdot u\, P_c = (x + i\xi) \cdot u\, P_c.$$

Therefore

$$\sigma_c'(B_u) = x \cdot u - i\xi \cdot u = \sigma_{(x,\xi)}(B_u),$$

$$\sigma_c'(A_u) = x \cdot u + i\xi \cdot u = \sigma_{(x,\xi)}(A_u),$$

as asserted. Q.E.D.

4.12 Bergman-Toeplitz Operators Over Symmetric Domains

In this section we study Toeplitz operators and their associated C^*-algebras, acting on the λ-Bergman space $H_\lambda^2(\Omega)$ over a symmetric domain $\Omega \subset Z$. For the structure theory of the weighted Bergman spaces, cf. Section 2.9.

4.12.1. DEFINITION. For any bounded function $f \in L^\infty(\Omega)$, the *multiplication operator* with *symbol* f is the bounded operator $f : L_\lambda^2(\Omega) \to L_\lambda^2(\Omega)$ defined for all $h \in L_\lambda^2(\Omega)$ and $z \in \Omega$ by

(4.12.2) $$(fh)(z) := f(z)h(z).$$

Identifying the operator (4.12.2) with its symbol yields an injective C^*-algebra homomorphism from $L^\infty(\Omega)$ onto an abelian C^*-algebra of $\mathcal{L}(L_\lambda^2(\Omega))$, the C^*-algebra of all bounded operators on $L_\lambda^2(\Omega)$. The right translation action (2.9.5) of K on $L_\lambda^2(\Omega)$ induces an adjoint action of K on $\mathcal{L}(L_\lambda^2(\Omega))$ which satisfies for every $s \in K$

$$\mathrm{Ad}(\rho_s)f = \rho_s f \qquad \text{(multiplication operator)}$$

where $(\rho_s f)(z) := f(zs)$ belongs to $L^\infty(\Omega)$. Now consider the λ-Bergman space $H^2_\lambda(\Omega)$ over Ω, with λ-Bergman projection $E_\lambda: L^2_\lambda(\Omega) \to H^2_\lambda(\Omega)$. For $\lambda = p$, we obtain the standard Bergman space $H^2(\Omega)$, with standard Bergman projection $E_\Omega : L^2(\Omega) \to H^2(\Omega)$.

4.12.3. DEFINITION. The *Bergman-Toeplitz operator* $T_\lambda(f)$ with symbol $f \in L^\infty(\Omega)$ is defined as the compression

(4.12.4) $$T_\lambda(f) := E_\lambda \circ f|_{H^2_\lambda(\Omega)}$$

of the multiplication operator (4.12.2). Thus

(4.12.5) $$T_\lambda(f)h = E_\lambda(fh)$$

for every $h \in H^2_\lambda(\Omega)$.

The right translation action (2.9.5) of K on $L^2_\lambda(\Omega)$ leaves $H^2_\lambda(\Omega)$ invariant and thus induces an adjoint action of K on $\mathcal{L}(H^2_\lambda(\Omega))$ which satisfies

(4.12.6) $$\mathrm{Ad}(\rho_s)T_\lambda(f) = T_\lambda(\rho_s f)$$

for all $s \in K$ and $f \in L^\infty(\Omega)$.

4.12.7. PROPOSITION. *For every* $f \in L^\infty(\Omega)$, $T_\lambda(f)$ *is a bounded operator on* $H^2_\lambda(\Omega)$ *satisfying*

(4.12.8) $$\|T_\lambda(f)\| \le \|f\|_\infty,$$

(4.12.9) $$T_\lambda(f)^* = T_\lambda(\bar{f}).$$

Moreover, if $\varphi \in H^\infty(\Omega) := \mathcal{O}(\Omega) \cap L^\infty(\Omega)$ *we have*

(4.12.10) $$T_\lambda(f)T_\lambda(\varphi) = T_\lambda(f\varphi),$$

(4.12.11) $$T_\lambda(\bar{\varphi})T_\lambda(f) = T_\lambda(\bar{\varphi}f).$$

Proof. As an operator on $L^2_\lambda(\Omega)$ we have

(4.12.12) $$T_\lambda(f) = E_\lambda \, f \, E_\lambda .$$ Q.E.D.

Let $\bar{\Omega}$ be the closure of a symmetric ball $\Omega \subset Z$. Then the algebra $\mathcal{C}(\bar{\Omega})$ of all continuous functions on $\bar{\Omega}$ becomes a subalgebra of $L^\infty(\Omega)$ via the (injective) restriction mapping $\mathcal{C}(\bar{\Omega}) \ni f \mapsto f|_\Omega \in L^\infty(\Omega)$.

4.12.13. DEFINITION. The *λ-Bergman-Toeplitz* C^**-algebra* over Ω is defined as the unital C^*-algebra

(4.12.14) $$\mathcal{T}_\lambda(\Omega) := C^*(T_\lambda(f) : f \in \mathcal{C}(\bar{\Omega}))$$

generated by all λ-Bergman-Toeplitz operators (4.12.4) with continuous symbol $f \in \mathcal{C}(\bar{\Omega})$.

For $\lambda = p$, we obtain the standard Bergman-Toeplitz C^*-algebra $\mathcal{T}(\Omega)$ on $H^2(\Omega)$. Since $\rho_t f \in \mathcal{C}(\bar{\Omega})$ whenever $t \in K$ and $f \in \mathcal{C}(\bar{\Omega})$, it follows that $\mathcal{T}_\lambda(\Omega)$ is invariant under the adjoint action (4.12.6) of K.

4.12.15. PROPOSITION. *$\mathcal{T}_\lambda(\Omega)$ is generated (as a C^*-algebra) by the operators $T_\lambda(p)$, where $p \in \mathcal{P}(Z)$ is a polynomial.*

Proof. Since the mapping $L^\infty(\Omega) \ni f \mapsto T_\lambda(f)$ is contractive and hence continuous, it follows from the Stone-Weierstrass Theorem applied to $\bar{\Omega}$ (= the closed unit ball for the norm $\|\cdot\|$ in Z) that $\mathcal{T}_\lambda(\Omega)$ is generated by the operators $T_\lambda(f)$ with f a real-analytic polynomial f. Writing

$$f(z) = \sum_j p_j(z) \, \overline{q_j(z)}$$

for finitely many $p_j, q_j \in \mathcal{P}(Z)$, the assertion follows with (4.12.11).

Q.E.D.

As in Proposition 4.11.14, $\mathcal{T}_\lambda(\Omega)$ acts irreducibly on $H^2_\lambda(\Omega)$.

4.12.16. THEOREM. *Let* p *be a polynomial in* k *non-commuting variables. Then we have for all* $f_1, ..., f_k \in \mathcal{C}(\bar{\Omega})$

$$\|p(T_\lambda(f_1), ..., T_\lambda(f_k))\| \geq \|p(f_1|_S, ..., f_k|_S)\|_\infty.$$

Here S *is the Shilov boundary of* Ω.

Proof. For each $s \in S$, there exists a peaking function $h_s \in \mathcal{A}(\Omega)$ at $\{s\}$ [FK4]. Consider the powers $h_s^n(z) := h_s(z)^n$ for all n. As in the proof of Theorem 4.11.16 this implies for all $f \in \mathcal{C}(\bar{\Omega})$

$$\frac{(fh_s^n|h_s^n)_\lambda}{(h_s^n|h_s^n)_\lambda} \to f(s).$$

In particular,

$$\inf_S |f| \geq \inf\{\frac{\|fh\|_\lambda}{\|h\|_\lambda} : 0 \neq h \in H_\lambda^2(\Omega)\}. \tag{4.12.17}$$

Now consider k-tuples $(\lambda_1, ..., \lambda_k) \in \sigma(f_1|_S, ..., f_k|_S)$ in the joint spectrum of $f_1|_S, ..., f_k|_S \in \mathcal{C}(S)$. Then the function

$$f := \sum_{j=1}^{k} |f_j - \lambda_j|^2 \in \mathcal{C}(\bar{\Omega})$$

has a zero on S. By (4.12.17), it follows that for each $\varepsilon > 0$ there exists a unit vector $h \in H_\lambda^2(\Omega)$ such that $\|fh\|_\lambda \leq \varepsilon$. Since

$$\sum_j \|T_\lambda(f_j)h - \lambda_j h\|_\lambda^2 \leq \sum_j \|f_j h - \lambda_j h\|_\lambda^2 = \|fh\|_\lambda^2 \leq \varepsilon^2,$$

it follows that $\|T_\lambda(f_j)h - \lambda_j h\|_\lambda \leq \varepsilon$ for every $1 \leq j \leq k$. Taking products, we see that for every $\delta > 0$ there exists a unit vector $h \in H_\lambda^2(\Omega)$ satisfying

$$\|p(T_\lambda(f_1), ..., T_\lambda(f_k))h - p(\lambda_1, ..., \lambda_k)h\|_\lambda \leq \delta.$$

Therefore

$$\|p(T_\lambda(f_1), ..., T_\lambda(f_k))\| \geq \|p(T_\lambda(f_1), ..., T_\lambda(f_k))h\|_\lambda \geq |p(\lambda_1, ..., \lambda_k)| - \delta.$$

For $\delta \to 0$, this implies

$$\|p(T_\lambda(f_1), ..., T_\lambda(f_k))\| \geq \sup |p(\lambda_1, ..., \lambda_k)| = \|p(f_1|_S, ..., f_k|_S)\|_\infty.$$

Q.E.D.

4.12.18. COROLLARY. $\|T_\lambda(f)\| \geq \|f|_S\|_\infty$ *for all* $f \in \mathcal{C}(\bar{\Omega})$.

We will now construct irreducible representations of the λ-Bergman-Toeplitz C^*-algebra $\mathcal{T}_\lambda(\Omega)$ over a symmetric ball Ω (with $\lambda > p - 1$), realized in geometric terms on the boundary components of Ω (cf. Section 1.5). The method is similar to the case of Hardy-Toeplitz operators considered in Section 4.11. For a different and more general approach, cf. [U11].

Let Z be an irreducible Jordan triple of rank r, with open unit ball Ω. Given a tripotent $0 \neq c \in Z$ of rank $1 \leq k \leq r$, consider the Peirce decomposition $Z = Z_1(c) \oplus Z_{1/2}(c) \oplus Z_0(c)$ and the bounded symmetric domain $\Omega_c := \Omega \cap Z_0(c)$ of rank $r - k$. By Theorem 1.5.47, the sets $c + \Omega_c$, for nonzero tripotents c, form the partition of $\partial\Omega$ into holomorphic boundary components.

4.12.19. LEMMA. *For every* $\alpha \in \vec{\mathbb{N}}^r$ *and* $p \in \mathcal{P}^\alpha(Z)$, *we have*

$$T_\lambda(\ell)^* p = \sum_{j=1}^{r} (\lambda + \alpha_j - 1 - \frac{a}{2}(j - 1))(\partial_v p)_{\alpha-\varepsilon_j} \tag{4.12.20}$$

where the subscript $\alpha - \varepsilon_j$ *denotes the corresponding Peter-Weyl component. Here* $\ell(z) = (z|v)$.

Proof. Suppose $(T_\lambda(\ell)^* p \mid q)_\lambda \neq 0$ for some $q \in \mathcal{P}^\beta(Z)$. Then

$$(p \mid \ell q)_\lambda = (p \mid T_\lambda(\ell) q)_\lambda = (T_\lambda(\ell)^* p \mid q)_\lambda \neq 0$$

and Theorem 4.11.86 implies $\alpha = \beta + \varepsilon_j$ for some $1 \leq j \leq r$. Further, Theorem 2.9.30 and Proposition 4.11.40 imply

$$(T_\lambda(\ell)^* p \mid q)_\lambda = (p \mid \ell q)_\lambda = \frac{1}{((\lambda))_\alpha}(p \mid \ell q)_Z = \frac{1}{((\lambda))_\alpha}(\partial_v p \mid q)_Z$$

$$= \frac{((\lambda))_{\alpha-\varepsilon_j}}{((\lambda))_\alpha}(\partial_v p \mid q)_\lambda = (\lambda + \alpha_j - 1 - \frac{a}{2}(j-1))^{-1}((\partial_v p)_{\alpha-\varepsilon_j} \mid q)_\lambda.$$

Since q is arbitrary, the assertion follows. Q.E.D.

Now consider the analytic function $H_c(z) := \exp(z|c) \in H^2_\lambda(\Omega)$ and the sequence of unit vectors

(4.12.21) $$h^i_\lambda(z) := H_c(z)^i / \|H^i_c\|_\lambda.$$

4.12.22. LEMMA. *Let* $f \in \mathcal{C}(\bar{\Omega}, \mathbb{R}_+)$ *satisfy* $f_c = 0$. *Then*

$$\lim_{i\to\infty} \int_{\bar{\Omega}} f(z)\ |h^i_\lambda(z)|^2\, d\mu_\lambda(z) = 0.$$

Proof. For every $\varepsilon > 0$ there exists an open neighborhood $U \subset \bar{\Omega}$ of $c + \bar{\Omega}_c$ satisfying $\sup f(U) \le \varepsilon$. By [L9; 6.2] we have $\operatorname{Re}(z|c) \le (c|c)$ on $\bar{\Omega}$ and $\operatorname{Re}(z|c) = (c|c)$ implies $z \in c + \bar{\Omega}_c$. Since $|H_c(z)| = \exp \operatorname{Re}(z|c)$ it follows that there exists an open neighborhood $V \subset U$ of $c + \bar{\Omega}_c$ satisfying

(4.12.23) $$q := \sup_{\bar{\Omega}\setminus U} |H_c| \,/\, \inf_V |H_c| < 1.$$

Since μ_λ is a probability measure, we obtain

$$\int_{\bar{\Omega}} f\ |h^i_\lambda|^2\, d\mu_\lambda = \int_U f\ |h^i_\lambda|^2\, d\mu_\lambda + \int_{\bar{\Omega}\setminus U} f\ |h^i_\lambda|^2\, d\mu_\lambda$$

$$\le \varepsilon + \sup_{\bar{\Omega}} f \cdot \int_{\bar{\Omega}\setminus U} |H_c|^{2i}\, d\mu_\lambda \Big/ \int_V |H_c|^{2i}\, d\mu_\lambda$$

$$\leq \varepsilon + \sup_{\bar{\Omega}} f \cdot q^{2i} \cdot \mathrm{Vol}_\lambda(\bar{\Omega}\setminus U)/\mathrm{Vol}_\lambda(V)^{-1}.$$

Since $q^{2i} \to 0$, it follows that

$$\overline{\lim_{i\to\infty}} \int_{\bar{\Omega}} f \; |h_\lambda^i|^2 \, d\mu_\lambda \leq \varepsilon. \qquad \text{Q.E.D.}$$

For two sequences (f_i), (g_i) in $L^2_\lambda(\Omega)$ we put

(4.12.24) $$f_i \underset{\lambda}{\sim} g_i$$

if $\lim_{i\to\infty} ||f_i - g_i||_\lambda = 0$.

4.12.25. LEMMA. *Let* $p \in \mathcal{P}(Z)$. *Then*

$$h_\lambda^i p \underset{\lambda}{\sim} h_\lambda^i p_c, \quad h_\lambda^i \bar{p} \underset{\lambda}{\sim} h_\lambda^i \bar{p}_c.$$

where we embed $\mathcal{P}(Z_0(c)) \subset \mathcal{P}(Z)$ *via the Peirce projection.*

Proof. Since $p - p_c$ vanishes on $c + \bar{\Omega}_c$, Lemma 4.12.22 implies

$$||h_\lambda^i p - h_\lambda^i p_c||_\lambda^2 = \int_{\bar{\Omega}} |p - p_c|^2 \; |h_\lambda^i|^2 \, d\mu_\lambda \to 0. \qquad \text{Q.E.D.}$$

4.12.26. LEMMA. *Let* $q \in \mathcal{P}(Z_0(c))$ *and* $\beta \in \vec{\mathbb{N}}^{r-k}$. *Then*

$$\pi_\beta(h_\lambda^i q) \underset{\lambda}{\sim} h_\lambda^i q_\beta.$$

Proof. Every $\gamma \in \mathrm{Aut}\, Z_0(c)^0$ has an extension $g \in K$ satisfying $g(c) = c$. It follows that we may assume that $q = \delta_\alpha$ is the conical polynomial in $Z_0(c)$ of type $\alpha \in \vec{\mathbb{N}}^{r-k}$. By (4.11.89), $\Delta_\alpha - q$ vanishes on $c + \bar{\Omega}_c$. Therefore Lemma 4.12.25 implies

$$h_\lambda^i q \underset{\lambda}{\sim} h_\lambda^i \Delta_\alpha$$

which gives

$$\pi_\beta(h^i_\lambda q) \underset{\lambda}{\sim} \pi_\beta(h^i_\lambda \Delta_\alpha)$$

since the projection π_β defined in (4.11.90) has a continuous extension to $H^2_\lambda(\Omega)$. Since h^i_λ belongs to the closure of $\mathcal{P}(Z_1(c))$ in $H^2_\lambda(\Omega)$, Lemma 4.11.91 implies

$$\pi_\beta(h^i_\lambda \Delta_\alpha) = \delta_{\alpha,\beta} h^i_\lambda \Delta_\alpha \underset{\lambda}{\sim} \delta_{\alpha,\beta} h^i_\lambda q = h^i_\lambda q_\beta. \qquad \text{Q.E.D.}$$

4.12.27. LEMMA. *Let* $p \in \mathcal{P}(Z_1(c))$ *and* $v \in Z_0(c)$. *Then* $\ell(z) := (z|v)$ *satisfies*

$$T_\lambda(\ell)^*(p\Delta^\beta) = \sum_{k<j\le r} \left[\beta_j + \lambda - 1 - \frac{a}{2}(j-1)\right]^{-1} \cdot \pi_{\beta-\varepsilon_j}(p \cdot \partial_v \Delta^\beta).$$

Proof. As in the proof of Lemma 4.11.91 we may assume that (4.11.92) holds. Then $p\Delta_\beta = \Delta_\alpha$ for some $\alpha = (\alpha_1, \ldots, \alpha_k, \beta) \in \vec{\mathbb{N}}^r$. Applying Proposition 4.11.40 and Lemma 4.12.19, we obtain

$$\begin{aligned} T_\lambda(\ell)^*(p\Delta_\beta) = T_\lambda(\ell)^*\Delta_\alpha &= \sum_{j=k+1}^{r} (\lambda + \alpha_j - 1 - \frac{a}{2}(j-1))(\partial_v\Delta_\alpha)_{\alpha-\varepsilon_j} \\ &= \sum_{j>k} (\lambda + \beta_j - 1 - \frac{a}{2}(j-1))^{-1}(p \cdot \partial_v\Delta_\beta)_{\alpha-\varepsilon_j}. \end{aligned} \tag{4.12.28}$$

Since $\mathcal{P}^{\alpha-\varepsilon_j}(Z) \subset \operatorname{Ran} \pi_{\beta-\varepsilon_j}$ for all $j > k$, the assertion follows. Q.E.D.

The symmetric domain Ω_c of rank $r - k$ has genus

$$p_c = 2 + a(r - k - 1) + b = p - ak.$$

Now choose $\lambda > p - 1$ and define

$$\lambda_c := \lambda - \frac{ak}{2}.$$

Then $\lambda_c > p_c - 1$, so that the λ_c-Bergman-Toeplitz operator

$$T_{\lambda_c}(\varphi) \in \mathcal{L}(H^2_{\lambda_c}(\Omega_c))$$

for $\varphi \in \mathcal{P}(Z_0(c))$ is well-defined. By Lemma 4.12.27 $T_{\lambda_c}(\varphi)$ and its adjoint $T_{\lambda_c}(\varphi)^*$ leave the dense subspace $\mathcal{P}(Z_0(c))$ invariant.

4.12.29. LEMMA. *Let* $p \in \mathcal{P}(Z)$ *and* $q \in \mathcal{P}(Z_0(c)) \subset \mathcal{P}(Z)$. *Then*

$$T_\lambda(p)(h^i_\lambda q) \underset{\lambda}{\sim} h^i_\lambda \cdot T_{\lambda_c}(p_c)q, \tag{4.12.30}$$

$$T_\lambda(p)^*(h^i_\lambda q) \underset{\lambda}{\sim} h^i_\lambda \cdot T_{\lambda_c}(p_c)^*q \tag{4.12.31}$$

where $\lambda_c := \lambda - \frac{ak}{2}$.

Proof. By Lemma 4.12.25

$$T_\lambda(p)h^i_\lambda q = ph^i_\lambda q \underset{\lambda}{\sim} h^i_\lambda p_c q = h^i_\lambda \cdot T_{\lambda_c}(p_c)q.$$

This proves (4.12.30). For (4.12.31) assume first that $p(z) = (z|v)$ is linear. In case $v \in Z_1(c) \oplus Z_{1/2}(c)$, p_c is constant and Lemma 4.12.25 implies

$$T_\lambda(p)^*(h^i_\lambda q) = E_\lambda(\bar{p}h^i_\lambda q) \underset{\lambda}{\sim} E_\lambda(\bar{p}_c h^i_\lambda q) = \bar{p}_c h^i_\lambda q = h^i_\lambda T_{\lambda_c}(p_c)^* q$$

since the λ-Bergman projection E_λ is continuous. In case $v \in Z_0(c)$ we may assume, as in the proof of Lemma 4.12.27, that $q = \delta_\beta$ is the conical polynomial of type $\beta \in \vec{\mathbb{N}}^{r-k}$ on $Z_0(c)$. Then $\Delta_\beta - q$ vanishes on $c + \bar{\Omega}_c$, and the same is true of $\partial_v(\Delta_\beta - q)$ since v is tangent to $Z_0(c)$. Applying Lemmas 4.12.26 and 4.12.27 we obtain

$$T_\lambda(p)^*(h^i_\lambda q) \underset{\lambda}{\sim} T_\lambda(p)^*(h^i_\lambda \Delta_\beta) = \sum_{j>k} (\beta_j + \lambda - 1 - \tfrac{a}{2}(j-1))^{-1}\, \pi_{\beta-\varepsilon_j}(h^i_\lambda \cdot \partial_v \Delta_\beta)$$

$$\underset{\lambda}{\sim} \sum_{j>k} (\beta_j + \lambda - 1 - \tfrac{a}{2}(j-1))^{-1}\, \pi_{\beta-\varepsilon_j}(h^i_\lambda \cdot \partial_v q)$$

$$\underset{\lambda}{\sim} \sum_{j>k} (\beta_j + \lambda - 1 - \frac{a}{2}(j - 1))^{-1}\, h_\lambda^i \cdot (\partial_v q)_{\beta-\varepsilon_j}$$

$$= h_\lambda^i \sum_{j>k} (\beta_j + \lambda_c - 1 - \frac{a}{2}(j - k - 1))\, (\partial_v q)_{\beta-\varepsilon_j} = h_\lambda^i\, T_{\lambda_c}(p_c)^* q$$

where the last identity follows from (4.12.28), applied to Ω_c, and the fact that $p_c = p$. Now suppose (4.12.31) is true for polynomials $\varphi, \psi \in \mathcal{P}(Z)$. Applying (4.12.31) to q and to $T_{\lambda_c}(\varphi_c)^* q \in \mathcal{P}(Z_0(c))$, we obtain

$$T_\lambda(\varphi\psi)^*(h_\lambda^i q) = T_\lambda(\psi)^*\, T_\lambda(\varphi)^* h_\lambda^i q \underset{\lambda}{\sim} T_\lambda(\psi)^*\, h_\lambda^i\, T_{\lambda_c}(\varphi_c)^* q$$

$$\underset{\lambda}{\sim} h_\lambda^i T_{\lambda_c}(\psi_c)^*\, T_{\lambda_c}(\varphi_c)^* q = h_\lambda^i T_{\lambda_c}((\varphi\psi)_c)^* q.$$

Thus (4.12.31) holds for $p = \varphi\psi$. Since we proved (4.12.31) for linear p, the assertion follows. Q.E.D.

4.12.32 THEOREM. *For each tripotent* $c \in Z$ *of rank* k *there exists an irreducible representation*

$$\sigma_c^\lambda : \mathcal{T}_\lambda(\Omega) \to \mathcal{L}(H^2_{\lambda_c}(\Omega_c))$$

on the Bergman space $H^2_{\lambda_c}(\Omega_c)$ *over* Ω_c *with parameter* $\lambda_c := \lambda - \frac{ak}{2}$, *which is uniquely determined by one of the following properties*

(4.12.33) $$\sigma_c^\lambda(T_\lambda(f)) = T_{\lambda_c}(f_c)$$

for all $f \in C(\bar{\Omega})$ *or*

(4.12.34) $$\lim_{i \to 0} \|A(h_c^i q) - h_c^i(\sigma_c^\lambda A) q\|_\lambda = 0$$

for all $q \in \mathcal{P}(Z_0(c)) \subset \mathcal{P}(Z)$ *and all operators* A *in the *-algebra* $\mathcal{T}_0$ *generated by* λ*-Bergman-Toeplitz operators with polynomial symbols.*

5. Index Theory for Multivariable Toeplitz Operators

5.0. Introduction

The results of Chapter IV, concerning the ideal structure of the Toeplitz C^*-algebra, enable us to define a refined notion of analytical index for multivariable Toeplitz operators which reflects the stratified nature of the boundary geometry. In this chapter we express these indices in topological or representation-theoretic terms.

For strictly pseudoconvex domains with smooth boundary, the Toeplitz index is the usual Fredholm index and its expression in topological terms is due to L. Boutet de Monvel. His proof, outlined in Section 5.2, reduces the Toeplitz index to the Atiyah-Singer index of a suitably constructed system of pseudo-differential operators. Specializing to the unit ball (resp., unit disk) one obtains the beautiful index theorems of Venugopalkrishna and Gohberg, resp. In Section 5.1 we recall the foundations of topological K-theory which is the generally accepted framework for modern index theory.

In order to treat domains with stratified boundary one has to consider more general "K-theory valued" Fredholm indices which are best defined in the setting of non-commutative K-theory. The basic notions of C^*-extensions and C^*-algebraic K-groups are introduced in Section 5.3. The following Sections 5.4 and 5.5 give a detailed account of (generalized) Fredholm indices for the bounded symmetric domains and symmetric tube domains. Here the theory is also illustrated by specific examples (Hilbert ball, Lie ball) where some indices are computed explicitly. For all these cases, the "highest" index is given in terms of a certain homogeneous vector bundle which we determine completely in Section 5.4, using the known classification of symmetric domains.

While the domains considered so far all give rise to Toeplitz C^*-algebras of type I (leading to "integer" Fredholm indices) the general K-circular domains have non-type I Toeplitz C^*-algebras, leading to a "real"-valued index theory. This is already apparent from the simplest case of two-dimensional bicircular domains such as the Hartogs' wedge or the "L-shaped" domains. In Section 5.6, the computation of such a non-standard index problem is carried out in this setting. The author expects that these results can be extended to the general setting of K-circular domains of arbitrary dimension, by using a "stratified" version of microlocal analysis and the theory of longitudinally elliptic pseudo-differential operators.

5.1   K-Theory for Topological Spaces

The modern formulation of index theory is usually done in terms of
K-theory.   In this section we review the basic notions of topological
K-theory [A1, K1].   Let   X   be a compact space.   Consider (topological)
complex vector bundles $\pi : E \to X$.   For each $x \in X$,

$$E_x := \pi^{-1}(x)$$

is a finite dimensional vector space called the *fibre* over   X.   We assume
that the dimension (or *rank*) $\dim(E) := \dim_{\mathbb{C}} E_x$ is independent of $x \in X$.
Let $\mathcal{E}_N(X)$ denote the set of all vector bundles of dimension   N   over   X
and   put

$$\mathcal{E}_\infty(X) := \bigcup_{N \geq 0} \mathcal{E}_N(X) \qquad \text{(disjoint union).}$$

Two vector bundles $\pi^i : E^i \to X$ $(i \in \{1,2\})$ are *isomorphic* if there exists
a bicontinuous map

$$
\begin{array}{ccc}
E^1 & \xrightarrow{\ \alpha\ } & E^2 \\
 & \searrow \pi^1 \quad \pi^2 \swarrow & \\
 & X &
\end{array}
$$

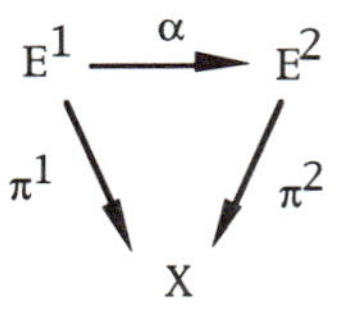

such that for each $x \in X$, the induced fibre map

$$E_x^1 \xrightarrow[\approx]{\ \alpha_x\ } E_x^2$$

is a linear isomorphism.   This implies $\dim(E^1) = \dim(E^2)$.   For each   N, let
$\tilde{\mathcal{E}}_N(X)$ be the set of equivalence classes   [E]   of vector bundles $E \in \mathcal{E}_N(X)$
modulo isomorphism and put

$$\tilde{\mathcal{E}}_\infty(X) = \bigcup_{N \geq 0} \tilde{\mathcal{E}}_N(X) \qquad \text{(disjoint union).}$$

The direct sum of two vector bundles $\pi^i : E^i \to X$ (not necessarily of same
rank) is the vector bundle $E^1 \oplus E^2$ over   X   having the fibres

$$(E^1 \oplus E^2)_x := E^1_x \oplus E^2_x \qquad (x \in X).$$

This defines a mapping

$$\mathcal{E}_m(X) \times \mathcal{E}_n(X) \xrightarrow{\oplus} \mathcal{E}_{m+n}(X)$$

which is compatible with isomorphism, resulting in a map

$$\tilde{\mathcal{E}}_\infty(X) \times \tilde{\mathcal{E}}_\infty(X) \xrightarrow{+} \tilde{\mathcal{E}}_\infty(X)$$

defined by $[E], [F] \mapsto [E \oplus F]$. In this way, $\tilde{\mathcal{E}}_\infty(X)$ becomes a commutative semigroup with neutral element $[0]$.

5.1.1. DEFINITION. For any compact space X, $K^0(X)$ is defined as the Grothendieck group associated with the monoid $\tilde{\mathcal{E}}_\infty(X)$ of all isomorphism classes of vector bundles over X. Hence by definition, $K^0(X)$ consists of all formal differences $[E] - [F]$, with $E,F \in \mathcal{E}_\infty(X)$. In $K^0(X)$, two vector bundles E and F are equivalent if $E \oplus G \approx F \oplus G$ for another vector bundle G.

5.1.2. EXAMPLE. Let $X = \{\infty\}$ be a singleton. Then the dimension function

$$\dim : \mathcal{E}_\infty(X) \to \mathbb{Z}, \; E \mapsto \dim E$$

induces an isomorphism $\dim : K^0(\infty) \xrightarrow[\approx]{} \mathbb{Z}$.

Let $\varphi : X \to Y$ be a continuous map between compact spaces. For any vector bundle $\pi : F \to Y$ consider the pullback

$$\begin{array}{ccc} \varphi^*F & & F \\ \downarrow & & \downarrow \pi \\ X & \longrightarrow & Y \end{array}$$

as a vector bundle over X. This process defines a homomorphism

$$\varphi^* : K^0(Y) \to K^0(X), \; [F] \mapsto [\varphi^*F].$$

If X is a non-compact but locally compact space, consider the 1-point compactification $X \cup \{\infty\}$. The canonical map $\{\infty\} \mapsto X \cup \{\infty\}$ induces a homomorphism of K-groups $K^0(X \cup \{\infty\}) \to K^0(\infty) \cong \mathbb{Z}$ and one defines

$$(5.1.3) \qquad K_c^0(X) := \mathrm{Ker}(K^0(X \cup \{\infty\}) \to K^0(\infty)).$$

This definition agrees with Definition 5.1.1 in case X is actually compact, since then $X \cup \{\infty\}$ is the topological sum of X and $\{\infty\}$. Thus one gets a contravariant functor K_c^0 from the category of locally compact spaces and proper maps to the category of (additive) abelian groups. In order to define the *relative* K-group $K_c^0(X,Y)$ for a compact space X and a closed subspace $Y \subset X$, consider homomorphisms

$$(5.1.4) \qquad E \xrightarrow{\alpha} F$$

of complex vector bundles over X such that the restriction

$$E|_Y \xrightarrow[\approx]{\alpha|_Y} F|_Y$$

is an isomorphism. By [K1; p. 97 ff], the set of all such triples (E,F,α) carries a natural equivalence relation, and $K_c^0(X,Y)$ is defined as the group of equivalence classes $d(E,F,\alpha)$. In case $Y = \{\}$, we have $K^0(X,\{\}) \xrightarrow[\approx]{} K^0(X)$ via the map

$$d(E,F,\{\}) \mapsto [E] - [F].$$

In case $Y = \{\infty\}$, X is the one-point compactification of $X\backslash\{\infty\}$ and $K_c^0(X,\{\infty\}) \approx K_c^0(X\backslash\{\infty\})$. More generally, $K^0(X,Y) \approx K^0(X\backslash Y)$. In this picture, $K_c^0(X)$ for a locally compact space X consists of classes $d(E,F,\alpha)$ of homomorphisms (5.1.4) such that the *support* $\mathrm{Supp}(\alpha) := \{x \in X: \alpha_x \text{ not invertible}\}$ is compact.

5.1.5. EXAMPLE. Let Z be a complex vector space, and consider the exterior powers $\Lambda^j Z$, $0 \le j \le \dim(Z)$. Put

$$\Lambda Z := \sum_{j\ge 0}^{\oplus} \Lambda^j Z = \Lambda^+ Z \oplus \Lambda^- Z,$$

where

(5.1.6)
$$\Lambda^{\pm}Z := \sum_{(-1)^j=\pm 1}^{\oplus} \Lambda^j Z.$$

For every $z \in Z$ we define the "creation" operator $\Lambda Z \xrightarrow{\partial_z} \Lambda Z$ by

(5.1.7)
$$\partial_z z_1 \wedge \cdots \wedge z_j := z \wedge z_1 \wedge \cdots \wedge z_j .$$

Now suppose Z is a hermitian space, with inner product $(z|w)$, complex-linear in z. Then ΛZ is a hermitian space, and the adjoint of (5.1.7) is the "annihilation" operator

(5.1.8)
$$\partial_z^*(z_1 \wedge \cdots \wedge z_j) = \sum_{i \geq 1} (-1)^{i-1}\, z_1 \wedge \cdots \wedge \hat{z}_i \wedge \cdots \wedge z_j\, (z_i|z).$$

The self-adjoint operator $d_z := \partial_z + \partial_z^*$ satisfies

(5.1.9)
$$d_z^2 = (z|z) \cdot \mathrm{Id}.$$

In particular, d_z is a symmetry (= self-adjoint unitary) if $||z|| = 1$. The unitary group $U(Z)$ acts on ΛZ via $s \mapsto \Lambda(s) = \sum^{\oplus} \Lambda^j(s) = \Lambda^+(s) \oplus \Lambda^-(s)$ $(s \in U(Z))$ and we have

(5.1.10)
$$\Lambda(s)\, d_z\, \Lambda(s)^* = d_{s \cdot z}$$

for all $z \in Z$ and $s \in U(Z)$. Now let $\pi : N \to X$ be a complex vector bundle over a compact space X, endowed with a hermitian fibre metric. Let $\bar{\pi} : \bar{N} \to X$ denote the dual bundle (i.e., $\bar{N}_x$ is the complex conjugate vector space of N_x, for every $x \in X$). Then the pull-backs

$$\begin{array}{ccc} \pi^*N & & N \\ \downarrow & & \downarrow \pi \\ N & \xrightarrow[\pi]{} & X \end{array} \quad , \quad \begin{array}{ccc} \pi^*\bar{N} & & \bar{N} \\ \downarrow & & \downarrow \bar{\pi} \\ N & \xrightarrow[\pi]{} & X \end{array}$$

become vector bundles over N, with exterior powers $\Lambda^j\pi^*(N)$ and $\Lambda^j\pi^*(\bar{N})$, respectively. For each $z \in N$, consider the endomorphisms

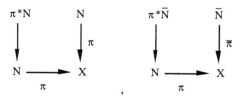

(5.1.11) $$d_z : \Lambda^+ N_{\pi(z)} \longrightarrow \Lambda^- N_{\pi(z)},$$

(5.1.12) $$d_{\bar{z}} : \Lambda^+ \bar{N}_{\pi(z)} \longrightarrow \Lambda^- \bar{N}_{\pi(z)}.$$

Now consider the *sphere bundle*

$$\mathbb{S}_N := \{z \in N : (z|z)_{\pi(z)} = 1\}$$

and the *ball bundle*

$$\mathbb{B}_N := \{z \in N : (z|z)_{\pi(z)} \leq 1\}$$

of N, respectively. Here $(z|w)_x$ is the hermitian product in N_x. Let $\pi_{\mathbb{S}} : \mathbb{S}_N \to X$, $\pi_{\mathbb{B}} : \mathbb{B}_N \to X$ denote the canonical projections. Since X is compact, $\mathbb{B}_N$ is a compact space containing $\mathbb{S}_N$ as a closed subspace. Moreover, there is a homeomorphism

$$N \xrightarrow[\approx]{} \mathbb{B}_N \backslash \mathbb{S}_N = \{z \in N : (z|z)_{\pi(z)} < 1\}, \; z \mapsto \frac{z}{1 + \|z\|}$$

where $\|z\| := (z|z)^{1/2}$. Therefore $K_c^0(\mathbb{B}_N, \mathbb{S}_N) \approx K_c^0(\mathbb{B}_N \backslash \mathbb{S}_N) \approx K_c^0(N)$. By (5.1.9), the operators (5.1.11) and (5.1.12) are unitary if $z \in \mathbb{S}_N$. We define the *Bott elements*

(5.1.13) $$\beta(N) := d(\Lambda^+ \pi_{\mathbb{B}}^*(N), \Lambda^- \pi_{\mathbb{B}}^*(N), d_z),$$

(5.1.14) $$\beta(\bar{N}) := d(\Lambda^+ \pi_{\mathbb{B}}^*(\bar{N}), \Lambda^- \pi_{\mathbb{B}}^*(\bar{N}), d_{\bar{z}})$$

in $K_c^0(\mathbb{B}_N, \mathbb{S}_N)$. Let X_1 and X_2 be locally compact spaces and, for $i \in \{1,2\}$, consider homomorphisms ${}_1E^i \xrightarrow{\alpha_i} {}_2E^i$ between hermitian vector bundles over X_i. For $j,k \in \{1,2\}$, the tensor product ${}_jE^1 \otimes {}_kE^2$ is a hermitian vector bundle over $X_1 \times X_2$, with fibres

$$({}_jE^1 \otimes {}_kE^2)_{(x_1,x_2)} := {}_jE^1_{x_1} \otimes {}_kE^2_{x_2}.$$

Consider the homomorphism $\alpha_1 \boxtimes \alpha_2$ over $X_1 \times X_2$ given in matrix form as follows:

$$({}_1E^1 \otimes {}_1E^2) \oplus ({}_2E^1 \otimes {}_2E^2) \xrightarrow{\begin{pmatrix} \alpha_1 \otimes {}_1I^2 & {}_2I^1 \otimes \alpha_2 \\ -{}_1I^1 \otimes \alpha_2^* & \alpha_1^* \otimes {}_2I^2 \end{pmatrix}} ({}_2E^1 \otimes {}_1E^2) \oplus ({}_1E^1 \otimes {}_2E^2).$$

Here ${}_jI^i$ is the identity on ${}_jE^i$. Since

$$(\alpha_1 \boxtimes \alpha_2)(\alpha_1 \boxtimes \alpha_2)^* = \begin{pmatrix} \alpha_1\alpha_1^* \otimes {}_1I^2 + {}_1I^1 \otimes \alpha_2\alpha_2^* & 0 \\ 0 & \alpha_1^*\alpha_1 \otimes {}_2I^2 + {}_2I^1 \otimes \alpha_2^*\alpha_2 \end{pmatrix}$$

it follows that $\mathrm{Supp}(\alpha_1 \boxtimes \alpha_2) = \mathrm{Supp}(\alpha_1) \times \mathrm{Supp}(\alpha_2)$. In this way we obtain a product $K_c^0(X_1) \times K_c^0(X_2) \to K_c^0(X_1 \times X_2)$ given by

$$d({}_1E^1, {}_2E^1, \alpha_1) \times d({}_1E^2, {}_2E^2, \alpha_2) :=$$
$$d(({}_1E^1 \otimes {}_1E^2) \oplus ({}_2E^1 \otimes {}_2E^2), ({}_2E^1 \otimes {}_1E^2) \oplus ({}_1E^1 \otimes {}_2E^2), \alpha_1 \boxtimes \alpha_2).$$

This product is associative and commutative in the sense that $(\alpha_1 \boxtimes \alpha_2) \boxtimes \alpha_3 \cong \alpha_1 \boxtimes (\alpha_2 \boxtimes \alpha_3)$ and $\alpha_1 \boxtimes \alpha_2 \cong \alpha_2 \boxtimes \alpha_1$ via certain permutation matrices. If $X_1 = X_2 = X$ and $\delta : X \mapsto X \times X$ is the diagonal embedding, we obtain a product

$$\begin{array}{ccc} K_c^0(X) \times K_c^0(X) & \xrightarrow{\otimes} & K_c^0(X) \\ & {\scriptstyle\times}\searrow \quad \nearrow{\scriptstyle\delta^*} & \\ & K_c^0(X \times X) & \end{array}$$

which makes $K_c^0(X)$ into a commutative ring. If $\pi : N \to X$ is a real vector bundle and $\delta := (\pi, \mathrm{id}) : N \to X \times N$ is the embedding $\delta(z) = (\pi(z), z)$, we obtain a product

$$\begin{array}{ccc} K_c^0(X) \times K_c^0(N) & \xrightarrow{\otimes} & K_c^0(N) \\ & {\scriptstyle\times}\searrow \quad \nearrow{\scriptstyle\delta^*} & \\ & K_c^0(X \times N) & \end{array}$$

which makes $K_c^0(N)$ into a $K_c^0(X)$-module.

5.1.15. THEOREM. *Let* $\pi : N \to X$ *be a complex vector bundle over a compact space* X *and consider the Bott element* $\beta(\bar{N})$ *defined in (5.1.14). Then the multiplication operator*

$$K^0(X) \to K_c^0(N) \tag{5.1.16}$$

given by $\xi \mapsto \xi \otimes \beta(\bar{N})$ *is an isomorphism.*

A modified version of Theorem 5.1.15 still holds in the locally compact case [K1; Theorem IV.1.11]. As a special case of Theorem 5.1.15 let N be a complex vector space and $X = \{\infty\}$. Then the element

$$\beta(\bar{N}) = d(N \times \Lambda^+\bar{N}, N \times \Lambda^-\bar{N}, d_z) \in K_c^0(N) \tag{5.1.17}$$

gives rise to an isomorphism $\mathbb{Z} \approx K_c^0(N)$, with 1 corresponding to $\beta(\bar{N})$.

If X is a locally compact space and $U \subset X$ is an open subset with injection $i : U \to X$, there is a canonical extension map

$$i_! : K_c^0(U) \to K_c^0(X) \tag{5.1.18}$$

defined as follows: Every element in $K_c^0(U)$ can be represented by a vector bundle homomorphism $E \xrightarrow{\alpha} U \times \mathbb{C}^N$ with compact support $K = \mathrm{Supp}(\alpha) \subset U$. Put $V := X \backslash K$. Since $\alpha|_{U \cap V}$ is an isomorphism, there exist a vector bundle $\tilde{E}$ over X and isomorphisms

$$\tilde{E}|_U \xrightarrow{\beta_U} E, \ \tilde{E}|_V \xrightarrow{\beta_V} V \times \mathbb{C}^N$$

such that the diagram

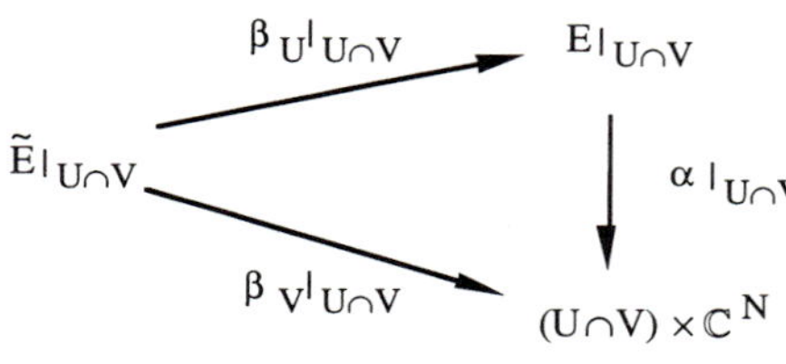

commutes [K1; Theorem I.3.2]. Therefore one can define a homomorphism

$\tilde{\alpha} : \tilde{E} \longrightarrow X \times \mathbb{C}^N$ of vector bundles over X by putting $\tilde{\alpha}|_U := \alpha \circ \beta_U$, $\tilde{\alpha}|_V := \beta_V$. Clearly, $\mathrm{Supp}(\tilde{\alpha}) = \mathrm{Supp}(\alpha)$. Define

(5.1.19) $$i_! \, d(E, U \times \mathbb{C}^N, \alpha) := d(\tilde{E}, X \times \mathbb{C}^N, \tilde{\alpha}).$$

Topological K-theory has also an "odd" version which is closer related to Toeplitz operators. Let X be a compact space and consider the $(N{\times}N)$-matrix groups $GL_N(\mathbb{C})$ with the embedding $GL_N(\mathbb{C}) \to GL_{N+1}(\mathbb{C})$ given by

$$g \mapsto \begin{pmatrix} g & 0 \\ 0 & 1 \end{pmatrix}.$$

Define the inductive limit

$$GL_\infty(\mathbb{C}) := \lim_{N\to\infty} \text{inj}\, GL_N(\mathbb{C}).$$

For $1 \le N \le \infty$, $GL_N(\mathbb{C})$ is a topological group. Let $\mathcal{G}_N(X) := \mathcal{C}(X, GL_N(\mathbb{C}))$ denote the topological group of all continuous mappings from X into $GL_N(\mathbb{C})$, under pointwise multiplication and uniform convergence. Put

$$\mathcal{G}_\infty(X) := \lim_{N\to\infty} \text{inj}\, \mathcal{G}_N(X).$$

Two such mappings $F_i : X \to GL_N(X)$ $(i \in \{0,1\})$ are *homotopic* if there exists a continuous path $F_t : X \to GL_N(X)$, $0 \le t \le 1$, connecting F_0 and F_1. For each n, let $\tilde{\mathcal{G}}_N(X)$ denote the set of all homotopy classes $[F]$ of mappings $F \in \mathcal{G}_N(X)$. Then

$$\tilde{\mathcal{G}}_\infty(X) = \lim_{N\to\infty} \text{inj}\, \tilde{\mathcal{G}}_N(X).$$

Since the group operations are compatible with homotopy, the $\tilde{\mathcal{G}}_N(X)$ are topological groups. $\tilde{\mathcal{G}}_\infty(X)$ is actually commutative since for $F \in \mathcal{G}_n(X)$, $F' \in \mathcal{G}_m(X)$ there exists a homotopy

$$\begin{pmatrix} F & 0 \\ 0 & 1 \end{pmatrix} \begin{pmatrix} F' & 0 \\ 0 & 1 \end{pmatrix} \sim \begin{pmatrix} F & 0 & 0 \\ 0 & F' & 0 \\ 0 & 0 & 1 \end{pmatrix}$$

in $\mathcal{G}_\infty(X)$. Here we write

$$\begin{pmatrix} F & 0 \\ 0 & 1 \end{pmatrix} := \begin{pmatrix} F-1_n & 0 \\ 0 & 0 \end{pmatrix} \oplus 1\!\!1_\infty .$$

5.1.20. DEFINITION. For any compact space X, define

$$K^1(X) := \tilde{\mathcal{G}}_\infty(X) = [X, GL_\infty(\mathbb{C})]$$

as the abelian (multiplicative) group of homotopy classes of continuous mappings $X \to GL_\infty(\mathbb{C})$.

5.1.21. EXAMPLE. For $X = \{\infty\}$ a singleton, we have

$$K^1(\infty) = \pi_0(GL_\infty(\mathbb{C})) = \{0\}$$

since $GL_\infty(\mathbb{C})$ is path-connected.

Let $\alpha : X \to Y$ be a continuous map between compact spaces. For any continuous mapping $F : Y \to GL_\infty(\mathbb{C})$ consider the pull-back $F \circ \alpha : X \to GL_\infty(\mathbb{C})$ as a continuous mapping on X. This process defines a group homomorphism

$$\alpha^{\#} : K^1(Y) \to K^1(X), \ [F] \mapsto [F \circ \alpha].$$

If X is a non-compact but locally compact space, consider the 1-point compactification $X \cup \{\infty\}$. The canonical map $\{\infty\} \mapsto X \cup \{\infty\}$ induces a homomorphism of K-groups $K^1(X \cup \{\infty\}) \to K^1(\infty) = \{0\}$ and one defines

$$K^1_c(X) := \mathrm{Ker}(K^1(X \cup \{\infty\}) \to K^1(\infty)) = K^1(X \cup \{\infty\}).$$

This definition agrees with Definition 5.1.20 in case X is actually compact, since then $X \cup \{\infty\}$ is the topological sum of X and $\{\infty\}$. Thus one gets a contravariant functor K^1_c from the category of locally compact spaces and proper maps to the category of (multiplicative) abelian groups. In order to define the relative K-group $K^1_c(X,Y)$ for a compact space X and a closed subspace $Y \subset X$ consider continuous mappings

(5.1.22) $$F : X \to GL_N(\mathbb{C})$$

such that the restriction

$$F|_Y = I_N \qquad \text{(unit matrix).}$$

By [K1], the set of all such F carries a natural equivalence relation, and $K_c^1(X,Y)$ is defined as the group of equivalence classes $[F]$. In case $Y = \{\}$, we have $K^1(X,\{\}) \approx K_c^1(X)$. In case $Y = \{\infty\}$, X is the one-point compactification of $X\backslash\{\infty\}$ and $K_c^1(X,\{\infty\}) \approx K_c^1(X\backslash\{\infty\})$. More generally, $K_c^1(X,Y) \approx K_c^1(X\backslash Y)$. In this picture, $K_c^1(X)$ for a locally compact space X consists of all classes $[F]$ of continuous mappings (5.1.22) such that the *support* $\operatorname{Supp}(F) := \{x \in X : F(x) \neq I_N\}^-$ is compact. If X is a locally compact space and $U \subset X$ is an open subset with injection $i : U \to X$, there is a canonical extension map

$$i_! : K_c^1(U) \to K_c^1(X) \tag{5.1.23}$$

defined as follows: Every element in $K_c^1(U)$ can be represented by a continuous map $F : U \to GL_N(\mathbb{C})$ with compact support $K = \operatorname{Supp}(F) \subset U$. Since $F|_{U\backslash K} = I_N$ (unit matrix), there exists a continuous mapping $\tilde{F} : X \to GL_N(\mathbb{C})$ satisfying $\tilde{F}|_U = F$, $\tilde{F}|_{X\backslash K} = I_N$. Now define

$$i_![F] := [\tilde{F}]. \tag{5.1.24}$$

A basic result in topological K-theory is the cyclic exact sequence:

5.1.25. THEOREM. *Let X be a locally compact space and Y a closed subspace. Then there exists a cyclic exact sequence*

$$\begin{array}{ccccc}
K_c^0(X\backslash Y) & \xrightarrow{p^*} & K_c^0(X) & \xrightarrow{i^*} & K_c^0(Y) \\
\partial \uparrow & & & & \downarrow \partial \\
K_c^1(Y) & \xleftarrow{i^*} & K_c^1(X) & \xleftarrow{p^*} & K_c^1(X\backslash Y)
\end{array}$$

Here $i : Y \to X$ *is the inclusion mapping, and* $p : X \to X\backslash Y$ *is given by* $p|_{X\backslash Y} := \mathrm{id}$ *and* $p(Y \cup \infty) = \infty$. *The homomorphisms* ∂ *are the so-called connecting maps.*

5.1.26. PROPOSITION. *There is an isomorphism*

(5.1.27) $$K_c^1(X) \xrightarrow[\approx]{\partial_X} K_c^0(X \times \mathbb{R}).$$

Proof. Let $F : X \to GL_N(\mathbb{C})$ have compact support $K \subset X$. Let

$$\alpha : X \times \mathbb{R} \to \mathbb{C}^{N\times N}$$

be any continuous function such that for some $t_0 >> 0$ we have $\alpha(x,t) = F(x)$ if $(x,t) \in X \times (t_0,\infty)$ and $\alpha(x,t) = I_N$ if $(x,t) \in (X \times (-\infty, -t_0)) \cup ((X\backslash K) \times \mathbb{R})$. Then the vector bundle homomorphism

$$X \times \mathbb{R} \times \mathbb{C}^N \xrightarrow{\alpha} X \times \mathbb{R} \times \mathbb{C}^N,$$

given by $(x,t,v) \to (x,t,\alpha(x,t)v)$ over $X \times \mathbb{R}$, has support $\mathrm{Supp}(\alpha) \subset K \times [-t_0, t_0]$. Put

(5.1.28) $$\partial_X [F] := d(X \times \mathbb{R} \times \mathbb{C}^N, X \times \mathbb{R} \times \mathbb{C}^N, \alpha).$$

Q.E.D.

In case $X = H\backslash K$ is a homogeneous space, for a compact Lie group K and a closed subgroup H, we may use the representation theory of K and H to construct elements in $K^1(X)$. We consider a finite dimensional Hilbert space E and its unitary group $U(E)$. Every representation $\rho: H \to U(E)$ induces a vector bundle

$$E \overset{\rho}{\underset{H}{\times}} K := \{[v,s] : v \in E, s \in K\}$$

over $X = H\backslash K$ which defines an element in $K^0(X)$. Here $[v,s]$ is an equivalence class, defined by

$$(v,s) \sim (\rho(\gamma)v, \gamma s)$$

for all $\gamma \in H$. The canonical projection is given by $[v,s] \mapsto Hs$. If $\sigma,\tau : K \to U(E)$ are representations which agree on H, then

(5.1.29) $$(\sigma\backslash\tau)(Hs) := \sigma(s)^* \tau(s)$$

defines a continuous map $\sigma\backslash\tau : H\backslash K \to U(E)$ and thus an element in $K^1(X)$. By definition, $\sigma\backslash\tau$ satisfies the covariance property

(5.1.30) $$(\sigma\backslash\tau)(xs) = \sigma(s)^* \, (\sigma\backslash\tau)(x) \, \tau(s)$$

for all $x \in H\backslash K$ and $s \in K$.

5.1.31. LEMMA. *Let* $\rho : H \to U(E)$ *be a representation and let* $G \subset H$ *be a closed subgroup. Let* $\pi : G\backslash K \to H\backslash K$ *be the canonical projection. Then*

(5.1.32) $$\pi^*(E \overset{\rho}{\underset{H}{\times}} K) \cong E \overset{\rho}{\underset{G}{\times}} K.$$

Proof. By definition, we have

$$\pi^*(E \overset{\rho}{\underset{H}{\times}} K) = \{([v,s]_H, Gt) \in (E \overset{\rho}{\underset{H}{\times}} K) \times G\backslash K : Hs = Ht\}$$

and

$$E \overset{\rho}{\underset{G}{\times}} K = \{[\![v,s]\!]_G = [\![\rho(g)v, \, gs]\!]_G : v \in E, s \in K, g \in G\}.$$

Now the mapping $([v,s]_H, Gt) \to [\![\rho(ts^{-1})v,t]\!]_G$ is a vector bundle isomorphism over $G\backslash K$. Q.E.D.

5.1.33. LEMMA. *Let* $\sigma,\tau : H \to U(E)$ *be representations which agree on a closed subgroup* $G \subset H$. *Then there is an isomorphism*

(5.1.34) $$\pi^*(E \overset{\sigma}{\underset{H}{\times}} K) \xrightarrow[\approx]{\underset{G}{\sigma\backslash\tau}} \pi^*(E \overset{\tau}{\underset{H}{\times}} K).$$

Proof. Realizing $\pi^*(E \underset{H}{\times} K) = E \underset{G}{\times} K$ for σ and τ, we define

$$\underset{G}{\sigma\backslash\tau} \, [\![v,s]\!]_\sigma := [\![v,s]\!]_\tau.$$ Q.E.D.

5.1.35. LEMMA. *Let* $\rho : K \to U(\tilde{E})$ *be a representation such that* $E \subset \tilde{E}$ *is an H-invariant subspace. Then we have for* $X = H\backslash K$

$$E \overset{\rho}{\underset{H}{\times}} K = \dot{\bigcup_{x \in X}} \rho(s)E \times \{x\}$$

where $s \in K$ *satisfies* $Hs = x$.

Proof. The map $[v,s] \mapsto (\rho(s)^{-1}v,\ Hs)$ is a vector bundle isomorphism.
Q.E.D.

For restrictions of K-actions, the isomorphisms (5.1.32) and (5.1.35) can be realized as follows: We have

$$\pi^*(E \overset{\rho}{\underset{H}{\times}} K) \xrightarrow[\approx]{} E \overset{\rho}{\underset{G}{\times}} K\,, \quad ((\rho(s)v,\ Hs),\ Gs) \mapsto (\rho(s)v,\ G(s))$$

and

$$\pi^*(E \overset{\sigma}{\underset{H}{\times}} K) \xrightarrow[\approx]{\overset{\sigma\backslash\tau}{G}} \pi^*(E \overset{\tau}{\underset{H}{\times}} K)\,, \quad (\sigma(s)v,\ Gs) \mapsto (\tau(s)v,\ Gs).$$

5.2 Index Theory for Strictly Pseudoconvex Domains

In this section we develop the index theory for Toeplitz operators over strictly pseudoconvex bounded domains $\Omega \subset \mathbb{C}^n$ with smooth boundary $\partial\Omega$. The analysis uses the structure theory of the Toeplitz C^*-algebra (of Hardy or Bergman type) developed in Sections 4.1 and 4.2. Let

(5.2.1) $$F = (F_{hk}) : \partial\Omega \to \mathbb{C}^{N\times N}$$

be a continuous matrix function, and consider the associated matrix Hardy-Toeplitz operator

(5.2.2) $$(T_{\partial\Omega}(F_{hk})) \in \mathcal{L}(H^2(\partial\Omega)^N)$$

over $\partial\Omega$. Under the assumption

(5.2.3) $$F(\partial\Omega) \subset GL_N(\mathbb{C}),$$

it follows from Theorem 4.2.24 that (5.2.2) is a Fredholm operator. The associated analytical index

(5.2.4) $$\mathrm{Ind}_{\partial\Omega}(F) := \mathrm{Index}(T_{\partial\Omega}(F_{hk}))$$

depends only on the homotopy class of F, and thus defines a homomorphism $\mathrm{Ind}_{\partial\Omega} : K^1(\partial\Omega) \to \mathbb{Z}$ called the *Hardy-Toeplitz index* over $\partial\Omega$. Our aim is to express (5.2.4) in terms of topological (i.e., K-theoretical or cohomological) properties of the "symbol" F.

5.2.5. DEFINITION. The *odd index character* of $\partial\Omega$ is defined as the homomorphism

$$\chi_{\partial\Omega} : K^1(\partial\Omega) \to \mathbb{Z} \tag{5.2.6}$$

satisfying the commuting diagram

$$\begin{array}{ccc} K^1(\partial\Omega) & \xrightarrow{\chi_{\partial\Omega}} & \mathbb{Z} \\ \partial \downarrow & & \approx \downarrow \beta(\bar{\mathbb{C}}^n) \\ K^0_c(\Omega) & \xrightarrow[i_!]{} & K^0_c(\mathbb{C}^n) \end{array}$$

Here ∂ is the connecting map for the pair $\partial\Omega \subset \bar{\Omega}$ (cf. Theorem 5.1.25), $i_!$ is the extension mapping (5.1.18) associated with the inclusion map $i : \Omega \to \mathbb{C}^n$ and $\beta(\bar{\mathbb{C}}^n)$ is the Bott element.

5.2.7. THEOREM. *For every* $F \in K^1(\partial\Omega)$ *we have*

$$\mathrm{Ind}_{\partial\Omega}(F) = \chi_{\partial\Omega}(F). \tag{5.2.8}$$

Since we assume that Ω is a bounded domain in $\mathbb{C}^n$, the Todd class $\tau(\Omega)$ vanishes and the cohomological version of (5.2.6) (cf. [AS]) yields the formula [B5, p. 263]

$$\mathrm{Ind}_{\partial\Omega}(F) = -\frac{(n-1)!}{(2n-1)!(2\pi i)^n} \int_{\partial\Omega} \mathrm{tr}(F^{-1}dF)^{2n-1} \tag{5.2.9}$$

where $\mathbb{C}^n$ has its usual orientation and $\partial\Omega$ is oriented as a boundary. Motivated by the Atiyah-Singer index theorem [AS], the *proof* [B5] of Theorem 5.2.7 uses the concept of pseudo-differential operator. Consider euclidean space $\mathbb{R}^n$ and its cotangent bundle $T^*(\mathbb{R}^n) \approx \mathbb{R}^n \times \mathbb{R}^n$. Denoting elements of $T^*(\mathbb{R}^n)$ as (x,ξ), with $x,\xi \in \mathbb{R}^n$, we consider the operator $P : C^\infty_c(\mathbb{R}^n) \to C^\infty(\mathbb{R}^n)$ defined by

$$Pu(x) = (2\pi)^{-n/2} \int e^{ix\cdot\xi}\, p(x,\xi)\, \hat{u}(\xi)\, d\xi \tag{5.2.10}$$

for all smooth functions $u \in C_c^\infty(\mathbb{R}^n)$ with compact support. Here $\hat{u}(\xi)$ is the Fourier transform and $p(x,\xi)$ is a smooth "symbol function" on $T^*(\mathbb{R}^n)$. In case

$$p(x,\xi) = \sum_{|\alpha|\leq m} p_\alpha(x)\xi^\alpha$$

is a polynomial in ξ, (5.2.10) defines a differential operator of order m. More generally, p is called a *classical symbol of order* m if its derivatives satisfy

$$|\partial_x^\alpha \partial_\xi^\beta p(x,\xi)| \leq C_{\alpha,\beta}(1 + |\xi|)^{m-|\beta|} \tag{5.2.11}$$

for all $(x,\xi) \in T^*(\mathbb{R}^n)$ and all multi-indices $\alpha,\beta \in \mathbb{N}^n$. Here $C_{\alpha,\beta}$ is a constant independent of x and ξ. One can show [LM; Proposition III.3.2] that in this case (5.2.10) defines a linear operator $P : \mathcal{S}(\mathbb{R}^n) \to \mathcal{S}(\mathbb{R}^n)$ (Schwartz space) which has a continuous Sobolev extension

$$P : L^2_{s+m}(\mathbb{R}^n) \to L^2_s(\mathbb{R}^n). \tag{5.2.12}$$

Here L^2_s are the classical Sobolev spaces of (generalized) functions having L^2-derivatives of order $\leq s$ in the sense of distributions. These operators are called *pseudo-differential operators of order* m. In case $m < 0$, P is called smoothing (of order $-m > 0$). A linear operator $P : \mathcal{S}(\mathbb{R}^n) \to \mathcal{S}(\mathbb{R}^n)$ is called *infinitely smoothing* if P has a continuous extension (5.2.12) for all values of s and m. Equivalently, the total symbol $p(x,\xi)$ is rapidly decreasing as $|\xi| \to \infty$.

Let Ψ denote the vector space of all pseudo-differential operators. Let $\Psi_{-\infty}$ denote the subspace of all infinitely smoothing operators. Given $P,Q \in \Psi$ we write $P \sim Q$ if $P - Q \in \Psi_{-\infty}$. By [LM, Proposition III.3.4], the quotient space $\Psi/\Psi_{-\infty}$ is in 1-1 correspondence with formal series

$$p(x,\xi) \sim \sum_{j\geq 0} p_j(x,\xi) \tag{5.2.13}$$

where p_j is a classical symbol of order m_j, the sequence $m_j \to -\infty$, and $\sim$ means that for each integer m there is k_0 such that

$$p(x,\xi) - \sum_{j=0}^{k} p_j(x,\xi)$$

is of order $-m$ whenever $k \geq k_0$. The well-known "symbolic calculus" [LM, §III.3] expresses the composition, adjoint and change of coordinates of pseudo-differential operators in terms of these formal series.

The principal idea of the proof of Theorem 5.2.7 is to relate the Toeplitz extension

$$0 \to \mathcal{K} \to \mathcal{T}(\partial\Omega) \to \mathcal{C}(\partial\Omega) \to 0 \tag{5.2.14}$$

to a C^*-extension of pseudodifferential type. Endow $\partial\Omega$ with the surface measure and define the Sobolev space $L^2_s(\partial\Omega)$ of (generalized) functions with L^2-derivatives of order $\leq s$ [H3, H4]. Let $\bar{\partial}_b$ be the tangential Cauchy-Riemann operator (cf. Section 4.2) and consider the subspace

$$H^2_s(\partial\Omega) = L^2_s(\partial\Omega) \cap \operatorname{Ker} \bar{\partial}_b$$

of all functions with analytic continuation in a neighborhood of $\partial\Omega$ in $\bar{\Omega}$. Then $H^2(\partial\Omega) = H^2_0(\partial\Omega)$ is the Hardy space. One can show [BS] that the Szegö projector is a continuous mapping $E : H^2_s(\partial\Omega) \to H^2_s(\partial\Omega)$ for every $s \in \mathbb{R}$. Moreover, E is pseudolocal, i.e., E decreases singular supports. Since Ω is strictly pseudoconvex, we may assume

$$\Omega = \{z \in \mathbb{C}^n : \rho(z) < 0\} \tag{5.2.15}$$

where $\rho : \mathbb{C}^n \to \mathbb{R}$ is a C^∞-function with differential $d\rho(z) \neq 0$ at every point $z \in \partial\Omega$, and the *Levi matrix*

$$\partial\bar{\partial}\rho(z) = \left(\frac{\partial^2\rho}{\partial z_i \partial \bar{z}_j}\right) > 0 \tag{5.2.16}$$

is *positive definite* at $z \in \partial\Omega$. Here $d = \partial + \bar{\partial}$ is the decomposition of the exterior derivative in holomorphic and antiholomorphic parts. As a consequence of (5.2.16), the differential 1-form

$$\alpha := \frac{1}{2i}(\partial\rho - \bar{\partial}\rho)|_{\partial\Omega} \tag{5.2.17}$$

on $\partial\Omega$ is a *contact form*, i.e., $\alpha \wedge (d\alpha)^{n-1}$ is a nowhere vanishing $(2n-1)$-form on $\partial\Omega$. Since $\partial\Omega$ is a smooth manifold (of real dimension $2n-1$), the cotangent bundle

$$T^*(\partial\Omega) = \{(z,\zeta) : z \in \partial\Omega,\ T_z(\partial\Omega) \xrightarrow[\text{linear}]{\zeta} \mathbb{R}\}$$

is a symplectic manifold (of double dimension) under the symplectic form

$$\omega_{z,\zeta}((z_1,\zeta_1), (z_2,\zeta_2)) := \zeta_2 z_1 - \zeta_1 z_2. \tag{5.2.18}$$

Here $(z,\zeta) \in T^*(\partial\Omega)$ and

$$(z_i,\zeta_i) \in T_{z,\zeta}(T^*(\partial\Omega)) \approx T_z(\partial\Omega) \oplus T_z^*(\partial\Omega).$$

Since α is a contact form, the half-line bundle

$$\Sigma^+ := \{t\alpha_z : t > 0, z \in \partial\Omega\} \subset T^*(\partial\Omega) \tag{5.2.19}$$

is a symplectic submanifold of dimension $2n$. Our first goal is to compare Σ^+ to the "flat" symplectic manifold $T^*(\mathbb{R}^n)$. To this end consider the hyperplane $\mathbb{R}^{2n-1} = \{(x,y) : x \in \mathbb{R}^n, y \in \mathbb{R}^{n-1}\}$ in $\mathbb{C}^n = \mathbb{R}^{2n}$, defined by $\rho_0(z) = \text{Im } z_n = 0$. Then

$$T^*(\mathbb{R}^{2n-1}) = \{(x,y,\xi,\eta) : x,\xi \in \mathbb{R}^n,\ y,\eta \in \mathbb{R}^{n-1}\}$$

and, by (5.2.18), we may identify $T^*(\mathbb{R}^n)$ with the symplectic subcone

$$\Sigma_0^+ := \{(x,0,\xi,0): x,\xi \in \mathbb{R}^n\} \subset T^*(\mathbb{R}^{2n-1}).$$

By [BS], we have the following microlocal description of E : For any $z \in \partial\Omega$, there exist a conic open set $U \subset T^*(\mathbb{R}^{2n-1}) \setminus$ (zero section) and a conic neighborhood V of $(z,\alpha_z) \in \Sigma^+$ in $T^*(\partial\Omega) \setminus$ (zero section), such that for a suitable symplectomorphism (canonical map) $\Phi : U \to V$ the restriction

$$\Phi|_{\Sigma_0^+} : U \cap \Sigma_0^+ \underset{\approx}{\to} V \cap \Sigma^+$$

is a symplectic isomorphism, and a suitable elliptic Fourier integral operator F associated with Φ (defined up to smoothing operators on V [H4, BG]) satisfies $E \sim H\,H^*$ (near $z \in \partial\Omega$), where

$$A \sim H_0^* F^* F H_0 \tag{5.2.20}$$

is an elliptic positive pseudo-differential operator and

$$H \sim F\, H_0\, A^{-1/2} \tag{5.2.21}$$

is a Fourier integral operator with complex phase. Here $H_0 : C^\infty(\mathbb{R}^n) \to C^\infty(\mathbb{R}^{2n-1})$ is the *Hermite operator* [B5] defined by

$$(H_0 u)(x,y) = (2\pi)^{-n} \int_{\mathbb{R}^n} e^{ix\cdot\xi - \frac{y\cdot y}{2}|\xi|} \left(\frac{|\xi|}{2\pi}\right)^{\frac{n-1}{4}} \hat{u}(\xi)\, d\xi. \tag{5.2.22}$$

The advantage of considering pseudodifferential operators and the "Hermite operators" (5.2.20), (5.2.21) is that one can define more general Toeplitz operators

$$T_{\partial\Omega}(Q) = EQE \tag{5.2.23}$$

where Q *is any* pseudo-differential operator of order m on $\partial\Omega$. Since $Q : L^2_{s+m}(\partial\Omega) \to L^2_s(\partial\Omega)$ it follows that

$$T_{\partial\Omega}(Q) : H^2_m(\partial\Omega) \to H^2_0(\partial\Omega) = H^2(\partial\Omega).$$

A non-trivial fact [B5, (1.7)] is that the generalized Toeplitz operators (5.2.23) form an algebra under composition. For $Q = f$ (multiplication operator) with $f \in C^\infty(\partial\Omega)$, we recover the usual Toeplitz operators (4.2.4) of order 0. More generally, one may consider $N \times N$-matrices $Q = (Q_{hk})$ of pseudo-differential operators on $\partial\Omega$, containing (5.2.1) as a special case. For any pseudo-differential operator Q of order m, let $\sigma_m(Q)$ denote its principal (or leading) symbol. By [LM; Corollary III.3.14], $\sigma_m(Q)$ is a well-defined function on $T^*(\partial Q)$, and we put

$$\sigma_m(T_{\partial\Omega}(Q)) := \sigma_m(Q)|_{\Sigma^+}. \tag{5.2.24}$$

By [B5, §1b], we have $\sigma_{m+m'}(T_{\partial\Omega}(Q)\cdot T_{\partial\Omega}(Q')) = \sigma_m(T_{\partial\Omega}(Q))\, \sigma_{m'}(T_{\partial\Omega}(Q'))$ for the product and

$$\sigma_{m+m'-1}[T_{\partial\Omega}(Q),\ T_{\partial\Omega}(Q')] = \frac{1}{i}\ \{\sigma_m(T_{\partial\Omega}(Q)),\ \sigma_{m'}(T_{\partial\Omega}(Q'))\}$$

where { } is the Poisson bracket on Σ^+.

Now let Q be an $N{\times}N$-matrix of pseudo-differential operators on $\partial\Omega$ which is elliptic (i.e., has invertible symbol) on $\Sigma^+ \subset T^*(\partial\Omega)$. Then the matrix Toeplitz operator $T_{\partial\Omega}(Q)$ has an index which depends only on the principal symbol (5.2.24). Since any Toeplitz operator with symbol $|\xi| \cdot I_N$ has index 0, we may suppose that Q is of order 1 (note that multiplication operators have order 0 instead). By modifying $\sigma(Q)$ outside Σ^+, we may also suppose $\sigma(Q) = |\xi|\, i_N$ on $-\Sigma^+$.

Let E be the sub-vector bundle of the complexified tangent bundle $T(\partial\Omega) \otimes \mathbb{C}$ spanned by all anti-holomorphic vectors tangent to $\partial\Omega$. The complex of first order differential operators

$$(5.2.25) \qquad 0 \to \mathcal{C}^\infty(\partial\Omega, \Lambda^0E^*) \xrightarrow{\bar\partial_b} \mathcal{C}^\infty(\partial\Omega, \Lambda^1E^*) \xrightarrow{\bar\partial_b} \cdots \longrightarrow \mathcal{C}^\infty(\partial\Omega, \Lambda^{n-1}E^*) \longrightarrow 0$$

is called the *tangential Cauchy-Riemann complex.* Here E^* is the dual bundle. The symbol of (5.2.25) is

$$\sigma(\bar\partial_b)(x,\xi) = i\ \partial_{\xi_E} : \Lambda^jE_x^* \to \Lambda^{j+1}E_x^*$$

where ∂_{ξ_E} is exterior multiplication (cf. (5.1.7)) by the natural projection $\xi_E \in E_x^*$ of $\xi \in T_x^*(\partial\Omega)$. By the assumptions on $\sigma(Q)$ made above, one defines the elliptic symbol complex

$$\sigma(Q) \boxtimes \sigma(\bar\partial_b) = \begin{pmatrix} \sigma(Q) \otimes I & I \otimes \sigma(\bar\partial_b) \\ -I \otimes \sigma(\bar\partial_b) & 0 \end{pmatrix}$$

on $E_j = (\mathbb{C}^N \otimes \Lambda^jE^*) \oplus (\mathbb{C}^N \otimes \Lambda^{j-1}E^*)$ and obtains a K-theory class

$$[\sigma(Q) \otimes \sigma(\bar\partial_b)] = i_![\sigma(T_{\partial\Omega}(Q))] \in K_c^0(T^*(\partial\Omega))$$

where $[\sigma(T_{\partial\Omega}(Q))] \in K^1(\partial\Omega) \approx K_c^0(\Sigma^+)$ and $i : \Sigma^+ \to T^*(\partial\Omega)$ is the inclusion mapping. By [B5] there exists a (non-classical) pseudo-differential operator A of order -1/2 (and type 1/2) such that $\bar{\partial}_b A$ is the orthogonal projector onto $\mathrm{Ran}(\bar{\partial}_b)$ and $A\bar{\partial}_b$ is the orthogonal projector onto $\mathrm{Ran}(\bar{\partial}_b^*)$. Then

$$I - \bar{\partial}_b A - A\bar{\partial}_b = \text{orthogonal projector onto } \mathrm{Ker}(\bar{\partial}_b + \bar{\partial}_b^*)$$

can be identified with the homology $\sum_{j=0}^{n-1} S_j$ of the operator complex (5.2.25). By definition, $S_0 = E$ is the Szegö projection, S_{n-1} is analogous to the Szegö projection but supported on $-\Sigma^+$ whereas the S_j, $1 \le j \le n-2$ have finite rank [B5]. By [B5; Lemma 3.2] there exists a system Q_0 of pseudo-differential operators of degree 1, acting on sections of $\mathbb{C}^N \otimes \bigoplus_0^{n-1} \Lambda^j E^*$, such that $\sigma(Q_0) = \sigma(Q) \otimes I$ and $Q_0\bar{\partial}_b = \bar{\partial}_b Q_0$, i.e., Q_0 is a homomorphism of the operator complexes (5.2.25). The associated double complex is elliptic and has Euler characteristic

$$\mathrm{Index}(Q_0 \otimes \bar{\partial}_b) = \sum_j (-1)^j \ \mathrm{Index}(S_j Q_0 S_j).$$

Since $\mathrm{rank}(S_j) < \infty$ for $j \ne 0, n-1$ we have $\mathrm{Index}(S_j Q_0 S_j) = 0$ for such j. For $j = 0$, we obtain a Toeplitz operator with index

$$\mathrm{Index}(S_0 Q_0 S_0) = \mathrm{Index}\ T_{\partial\Omega}(Q_0) = \mathrm{Index}\ T_{\partial\Omega}(Q).$$

For $j = n - 1$, we obtain a "dual" Toeplitz operator (supported by $-\Sigma^+$) which has index 0 since its symbol $|\xi| \cdot I_N$ is self-adjoint. It follows that

$$\mathrm{Index}\ T_{\partial\Omega}(Q) = \mathrm{Index}(Q_0 \otimes \bar{\partial}_b).$$

Since $Q_0 \otimes \bar{\partial}_b$ has symbol $\sigma(Q) \otimes \sigma(\bar{\partial}_b)$, the Atiyah-Singer index theorem [AS] for (complexes of) pseudo-differential operators on the compact manifold $\partial\Omega$ implies the assertion (5.2.7). Q.E.D.

We now consider the Bergman-Toeplitz operators. Let

(5.2.26) $$F = (F_{hk}) : \bar{\Omega} \to \mathbb{C}^{N \times N}$$

be a continuous matrix function, and consider the associated matrix Bergman-Toeplitz operator

(5.2.27) $$(T_\Omega(F_{hk})) \in \mathcal{L}(H^2(\Omega)^N)$$

over Ω. Under the assumption

(5.2.28) $$F(\partial\Omega) \subset GL_N(\mathbb{C}),$$

it follows from Theorem 4.1.25 that (5.2.27) is a Fredholm operator. The associated analytic index

(5.2.29) $$\mathrm{Ind}_\Omega(F) := \mathrm{Index}(T_\Omega(F_{hk}))$$

depends only on the homotopy class of F, and thus defines a homomorphism $\mathrm{Ind}_\Omega : K_c^0(\Omega) \to \mathbb{Z}$ called the *Bergman-Toeplitz index over* Ω. Our aim is to express (5.2.29) in terms of topological (i.e., K-theoretical or cohomological) properties of the "symbol" F. Consider the "graph" of F, which is a vector bundle homomorphism

$$\mathcal{G}_F : \bar{\Omega} \times \mathbb{C}^N \longrightarrow \bar{\Omega} \times \mathbb{C}^N$$

defined by $(z,v) \mapsto (z,F(z)v)$. By (5.2.28), we obtain an element

(5.2.30) $$[F] := d(\Omega \times \mathbb{C}^N, \Omega \times \mathbb{C}^N, \mathcal{G}_F) \in K_c^0(\bar{\Omega}, \partial\Omega) = K_c^0(\Omega).$$

5.2.31. DEFINITION. The *even index character* of Ω is defined as the homomorphism

(5.2.32) $$\chi_\Omega : K_c^0(\Omega) \to \mathbb{Z}$$

satisfying the commuting diagram

$$\begin{array}{ccc} K_c^0(\Omega) & \xrightarrow{\ \chi_\Omega\ } & \mathbb{Z} = K^0(\infty) \\ & {\scriptstyle i_!}\searrow \quad \swarrow{\scriptstyle \beta(\overline{\mathbb{C}}^n)} & \\ & K_c^0(\mathbb{C}^n) & \end{array}$$

Here $i_!$ is the extension mapping (5.1.18) associated with the inclusion map $i : \Omega \to \mathbb{C}^n$ and $\beta(\bar{\mathbb{C}}^n)$ denotes (multiplication by) the Bott element (5.1.17).

5.2.33. PROPOSITION. *For a complex manifold* X, *the even index character* $\chi_X : K_c^0(X) \to \mathbb{Z}$ *is given by*

$$\chi_X(\alpha) = (\mathrm{ch}(\alpha)\ \mathrm{Td}(TX))[X]. \tag{5.2.34}$$

Here $\mathrm{ch} : K_c^0(X) \to H^*(X,\mathbb{Q})$ *is the even Chern character and* $\mathrm{Td}(TX)$ *is the Todd class of the holomorphic tangent bundle* TX.

5.2.35. THEOREM. *For every* $F \in K_c^0(\bar{\Omega}, \partial\Omega)$ *we have*

$$\mathrm{Ind}_\Omega(F) = \chi_\Omega[F]\ (= \chi_\Omega(\mathcal{G}_F)). \tag{5.2.36}$$

In cohomological terms (cf. (5.2.9)), (5.2.36) implies

$$\mathrm{Ind}_\Omega(F) = \langle \mathrm{ch}[F], [\Omega]\rangle \tag{5.2.37}$$

since the Todd class is trivial for domains in $\mathbb{C}^n$.

The *proof* of Theorem 5.2.35 [B5] can be reduced to Theorem 5.2.7 along the following lines. Consider the connecting map

$$\partial : K^1(\partial\Omega) \to K_c^0(\bar{\Omega}, \partial\Omega) = K_c^0(\Omega)$$

and let $\Phi : \Sigma_+ \xrightarrow[\approx]{} U$ be an isomorphism onto a tubular neighborhood U of $\partial\Omega$ so that Σ_+ points outwards and $\Phi(z, \alpha(z)) = z$ for all z. Here α is the contact form (5.2.17). Then there is a commuting diagram

$$\begin{array}{ccc} K^1(\partial\Omega) & \xrightarrow{\ \partial\ } & K_c^0(\Omega) \\ \approx\downarrow & & \uparrow i_! \\ K_c^0(\Sigma^+) & \xrightarrow[\ \Phi_*\ ]{} & K_c^0(U) \end{array}$$

where Φ_* is the push-forward, $i : U \to \Omega$ is the inclusion map and $K^1(\partial\Omega) \approx K_c^0(\Sigma^+)$ is the canonical isomorphism. In terms of a defining function ρ of Ω (cf. (5.2.15)) consider the "positive" symplectic form

$$\omega = i\partial\bar{\partial}\rho = d\alpha$$

on U satisfying $\omega\left(\frac{\partial}{\partial n}, J\frac{\partial}{\partial n}\right) > 0$ where $\frac{\partial}{\partial n}$ is the outward normal and J is the complex structure. Similarly, the restricted symplectic form ω_{Σ_+} on Σ^+ satisfies

$$\omega_{\Sigma_+}\left(\rho\frac{\partial}{\partial\rho}, J\frac{\partial}{\partial n}\right) > 0$$

where $\rho\frac{\partial}{\partial\rho} = \Sigma_j \xi_j \frac{\partial}{\partial\xi_j}$ is the "radial" vector field on Σ^+. It follows that the pull-back of the complex structure on U to Σ^+ is homotopic to a "positive" structure (in the sense of [B5; définition (2.5)] so that, on the level of K-theory,

(5.2.38) $$\chi_{\partial\Omega} = \chi_\Omega \circ \partial.$$

Since the C^*-extensions

$$0 \to \mathcal{K}(H^2(\partial\Omega)) \to \mathcal{T}(\partial\Omega) \to C(\partial\Omega) \to 0,$$

$$0 \to \mathcal{K}(H^2(\Omega)) \to \mathcal{T}(\Omega) \to C(\partial\Omega) \to 0$$

are equivalent [R1] it follows that

$$\mathrm{Ind}_\Omega(F) = \mathrm{Ind}_{\partial\Omega}(F|_{\partial\Omega}) = \chi_{\partial\Omega}(F|_{\partial\Omega}) = \chi_\Omega(\partial F|_{\partial\Omega}) = \dot{\chi}_\Omega(F).$$

This proves Theorem 5.2.35. Q.E.D.

5.3 K-Theory for C^*-Algebras

In order to formulate an index theory for Toeplitz C^*-algebras which are not essentially commutative, it is necessary to use K-theory of C^*-algebras. In this section we review the basic properties of this theory [B2] which closely parallels the corresponding "commutative" theory for topological spaces (cf. Section 5.1). Let A be a unital C^*-algebra. Consider the $(N\times N)$-matrix algebras

$$M_N(A) := A^{N\times N}$$

with the embedding $M_N(A) \mapsto M_{N+1}(A)$ given by

$$a \mapsto \begin{pmatrix} a & 0 \\ 0 & 0 \end{pmatrix}.$$

Define the inductive limit

$$M_\infty(A) := \lim_{N\to\infty} \text{inj}\, M_N(A).$$

For $1 \leq N \leq \infty$, $M_N(A)$ is an associative *-algebra. Let

$$P_N(A) := \{p \in M_N(A): p = p^* = p^2\}$$

denote the set of all *projections* (i.e., self-adjoint idempotents) in $M_N(A)$. Then

$$P_\infty(A) = \bigcup_{N\geq 0} P_N(A).$$

Two projections $p,q \in P_\infty(A)$ are called *equivalent* if

$$p = uu^*,\ q = u^*u$$

for some partial isometry $u = uu^*u \in M_\infty(A)$. Let $\tilde{P}_\infty(A)$ be the set of equivalence classes $[p]$ of projections $p \in P_\infty(A)$ modulo this relation. Given $p \in P_n(A)$ and $q \in P_m(A)$, define

$$p \oplus q := \begin{pmatrix} p & 0 \\ 0 & q \end{pmatrix} \in P_{n+m}(A).$$

This defines a mapping

$$P_m(A) \times P_n(A) \xrightarrow{\oplus} P_{m+n}(A)$$

which is compatible with equivalence, resulting in a map

$$\tilde{P}_\infty(A) \times \tilde{P}_\infty(A) \xrightarrow{+} \tilde{P}_\infty(A)$$

given by $[p], [q] \mapsto [p \oplus q]$. In this way $\tilde{P}_\infty(A)$ becomes a commutative semigroup with neutral element $[0]$.

5.3.1. DEFINITION. For a unital C^*-algebra A, define $K_0(A)$ as the Grothendieck group associated with the monoid $\tilde{P}_\infty(A)$ of all equivalence classes of projections in $M_\infty(A)$.

Hence, by definition, $K_0(A)$ consists of all formal differences $[p] - [q]$, with $p,q \in P_\infty(A)$. In $K_0(A)$, two projections p and q are equivalent if $p \oplus r \approx q \oplus r$ for another projection r.

5.3.2. EXAMPLE. For $A = \mathbb{C}$, the dimension function

$$\dim : P_\infty(\mathbb{C}) \to \mathbb{Z}, \ p \mapsto \operatorname{rank} p$$

induces an isomorphism $\dim : K_0(\mathbb{C}) \underset{\approx}{\to} \mathbb{Z}$.

Let $\varphi : A \to B$ be a unital C^*-algebra homomorphism. Then φ induces matrix homomorphisms $\varphi_N : M_N(A) \to M_N(B)$ given by

$$(a_{ij}) \mapsto (\varphi(a_{ij}))$$

for each $N \geq 1$, mapping $P_N(A)$ into $P_N(B)$. Thus we obtain a group homomorphism

$$\varphi_* : K_0(A) \to K_0(B)$$

given by $[p] \mapsto [\varphi_\infty(p)]$. If A is a non-unital C^*-algebra, the unitization $A \oplus \mathbb{C}$ becomes a unital C^*-algebra in a natural way [D1]. The canonical homomorphism $A \oplus \mathbb{C} \to \mathbb{C}$ induces a homomorphism of K-groups $K_0(A \oplus \mathbb{C}) \to K_0(\mathbb{C}) \cong \mathbb{Z}$ and one defines

$$K_0(A) := \operatorname{Ker}[K_0(A \oplus \mathbb{C}) \to K_0(\mathbb{C})]. \tag{5.3.3}$$

This definition agrees with Definition 5.3.1 in case A has a unit, since then $K_0(A \oplus \mathbb{C}) = K_0(A) \oplus K_0(\mathbb{C}) = K_0(A) \oplus \mathbb{Z}$. Thus one gets a covariant functor K_0 from the category of (not necessarily unital) C^*-algebras to the category of (additive) abelian groups.

K-theory of C^*-algebras has also an "odd" version which is closer related to Toeplitz operators. Let A be a unital C^*-algebra and consider the group $GL_N(A)$ of invertible elements in $M_N(A)$, with the embedding $GL_N(A) \mapsto GL_{N+1}(A)$ given by

$$g \mapsto \begin{pmatrix} g & 0 \\ 0 & 1 \end{pmatrix}.$$

Define the inductive limit

$$GL_\infty(A) := \lim_{N\to\infty} \text{inj}\, GL_N(A).$$

For $1 \leq N \leq \infty$, $GL_N(A)$ is a topological group under pointwise multiplication. Two elements $g_0, g_1 \in GL_N(A)$ are *homotopic* if there exists a continuous path $g_t \in GL_N(A)$, $0 \leq t \leq 1$, connecting g_0 and g_1. For each n, let $GL_N^\sim(A)$ denote the set of all homotopy classes (i.e., path components) in $GL_N(A)$. Then

$$GL_\infty^\sim(A) = \lim_{N\to\infty} \text{inj}\, GL_N^\sim(A).$$

Since the group operations are compatible with homotopy, the $GL_N^\sim(A)$ are topological groups. $GL_\infty^\sim(A)$ is actually commutative since for $g \in GL_N(A)$, $h \in GL_m(A)$ there exists a homotopy

$$\begin{pmatrix} g & 0 \\ 0 & 1 \end{pmatrix}\begin{pmatrix} h & 0 \\ 0 & 1 \end{pmatrix} \sim \begin{pmatrix} g & 0 & 0 \\ 0 & h & 0 \\ 0 & 0 & 1 \end{pmatrix}$$

in $GL_\infty(A)$. Here we write

$$\begin{pmatrix} g & 0 \\ 0 & 1 \end{pmatrix} := \begin{pmatrix} g\text{-}1_n & 0 \\ 0 & 1 \end{pmatrix} \oplus 1_\infty.$$

5.3.4. DEFINITION. For any unital C^*-algebra A, define

(5.3.5) $$K_1(A) := GL_\infty^\sim(A) = \pi_0(GL_\infty(A))$$

as the abelian (multiplicative) group of path components in $GL_\infty(A)$.

5.3.6. EXAMPLE. For $A = \mathbb{C}$, we have $K_1(A) = \{0\}$ since $GL_\infty(\mathbb{C})$ is path-connected.

Let $\varphi : A \to B$ be a unital C^*-algebra homomorphism. Then the induced matrix homomorphism $\varphi_N : M_N(A) \to M_N(B)$ maps $GL_N(A)$ into $GL_N(B)$. This process defines a group homomorphism

$$\varphi_* : K_1(A) \to K_1(B)$$

given by $[g] \mapsto [\varphi_\infty(g)]$. If A is a non-unital C^*-algebra, the unitization $A \oplus \mathbb{C}$ becomes a unital C^*-algebra and the canonical homomorphism $A \oplus \mathbb{C} \to \mathbb{C}$ induces a homomorphism of K-groups $K_1(A \oplus \mathbb{C}) \to K_1(\mathbb{C}) = \{0\}$ and one defines

$$K_1(A) := \mathrm{Ker}(K_1(A \oplus \mathbb{C}) \to K_1(\mathbb{C})) = K_1(A \oplus \mathbb{C}). \tag{5.3.7}$$

This definition agrees with Definition 5.3.4 in case A has a unit, since then $K_1(A \oplus \mathbb{C}) = K_1(A) \oplus K_1(\mathbb{C}) = K_1(A)$. Thus one gets a covariant functor K_1 from the category of (not necessarily unital) C^*-algebras to the category of (multiplicative) abelian groups.

A basic result in K-theory of C^*-algebras is the cyclic exact sequence.

5.3.8. THEOREM. *Let $\mathcal{J}$ be an ideal in a C^*-algebra A. Then there exists a cyclic exact sequence*

$$\begin{array}{ccccc}
K_0(\mathcal{J}) & \xrightarrow{i_*} & K_0(A) & \xrightarrow{p_*} & K_0(A/\mathcal{J}) \\
\partial \uparrow & & & & \downarrow \partial \\
K_1(A/\mathcal{J}) & \xleftarrow[p_*]{} & K_1(A) & \xleftarrow[i_*]{} & K_1(\mathcal{J})
\end{array}$$

Here $i : \mathcal{J} \to A$ is the inclusion, $p : A \to A/\mathcal{J}$ is the canonical projection and ∂ are the so-called connecting homomorphisms.

5.3.9. DEFINITION. Let A and B be C^*-algebras. An *extension* of A by B is a short exact sequence of C^*-homomorphisms

(5.3.10) $$0 \leftarrow A \xleftarrow{\;p\;} E \xleftarrow{\;j\;} B \leftarrow 0$$

where E is another C^*-algebra. Two extensions

$$0 \leftarrow A \xleftarrow{\;p_\nu\;} E_\nu \xleftarrow{\;j_\nu\;} B \leftarrow 0 \qquad (\nu \in \{1,2\})$$

are called (strongly) *equivalent* if there is a commuting diagram

$$\begin{array}{ccccccccc} & & & \swarrow^{p_1} & E_1 & \nwarrow^{j_1} & & & \\ 0 & \longleftarrow & A & & \downarrow \gamma & & B & \longleftarrow & 0 \\ & & & \nwarrow_{p_2} & E_2 & \swarrow_{j_2} & & & \end{array}$$

where γ is a C^*-algebra isomorphism. An extension (5.3.10) is said to be *split* if there is a cross-section τ of p,

$$0 \leftarrow A \underset{\tau}{\overset{p}{\rightleftarrows}} E \xleftarrow{\;j\;} B \leftarrow 0$$

which is a C^*-algebra homomorphism. Now assume that $B \approx B \otimes \mathcal{K}$ is *stable* [B2]. Using the so-called Busby invariant

(5.3.11) $$\tau : A \to \bar{B}/B$$

into the outer multiplier algebra of B [B2; 15.2] one can define the *direct sum* of (strong equivalence classes of) extensions of A and B.

5.3.12. DEFINITION. Let A and B be C^*-algebras, with A nuclear. Then the set E(A,B) of strong equivalence classes of extensions of A by $B \otimes \mathcal{K}$ is a semi-group under direct sum, and the quotient

$$KK^1(A,B) := E(A,B)/\{\text{split extensions}\}$$

is an abelian group. The importance of nuclearity of A stems from the fact that every extension (5.3.10) of A by B admits a *completely positive* cross-section τ [CE].

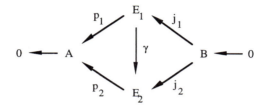

5.4 Index Theory for Symmetric Domains

In this section we develop the index theory for Toeplitz operators over a symmetric domain $\Omega \subset Z$ with Shilov boundary S. We assume that Ω is irreducible of rank r. Our analysis is based on the structure theory of the Toeplitz C^*-algebra developed in Section 4.11 (for the case of Hardy spaces). Since the Hardy-Toeplitz C^*-algebra $\mathcal{T}(S)$ over S is not commutative modulo $\mathcal{K}(H^2(S))$ if $r > 1$, it will be necessary to consider several index homomorphisms $\mathrm{Ind}_1^S, \ldots, \mathrm{Ind}_r^S$ adapted to the C^*-filtration $\mathcal{J}_j := \mathrm{Ker}\ \sigma_j$ of $\mathcal{T}(S)$ (Theorem 4.11.133), where

$$\sigma_j := (\sigma_c)_{c \in S_j}$$

is the j-th symbol homomorphism. Here

$$\sigma_c : \mathcal{T}(S) \to \mathcal{L}(H^2(S_c))$$

is the irreducible representation corresponding to the boundary component $\Omega_c := \Omega \cap Z_0(c)$ in the Jordan subtriple $Z_0(c)$, acting on the Hardy space over the Shilov boundary $S_c = Z_0(c) \cap S_{r-j}$ of Ω_c. Consider the field C^*-algebra

$$\mathcal{K}(\mathcal{E}_j) := \int_{c \in S_j}^{\oplus} \mathcal{K}(H^2(S_c))$$

of the continuous bundle of elementary C^*-algebras [D1] associated with the continuous bundle

(5.4.1) $$\mathcal{E}_j := (H^2(S_c))_{c \in S_j}$$

of Hilbert spaces over S_j. There is an embedding

$$\mathcal{C}(S_j) \subset \mathcal{K}(\mathcal{E}_j)$$

given by

(5.4.2) $$f \mapsto (f(c)\ 1_c \otimes 1_c)_{c \in S_j}$$

where $1_c \in H^2(S_c)$ is the constant function one.

By the *spectral theorem* [L8, L9], every $z \in Z$ has a unique "spectral resolution"

(5.4.3) $$z = z_1 c_1 + \cdots + z_r c_r$$

where $\{c_1, \ldots, c_r\}$ is a frame of minimal orthogonal tripotents in Z, and the "singular numbers" $z_1, \ldots, z_r$ satisfy $z_1 \geq \cdots \geq z_r \geq 0$. We say that z has *rank* j, if $z_1 \geq \cdots \geq z_j > 0$ but $z_{j+1} = 0$. For example, every tripotent $c \in S_j$ has the singular numbers $(1, \ldots, 1, 0, \ldots, 0)$ (j ones) and is therefore of rank j. We put

(5.4.4) $$S_j^{\mathbb{C}} := \{z \in Z : \mathrm{rank}(z) = j\}$$

and consider the closure

(5.4.5) $$\bar{S}_j^{\mathbb{C}} = \{z \in Z : \mathrm{rank}(z) \leq j\}.$$

5.4.6. PROPOSITION. $\bar{S}_j^{\mathbb{C}}$ *is an algebraic variety which contains* $S_j^{\mathbb{C}}$ *as an open dense subset and has no singularities near* S_j.

Proof. An element z in a Jordan algebra of rank r has $\mathrm{rank}(z) < r$ if and only if the determinant $\Delta(z)$ vanishes. Applying this condition to all irreducible Jordan subalgebras $Z' \subset Z$ of rank $j + 1$, we see that

$$\bar{S}_j^{\mathbb{C}} = \{z \in Z : p(z) = 0 \ \forall\ p \in \mathcal{P}^{1\ldots10\ldots0}(Z)\}$$

($j + 1$ ones) since $\mathcal{P}^{1\ldots10\ldots0}(Z)$ contains all determinants of the subalgebras Z' and $\bar{S}_j^{\mathbb{C}}$ is K-invariant. Similarly,

$$\bar{S}_{j-1}^{\mathbb{C}} = \{z \in \bar{S}_j^{\mathbb{C}} : q(z) = 0 \ \forall\ q \in \mathcal{P}^{1\ldots10\ldots0}(Z)\}$$

(j ones) is a proper algebraic subset of $\bar{S}_j^{\mathbb{C}}$, so that $S_j^{\mathbb{C}} := \bar{S}_j^{\mathbb{C}} \setminus \bar{S}_{j-1}^{\mathbb{C}}$ is open and dense. It is known [L9] that the complex Lie group $K^{\mathbb{C}}$ acts transitively on $S_j^{\mathbb{C}}$. Thus $S_j^{\mathbb{C}}$ is a manifold and the singularities of $\bar{S}_j^{\mathbb{C}}$ are at $\bar{S}_{j-1}^{\mathbb{C}}$.

Q.E.D.

Since the higher indices Ind_j^S, $j \geq 2$, are essentially "family" versions of the basic index Ind_1^S, we will first consider the case $j = 1$. By Theorem 4.11.133, there is a C^*-extension

$$(5.4.7) \qquad 0 \leftarrow \mathcal{K}(\mathcal{E}_1) \xleftarrow{\sigma_1} \mathcal{J}_2 \leftarrow \mathcal{K}(H^2(S)) \leftarrow 0.$$

Its Busby invariant is the C^*-homomorphism

$$(5.4.8) \qquad \tau_1(S) : \mathcal{C}(S_1) \to \mathcal{L}(H^2(S))/\mathcal{K}(H^2(S))$$

into the Calkin algebra, defined as the composition

$$\mathcal{C}(S_1) \to \mathcal{K}(\mathcal{E}_1) \xrightarrow{\tau_1} \mathcal{J}_2 \subset \mathcal{L}(H^2(S)) \to \mathcal{L}(H^2(S))/\mathcal{K}(H^2(S)).$$

Here τ_1 is any completely positive cross-section of σ_1. The homomorphism property follows from the fact that

$$(\tau_1 F)(\tau_1 \tilde{F}) - \tau_1(F\tilde{F}) \in \mathrm{Ker}(\sigma_1) = \mathcal{K}(H^2(S))$$

for all $F, \tilde{F} \in \mathcal{K}(\mathcal{E}_1)$. Any element in $K^1(S)$ can be represented by a continuous matrix function

$$(5.4.9) \qquad F = (F_{hk}) : S_1 \to GL_N(\mathbb{C})$$

for some N. Let (δ_{hk}) be the unit matrix. Then we obtain a function matrix

$$(5.4.10) \qquad (F_{hk} - \delta_{hk}) \in \mathcal{C}(S_1)^{N\times N}.$$

Consider the vector-valued Hardy space $H^2(S,\mathbb{C}^N) = H^2(S) \otimes \mathbb{C}^N$. Then we have

$$\mathcal{L}(H^2(S,\mathbb{C}^N)) = \mathcal{L}(H^2(S)) \otimes \mathbb{C}^{N\times N},$$

$$\mathcal{K}(H^2(S,\mathbb{C}^N)) = \mathcal{K}(H^2(S)) \otimes \mathbb{C}^{N\times N}.$$

5.4.11. PROPOSITION. *The operator $N\times N$-matrix*

$$(5.4.12) \qquad I + (\tau_1(F_{hk} - \delta_{hk}))$$

defines a Fredholm operator on $H^2(S)^N$. *Here* I *denotes the identity.*

Proof. Taking N×N-matrices, (5.4.7) yields an exact sequence

$$(5.4.13) \qquad 0 \leftarrow \mathcal{K}(\mathcal{E}_1 \otimes \mathbb{C}^N) \xleftarrow{\sigma_1^{N\times N}} \mathcal{J}_2^{N\times N} \leftarrow \mathcal{K}(H^2(S)^N) \leftarrow 0.$$

The operator matrix (5.4.12) belongs to the unitization of $\mathcal{J}_2^{N\times N}$ (in case $r = 1$, $\mathcal{J}_2 = \mathcal{T}(S)$ is unital) and satisfies

$$\sigma_1^{N\times N}(I + (\tau_1(F_{hk} - \delta_{hk}))) = I + (\sigma_1\tau_1(F_{hk} - \delta_{hk})) = I + (F_{hk} - \delta_{hk}) = \begin{pmatrix} F & 0 \\ 0 & I \end{pmatrix}$$

in the unitization of $\mathcal{K}(\mathcal{E}_1 \otimes \mathbb{C}^N)$ (in case $r = 1$, $\mathcal{K}(\mathcal{E}_1 \otimes \mathbb{C}^N) = \mathcal{C}(S_1)^{N\times N}$ is unital). Since F is invertible, the assertion follows. Q.E.D.

5.4.14. DEFINITION. The analytic *Hardy-Toeplitz index*

$$\mathrm{Ind}_1^S : K^1(S_1) \to \mathbb{Z}$$

is defined for all matrix symbols $F = (F_{hk})$ by

$$(5.4.15) \qquad \mathrm{Ind}_1^S(F) := \mathrm{Index}(I + (\tau_1(F_{hk} - \delta_{hk}))).$$

It is clear that (5.4.15) does not depend on the choice of cross-section τ_1, since another cross-section $\bar{\tau}_1$ differs only by compact operators. Also, (5.4.15) depends only on the homotopy class of F. The topological (i.e., K-theoretical and cohomological) description of (5.4.15) is our next aim. For $0 \le j \le r$, let $H_j^2(S)$ denote the closure (in $L^2(S)$) of the direct sum

$$(5.4.16) \qquad \mathcal{P}_j(Z) = \sum_{\alpha \in \vec{\mathbb{N}}^j} \mathcal{P}^\alpha(Z),$$

where $\vec{\mathbb{N}}^j := \{(\alpha_1, \ldots, \alpha_j, 0, \ldots, 0) : \alpha_1 \ge \cdots \ge \alpha_j \ge 0 \text{ integers}\}$.

5.4.17. PROPOSITION. *The orthogonal projection*

(5.4.18) $$E_j^S : H^2(S) \to H_j^2(S)$$

belongs to $\mathcal{T}(S)$, *and satisfies*

(5.4.19) $$\sigma_c(E_j^S) = E_{j-k}^{S_c}$$

if $k \le j$ *and* $c \in S_k$.

Proof. The first assertion is proved in [U2; Theorem 1.4]. Now let $c \in S_k$. Since K acts transitively on S_k, we may assume $c = e_1 + \cdots + e_k$. For a signature $\mu = (\alpha_{k+1}, \ldots, \alpha_r) \in \vec{\mathbb{N}}^{r-k}$, let $\delta_\mu \in \mathcal{P}^\mu(Z_0(c))$ be the corresponding conical polynomial and let $\Delta_\alpha \in \mathcal{P}^\alpha(Z)$ be the conical polynomial of signature $\alpha := (\alpha_{k+1}, \ldots, \alpha_{k+1}, \mu) \in \vec{\mathbb{N}}^r$. Then $\delta_\mu - \Delta_\alpha$ vanishes on $c + S_c \subset S$, implying

(5.4.20) $$\lim_{i\to\infty} \|h_c^i(\delta_\mu - \Delta_\alpha)\|_S = 0$$

for the peaking functions h_c^i defined in 4.11.96. In case $\alpha_{j+1} > 0$ we have

$$E_j^S(h_c^i\Delta_\alpha) = 0, \quad E_{j-k}^{S_c}\,\delta_\mu = 0$$

since $\Delta_\alpha \in \mathcal{P}_j(Z)^\perp$ and $\mathcal{P}_j(Z)^\perp$ is an ideal by Theorem 4.11.86. In case $\alpha_{j+1} = 0$ we have

$$E_j^S(h_c^i\Delta_\alpha) = h_c^i\Delta_\alpha, \quad E_{j-k}^{S_c}\,\delta_\mu = \delta_\mu$$

since $h_c^i \in \overline{\mathcal{P}(Z_1(c))}$ and $\mathcal{P}(Z_1(c)) \cdot \Delta_\alpha \subset \mathcal{P}_j(Z)$ by [U4; Lemma 3.5]. In both cases it follows from (5.4.20) and the boundedness of E_j^S that $q := \delta_\mu$ satisfies

(5.4.21) $$\lim_{i\to\infty} \|E_j^S(h_c^i q) - h_c^i E_{j-k}^{S_c} q\|_S \to 0.$$

Since $\mathcal{P}(Z_0(c))$ is spanned by polynomials of the form $\gamma \cdot \delta_\mu$, $\gamma \in GL(\Omega_c)$, it follows that (5.4.21) holds for all $q \in \mathcal{P}(Z_0(c))$. By definition (4.11.109) of σ_c, the assertion follows. Q.E.D.

The manifold S_j of all rank j tripotents has the tangent space

(5.4.22) $$T_c(S_j) = iX(c) \oplus Z_{1/2}(c)$$

where $Z = Z_1(c) \oplus Z_{1/2}(c) \oplus Z_0(c)$ is the Peirce decomposition (1.5.46) and

(5.4.23) $$X(c) := \{a \in Z_1(c): \{ca^*c\} = a\}$$

is the real form of $Z_1(c)$. The complex subspace $Z_{1/2}(c)$ is called the *holomorphic tangent space*. The group K acts transitively on S_j, and its Lie algebra $\mathfrak{k}$ induces smooth vector fields on S_j. Similarly, the complexification $\mathfrak{k}^{\mathbb{C}}$ induces "complex" vector fields on S_j. By [U8; p. 813], there is a decomposition $\mathfrak{k}^{\mathbb{C}} = \mathfrak{q}_+ \oplus \mathfrak{m}^{\mathbb{C}} \oplus \mathfrak{q}_-$, where

$$\mathfrak{m}^{\mathbb{C}} = \{A \in \mathfrak{k}^{\mathbb{C}} : Ac = 0\} \oplus \{a \square c^* : a \in Z_1(c)\},$$

$$\mathfrak{q}_+ = \{b \square c^* : b \in Z_{1/2}(c)\}, \; \mathfrak{q}_- = \{c \square b^* : b \in Z_{1/2}(c)\}.$$

Here $(a \square c^*)z := \{ac^*z\}$ is the Jordan triple product. For every $b \in Z_{1/2}(c)$, the vector field $d_b := 2(b \square c^* - c \square b^*) \in \mathfrak{k}$ satisfies $d_b c = b$ since $\{bc^*c\} = \frac{b}{2}$ and $\{cb^*c\} = 0$. The real-linear mapping $b \mapsto d_b$ decomposes into a complex-linear part

$$\partial_b := \frac{1}{2}(d_b - i\, d_{ib}) = 2b \square c^*$$

and a complex-antilinear part

$$\bar{\partial}_b := \frac{1}{2}(d_b + i\, d_{ib}) = -2c \square b^*.$$

It follows that q_+ (resp., q_-) corresponds to the holomorphic (resp., antiholomorphic) complex vector fields on S_j.

5.4.24. DEFINITION. The *Hardy space* $H^2(S_j)$ over S_j is defined as the closed subspace of all $\varphi \in L^2(S_j)$ (for the K-invariant probability measure) satisfying the *tangential Cauchy-Riemann equations*

$$\bar{\partial}_b \varphi = 0 \qquad \text{(as distributions)} \tag{5.4.25}$$

for all $b \in Z_{1/2}(c)$. Here $\bar{\partial}_b$ is the corresponding right-invariant complex vector field. Let

$$E^{S_j} : L^2(S_j) \to H^2(S_j) \tag{5.4.26}$$

denote the orthogonal projection.

5.4.27. PROPOSITION. *The map*

$$\tau(S_1)f := E^{S_1}\, f\, E^{S_1} \qquad (f \in \mathcal{C}(S_1)) \tag{5.4.28}$$

induces a C^**-homomorphism*

$$\tau(S_1) : \mathcal{C}(S_1) \to \mathcal{L}(H^2(S_1))/\mathcal{K}(H^2(S_1)) \tag{5.4.29}$$

into the Calkin algebra of the Hardy space $H^2(S_1)$ *over* S_1.

Proof. For $r = 1$, (5.4.28) is the Toeplitz mapping. Now assume $r > 1$. By Proposition 5.4.11,

$$\Omega_1 := \Omega \cap \bar{S}_1^{\mathbb{C}} = \{z \in \bar{S}_1^{\mathbb{C}} : (z|z) < 1\} \tag{5.4.30}$$

is a strictly pseudoconvex domain in the algebraic variety $\bar{S}_1^{\mathbb{C}}$ which is singular at 0. Its boundary is

$$\partial\Omega_1 = \{z \in \bar{S}_1^{\mathbb{C}} : (z|z) = 1\} = S_1. \tag{5.4.31}$$

Moreover, the Hardy space $H^2(\partial\Omega_1)$, defined in terms of the tangential Cauchy-Riemann equations (cf. (2.2.12)), coincides with the space

$H^2(S_1)$ defined in Definition 5.4.24. Thus Theorem 4.2.24 implies that the operators (5.4.28) commute modulo the compact operators on $H^2(S_1)$.
Q.E.D.

Since S_1 is a strictly pseudoconvex boundary, the C^*-extension (5.4.29) has an index mapping [B5]

$$\text{Ind}^{S_1}(F) := \text{Index } I + (E^{S_1}(F_{hk} - \delta_{hk})E^{S_1}) \tag{5.4.32}$$

for $F = (F_{hk}) \in K^1(S_1)$.

5.4.33. THEOREM. *For every* $F \in K^1(S_1)$ *we have*

$$\text{Ind}_1^S(F) = \text{Ind}^{S_1}(F). \tag{5.4.34}$$

Proof. Consider the orthogonal projection E_1^S onto the closed subspace $H_1^2(S)$. For every $f \in \mathcal{C}(\bar{\Omega})$, the operator

$$E_1^S\, f\, E_1^S = E_1^S\, T_S(f)\, E_1^S \in \mathcal{T}(S) \tag{5.4.35}$$

has the symbol

$$\sigma_c(E_1^S\, f\, E_1^S) = \sigma_c(E_1^S)\, \sigma_c(T_S(f))\, \sigma_c(E_1^S) = E_0^{S_c}\, T_{S_c}(f_c)\, E_0^{S_c}$$

$$= (1_c \otimes 1_c)\, T_{S_c}(f_c)\, (1_c \otimes 1_c) = (1_c \otimes 1_c)\, (T_{S_c}(f_c)1_c \otimes 1_c)$$

$$= (1_c \mid T_{S_c}(f_c)1_c)\, 1_c \otimes 1_c = f(c)1_c \otimes 1_c$$

at $c \in S_1$, according to Proposition 5.4.17. It follows that

$$\sigma_1(E_1^S\, f\, E_1^S) = f|_{S_1}$$

for all $f \in \mathcal{C}(\bar{\Omega})$, so that

$$E_1^S\, f\, E_1^S \in \mathcal{K}(H^2(S)) \cap \mathcal{Z}(H_1^2(S)) = \mathcal{K}(H_1^2(S))$$

whenever f vanishes on S_1. Therefore there exists a C^*-algebra homomorphism

$$\mathcal{C}(S_1) \to \mathcal{L}(H_1^2(S))/\mathcal{K}(H_1^2(S)), \quad f \mapsto E_1^S \tilde{f} E_1^S \tag{5.4.36}$$

into the Calkin algebra, where $\tilde{f} \in \mathcal{C}(\bar{\Omega})$ is any extension of f. Moreover,

$$\sigma_1(E_1^S \tilde{f} E_1^S) = f = \sigma_1 \tau_1 f$$

which implies

$$E_1^S \tilde{f} E_1^S - \tau_1 f \in \mathcal{K}(H^2(S)).$$

It follows that

$$\mathrm{Ind}_1^S(F) = \mathrm{Index}(I + (E_1^S(\tilde{F}_{hk} - \delta_{hk})E_1^S)). \tag{5.4.37}$$

By [U8; Theorem 1.7], there exists a Hilbert space isomorphism $U : H_1^2(S) \xrightarrow[\approx]{} H^2(S_1)$ which maps $p \in \mathcal{P}^{m0\cdots 0}(Z)$ to

$$Up := \Lambda_m \, p|_{S_1} \tag{5.4.38}$$

where Λ_m is a constant defined by

$$(p|p)_S = \Lambda_m^2 \, (p|p)_{S_1}$$

for all $p \in \mathcal{P}^{m0\cdots 0}(Z)$. In order to compute Λ_m, let $p(z) = \Delta_{m0\ldots0}(z) = (z|e_1)^m$ be the conical polynomial. By Example 2.8.25, we have

$$(\Delta_m|\Delta_m)_S = \frac{m!}{(n/r)_m}$$

and therefore

$$\frac{(\Delta_{m+1}|\Delta_{m+1})_S}{(\Delta_m|\Delta_m)_S} = \frac{m+1}{\frac{n}{r}+m} \to 1 \tag{5.4.39}$$

as $m \to \infty$. On the other hand, Δ_m is the unique element in

$$\mathcal{P}^m(S_1) := \mathcal{P}^{m0\cdots 0}(Z)|_{S_1}$$

which is invariant under $L_1 := \{s \in K: e_1 \cdot s = e_1\}$ and satisfies $\Delta_m(e_1) = 1$. This follows from Frobenius reciprocity

$$\frac{K \ltimes L^2(S_1)}{K \ltimes \mathcal{P}^m(S_1)} = \frac{L_1 \ltimes \mathcal{P}^m(S_1)}{L_1 \ltimes \mathbb{C}}, \tag{5.4.40}$$

since the irreducible K-module $\mathcal{P}^m(S_1)$ occurs only once in $L^2(S_1)$ by [U8; Theorem 1.7]. (In (5.4.40), $\frac{\pi}{\sigma}$ denotes the multiplicity of a representation σ in a representation π of the same group). Therefore

$$(\Delta_m|\Delta_m)_{S_1} = \dim \mathcal{P}^m(S_1)^{-1} = \dim \mathcal{P}^{m0\cdots 0}(Z)^{-1}$$

and the known dimension formula [U4] yields for $m \to \infty$

$$\frac{(\Delta_{m+1}|\Delta_{m+1})_{S_1}}{(\Delta_m|\Delta_m)_{S_1}} \to 1.$$

Comparing with (5.4.39), we obtain

$$\lim_{m\to\infty} \frac{\Lambda_{m+1}}{\Lambda_m} = 1. \tag{5.4.41}$$

We will now show that

$$E_1^S \tilde{f} E_1^S - U^* E^{S_1} f E^{S_1} U \in \mathcal{K}(H_1^2(S)) \tag{5.4.42}$$

whenever $f \in \mathcal{C}(S_1)$. Equivalently, there is a commuting diagram

$$\begin{array}{ccc} & \nearrow & \mathcal{L}(H_1^2(S))/\mathcal{K}(H_1^2(S)) \\ \mathcal{C}(S_1) & & \big\downarrow \approx \ \mathrm{Ad}(U) \\ & \searrow & \mathcal{L}(H^2(S_1))/\mathcal{K}(H^2(S_1)) \end{array} \tag{5.4.43}$$

for the C^*-homomorphisms defined in (5.4.29) and (5.4.36), where we put $Ad(U)T := UTU^*$. In order to show (5.4.43), we may assume that $\tilde{f}(z) = (z|b)$, $b \in Z$, is linear. Then Theorem 4.11.86 implies $\tilde{f} \cdot p = q + h$ for all $p \in \mathcal{P}^{m0\cdots0}(Z)$, where $q \in \mathcal{P}^{m+1,0,\cdots,0}(Z)$ and $h \in \mathcal{P}^{m,1,0\cdots0}(Z)$. We have $h|_{S_1} = 0$ and hence

$$(E^{S_1} f E^{S_1})Up = \Lambda_m(E^{S_1} f E^{S_1}p|_{S_1}) = \Lambda_m E^{S_1}q|_{S_1} = \Lambda_m \cdot q|_{S_1},$$

whereas

$$U E_1^S \tilde{f} E_1^S p = U E_1^S(\tilde{f}p) = U E_1^S(q + h) = Uq = \Lambda_{m+1} \cdot q|_{S_1}.$$

It follows that

$$K_f := E_1^S \tilde{f} E_1^S - U^* E^{S_1} f E^{S_1} U = \sum_m (1 - \frac{\Lambda_m}{\Lambda_{m+1}})P_{m+1} \tilde{f} P_m,$$

where $P_m : H_1^2(S) \to \mathcal{P}^{m0\cdots0}(Z)$ is the orthogonal projection. Since K_f is compact by (5.4.41), the assertion (5.4.42) follows. Applying (5.4.42) to (F_{hk}), we obtain

$$\text{(5.4.44)} \qquad \text{Index } I + (E_1^S(\tilde{F}_{hk} - \delta_{hk})E_1^S) = \text{Index } I + (E^{S_1}(F_{hk} - \delta_{hk})E^{S_1}).$$

Combining (5.4.37) and (5.4.44), the assertion follows. Q.E.D.

We now pass to the general case $1 \le j \le r$. By Theorem 4.11.133, there is a C^*-extension

$$\text{(5.4.45)} \qquad 0 \leftarrow \mathcal{K}(\mathcal{E}_j) \xleftarrow{\sigma_j} \mathcal{J}_{j+1}/\mathcal{J}_{j-1} \leftarrow \mathcal{J}_j/\mathcal{J}_{j-1} \leftarrow 0$$

whose Busby invariant is the C^*-homomorphism

$$\text{(5.4.46)} \qquad \tau_j(S) : \mathcal{C}(S_j) \to \overline{\mathcal{K}(\mathcal{E}_{j-1})} / \mathcal{K}(\mathcal{E}_{j-1})$$

into the outer multiplier algebra, obtained as the composition

$$\mathcal{C}(S_j) \to \mathcal{K}(\mathcal{E}_j) \xrightarrow{\tau_j} \mathcal{J}_{j+1}/\mathcal{J}_{j-1} \subset \overline{\mathcal{J}_j/\mathcal{J}_{j-1}} \xrightarrow[\approx]{\overline{\sigma_{j-1}}} \overline{\mathcal{K}(\mathcal{E}_{j-1})} \to \overline{\mathcal{K}(\mathcal{E}_{j-1})}/\mathcal{K}(\mathcal{E}_{j-1}).$$

Here τ_j is any completely positive cross-section of σ_j. By [R5; Theorem 4.9], the embedding (5.4.46) induces K-theory isomorphisms

(5.4.47) $$K^{\cdot}(S_j) = K_{\cdot}(\mathcal{C}(S_j)) \xrightarrow[\approx]{} K_{\cdot}(\mathcal{K}(\mathcal{E}_j)).$$

5.4.48. DEFINITION. The C^*-algebra extension

(5.4.49) $$[\tau_j(S)] \in KK^1(\mathcal{C}(S_j), \mathcal{K}(\mathcal{E}_{j-1}))$$

defined by the exact sequence (5.4.45) or the Busby invariant (5.4.46) is called the j-*th Hardy-Toeplitz extension* over S.

Applying the Kasparov product [B2] and the identification (5.4.47) (for j and j - 1) we obtain a homomorphism

(5.4.50) $$\mathrm{Ind}_j : K^1(S_j) \longrightarrow K^0(S_{j-1}), \ [F] \mapsto [\tau_j(S)] \otimes [F]$$

called the *j-th analytic Hardy-Toeplitz index* over S. For $j = 1$, we have $K^0(S_{j-1}) = \mathbb{Z}$ since $S_0 = \{0\}$, and

$$\mathrm{Ind}_1 : K^1(S_1) \longrightarrow \mathbb{Z}$$

is the index homomorphism studied above, corresponding to the *first Hardy-Toeplitz extension*

(5.4.51) $$[\tau_1(S)] \in KK^1(\mathcal{C}(S_1), \mathbb{C})$$

over S. In order to describe the analytic index (5.4.50) in terms of Fredholm theory, we need the following concept:

5.4.52. DEFINITION. An operator $A \in \mathcal{T}(S)$ is called *j-Fredholm* if it is invertible modulo $\mathcal{J}_j$, i.e., in the quotient algebra $\mathcal{T}(S)/\mathcal{J}_j$.

Since $\mathcal{J}_1 = \mathcal{K}(H^2(S))$ by Proposition 4.11.117, 1-Fredholm is the same as Fredholm. The notion of j-Fredholm operator makes also sense in the matrix algebra $\mathcal{T}(S)^{N\times N}$, acting on $H^2(S,\mathbb{C}^N)$.

5.4.53. PROPOSITION. *Let* $A \in \mathcal{T}(S)$ *be a j-Fredholm operator. Then*

(5.4.54) $$\sigma_{j-1}(A) := (\sigma_c(A))_{c \in S_{j-1}}$$

is a continuous field of Fredholm operators on $\mathcal{E}_{j-1}$.

Proof. By assumption, there exists $B \in \mathcal{T}(S)$ such that

(5.4.55) $$\sigma_j(AB) = I = \sigma_j(BA).$$

Now fix $c \in S_{j-1}$ and let $a \in S_1 \cap Z_0(c)$ be arbitrary. Then $a + c \in S_j$, and (5.4.55) implies

$$\sigma_a(\sigma_c(AB)) = \sigma_{a+c}(AB) = I_{a+c} = \sigma_a(I_c)$$

where I denotes the identity operators. Thus

$$\sigma_c(AB) - I_c \in \bigcap_{a \in S_1 \cap Z_0(c)} \operatorname{Ker} \sigma_a = \mathcal{K}(H^2(S_c))$$

according to Proposition 4.11.117, applied to Ω_c. Similarly, $\sigma_c(BA) - I_c \in \mathcal{K}(H^2(S_c))$. Thus $\sigma_c(A)$ is a Fredholm operator. Q.E.D.

By [A1], every continuous field (T_x) of Fredholm operators on a compact space X has a "family" index in $K^0(X)$, and every element in $K^0(X)$ can be obtained this way. In case the vector spaces $\operatorname{Ker} T_x$ and $\operatorname{Ker} T_x^*$ have (finite) dimension independent of $x \in X$, we can write

(5.4.56) $$\operatorname{Index}_X(T_x) := \{\operatorname{Ker} T_x\} - \{\operatorname{Ker} T_x^*\} \in K^0(X)$$

as a formal difference of topological vector bundles over X. Applied to (5.4.54), we obtain a family index

(5.4.57) $$\operatorname{Index}_{S_{j-1}} \sigma_{j-1}(A) \in K^0(S_{j-1})$$

for every j-Fredholm operator $A \in \mathcal{T}(S)$. Every element in $K^1(S_j)$ can be realized as (the homotopy class of) a continuous matrix function

(5.4.58) $$F = (F_{hk}) : S_j \to U_N(\mathbb{C})$$ (unitary group)

for some N. Choose a cross-section τ_j of σ_j.

5.4.59. PROPOSITION. *The operator N×N-matrix*

(5.4.60) $$I + (\tau_j(F_{hk} - \delta_{hk}))$$

defines a j-Fredholm operator in $\mathcal{T}(S)^{N\times N} \subset \mathcal{L}(H^2(S,\mathbb{C}^N))$.

Proof. Taking N×N-matrices, (5.4.45) yields an exact sequence

$$0 \leftarrow \mathcal{K}(\mathcal{E}_j \otimes \mathbb{C}^N) \xleftarrow{\sigma_j^{N\times N}} \mathcal{J}_{j+1}^{N\times N} \leftarrow \mathcal{J}_j^{N\times N} \leftarrow 0.$$

The operator matrix (5.4.60) belongs to the unitization of $\mathcal{J}_{j+1}^{N\times N}$ (in case $j = r$, $\mathcal{J}_{j+1} = \mathcal{T}(S)$ is unital) and satisfies

$$\sigma_j^{N\times N}(I + (\tau_j(F_{hk} - \delta_{hk}))) = I + (\sigma_j\tau_j(F_{hk} - \delta_{hk})) = I + (F_{hk} - \delta_{hk}) = \begin{pmatrix} F & 0 \\ 0 & I \end{pmatrix}$$

in the unitization of $\mathcal{K}(\mathcal{E}_j \otimes \mathbb{C}^N)$. (In case $j = r$, $\mathcal{K}(\mathcal{E}_j \otimes \mathbb{C}^N) = \mathcal{C}(S,\mathbb{C}^{N\times N})$ is unital.) Since F is invertible, the assertion follows. Q.E.D.

By analyzing the Kasparov product one can show that

(5.4.61) $$\mathrm{Ind}_j^S(F) = \mathrm{Index}_{S_{j-1}}\, I + (\sigma_{j-1}\tau_j(F_{hk} - \delta_{hk})) \in K^0(S_{j-1})$$

agrees with the family index of the continuous field of Fredholm operators over S_{j-1} associated with the j-Fredholm operators in $\mathcal{T}(S)^{N\times N}$ defined in (5.4.60). It is clear that (5.4.61) does not depend on the choice of cross-section τ_j, since another cross-section $\tilde{\tau}_j$ differs only by elements in $\mathcal{J}_j$ which are mapped into compact operators by σ_{j-1}. Also, (5.4.61) depends only on the homotopy class of F.

5.4.62. EXAMPLE. For $j = r$, the analytic index

$$\mathrm{Ind}_r : K^1(S) \to K^0(S_{r-1})$$

can be directly described in terms of Toeplitz operators. Given a continuous mapping $F = (F_{hk}) : S \to GL_N(\mathbb{C})$, we form the matrix Toeplitz operator

$$T_S(F_{hk}) \in \mathcal{T}(S)^{N\times N}$$

which is an r-Fredholm operator in the sense of Definition 5.4.52. Then

$$\text{(5.4.63)} \qquad \mathrm{Ind}_r(F) = \mathrm{Index}_{S_{r-1}}(\sigma_{r-1}T_S(F_{hk})) \in K^0(S_{r-1}).$$

Thus the "Toeplitz map" plays precisely the role of the cross-section in the previous construction.

5.4.64. EXAMPLE. For $j = 1$, the analytic index

$$\mathrm{Ind}_1 : K^1(S_1) \to K^0(S_0) = \mathbb{Z}$$

is integer-valued, but the relevant Fredholm operators are not of Toeplitz type if $r > 1$.

We will prove the index theorem for the higher indices Ind_j^S by comparing the j-th Hardy-Toeplitz extension $\tau_j(S)$ over S with another extension related to a family of strictly pseudoconvex boundaries. For each $c \in S_{j-1}$, the space

$$S_1^c := S_j \cap Z_0(c)$$

consists of all minimal tripotents in $Z_0(c)$. The "partial" Hardy spaces (cf. Definition 5.4.24) in $Z_0(c)$ define a continuous bundle of Hilbert spaces

$$\text{(5.4.65)} \qquad \mathcal{F}_{j-1} := \{H^2(S_1^c)\}_{c\in S_{j-1}}$$

over S_{j-1}. Viewing $\mathcal{F}_{j-1}$ as a Hilbert module over $\mathcal{C}(S_{j-1})$, let

$$\mathcal{K}(\mathcal{F}_{j-1}) = \int_{c\in S_{j-1}}^{\oplus} \mathcal{K}(H^2(S_1^c))$$

denote the corresponding C^*-algebra of "compact" endomorphisms. Let

(5.4.66) $$E^{S_1^c} : L^2(S_1^c) \to H^2(S_1^c)$$

denote the orthogonal projection.

5.4.67. PROPOSITION. *The map*

(5.4.68) $$\tau(S_j)f := \{E^{S_1^c} f_c E^{S_1^c}\}_{c \in S_{j-1}} \qquad (f \in \mathcal{C}(S_j))$$

induces a C^**-homomorphism*

(5.4.69) $$\tau(S_j) : \mathcal{C}(S_j) \to \overline{\mathcal{K}(\mathcal{F}_{j-1})} / \mathcal{K}(\mathcal{F}_{j-1})$$

into the outer multiplier algebra. Here $f_c(w) := f(c + w)$ *for all* $w \in S_1^c$.

Proof. For every $c \in S_{j-1}$, S_1^c is the Shilov boundary of a strictly pseudoconvex (singular) domain in $Z_0(c)$ according to (5.4.31). It follows from Theorem 4.2.24 that for any $\varphi, \psi \in \mathcal{C}(S_j)$, the commutator

(5.4.70) $$[E^{S_1^c} \varphi_c E^{S_1^c}, E^{S_1^c} \psi_c E^{S_1^c}] \in \mathcal{K}(H^2(S_1^c))$$

is compact. Using the fact that S_{j-1} is homogeneous under K, one shows [U8; Lemma 3.5] that the operator fields (5.4.68) and (5.4.70) depend in a *-strongly continuous (resp., norm continuous) way on $c \in S_{j-1}$. Now apply [D1; Theorem 10.5.4 and Lemma 10.7.6] and [U8; Corollary 3.5]. Q.E.D.

5.4.71. DEFINITION. The C^*-algebra extension

(5.4.72) $$[\tau(S_j)] \in KK^1(\mathcal{C}(S_j), \mathcal{K}(\mathcal{F}_{j-1}))$$

with Busby invariant (5.4.69) is called the *Hardy-Toeplitz extension* over S_j.

The C^*-extension (5.4.72) induces an index homomorphism

$$\mathrm{Ind}^{S_j} : K^1(S_j) \to K^0(S_{j-1})$$

which is defined as the family index [A1]

(5.4.73) $\quad \mathrm{Ind}^{S_j}(F) := \mathrm{Index}_{S_{j-1}}(I + (E^{S_1^c}(F_{hk} - \delta_{hk})_c\, E^{S_1^c}))_{c\in S_{j-1}}$

over S_{j-1}, for any $F = (F_{hk}) \in K^1(S_j)$.

5.4.74. THEOREM. *The extensions* $\tau_j(S)$ *and* $\tau(S_j)$ *in* $KK^1(\mathcal{C}(S_j), \mathcal{C}(S_{j-1}))$ *are stably equivalent, and thus induce the same index homomorphism.*

Proof. For each $c \in S_{j-1}$, consider the orthogonal projection

$$E_1^{S_c} : H^2(S_c) \to H_1^2(S_c).$$

For every $f \in \mathcal{C}(\bar{\Omega})$, the operator

$$E_1^{S_c} f_c\, E_1^{S_c} = E_1^{S_c}\, T_{S_c}(f_c)\, E_1^{S_c} \in \mathcal{T}(S_c)$$

has the symbol

$$\sigma_a(E_1^{S_c} f_c\, E_1^{S_c}) = \sigma_a(E_1^{S_c})\, \sigma_a(T_{S_c}(f_c))\, \sigma_a(E_1^{S_c}) = E_0^{S_{c+a}}\, T_{S_{c+a}}(f_{c+a})\, E_0^{S_{c+a}}$$

$$= 1_{c+a} \otimes 1_{c+a}\ T_{S_{c+a}}(f_{c+a})\ 1_{c+a} \otimes 1_{c+a} = f(c+a)1_{c+a} \otimes 1_{c+a}$$

at $a \in S_1^c$, according to Proposition 5.4.17. It follows that

$$\sigma_1^c(E_1^{S_c} f_c\, E_1^{S_c}) = f|_{S_1^c}$$

for all $f \in \mathcal{C}(\bar{\Omega})$, so that

$$E_1^{S_c} f_c\, E_1^{S_c} \in \mathcal{K}(H_1^2(S_c))$$

for any $c \in S_{j-1}$ whenever f vanishes on S_j. Therefore there exists a C^*-algebra homomorphism

(5.4.75) $\quad \check{\tau}_j(S) : \mathcal{C}(S_j) \to \overline{\mathcal{K}(\check{\mathcal{E}}_{j-1})} / \mathcal{K}(\check{\mathcal{E}}_{j-1}),\ f \mapsto (E_1^{S_c}\, \tilde{f}_c\, E_1^{S_c})_{c\in S_{j-1}}$

into the outer multiplier algebra, where $\tilde{f} \in \mathcal{C}(\bar{\Omega})$ is any extension of f. Here

$$\check{\mathcal{E}}_{j-1} := (H_1^2(S_c))_{c \in S_{j-1}}$$

is a continuous bundle of Hilbert spaces over S_{j-1}. Since

$$\sigma_1^c(E_1^{S_c}\, \tilde{f}_c\, E_1^{S_c}) = f|_{S_1^c} = \sigma_1^c(\sigma_{j-1}\tau_j f)$$

for all $c \in S_{j-1}$, it follows that

$$(E_1^{S_c}\, \tilde{f}_c\, E_1^{S_c})_{c \in S_{j-1}} - \sigma_{j-1}(\tau_j f) \in \mathcal{K}(\mathcal{E}_{j-1})$$

and therefore

$$\mathrm{Ind}_j^S(F) = \mathrm{Index}_{S_{j-1}}\, I + (E_1^{S_c}((\tilde{F}_{hk})_c - \delta_{hk})E_1^{S_c})_{c \in S_{j-1}}.$$

For each $c \in S_{j-1}$, there exists a Hilbert space isomorphism

$$H_1^2(S_c) \xrightarrow[\approx]{U_c} H^2(S_1^c)$$

which maps $p \in \mathcal{P}^{m0\cdots0}(Z_0(c))$ (signature of length $r - j$) to

$$U_c p := \lambda_m\, p|_{S_1^c}$$

where λ_m is a constant independent of c defined by

$$(p|p)_{S_c} = \lambda_m^2 (p|p)_{S_1^c}$$

for all $p \in \mathcal{P}^{m0\cdots0}(Z_0(c))$. Using covariance under the transitive group K, it follows that

$$U_{j-1} := (U_c)_{c \in S_{j-1}} : \check{\mathcal{E}}_{j-1} \to \mathcal{F}_{j-1}$$

defines an isometric isomorphism of Hilbert $\mathcal{C}(S_{j-1})$-modules. Applying (5.4.41) to $Z_0(c)$ it follows that

$$\lim_{m\to\infty} \frac{\lambda_{m+1}}{\lambda_m} = 1. \tag{5.4.76}$$

We will now show that

$$(E_1^{S_c}\,\tilde{f}_c\,E_1^{S_c})_{c\in S_{j-1}} - U_{j-1}^*(E^{S_1^c}\,f_c\,E^{S_1^c})_{c\in S_{j-1}}\,U_{j-1} \in \mathcal{K}(\check{\mathcal{E}}_{j-1}) \tag{5.4.77}$$

whenever $f \in \mathcal{C}(S_j)$. Equivalently, there is a commuting diagram

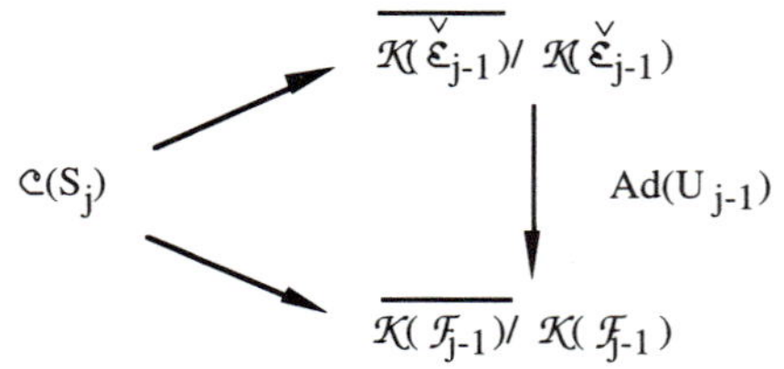

for the C^*-homomorphisms (5.4.75) and (5.4.69), where $Ad(U_{j-1})T := U_{j-1}TU_{j-1}^*$. In order to show (5.4.77), we may assume that $\tilde{f}(z) = (z|b)$, $b \in Z$, is linear. Applying Theorem 4.11.86 to $Z_0(c)$, we obtain $\tilde{f}_c \cdot p = (c|b)p + q + h$ for all $p \in \mathcal{P}^{m0\cdots0}(Z_0(c))$, where $q \in \mathcal{P}^{m+1,0\cdots0}(Z_0(c))$ and $h \in \mathcal{P}^{m,1,0\cdots0}(Z_0(c))$. We have $h|_{S_1^c} = 0$ which implies

$$(E^{S_1^c}\,f_c\,E^{S_1^c})U_c p = \lambda_m(E^{S_1^c}\,f_c\,E^{S_1^c})\,p|_{S_1^c} = \lambda_m\,E^{S_1^c}(f_c \cdot p|_{S_1^c})$$
$$= \lambda_m\,E^{S_1^c}((c|b)\cdot p|_{S_1^c} + q|_{S_1^c}) = \lambda_m((c|b)\cdot p|_{S_1^c} + q|_{S_1^c})$$

whereas

$$U_c\,E_1^{S_c}\,\tilde{f}_c\,E_1^{S_c}p = U_c\,E_1^{S_c}(\tilde{f}_c p) = U_c\,E_1^{S_c}((c|b)p + q + h)$$
$$= U_c((c|b)p + q) = \lambda_m(c|b)\cdot p|_{S_1^c} + \lambda_{m+1}\cdot q|_{S_1^c}.$$

It follows that

$$K_f^c := (E_1^{S_c}\,\tilde{f}_c\,E_1^{S_c})_{c\in S_{j-1}} - U_c^*\,(E^{S_1^c}\,f_c\,E^{S_1^c})_{c\in S_{j-1}}\,U_c = \sum_m \left(1 - \frac{\lambda_m}{\lambda_{m+1}}\right) P_{m+1}^c\,\tilde{f}_c\,P_m^c,$$

where $P_m^c : H_1^2(S_c) \to \mathcal{P}^{m0\cdots0}(Z_0(c))$ is the orthogonal projection. Since (5.4.76) implies

$$K_f := (K_f^c)_{c \in S_{j-1}} \in \mathcal{K}(\check{\mathcal{E}}_{j-1}),$$

the assertion (5.4.77) follows. It follows that

$$\mathrm{Index}_{S_{j-1}}\, I + (E_1^{S_c}\, (\tilde{F}_{hk} - \delta_{hk})_c\, E_1^{S_c})_{c \in S_{j-1}}$$

$$= \mathrm{Index}_{S_{j-1}}\, I + (E^{S_1^c}\, (F_{hk} - \delta_{hk})_c\, E^{S_1^c})_{c \in S_{j-1}}.$$

Q.E.D.

We will now express the analytic Hardy-Toeplitz indices Ind_j^S over S in topological terms, starting with the basic case $j = 1$. As a strictly pseudoconvex boundary, S_1 has a K-theoretic index character

$$\chi_{S_1} : K^1(S_1) \to \mathbb{Z}.$$

Combining Theorem 5.4.33 and Theorem 5.2.10, we obtain the *K-theoretic index formula*

(5.4.79) $$\mathrm{Ind}_1^S(F) = \chi_{S_1}(F)$$

for all $F \in K^1(S_1)$. Realizing F as a continuous matrix function

$$F = (F_{hk}) : S_1 \to U_N(\mathbb{C})$$

we consider the *generators* $h_1, \ldots, h_N$ of the exterior cohomology algebra $H^*(U_N(\mathbb{C}), \mathbb{Q})$ [B4; p. 601]. Then the *odd Chern character*

$$\mathrm{ch} : K^1(X) \to H^*(X,\mathbb{Q})$$

for any compact space X has the form

(5.4.80) $$\mathrm{ch}(F) = \sum_{k \geq 1} \frac{-1}{(k-1)!}\, F^* h_k$$

where $F^* h_k$ is the pull back of h_k under the matrix function $F : X \to U_N(\mathbb{C})$ [U8; Lemma 4.4].

5.4.81. THEOREM. *For every* $F \in K^1(S_1)$ *we have*

$$\begin{aligned} \operatorname{Ind}_1^S(F) &= ch(F) \cdot Td(T_{\mathbb{C}}(S_1))[S_1] \\ &= \sum_{k\geq 1} \frac{-1}{(k-1)!} F^* h_k \cdot Td(T_{\mathbb{C}}(S_1))[S_1]. \end{aligned} \tag{5.4.82}$$

Here $Td(T_{\mathbb{C}}(S_1))$ *is the Todd class of the holomorphic tangent bundle*

$$T_{\mathbb{C}}(S_1) = \bigcup_{c \in S_1} Z_{1/2}(c) \times \{c\} \tag{5.4.83}$$

of S_1 (cf. (5.4.22)).

Proof. The contact form θ on S_1, regarded as the boundary of $\Omega \cap S_1^{\mathbb{C}}$, is given by $\theta_c v := \operatorname{Im}(v|c)$. By [B5; (1.2)], this form generates a half-line bundle

$$\Sigma \approx S_1^{\mathbb{C}}, \quad (t\theta_c, c) \mapsto \sqrt{2t}\, c \tag{5.4.84}$$

for $t > 0$. Endowing $S_1^{\mathbb{C}}$ with the "positive" 1-form $\tilde{\theta}_z v := \frac{1}{2} \operatorname{Im}(v|z)$, the mapping (5.4.84) becomes a symplectic isomorphism, so that the inherited complex structure on Σ is positive [B5; §2.h]. Let $p : \Sigma \to S_1$ be the projection. Then the complex tangent bundle of Σ is $T\Sigma = p^*(T_{\mathbb{C}}(S_1) \oplus L)$, where

$$L := \bigcup_{c \in S_1} \mathbb{C}c \times \{c\}$$

is a trivial line bundle. With the connecting homomorphism

$$\begin{array}{ccc} K^1(S_1) & \xrightarrow{\ \partial\ } & K_c^0(\Sigma) \\ {\scriptstyle ch}\downarrow & & \downarrow{\scriptstyle ch} \\ H^*(S_1, \mathbb{Q}) & \xrightarrow[\ \delta\ ]{} & H_c^*(\Sigma, \mathbb{Q}) \end{array}$$

we obtain from Theorem 5.4.79 and Proposition 5.2.8

$$\mathrm{Ind}_1^S(F) = \chi_{S_1}(F) = \chi_\Sigma(\partial F) = \mathrm{ch}(\partial(F)) \cdot \mathrm{Td}(T\Sigma)[\Sigma] = \delta(\mathrm{ch}F)) \cdot \mathrm{Td}\,(T\Sigma)[\Sigma]$$

$$= \delta(\mathrm{ch}F \cdot \mathrm{Td}(T_{\mathbb{C}}(S_1)))[\Sigma] = \mathrm{ch}F \cdot \mathrm{Td}(T_{\mathbb{C}}(S_1))[S_1].$$

The expression (5.4.82) follows with (5.4.80). Q.E.D.

For $j \geq 1$ consider the compact K-homogeneous real analytic sphere bundle

(5.4.85)
$$\mathbb{S}(S_{j-1}) := \bigcup_{c \in S_{j-1}} S_1^c \times \{c\}$$

where each fibre

$$S_1^c := S_1 \cap \bar{\Omega}_c \approx \mathbb{S}^{2b+1}$$

is an oriented contact manifold, being a strictly pseudoconvex boundary in $Z_0(c)$. Therefore $\mathbb{S}(S_{j-1})$ has a K-theoretic family index character

$$\chi_{\mathbb{S}(S_{j-1})} : K^1(\mathbb{S}(S_{j-1})) \to K^0(S_{j-1}).$$

Define $\beta_j : \mathbb{S}(S_{j-1}) \to S_j$ by $(\zeta, c) \mapsto \zeta + c$. Geometrically, β_j realizes a maximal boundary component of Ω_c, $c \in S_{j-1}$, as a boundary component of Ω itself. This follows from the "transitivity" relation $(\Omega_c)_\zeta = \Omega_{c+\zeta}$ valid for $c \in S_{j-1}$ and $\zeta \in S_1^c$. Define

$$\chi_{S_j} := \chi_{\mathbb{S}(S_{j-1})} \circ \beta_j^* : K^1(S_j) \to K^0(S_{j-1}).$$

Combining Theorem 5.4.75 and Theorem 5.2.7, we obtain the *K-theoretic family index formula*

(5.4.86)
$$\mathrm{Ind}_j^S(F) = \chi_{S_j}(F)$$

for all $F \in K^1(S_j)$. For the *cohomological family index formula*, consider the complex vector bundle

(5.4.87) $$T_{\mathbb{C}}(\mathbb{S}(S_{j-1})) := \bigcup_{(\zeta,c)\in\mathbb{S}(S_{j-1})} (Z_{1/2}(\zeta) \cap Z_0(c)) \times \{(\zeta,c)\}$$

over $\mathbb{S}(S_{j-1})$, whose fibres are the holomorphic tangent spaces of S_1^c at $\zeta \in S_1^c$. Applying the proof of Theorem 5.4.81 to the manifolds S_1^c, we obtain the cohomological version:

5.4.88. THEOREM. *For every* $F \in K^1(S_j)$ *we have*

(5.4.89) $$\mathrm{ch}(\mathrm{Ind}_j^S(F)) = \pi_*(\mathrm{ch}(F \circ \beta_j)) \cdot \mathrm{Td}(T_{\mathbb{C}}(\mathbb{S}(S_{j-1}))).$$

Here $\pi : \mathbb{S}(S_{j-1}) \to S_{j-1}$ *is the projection and* π_* *denotes (cohomological) integration along the fibres of* π.

5.4.90. EXAMPLE. Let $\Omega = \{Z \in \mathbb{C}^n : (z|z) < 1\}$ denote the Hilbert ball of rank 1, with Shilov boundary $S = \mathbb{S}^{2n-1}$. Let $F = (F_{hk}) : \mathbb{S}^{2n-1} \to U_N(\mathbb{C})$ be a continuous matrix function. The *degree* of F [V2] has the expression

$$\deg(F) = \sum_{k\geq 1} \frac{(-1)^{k-1}}{(k-1)!} F^* h_k\, [\mathbb{S}^{2n-1}]$$

in terms of the generators $h_1, \ldots, h_N$ of $H^*(U_N(\mathbb{C}), \mathbb{Q})$. The holomorphic tangent bundle

$$T^{\mathbb{C}}(S) = \bigcup_{c\in S} Z_{1/2}(c) \times \{c\}$$

has trivial Todd class $\mathrm{Td}(T^{\mathbb{C}}(S)) = 1$ since the trivial line bundle

$$L := \bigcup_{c\in S} \mathbb{C}c \times \{c\}$$

satisfies $L \oplus T^{\mathbb{C}}(S) = \mathbb{C}^n \times S$. Since $r = 1$, we have $\mathcal{J}_2 = \mathcal{T}(S)$ and $f \mapsto T_S(f)$ is a completely positive cross-section of σ_1. Since $\deg h_k = 2k - 1$, Theorem 5.4.8 implies

$$\mathrm{Index}\ T_S(F_{hk}) = \mathrm{Ind}_1^S(F) = \mathrm{ch}(F)[S] = \frac{-1}{(n-1)!} F^* h_n[S] = (-1)^n \deg(F),$$

a formula due to Venugopalkrishna [V2]. In the special case $n = 1$, i.e., $S = \mathbb{T}$ we obtain Gohberg's index formula for Toeplitz operators on $H^2(\mathbb{T})$

$$\text{Index } T_{\mathbb{T}}(F_{hk}) = - \deg \text{Det}(F_{hk}),$$

where

$$\deg(f) = \frac{1}{2\pi i} \int_{\mathbb{T}} \frac{df}{f}$$

is the winding number of f.

Since the spaces $S_1, \ldots, S_r$ are homogeneous under the compact Lie group K, one may use the representation theory of K to express the analytic indices $\text{Ind}_1^S, \ldots, \text{Ind}_r^S$. We will now describe this approach for the highest index

$$\text{Ind}_r^S : K^1(S) \to K^0(S_{r-1}).$$

In this case the basic geometric object is the "Peirce 0-bundle"

$$Z^0 = \bigcup_{c \in S_{r-1}} Z_c^0 \times \{c\} \tag{5.4.91}$$

over S_{r-1}, where $Z_c^0 := Z_0(c)$ is the Peirce 0-space. In case Ω is irreducible, we have $\dim Z_c^0 = b + 1$ for all $c \in S_{r-1}$, where b is a characteristic multiplicity (1.5.41). In case Ω is of tube type, we have $b = 0$ and (5.4.91) is a (trivial) line bundle. Let $\pi : Z^0 \to S_{r-1}$ denote the canonical projection.

5.4.92. THEOREM. *Consider the sphere bundle*

$$\mathbb{S}(S_{r-1}) := \bigcup_{c \in S_{r-1}} S_c \times \{c\} \xrightarrow{\pi_{\mathbb{S}}} S_{r-1}$$

of Z^0 *and define* $\alpha : \mathbb{S}(S_{r-1}) \to S$ *by* $(\zeta, c) \mapsto \zeta + c$. *Then there exist representations* $\sigma, \tau : K \to U(E)$ *which induce an element* $\Phi = \sigma \backslash \tau \in K^1(S)$ *such that*

(5.4.93) $$\alpha^*F = \pi_{\mathbb{S}}^*F_1 + \pi_{\mathbb{S}}^*F_0 \otimes \alpha^*(\Phi)$$

for all $F \in K^1(S)$, *where* $F_1 \in K^1(S_{r-1})$ *and*

(5.4.94) $$F_0 = (-1)^{b+1}\ \mathrm{Ind}_r(F) \in K^0(S_{r-1})$$

are uniquely determined by F. *For the connecting map*

$$\partial : K^1(\mathbb{S}(S_{r-1})) \underset{\approx}{\longrightarrow} K_c^0(\tilde{Z}^0),$$

we have also

(5.4.95) $$\partial\alpha^*F = \pi^*F_0 \otimes \pi^*\ \overline{\Lambda^{b+1}Z^0} \otimes \beta(Z^0),$$

where $\beta(Z^0)$ *is the Bott element.*

Proof. Fix a base-point $(p,q) \in \mathbb{S}(S_{r-1})$, i.e., $q \in S_{r-1}$ and $p \in S_q$. Put $e := p + q$ and define $H := \{s \in K : q \cdot s = q\}$ and $L := \{s \in K : e \cdot s = e\}$. Using the classification of irreducible bounded symmetric domains one can construct representations (cf. [U6]) $\sigma^+, \sigma^- : K \to U(\tilde{E})$ satisfying the following properties:

(5.4.96) $$\sigma^+|_L = \sigma^-|_L;$$

(5.4.97) $\tilde{E}$ contains a subspace E invariant under $\sigma^{\pm}(H)$, such that there is a commuting diagram

$$\begin{array}{ccc} E & \xrightarrow{\ \sigma^{\pm}(\gamma)\ } & E \\ {\scriptstyle \tau_\pm}\uparrow & & \uparrow{\scriptstyle \tau_\pm} \\ \lambda^{\pm}(Z_q^0) & \xrightarrow[\ \lambda^{\pm}(\gamma)\ ]{} & \lambda^{\pm}(Z_q^0) \end{array}$$

for all $\gamma \in H$. Here $\tau_{\pm}$ are unitary, we put

$$\lambda^{\pm}(Z_q^0) := \overline{\Lambda^{b+1}Z_q^0} \otimes \Lambda^{\pm}(Z_q^0)$$

and define $\lambda^{\pm}(\gamma)$ as the corresponding representation;

(5.4.98) The diagram

$$\begin{array}{ccc} & E & \\ {\scriptstyle \tau_{\pm}}\nearrow & & \nwarrow{\scriptstyle \tau_{\mp}} \\ \lambda^{\pm}(Z_q^0) & \xrightarrow[\mathrm{id}\,\otimes\, d_p]{} & \lambda^{\mp}(Z_q^0) \end{array}$$

commutes, where d_p is the symmetry defined in (5.1.9).

(5.4.99) There is a homotopy $\sigma_\lambda \in U(E^\perp)$, $0 \le \lambda \le 1$, commuting with $\sigma^{\pm}(H \cap L)$ such that $\sigma_0 = \mathrm{id}$ and σ_1 yields, for every $\gamma \in H$, a commuting diagram

$$\begin{array}{ccc} E^\perp & \xrightarrow{\sigma^-(\gamma)} & E^\perp \\ {\scriptstyle \sigma_1}\uparrow & & \uparrow{\scriptstyle \sigma_1} \\ E^\perp & \xrightarrow[\sigma^+(\gamma)]{} & E^\perp \end{array}$$

Using (5.4.96), we define $\Phi = \sigma^+\backslash\sigma- : S \to U(\tilde{E})$ by putting

$$\Phi(es) := \sigma^+(s)^* \, \sigma^-(s)$$

for all $s \in K$. We will first compute the r-index of $[\Phi] \in K^1(S)$. Define a homotopy $\sigma_\lambda^0 \in \mathrm{Hom}(K, U(\tilde{E}))$, for $0 \le \lambda \le 1$, by putting

$$\sigma_\lambda^+(s) := \begin{bmatrix} \mathrm{id}_E & 0 \\ 0 & \sigma_\lambda \end{bmatrix} \sigma^+(s) \begin{bmatrix} \mathrm{id}_E & 0 \\ 0 & \sigma_\lambda^* \end{bmatrix}$$

for all $s \in K$. Then $\sigma_0^+(s) = \sigma^+(s)$ and

$$\sigma_1^+(\gamma) = \begin{bmatrix} 1 & 0 \\ 0 & \sigma_1 \end{bmatrix} \sigma^+(\gamma) \begin{bmatrix} 1 & 0 \\ 0 & \sigma_1^* \end{bmatrix} = \begin{bmatrix} \sigma^+(\gamma) & 0 \\ 0 & \sigma^-(\gamma) \end{bmatrix} \tag{5.4.100}$$

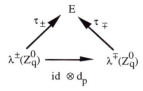

for all $\gamma \in H$. Since $\sigma_\lambda^+|_{H\cap L} = \sigma^-|_{H\cap L}$ by (5.4.99) and (5.4.96), we may define $\Phi_\lambda := \sigma_\lambda^+\backslash\sigma^- : \mathbb{S}(S_{r-1}) \to U(E)$ by putting

$$\Phi_\lambda((p,q) \cdot s) := \sigma_\lambda^+(s)^* \, \sigma^-(s)$$

for all $s \in K$. Then $\Phi_0 = \Phi \circ \alpha$. For $\gamma \in H$ and $\zeta = p \cdot \gamma$, we have by (5.4.100)

$$\Phi_1(\zeta,q) = \Phi_1((p,q) \cdot \gamma) = \sigma_1^+(\gamma)^* \, \sigma^-(\gamma) = \begin{bmatrix} \sigma^+(\gamma)^*\sigma^-(\gamma) & 0 \\ 0 & \mathrm{id} \end{bmatrix},$$

and (5.4.98) implies

$$\tau_+^* \, \sigma^+(\gamma)^* \, \sigma^-(\gamma) \, \tau_- = \lambda^+(\gamma)^* \, \tau_+^* \tau_- \, \lambda^-(\gamma) = \lambda^+(\gamma)^* \, (\mathrm{id} \otimes d_p) \, \lambda^-(\gamma)$$

(5.4.101) $$= \mathrm{id} \otimes d_{p\cdot\gamma} = \mathrm{id} \otimes d_\zeta.$$

Now consider the (matrix symbol) Toeplitz operator

$$T_c := T_{S_c}(\Phi_1(\_,c)) \in \mathcal{T}(S_c) \otimes \mathcal{L}(\tilde{E}) \subset \mathcal{L}(H^2(S_c,\tilde{E}))$$

over $S_c \approx \mathbb{S}^{2b+1}$, where $c = q \cdot s \in S_{r-1}$ and $s \in K$. Suppose first that $b+1$ is even. Then $\overline{\Lambda^{b+1}Z_q^0} \otimes \Lambda^{b+1}Z_q^0 \subset \lambda^+(Z_q^0)$, and [V2; Theorem 5.8] together with (5.4.101) imply

(5.4.102) $$\mathrm{Ker}\ T_q = \tau_+(\overline{\Lambda^{b+1}Z_q^0} \otimes \Lambda^{b+1}Z_q^0)$$

and $\mathrm{Ker}\ T_q^* = \{0\}$. Since $s : \Omega_q \to \Omega_c$ is biholomorphic and (5.4.102) consists of constant $\tilde{E}$-valued functions (independent of $\zeta \in S_q$), the covariance property

$$\Phi_1((\zeta,q) \cdot s) = \sigma_1^+(s)^* \, \Phi_1(\zeta,q) \, \sigma^-(s)$$

(cf. (5.1.30)) implies that

$$\mathrm{Ker}\ T_c = \sigma_1^+(s)(\mathrm{Ker}\ T_q)$$

and $\operatorname{Ker} T_c^* = \{0\}$. For every $\gamma \in H$, $\lambda^+(\gamma)$ acts trivially on $\overline{\Lambda^{b+1}Z_q^0} \otimes \Lambda^{b+1}Z_q^0$ since γ is unitary on Z_q^0. Hence (5.4.97) and (5.4.102) imply that $\sigma_1^+(\gamma)$ acts trivially on $\operatorname{Ker} T_q$. Therefore

$$\operatorname{Ker} T_q \times S_{r-1} \xrightarrow[\approx]{} (\operatorname{Ker} T_c)_{c \in S_{r-1}}, \quad (\psi, qs) \mapsto (\sigma_1^+(s)\psi, qs)$$

is a vector bundle isomorphism over S_{r-1}, realizing the right-hand side as a trivial line bundle. In case $b + 1$ is odd, we have similarly

$$\operatorname{Ker} T_q^* = \tau_-(\overline{\Lambda^{b+1}Z_q^0} \otimes \Lambda^{b+1}Z_q^0)$$

and $\operatorname{Ker} T_q = \{0\}$. Therefore $\operatorname{Ker} T_c = \{0\}$ for all $c \in S_{r-1}$ and

$$\operatorname{Ker} T_q^* \times S_{r-1} \xrightarrow[\approx]{} (\operatorname{Ker} T_c^*)_{c \in S_{r-1}}, \quad (\psi, qs) \mapsto (\sigma^-(s)\psi, qs).$$

In both cases, we obtain by homotopy invariance

(5.4.103) $\operatorname{Ind}_r \Phi = \operatorname{Index}_{S_{r-1}} T_{\Phi_0} = \operatorname{Index}_{S_{r-1}} T_{\Phi_1} = (-1)^{b+1} \in K^0(S_{r-1})$.

Now consider the vector bundles

$$E \overset{\sigma^-}{\underset{H}{\times}} K \text{ and } E^\perp \overset{\sigma^-}{\underset{H}{\times}} K$$

over S_{r-1} (well-defined by (5.4.97)), and the analogous vector bundles induced by σ_1^+. By (5.4.100) and Lemma 5.1.33, there exists an isomorphism

$$E^\perp \overset{\sigma_1^+}{\underset{H}{\times}} K \xrightarrow[\approx]{\sigma_1^+ \backslash \sigma^- \atop H} E^\perp \overset{\sigma^-}{\underset{H}{\times}} K.$$

Similarly, (5.4.96) and Lemma 5.1.33 yield an isomorphism

$$E \underset{H\cap L}{\overset{\sigma_1^+}{\times}} K = \pi_{\mathbb{S}}^*(E \underset{H}{\overset{\sigma_1^+}{\times}} K) \xrightarrow[\approx]{\sigma_1^+ \underset{H\cap L}{\backslash} \sigma^-} \pi_{\mathbb{S}}^*(E \underset{H}{\overset{\sigma^-}{\times}} K) = E \underset{H\cap L}{\overset{\sigma^-}{\times}} K .$$

By (5.4.97), we have for the Peirce 0-bundle Z^0

$$\lambda^{\pm}(Z^0) = \lambda^{\pm}(Z_q^0) \underset{H}{\overset{\lambda^{\pm}}{\times}} K \xrightarrow[\approx]{\tau_{\pm}} E \underset{H}{\overset{\sigma^{\pm}}{\times}} K.$$

We claim that the diagram

$$\text{(5.4.104)} \qquad \begin{array}{ccc} \pi_{\mathbb{S}}^*(E \underset{H}{\overset{\sigma_1^+}{\times}} K) & \xrightarrow{\sigma_1^+ \underset{H\cap L}{\backslash}\ \sigma^-} & \pi_{\mathbb{S}}^*(E \underset{H}{\overset{\sigma^-}{\times}} K) \\ \pi_{\mathbb{S}}^*(\tau_+) \uparrow \approx & & \approx \uparrow \pi_{\mathbb{S}}^*(\tau_-) \\ \pi_{\mathbb{S}}^*(\lambda^+(Z^0)) & \xrightarrow[\text{id} \otimes d]{} & \pi_{\mathbb{S}}^*(\lambda^-(Z^0)) \end{array}$$

commutes. In fact, we have by Lemma 5.1.31

$$\pi_{\mathbb{S}}^*(\lambda^{\pm}(Z^0)) = \lambda^{\pm}(Z_q^0) \underset{H\cap L}{\overset{\lambda^{\pm}}{\times}} K .$$

Now let $\omega \in \lambda^+(Z_q^0)$ and $s \in K$. Realizing all vector bundles in (5.4.104) as homogeneous bundles with respect to $H \cap L$, we obtain

$$\sigma_1^+ \underset{H\cap L}{\backslash} \sigma^- \ \pi_{\mathbb{S}}^*(\tau_+)[\omega,s]_{\lambda^+} = \sigma_1^+ \underset{H\cap L}{\backslash} \sigma^- \, [\tau_+\omega,s]_{\sigma^+}$$

$$= \sigma_1^+ \underset{H\cap L}{\backslash} \sigma^- \, [\tau_+\omega,s]_{\sigma_1^+} = [\tau_+\omega,s]_{\sigma^-}$$

since σ^+ and σ_1^+ agree on $H \cap L$. On the other hand, $\text{id} \otimes d_p$ commutes with $H \cap L$ so that (5.4.98) implies

$$\pi_{\mathbb{S}}^*(\tau\_)(\text{id} \otimes d)[\omega,s]_{\lambda^+} = \pi_{\mathbb{S}}^*(\tau\_)[(\text{id} \otimes d_p)\omega,s]_{\lambda^-}$$

$$= [\tau\_(\text{id} \otimes d_p)\omega,s]_{\sigma^-} = [\tau_+\omega,s]_{\sigma^-} .$$

This proves that the diagram (5.4.104) commutes. Consider the ball bundle

$$\mathbb{B}(S_{r-1}) = \bigcup_{c \in S_{r-1}} \bar{\Omega}_c \times \{c\} \xrightarrow{\pi_{\mathbb{B}}} S_{r-1}$$

of Z^0. The connecting map

$$\partial: K^1(\mathbb{S}(S_{r-1})) \to K_c^0(\mathbb{B}(S_{r-1}), \mathbb{S}(S_{r-1})) \approx K_c^0(Z^0)$$

satisfies, via [K1; II.3.21],

$$\partial\alpha^*[\Phi] = \partial[\Phi_0] = \partial[\Phi_1] = d(\tilde{E} \times \mathbb{B}(S_{r-1}), \tilde{E} \times \mathbb{B}(S_{r-1}), \Phi_1)$$

$$= d(\pi_{\mathbb{B}}^*(E \overset{\sigma_1^+}{\underset{H}{\times}} K), \pi_{\mathbb{B}}^*(E \overset{\sigma^-}{\underset{H}{\times}} K), \sigma_1^+ \setminus_{H\cap L} \sigma^-) + d(\pi_{\mathbb{B}}^*(E^\perp \overset{\sigma_1^+}{\underset{H}{\times}} K), \pi_{\mathbb{B}}^*(E^\perp \overset{\sigma^-}{\underset{H}{\times}} K), \pi_{\mathbb{S}}^*(\sigma_1^+ \setminus_H \sigma^-))$$

$$= d(\pi_{\mathbb{B}}^*(\lambda^+ Z^0), \pi_{\mathbb{B}}^*(\lambda^- Z^0), \text{id} \otimes d) = \pi_{\mathbb{B}}^*(\overline{\Lambda^{b+1}Z^0}) \otimes d(\pi_{\mathbb{B}}^*(\Lambda^+ Z^0), \pi_{\mathbb{B}}^*(\Lambda^- Z^0), d)$$

$$= \pi_{\mathbb{B}}^*(\overline{\Lambda^{b+1}Z^0}) \otimes \beta(Z^0).$$

Since the evaluation mapping $s \mapsto cs$ is a submersion from K onto S_{r-1}, the sphere bundle $\mathbb{S}(S_{r-1})$ is locally trivial. This implies [K1; p. 368] that

$$K^{\cdot}(\mathbb{S}(S_{r-1})) = K^{\cdot}(S_{r-1}) < 1, \alpha^*\Phi >$$

as a free module (via $\pi_{\mathbb{S}}$). Thus every $F \in K^1(S)$ admits a unique representation

$$\alpha^*(F) = \pi_{\mathbb{S}}^* F_1 + \pi_{\mathbb{S}}^* F_0 \otimes \alpha^*\Phi$$

where $F_1 \in K^1(S_{r-1})$ and $F_0 \in K^0(S_{r-1})$. By (5.4.103), we have

$$\mathrm{Ind}_r(F) = \mathrm{Index}_{S_{r-1}}\, \alpha^*(F) = F_0 \otimes \mathrm{Index}_{S_{r-1}}\, \alpha^*\Phi = (-1)^{b+1} F_0$$

which proves (5.4.94). On the other hand, the K-theoretic exact sequence [K1; IV.1.13] and (5.4.105) imply

$$\partial\alpha^*(F) = F_0 \otimes \partial\alpha^*\Phi = F_0 \otimes \pi_{\mathbb{B}}^*(\overline{\Lambda^{b+1}Z^0}) \otimes \beta(Z^0)$$

which gives (5.4.95). Q.E.D.

5.4.106. REMARK. Let $\Omega \subset \mathbb{C}$ be the unit disk with boundary $\partial\Omega = \mathbb{T}$. Coburn's Lemma [C1] states that a Toeplitz operator $T_{\mathbb{T}}(f)$ $(f \in \mathcal{C}(\mathbb{T}))$ satisfies

$$\mathrm{Ker}(T_{\mathbb{T}}(f)) = \{0\} \quad \text{or} \quad \mathrm{Ker}(T_{\mathbb{T}}(f)^*) = \{0\}.$$

This is a consequence of the fact that

$$L^2(\mathbb{T}) = H^2(\mathbb{T}) \oplus \overline{\zeta \cdot H^2(\mathbb{T})}$$

(with $\zeta \in \mathbb{T}$ the independent variable) and implies, for example that every Fredholm Toeplitz operator of index 0 (in particular every operator $T_{\mathbb{T}}(\exp\varphi)$, $\varphi \in \mathcal{C}(\mathbb{T})$) is invertible. The following example shows that none of these properties generalizes to any other symmetric domain. Let S be the Shilov boundary of an irreducible symmetric ball of rank r and dimension $n > r$. Let $f \in \mathcal{C}(S)$ be invariant under the circle group $\mathbb{T}$, acting by rotations of S. Then

$$(f|p)_S = \int_S \overline{f(z)}\, p(z)\, dz = \int_S \overline{f(z)}\, p(e^{it} z)\, dz = e^{int} \int_S \overline{f(z)}\, p(z)\, dz = e^{int}(f|p)_S$$

for every $p \in \mathcal{P}^n(Z)$ and every $t \in \mathbb{R}$. It follows that $(f \mid \mathcal{P}^n(Z))_S = 0$ for all $n \geq 1$ and therefore

$$T_S(f)1 = E^S(f) = (1 \mid f)_S = \int_S f(z)\,dz.$$

Now let e_1 be a minimal tripotent and let φ be a complex continuous function on the closed unit disk. Then we have

$$\int_S \varphi((z|e_1))\, dz = \frac{\frac{n}{r}-1}{\pi} \int_0^{2\pi} \int_0^1 \rho(1-\rho^2)^{(n/r)-2}\, \varphi(\rho e^{it})\, d\rho\, dt,$$

a formula generalizing [R7; p. 15, Lemma] for the Hilbert ball in $\mathbb{C}^n$, where $r = 1$ and $S = \mathbb{S}^{2n-1}$. Now let

$$\psi_a(z) = \exp(a \cdot (1 - |(z|e_1)|^2)^{(n/r)-1}),$$

where $a \in \mathbb{C}$ is non-zero. The change of variables $u := (1-\rho^2)^{(n/r)-1}$ gives

$$\int_S \psi_a(z)\, dz = \frac{1}{a}(e^a - 1) = T_S(\psi_a)1 = E^S(\psi_a),$$

since ψ_a is invariant under the circle group. Now choose $a = 2\pi i$. Then $T_S(\psi_a)1 = 0$ showing that $T_S(\psi_a)$ is not invertible. Similarly,

$$T_S(\psi_a)^* 1 = T_S(\psi_{-a})1 = 0,$$

showing that both $T_S(\psi_a)$ and $T_S(\psi_a)^*$ have a null-space. Now assume that Ω is of tube type and let Δ be its Jordan algebra determinant. Then

$$\overline{\Delta H^2(S)} \subset H^2(S)^\perp \tag{5.4.107}$$

since $\Delta(0) = 0$. Assume that ψ_a belongs to the direct sum

$$\psi_a \in H^2(S) \oplus \overline{\Delta \cdot H^2(S)}.$$

Then $\psi_a = f + \overline{\Delta g}$ on S, with f and g holomorphic. By (5.4.107), we have $f = E^S(\psi_a) = 0$, i.e., $\bar{\psi}_a = \psi_{-a} = \Delta g$ is holomorphic, a contradiction. This shows that the inclusion (5.4.107) is proper. A related example uses the function $\Delta_1(z) = (z|e_1)$, for which

$$\|\Delta_1^m\|_S^2 = m! \frac{(\frac{n}{r} - 1)!}{(m + \frac{n}{r} - 1)!}$$

for every $m \geq 0$ (Example 2.8.25) and therefore

$$\int_S \exp(a \cdot |(z|e_1)|^2)\, dz = \sum_{m\geq 0} \frac{a^m}{m!} \|\Delta_1^m\|_S^2 = (\frac{n}{r} - 1)! \sum_{m\geq 0} \frac{a^m}{(m + \frac{n}{r} - 1)!}$$

which vanishes for a suitable choice of $a \in \mathbb{C}$.

5.5 Index Theory for Tubular Domains

In this section we develop the index theory for Hardy-Toeplitz operators over a tubular domain $\Pi = \Lambda \times iX$ whose base Λ is a symmetric cone in a real Jordan algebra X. More generally, we consider also symmetric Siegel domains

(5.5.1) $$\Pi = \{(u,v) \in X^{\mathbb{C}} \times V : u + u^* + \Phi(v,v) \in \Lambda\}$$

where $\Phi : V \times V \to U := X^{\mathbb{C}}$ is a positive hermitian mapping. We assume in both cases that Π is irreducible of rank r. Our analysis is based on the structure theory of Toeplitz C^*-algebras carried out in Sections 4.4 and 4.5. We will concentrate on the case of Hardy-Toeplitz operators. For $0 \leq j \leq r$, let P_j denote the compact manifold of all projections of rank j in X. Each $p \in P_j$ induces Peirce decompositions

$$X = X_1(p) \oplus X_{1/2}(p) \oplus X_0(p) ,$$

$$Z = Z_1(p) \oplus Z_{1/2}(p) \oplus Z_0(p)$$

of $Z := U \oplus V$. For $\alpha = 1, 1/2, 0$ we put $U_\alpha(p) := U \cap Z_\alpha(p)$ and $V_\alpha(p) := V \cap Z_\alpha(p)$. For $a \in iX$ and $b \in V$, consider the quasi-translation

(5.5.2) $$h_{a,b}(u,v) := (u + a - \Phi(v,b) - \frac{\Phi(b,b)}{2}, v + b)$$

of Π. The transformations (5.5.2) form a nilpotent subgroup of $\mathrm{Aut}(\Pi)$. In the tubular case $(V = 0)$, $h_a(u) = u + a$ is a translation. By Theorem 1.3.82, the boundary components of Π have the form

$$(5.5.3) \qquad h_{a,b}(\Pi_p),$$

where $p \in P_j$ for some $j \geq 1$, $ia \in X_1(p) \oplus X_{1/2}(p)$ and $b \in V_{1/2}(p)$. Moreover

$$(5.5.4) \qquad \Pi_p := \{(u,v) \in U_0(p) \times V_0(p) : u + u^* + \Phi(v,v) \in \Lambda_p\}$$

is a symmetric Siegel domain in $Z_0(p) = U_0(p) \oplus V_0(p)$, whose base Λ_p is the strictly negative cone of the real Jordan algebra $X_0(p)$ of rank $r - j$. If Π is a tubular domain, then

$$\Pi_p = \Lambda_p \times iX_0(p)$$

is the tubular domain with base Λ_p. Let e be the unit element of X. Taking the base point $p\text{-}e \in \Pi_p$, we obtain a submanifold

$$(5.5.5) \qquad \Sigma_j := \{ h_{a,b}(p-e) : p \in P_j, ia \in X_1(p) \oplus X_{1/2}(p), b \in V_{1/2}(p)\}$$

of $\partial\Pi$, called the *j-th extreme boundary* of Π. For $j = r$, we obtain the *extreme boundary*

$$(5.5.6) \qquad \Sigma = \Sigma_r = \{(a - \frac{\Phi(b,b)}{2}, b) : a \in iX, b \in V\}.$$

We are now going to define the index theoretic concepts for the Hardy-Toeplitz C^*-algebra $\mathcal{T}(\Sigma)$. Since $\mathcal{T}(\Sigma)$ is not commutative modulo $\mathcal{K}(H^2(\Sigma))$ if $r > 1$, it will be necessary to consider several index homomorphisms $\mathrm{Ind}_1^\Sigma, \ldots, \mathrm{Ind}_r^\Sigma$ adapted to the C^*-filtration $\mathcal{J}_j^\Sigma := \mathrm{Ker}\,\sigma_j$ of $\mathcal{T}(\Sigma)$ (Theorem 4.4.51), where

$$\sigma_j := (\sigma_{p,a,b})_{(p,a,b) \in \Sigma_j}$$

is the j-th symbol homomorphism. Here

$$\sigma_{p,a,b} : \mathcal{T}(\Sigma) \to \mathcal{L}(H^2(\Sigma_p))$$

is the irreducible representation corresponding to the boundary component (5.5.3), acting on the Hardy space over the extreme boundary

$$\Sigma_p = \{(a - \frac{\Phi(b,b)}{2}, b) : a \in iX_0(p), b \in V_0(p)\} \tag{5.5.7}$$

of Π_p. Let $1 \le j \le r$ and consider the field C^*-algebra

$$\mathcal{K}_0(\mathcal{E}_j) := \int_{(p,a,b)\in\Sigma_j}^{\oplus} \mathcal{K}(H^2(\Sigma_p))$$

of the continuous bundle of elementary C^*-algebras [D1] associated with the continuous bundle

$$\mathcal{E}_j := (H^2(\Sigma_p))_{(p,a,b)\in\Sigma_j} \tag{5.5.8}$$

of Hilbert spaces over Σ_j. There is an embedding

$$\mathcal{C}_0(\Sigma_j) \to \mathcal{K}_0(\mathcal{E}_j) \tag{5.5.9}$$

given by

$$f \mapsto (f(p,a,b)\ \psi_{p-e} \otimes \psi_{p-e})_{(p,a,b)\in\Sigma_j},$$

where ψ_{p-e} is the normalized Szegö kernel vector of $H^2(\Sigma_p)$, explicitly given by

$$\psi_{p-e}(u,v) := (\sqrt{2})^{n_p}\ \Delta_p(-u + e - p)^{-n_p/r-j}$$

where Δ_p is the determinant of $X_0(p)$ and n_p is the dimension.

Since the "higher" indices Ind_j^Σ, $j \ge 2$, are essentially "family" versions of the basic index Ind_1^Σ, we will first consider the case $j = 1$. By Theorem 4.4.51, there is a C^*-extension

$$0 \leftarrow \mathcal{K}_0(\mathcal{E}_1) \xleftarrow{\sigma_1} \mathcal{I}_2 \leftarrow \mathcal{K}(H^2(\Sigma)) \leftarrow 0 \tag{5.5.10}$$

whose Busby invariant is the C^*-homomorphism

(5.5.11) $$\tau_1(\Sigma) : \mathcal{C}_0(\Sigma_1) \to \mathcal{L}(H^2(\Sigma))/\mathcal{K}(H^2(\Sigma))$$

into the Calkin algebra, defined as the composition

$$\mathcal{C}_0(\Sigma_1) \to \mathcal{K}_0(\mathcal{E}_1) \xrightarrow{\tau_1} \mathcal{J}_2 \subset \mathcal{L}(H^2(\Sigma)) \to \mathcal{L}(H^2(\Sigma))/\mathcal{K}(H^2(\Sigma))$$

where τ_1 is any completely positive cross-section of σ_1. The *analytic index*

$$\mathrm{Ind}_1^\Sigma : K^1(\Sigma_1) \to \mathbb{Z}$$

is then defined as

(5.5.12) $$\mathrm{Ind}_1^\Sigma(F) := \mathrm{Index}\ I + (\tau_1(F_{hk} - \delta_{hk}))$$

where $F = (F_{hk}) : \Sigma_1 \to GL_N(\mathbb{C})$ is continuous and unity at ∞, and

$$I + (\tau_1(F_{hk} - \delta_{hk}))$$

is a Fredholm operator on $H^2(\Sigma,\mathbb{C}^N)$. Clearly, (5.5.12) is independent of the choice of τ_1 and depends only on the homotopy class of F. In order to express (5.5.12) in topological terms, consider the *Cayley transformation*

(5.5.13) $$g(u,v) := ((u + e) \circ (u - e)^{-1}, \sqrt{2}\, v \circ (u - e)^{-1})$$

defined in terms of the Jordan algebra $Z = U \oplus V$ and the unit element $e \in X$. One can show [L9, KU] that

(5.5.14) $$g : \Pi \xrightarrow[\approx]{} \Omega$$

is a biholomorphic mapping onto a bounded symmetric domain Ω realized as the open unit ball of Z for a Jordan triple product $\{z_1 z^* z_2\}$ specializing to $z_1 \circ z_2 = \{z_1 e^* z_2\}$ and $\Phi(v,b) = 2\{eb^* v\}$. The Cayley transform is an open dense embedding

(5.5.15) $$g : \Sigma \to S$$

which gives rise to a Hilbert space isomorphism

(5.5.16) $$H^2(\Sigma) \xrightarrow{U} H^2(S)\,, \quad \varphi \mapsto \varphi \circ g^{-1}(z)\, \frac{E_\Sigma(-e,-e)^{1/2}}{E_\Sigma(g^{-1}(z),-e)}$$

inducing a commuting diagram

$$\begin{array}{ccc} H^2(\Sigma) & \xrightarrow{\quad U \quad} & H^2(S) \\ {\scriptstyle T_\Sigma(f)}\Big\downarrow & & \Big\downarrow{\scriptstyle T_S(f\circ g^{-1})} \\ H^2(\Sigma) & \xrightarrow[\quad U \quad]{} & H^2(S) \end{array}$$

for the respective Hardy-Toeplitz operators. Here $f \in \mathcal{C}_0(\Sigma)$, and $f \circ g^{-1} \in \mathcal{C}(S)$ is defined as zero on $S \backslash g(\Sigma)$. Generalizing (5.5.15), there exist open dense embeddings

(5.5.17) $$g_j : \Sigma_j \to S_j$$

defined as follows: For each $(p,a,b) \in \Sigma_j$,

(5.5.18) $$g(h_{a,b}(\Pi_p)) = c + \Omega_c$$

is a boundary component of Ω (Theorem 1.5.47) for some unique tripotent

(5.5.19) $$c = g_j(p,a,b) = g_j(h_{a,b}(p-e)) \in S_j.$$

Only in case $j = r$ does g_j coincide with g. The biholomorphic mapping

(5.5.20) $$\Pi_p \xrightarrow{g_{p,a,b}} \Omega_c\,, \quad z \mapsto g(h_{a,b}(z)) - c$$

defined via (5.5.18) induces an isometric isomorphism

(5.5.21) $$H^2(\Sigma_p) \xrightarrow[\approx]{U_{p,a,b}} H^2(S_c)$$

such that there is a commuting diagram

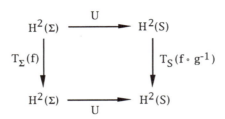

$$\begin{array}{ccc} \mathcal{T}_0(\Sigma) & \xrightarrow{\ \sigma_{p,a,b}\ } & \mathcal{L}(H^2(\Sigma_p)) \\ {\scriptstyle Ad(U)}\downarrow & & \downarrow{\scriptstyle Ad(U_{p,a,b})} \\ \mathcal{T}(S) & \xrightarrow[\ \sigma_c\ ]{} & \mathcal{L}(H^2(S_c)) \end{array}$$

where $Ad(U)T := UTU^*$ maps $\mathcal{T}_0(\Sigma)$ onto an ideal of $\mathcal{T}(S)$ and $Ad(U_{p,a,b})$ is defined similarly.

5.5.22. LEMMA. $Ad(U)\mathcal{J}_j^\Sigma \subset \mathcal{J}_j^S$ *for all* j.

Proof. By definition, $\mathcal{J}_j^\Sigma$ (resp., $\mathcal{J}_j^S$) is the joint null-space of the representations $\sigma_{p,a,b}$ (resp., σ_c). Let $T \in \mathcal{J}_j^\Sigma$ and suppose $c \in S_j$ satisfies (5.5.19). Then

$$\sigma_c(Ad(U)T) = Ad(U_{p,a,b})\sigma_{p,a,b}T = Ad(U_{p,a,b})0 = 0.$$

On the other hand, [U4] implies

$$\sigma_c(Ad(U)\mathcal{T}_0(\Sigma)) = 0 \tag{5.5.23}$$

whenever $c \in S_j \backslash g_j(\Sigma_j)$. Thus $\sigma_c(Ad(U)T) = 0$ in this case also, and hence $Ad(U)T \in \mathcal{J}_j^S$. Q.E.D.

For every $f \in \mathcal{C}_0(\Sigma_j)$, define a continuous function $\hat{f} \in \mathcal{C}(S_j)$ by putting $\hat{f} \circ g_j := f$ and

$$\hat{f}|_{S_j \backslash g_j(\Sigma_j)} := 0 \tag{5.5.24}$$

5.5.25. LEMMA. *For all* $c \in S_j$ *and* $f \in \mathcal{C}_0(\Sigma_j)$, *we have*

$$\sigma_c(Ad(U)\tau_j f) = \sigma_c(\tau_j \hat{f}). \tag{5.5.26}$$

Proof. Suppose $c \in S_j$ satisfies (5.5.19). Then

$$\sigma_c(Ad(U)\tau_j f) = Ad(U_{p,a,b})\sigma_{p,a,b}\tau_j f$$

$$= \mathrm{Ad}(U_{p,a,b})\ f(p,a,b)\ \psi_{p-e} \otimes \psi_{p-e} = \hat{f}(c) \cdot 1_c \otimes 1_c = \sigma_c(\tau_j \hat{f})$$

since we have $\mathrm{Ad}(U_{p,a,b})\psi_{p-e} = 1_c$ for the normalized kernel vectors. On the other hand, if $c \in S_j \backslash g_j(\Sigma_j)$ we have $\sigma_c(\mathrm{Ad}(U)\tau_j f) = 0$ by (5.5.23), whereas $\sigma_c(\tau_j \hat{f}) = \hat{f}(c)\ 1_c \otimes 1_c = 0$ by (5.5.24). Q.E.D.

Consider the canonical K-theory extension mapping (cf. (5.1.23))

(5.5.27) $$(g_j)_! : K^1(\Sigma_j) \to K^1(S_j)$$

defined by the open embedding (5.5.17).

5.5.28. THEOREM. *For every* $F \in K^1(\Sigma_1)$ *we have*

(5.5.29) $$\mathrm{Ind}_1^{\Sigma}(F) = \mathrm{Ind}_1^{S}((g_1)_! F)$$

where $\mathrm{Ind}_1^S : K^1(S_1) \to \mathbb{Z}$ *is the corresponding index mapping* (5.4.15) *for* $\mathcal{T}(S)$.

Proof. Assuming $F = (F_{hk}) : \Sigma_1 \to U_N(\mathbb{C})$ is continuous and unity at ∞, we have

$$((g_1)_!\ F)_{hk} - \delta_{hk} = \widehat{F_{hk} - \delta_{hk}}$$

in the sense of (5.5.24). By Lemma 5.5.25, we have

$$\mathrm{Ad}(U)\tau_1 f - \tau_1 \hat{f} \in \mathcal{K}(H^2(S))$$

for all $f \in \mathcal{C}_0(\Sigma_1)$. It follows that

$$\mathrm{Ind}_1^S((g_1)_!\ F) = \mathrm{Index}\ I + \tau_1(((g_1)_! F)_{hk} - \delta_{hk})$$

$$= \mathrm{Index}\ I + (\tau_1 \widehat{F_{hk} - \delta_{hk}}) = \mathrm{Index}\ I + (\mathrm{Ad}(U)\tau_1(F_{hk} - \delta_{hk}))$$

$$= \mathrm{Index}\ \mathrm{Ad}(U)(I + (\tau_1(F_{hk} - \delta_{hk}))) = \mathrm{Index}\ I + (\tau_1(F_{hk} - \delta_{hk})) = \mathrm{Ind}_1^{\Sigma}(F).$$

Q.E.D.

We now pass to the general case $1 \le j \le r$. By Theorem 4.4.51, there is a C^*-extension

(5.5.30) $$0 \leftarrow \mathcal{K}_0(\mathcal{E}_j) \xleftarrow{\sigma_j} \mathcal{I}_{j+1}/\mathcal{I}_{j-1} \leftarrow \mathcal{I}_j/\mathcal{I}_{j-1} \leftarrow 0$$

whose Busby invariant is the C^*-homomorphism

(5.5.31) $$\tau_j(\Sigma) : \mathcal{C}_0(\Sigma_j) \to \overline{\mathcal{K}_0(\mathcal{E}_{j-1})}/\mathcal{K}_0(\mathcal{E}_{j-1})$$

into the outer multiplier algebra, obtained as the composition

$$\mathcal{C}_0(\Sigma_j) \to \mathcal{K}_0(\mathcal{E}_j) \xrightarrow{\tau_j} \mathcal{I}_{j+1}/\mathcal{I}_{j-1} \subset \overline{\mathcal{I}_j/\mathcal{I}_{j-1}} \xrightarrow{\overline{\sigma_{j-1}}} \overline{\mathcal{K}_0(\mathcal{E}_{j-1})} \to \overline{\mathcal{K}_0(\mathcal{E}_{j-1})}/\mathcal{K}_0(\mathcal{E}_{j-1})$$

where τ_j is any completely positive cross-section of σ_j. By [R5; Theorem 4.9], the embedding (5.5.9) induces K-theory isomorphisms

(5.5.32) $$K_c^{\cdot}(\Sigma_j) = K_{\cdot}(\mathcal{C}_0(\Sigma_j)) \xrightarrow[\approx]{} K_{\cdot}(\mathcal{K}_0(\mathcal{E}_j)).$$

5.5.33. DEFINITION. The C^*-algebra extension

(5.5.34) $$[\tau_j(\Sigma)] \in KK^1(\mathcal{C}_0(\Sigma_j), \mathcal{K}_0(\mathcal{E}_{j-1}))$$

defined by the exact sequence (5.5.30) or the Busby invariant (5.5.31) is called the *j-th Hardy-Toeplitz extension* over Σ.

Applying the Kasparov product and the identification (5.5.32) (for j and $j - 1$), we obtain a homomorphism

$$\mathrm{Ind}_j^\Sigma : K_c^1(\Sigma_j) \longrightarrow K_c^0(\Sigma_{j-1}), \quad [F] \mapsto [\tau_j(\Sigma)] \otimes [F]$$

called the *j-th analytic Hardy-Toeplitz index* over Σ. For $j = 1$, we have $K_c^0(\Sigma_{j-1}) = \mathbb{Z}$ since $\Sigma_0 = \{-e\}$, and

(5.5.35) $$\mathrm{Ind}_1^\Sigma : K_c^1(\Sigma_1) \longrightarrow \mathbb{Z}$$

is the index homomorphism studied above, corresponding to the first Hardy-Toeplitz extension

$$[\tau_1(\Sigma)] \in KK^1(\mathcal{C}_0(\Sigma_1), \mathbb{C})$$

over Σ. Every element in $K_c^1(\Sigma_j)$ can be realized as (the homotopy class of) a continuous matrix function $F = (F_{hk}) : \Sigma_j \to U_N(\mathbb{C})$ which is unity (i.e., $F = I_N$) at ∞. As in Section 5.4 one shows that

$$(5.5.36)\quad I + (\sigma_{j-1}\tau_j(F_{hk} - \delta_{hk})) := (I + \sigma_{q,u,v}\tau_j(F_{hk} - \delta_{hk})))_{(q,u,v)\in\Sigma_{j-1}}$$

is a continuous field of Fredholm operators (on $H^2(\Sigma_q, \mathbb{C}^N)$) over Σ_{j-1}. By the next Lemma, the Fredholm field (5.5.36) over Σ_{j-1} is trivial at infinity and thus has a *family index* [A1]

$$(5.5.37)\qquad \mathrm{Ind}_j^{\Sigma}[F] := \mathrm{Index}_{\Sigma_{j-1}}\, I + (\sigma_{j-1}\tau_j(F_{hk} - \delta_{hk})) \in K_c^0(\Sigma_{j-1})$$

which is independent of the choice of cross-section τ_j and depends only on the homotopy class of F. Thus we obtain a homomorphism

$$\mathrm{Ind}_j^{\Sigma} : K_c^1(\Sigma_j) \to K_c^0(\Sigma_{j-1})$$

called the *j-th analytic Hardy-Toeplitz index* over Σ.

5.5.38. LEMMA. *The Fredholm family* (5.5.36) *over* Σ_{j-1} *is trivial, i.e., identity + compact, at infinity.*

Proof. Consider the compact fibre bundle

$$\mathcal{P}_j := \{(q,p) : q \in P_{j-1}, p \in P_1 \cap X_0(q)\}$$

over P_{j-1}, and define the mapping

$$\eta : \mathcal{P}_j \to P_j\,,\quad (q,p) \mapsto q + p.$$

By (5.5.7), Σ_j is a real vector bundle over P_j. Therefore the pull-back

$$(5.5.39)\qquad \begin{array}{ccc} \eta^*\Sigma_j & \xrightarrow{\ \pi\ } & \Sigma_j \\ \downarrow & & \downarrow \\ \mathcal{P}_j & \xrightarrow[\ \eta\ ]{} & P_j \end{array}$$

becomes a real vector bundle over $\mathcal{P}_j$, whose elements have the form $((q,p),z)$ with $(q,p) \in \mathcal{P}_j$ and

(5.5.40) $$z = h_{\alpha,\beta}(p+q-e) \in \Sigma_j$$

(cf. (5.5.19)). The projection map π in (5.5.39) is proper. According to the Peirce multiplication rules [L8, L9], the element z has a unique representation

(5.5.41) $$z = h_{u,v}(h_{a,b}(p+q-e))$$

where

(5.5.42) $$w = h_{u,v}(q-e) \in \Sigma_{j-1} ,$$

(5.5.43) $$h_{\alpha,\beta} = h_{u,v}\ h_{a,b}.$$

(Thus, $(\alpha,\beta) = (u,v)(a,b)$ in the Heisenberg type group multiplication determined by the transformations (5.5.2).) Thus we obtain a fibre bundle

$$\eta^*\Sigma_j \xrightarrow{\beta} \Sigma_{j-1}$$

with projections $((q,p),z) \mapsto w$.

Geometrically, the fibre over w consists of all maximal boundary components of $h_{u,v}(\Pi_q)$, regarded as boundary components of Π itself. Now let $K \subset \Sigma_j$ be a compact subset such that $F = I_N$ on $\Sigma_j \backslash K$. Since π is proper,

$$\beta(\pi^{-1}(K)) = \{w \in \Sigma_{j-1} : \exists\ ((q,p), z) \in \beta^{-1}(w),\ z \in K\}$$

is a compact subset of Σ_{j-1}. For $w \in \Sigma_{j-1}\backslash\beta(\pi^{-1}(K))$, every maximal boundary component of $h_{u,v}(\Pi_q)$ is contained in $\Sigma_j\backslash K$. Therefore

$$\sigma_{p,a,b}\sigma_{q,u,v}\tau_j(F_{hk} - \delta_{hk}) = \sigma_{p+q,(u,v)(a,b)}\ \tau_j(F_{hk} - \delta_{hk}) = (F_{hk} - \delta_{hk})(z) = 0$$

for all representations $\sigma_{p,a,b}$ of $\mathcal{T}(\Sigma_q)$ with $p \in P_1 \cap X_0(q)$. Applying Theorem 4.4.51 to Σ_q, it follows that

$$\sigma_{q,u,v}\tau_j(F_{hk} - \delta_{hk}) \in \mathcal{K}(H^2(\Sigma_q))$$

whenever (q,u,v) does not belong to $\beta(\pi^{-1}(K))$. Q.E.D.

We will now prove the index theorem for the higher indices Ind_j^Σ by comparing the j-th Hardy-Toeplitz extension $\tau_j(\Sigma)$ over Σ with the j-th Hardy-Toeplitz extension $\tau_j(S)$ over the Shilov boundary S of the bounded symmetric domain $\Omega = g(\Pi)$. Here g is the Cayley transformation (5.5.13). Consider the embedding $g_j : \Sigma_j \to S_j$ defined by (5.5.17).

5.5.44. LEMMA. *Let* $d \in S_{j-1} \backslash g_{j-1}(\Sigma_{j-1})$ *and* $c \in S_1 \cap Z_0(d)$. *Then* $c + d \in S_j \backslash g_j(\Sigma_j)$.

Proof. Extend g to a biholomorphic mapping $g : M \to M$ of the compact symmetric space M which is dual to Ω [L9]. Since Z is an open subset of M, g maps the closure $\bar{\Pi} \cap Z$ onto an open subset of $\bar{\Omega}$. Since $d \notin g_{j-1}(\Sigma_{j-1})$, it follows from (5.5.18) that $d + \Omega_d \subset \bar{\Omega} \backslash g(\bar{\Pi} \cap Z)$. Therefore

$$c + d + \Omega_{c+d} = d + (c + (\Omega_d)_c) \subset d + \bar{\Omega}_d \subset \bar{\Omega} \backslash g(\bar{\Pi} \cap Z)$$

since $g(\bar{\Pi} \cap Z)$ is open in $\bar{\Omega}$. By definition (5.5.18), $c + d \notin g_j(\Sigma_j)$. Q.E.D.

5.5.45. LEMMA. *For any* $F \in K_c^1(\Sigma_j)$, *the Fredholm family*

$$I + (\sigma_{j-1} \tau_j(((g_j)_! F)_{hk} - \delta_{hk})) \tag{5.5.46}$$

over S_{j-1} *is trivial (i.e., identity + compact) on* $S_{j-1} \backslash g_{j-1}(\Sigma_{j-1})$.

Proof. Assuming $F = (F_{hk}) : \Sigma_j \to U_N(\mathbb{C})$ is continuous and unity at ∞, we have

$$((g_j)_! F)_{hk} - \delta_{hk} = \widehat{F_{hk} - \delta_{hk}}$$

in the sense of (5.5.24). For every $d \in S_{j-1} \backslash g_{j-1}(\Sigma_{j-1})$ and $c \in S_1 \cap Z_0(d)$, Lemma 5.5.44 implies

$$\sigma_c\, \sigma_d\, \tau_j\, \widehat{F_{hk} - \delta_{hk}} = \sigma_{c+d}\, \tau_j\, \widehat{F_{hk} - \delta_{hk}} = \widehat{F_{hk} - \delta_{hk}}(c + d) = 0$$

since $c + d \in S_j \backslash g_j(\Sigma_j)$. Applying Theorem 4.4.51 to $Z_0(d)$, it follows that

$$\sigma_d \, \tau_j \, \widehat{F_{hk} - \delta_{hk}} \in \mathcal{K}(H^2(S_d))$$

whenever $d \in S_{j-1} \backslash g_{j-1}(\Sigma_{j-1})$. Hence (5.5.46) is trivial on $S_{j-1} \backslash g_{j-1}(\Sigma_{j-1})$.
Q.E.D.

5.5.47. THEOREM. *For every* $F \in K^1_c(\Sigma_j)$ *we have*

(5.5.48) $$(g_{j-1})_! \, \mathrm{Ind}^{\Sigma}_j(F) = \mathrm{Ind}^S_j((g_j)_! F)$$

where $\mathrm{Ind}^S_j : K^1(S_j) \to K^0(S_{j-1})$ *is the corresponding index* (5.4.61) *for* $\mathcal{T}(S)$.

Proof. For every $(q,u,v) \in \Sigma_{j-1}$, define the Hilbert space isomorphism

$$U_{q,u,v} : H^2(\Sigma_q) \xrightarrow[\approx]{} H^2(S_d)$$

as in (5.5.21). Here $d \in S_{j-1}$ is given by $d = g_{j-1}(h_{u,v}(q-e))$. By construction,

$$U_{j-1} := (U_{q,u,v})_{(q,u,v) \in \Sigma_{j-1}}$$

is a strongly continuous field of unitaries over Σ_{j-1}. By (5.5.26) we have

$$\mathrm{Ad}(U_{q,u,v})\sigma_{q,u,v} \, \tau_j \, f - \sigma_d \, \tau_j \, \hat{f} = \sigma_d(\mathrm{Ad}(U)\tau_j f - \tau_j \hat{f})$$

for all $f \in \mathcal{C}_0(\Sigma_j)$. For all $c \in S_1 \cap Z_0(d)$, Lemma 5.5.44 implies

$$\sigma_c(\sigma_d(\mathrm{Ad}(U)\tau_j f - \tau_j \hat{f})) = \sigma_{c+d}(\mathrm{Ad}(U)\tau_j f - \tau_j \hat{f}) = 0$$

since $c + d \in S_j$. Therefore

(5.5.49) $$\mathrm{Ad}(U_{q,u,v})\sigma_{q,u,v}\tau_j f - \sigma_d \, \tau_j \hat{f} \in \mathcal{K}(H^2(S_d))$$

for all $(q,u,v) \in \Sigma_{j-1}$. Since the Fredholm family

$$I + (\sigma_{j-1} \, \tau_j \, \widehat{F_{hk} - \delta_{hk}})$$

over S_{j-1} is trivial outside $g_{j-1}(\Sigma_{j-1})$ by Lemma 5.5.45, it follows from (5.5.49) that

$$(g_{j-1})_! \mathrm{Index}_{\Sigma_{j-1}}[I + \mathrm{Ad}(U_{j-1})\sigma_{j-1}\tau_j(F_{hk} - \delta_{hk})] = \mathrm{Index}_{S_{j-1}}[I + \sigma_{j-1}\widehat{\tau_j F_{hk} - \delta_{hk}}].$$

Therefore

$$\begin{aligned}
\mathrm{Ind}_j^S((g_j)_!F) &= \mathrm{Index}_{S_{j-1}} [I + (\sigma_{j-1}\tau_j(((g_j)_!F)_{hk}) - \delta_{hk}))] \\
&= \mathrm{Index}_{S_{j-1}} [I + (\sigma_{j-1}\widehat{\tau_j F_{hk} - \delta_{hk}})] \\
&= (g_{j-1})_! \ \mathrm{Index}_{\Sigma_{j-1}} [I + (\mathrm{Ad}(U_{j-1})\ \sigma_{j-1}\ \tau_j\ (F_{hk} - \delta_{hk}))] \\
&= (g_{j-1})_! \ \mathrm{Index}_{\Sigma_{j-1}} \ \mathrm{Ad}(U_{j-1})[I + (\sigma_{j-1}\tau_j(F_{hk} - \delta_{hk}))] \\
&= (g_{j-1})_! \ \mathrm{Index}_{\Sigma_{j-1}} [I + (\sigma_{j-1}\tau_j(F_{hk} - \delta_{hk}))] = (g_{j-1})_! \ \mathrm{Ind}_j^{\Sigma}(F).
\end{aligned}$$

Q.E.D.

We will now express the analytic Hardy-Toeplitz index Ind_j^{Σ}, $j \geq 1$, over Σ in topological terms, starting with the basic case $j = 1$. Consider the compact symmetric space P_1 of all minimal projections in X. Let $t \mapsto p_t$ be a curve in P_1 passing through $p_0 = p$. Then the derivative $x := \dot{p}_t|_{t=0}$ satisfies $x = x \circ p + p \circ x = 2x \circ p$ since $p_t \circ p_t = p_t$ for all t. Thus the real submanifold $P_1 \subset X$ has the tangent space

$$T_p(P_1) = X_{1/2}(p)$$

at $p \in P_1$. Identifying the dual space $X^\# = iX$, we obtain the *cotangent bundle*

$$T^\#(P_1) = \{p + ix : p \in P_1, x \in X_{1/2}(p)\} \tag{5.5.50}$$

as a real submanifold of $U \subset Z$. Let $\nu : P_1 \to T^\#(P_1)$ denote the zero-section map $p \mapsto p + i0$. At the points of the zero-section, $T^\#(P_1)$ has the tangent space

$$T_p(T^\#(P_1)) = T_p(P_1) \oplus T_p^\#(P_1) = U_{1/2}(p)$$

which has a canonical complex structure

$$\mathcal{J}_p(x + i\xi) = i(x + i\xi) = -\xi + ix \tag{5.5.51}$$

for all $x,\xi \in X_{1/2}(p)$.

5.5.52. LEMMA. *Let* $\pi : E \to M$ *be a smooth real vector bundle over a manifold* M, *with zero-section* $\nu : M \to E$. *Suppose that at every point of the zero-section, there exists a complex structure*

$$\mathcal{J}_m : T_m(E) \to T_m(E), \quad \mathcal{J}_m^2 = -\mathrm{id}, \tag{5.5.53}$$

depending smoothly on $m \in M$. *Then there exists an almost-complex structure* $\mathcal{J}$ *on* E *extending* (5.5.53), *and any two such almost-complex structures on* E *are homotopic.*

Proof. A linear connection on E gives rise to a smooth family of linear isomorphisms

$$\Lambda_z : T_z(E) \xrightarrow[\approx]{} T_m(E) \ . \tag{5.5.54}$$

for $z \in E_m$, $m \in M$, such that $\Lambda_m = \mathrm{id}$. Define $\mathcal{J}_z$ by the commuting diagram

$$\begin{array}{ccc} T_z(E) & \xrightarrow{\ \mathcal{J}_z\ } & T_z(E) \\ {\scriptstyle \Lambda_z}\downarrow & & \downarrow{\scriptstyle \Lambda_z} \\ T_m(E) & \xrightarrow[\ \mathcal{J}_m\ ]{} & T_m(E) \end{array} \ .$$

This shows the existence of $\mathcal{J}$. Now suppose that $\tilde{\mathcal{J}}$ is another almost-complex structure on E which coincides with (5.5.53) at the zero-section. For $0 \le t \le 1$, define an almost-complex structure $\tilde{\mathcal{J}}^t$ on E by the commuting diagram

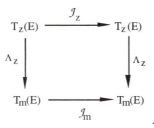

$$\begin{array}{ccc}
T_z(E) & \xrightarrow{\ \tilde{\mathcal{J}}_z^t\ } & T_z(E) \\
\downarrow{\scriptstyle \Lambda_z} & & \downarrow{\scriptstyle \Lambda_z} \\
T_m(E) & & T_m(E) \\
\downarrow{\scriptstyle \Lambda_{tz}} & & \downarrow{\scriptstyle \Lambda_{tz}} \\
T_{tz}(E) & \xrightarrow[\ \tilde{\mathcal{J}}_{tz}\ ]{} & T_{tz}(E)
\end{array}$$

Putting $t = 0$, the diagram becomes

$$\begin{array}{ccc}
T_z(E) & \xrightarrow{\ \tilde{\mathcal{J}}_z^0\ } & T_z(E) \\
\downarrow{\scriptstyle \Lambda_z} & & \downarrow{\scriptstyle \Lambda_z} \\
T_m(E) & \xrightarrow[\ \tilde{\mathcal{J}}_m\ ]{} & T_m(E)
\end{array}$$

with $\tilde{\mathcal{J}}_m = \mathcal{J}_m$. Thus $\tilde{\mathcal{J}}^0 = \mathcal{J}$ and hence $\tilde{\mathcal{J}} = \tilde{\mathcal{J}}^1 \sim \tilde{\mathcal{J}}^0 = \mathcal{J}$. Q.E.D.

Let $\mathcal{J}$ denote the almost-complex structure on $T^\#(P_1)$ determined, up to homotopy, by (5.5.51). Let

$$\chi_{T^\#(P_1)} : K^0(T^\#(P_1)) \to \mathbb{Z}$$

denote the corresponding K-theoretic index character.

5.5.55. LEMMA. $T^\#(P_1)$ *is a symplectic manifold with symplectic form*

$$\omega_{x,\xi}((y_1,\eta_1) \otimes (y_2,\eta_2)) = y_1\eta_2 - y_2\eta_1$$

for all $(x,\xi) \in T^\#(P_1)$ *and* $(y_i,\eta_i) \in T_{x,\xi}(T^\#(P_1))$.

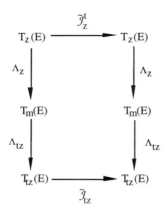

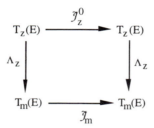

Proof. For any smooth vector bundle $\pi : E \to M$ over a manifold M, there exists a "rhombus", i.e. a commuting diagram

$$\begin{array}{ccc} T(E) & \xrightarrow{T(\pi)} & T(M) \\ {\scriptstyle \tau_E}\downarrow & & \downarrow{\scriptstyle \tau_M} \\ E & \xrightarrow[\pi]{} & M \end{array}$$

for the respective tangent bundles with projection τ. Specializing to the cotange bundle $\tau^{\#}_M : T^{\#}(M) \longrightarrow M$ we obtain the commuting diagram

$$\begin{array}{ccc} T(T^{\#}(M)) & \xrightarrow{T(\tau^{\#}_M)} & T(M) \\ {\scriptstyle \tau_{T^{\#}(M)}}\downarrow & & \downarrow{\scriptstyle \tau_M} \\ T^{\#}(M) & \xrightarrow[\tau^{\#}_M]{} & M \end{array}.$$

Now the canonical 1-form on $T^{\#}(M)$ is defined by

$$T_{x,\xi}(T^{\#}(M)) \xrightarrow{T_{x,\xi}(\tau^{\#}_M)} T_x(M) \xrightarrow{\xi} \mathbb{R}, \qquad \theta_{x,\xi} = \xi \circ T_{x,\xi}(\tau^{\#}_M)$$

for all $\xi \in T^{\#}_x(M)$. By definition, $\omega = d\theta$ is the symplectic form on $T^{\#}(M)$. In case $M \subset X$ is embedded in a real vector space X, the commuting diagram

$$\begin{array}{ccc} T^{\#}(M) & \searrow^{\tau^{\#}_M} & \\ \cap & & M \\ M \times X^{\#} & \nearrow_{pr_M} & \end{array}$$

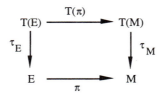

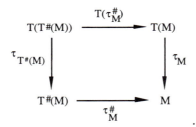

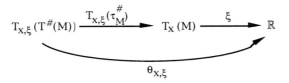

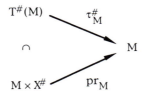

realizes $\tau_M^\#$ as the projection pr_M onto the first factor, so that $\theta_{x,\xi}(y,\eta) = y\xi$ for all $(y,\eta) \in T_{x,\xi}(T^\#(M)) \subset X \times X^\#$. Taking derivatives, we obtain

$$\omega_{x,\xi}((y_1,\eta_1) \otimes (y_0,\eta_0)) = y_1\eta_2 - y_2\eta_1. \qquad \text{Q.E.D.}$$

The set Σ_1 of all maximal boundary components of Π can be identified with the real submanifold

$$\Sigma_1 = \{p - e + ia - \frac{\Phi(b,b)}{2} + b : p \in P_1,\ a \in \mathbb{R}p \oplus X_{1/2}(p),\ b \in V_{1/2}(p)\}$$

of Z, since the point

$$z = p - e + ia - \frac{\Phi(b,b)}{2} + b \tag{5.5.56}$$

satisfies $b = pr_V(z)$ and

$$ia = pr_{iX}(z - b + \frac{\Phi(b,b)}{2}),\quad p - e = pr_X(z - b + \frac{\Phi(b,b)}{2}).$$

Differentiating a curve z_t of the form (5.5.56), we see that

$$T_{p-e}(\Sigma_1) = i\mathbb{R}p + Z_{1/2}(p) \subset Z.$$

More generally, the set

$$\Sigma_1^{\mathbb{C}} := \{p - e + (s + it)p + i\xi - \frac{\Phi(b,b)}{2} + b :$$

$$p \in P_1,\ s,t \in \mathbb{R},\ \xi \in X_{1/2}(p),\ b \in V_{1/2}(p)\}$$

is a real submanifold of Z with tangent space

$$T_{p-e}(\Sigma_1^{\mathbb{C}}) = \mathbb{C}\,p + Z_{1/2}(p) \subset Z. \tag{5.5.57}$$

5.5.58. LEMMA. *The open embedding* $g_1 : \Sigma_1 \to S_1$ *has the derivative*

$$T_{p-e}(g_1)(itp + u + b) = -2itp - u - b/\sqrt{2}$$

for all $t \in \mathbb{R}$, $u \in U_{1/2}(p)$ *and* $b \in V_{1/2}(p)$.

Proof. By definition, $g_1 = \pi \circ g$ where $g : \Sigma_1 \to \partial_1\Omega$ is the Cayley transform (5.5.13) and $\pi : \partial_1\Omega \to S_1$ is the projection $\pi(c + \Omega_c) := c$ from the partial boundary $\partial_1\Omega$ onto S_1. As a real submanifold of Z, $\partial_1\Omega$ has the tangent space

$$T_c(\partial_1\Omega) = T_c(S_1) \oplus X_0(c) \subset Z$$

at the points $c \in S_1 \subset \partial_1\Omega$ of the zero-section, and

(5.5.59) $$T_c(\pi) : T_c(\partial_1\Omega) \to T_c(S_1)$$

is the orthogonal projection. By [U9; Lemma 3.1], we have $g(p-e) = -p$ and

$$T_{p-e}(g)(itp + u + b) = -2itp - u - b/\sqrt{2} \in T_{-p}(\partial_1\Omega)$$

for all $t \in \mathbb{R}$, $u \in U_{1/2}(p)$ and $b \in V_{1/2}(p)$. Since this vector lies in $T_{-p}(S_1) \subset T_{-p}(\partial_1\Omega)$, the assertion follows. Q.E.D.

As a complex-algebraic variety, the set $S_1^{\mathbb{C}}$ has the tangent space

$$T_c(S_1^{\mathbb{C}}) = \mathbb{C}c \oplus Z_{1/2}(c) \subset Z.$$

Consider the open embedding $g_1^{\mathbb{C}} : \Sigma_1^{\mathbb{C}} \longrightarrow S_1^{\mathbb{C}}$ defined by

(5.5.60) $$\begin{aligned} &g_1^{\mathbb{C}}\left(p - e + (s + it)p + ia - \frac{\Phi(b,b)}{2} + b\right) \\ &:= e^{2s}\, g_1\left(p - e + itp + ia - \frac{\Phi(b,b)}{2} + b\right) \end{aligned}$$

for all $p \in P_1$, $s,t \in \mathbb{R}$, $a \in X_{1/2}(p)$ and $b \in V_{1/2}(p)$. Applying Lemma 5.5.60, we obtain

(5.5.61) $$T_{p-e}(g_1^{\mathbb{C}})(\lambda p + a + b) = 2\bar{\lambda}p - a - b/\sqrt{2}$$

for all $\lambda \in \mathbb{C}$, $a \in U_{1/2}(p)$ and $b \in V_{1/2}(p)$. Since $S_1^{\mathbb{C}}$ is a complex submanifold of Z, the open embedding $g_1^{\mathbb{C}}$ defines a complex structure $\mathcal{J}^g$ on $\Sigma_1^{\mathbb{C}}$ such that the mapping (5.5.61) becomes complex-linear. More explicitly, we have

$$\mathcal{J}^g_{p-e}(\lambda p + a + b) = -i\lambda p + ia + ib \tag{5.5.62}$$

as follows from the commuting diagram

$$\begin{array}{ccc} T_{p-e}(\Sigma_1^{\mathbb{C}}) & \xrightarrow{T_{p-e}(g_1^{\mathbb{C}})} & T_p(S_1^{\mathbb{C}}) \\ \Big\downarrow \mathcal{J}^g_{p-e} & & \Big\downarrow i \\ T_{p-e}(\Sigma_1^{\mathbb{C}}) & \xrightarrow[T_{p-e}(g_1^{\mathbb{C}})]{} & T_p(S_1^{\mathbb{C}}) \end{array}$$

On the other hand, $\Sigma_1^{\mathbb{C}}$ becomes a complex vector bundle over $T^{\#}(P_1)$ via the projection

$$\pi : \Sigma_1^{\mathbb{C}} \to T^{\#}(P_1), \quad p - e + \lambda p + i\xi - \frac{\Phi(b,b)}{2} + b \mapsto p + i\xi$$

for all $p \in P_1$, $\lambda \in \mathbb{C}$, $\xi \in X_{1/2}(p)$ and $b \in V_{1/2}(p)$.

5.5.63. LEMMA. *Let* $\pi : E \to M$ *be a complex vector bundle over an almost-complex manifold* M. *Let* $\nu : M \to E$ *denote the zero-section. Then* E *has an almost-complex structure such that* ν *is a complex embedding and* E *is a normal bundle along* ν.

Proof. Endow the tangent spaces

$$T_m(E) = T_m(M) \oplus E_m$$

at the zero-section $m \in M \subset E$ with the product complex structure and define $\mathcal{J}_z$, $z \in E$, so that the isomorphisms Λ_z (cf. (5.5.54)) are $\mathbb{C}$-linear.

Then ν is a complex embedding, and E_m is a complex complementary subspace to $T_m(M)$, making E a normal bundle along ν. Q.E.D.

Using Lemma 5.5.63, we may endow $\Sigma_1^{\mathbb{C}}$ with an almost-complex structure $\mathcal{J}$ by combining the almost-complex structure on the base $T^{\#}(P_1)$, determined up to homotopy by (5.5.51), with a complex structure on each fibre

$$\pi^{-1}(p + ia) = \{p - e + \lambda p + ia - \frac{\Phi(b,b)}{2} + b \colon \lambda \in \mathbb{C},\ b \in V_{1/2}(p)\}.$$

Consider the complex vector bundle

$$V := \bigcup_{p \in P_1} \{p\} \times V_{1/2}(p)$$

over P_1, and its direct sum $\bar{\mathbb{C}} \oplus V$ with the dual trivial line bundle $\bar{\mathbb{C}}$. Then the pull-back

$$\begin{array}{ccc} \tau^*(\bar{\mathbb{C}} \oplus V) & \longrightarrow & \bar{\mathbb{C}} \oplus V \\ \pi \big\downarrow & & \big\downarrow \\ T^{\#}(P_1) & \xrightarrow[\tau]{} & P_1 \end{array}$$

via $\tau = \tau^{\#}_{P_1}$ is a complex vector bundle over $T^{\#}(P_1)$ and we make the natural bijection $\Sigma_1^{\mathbb{C}} \xrightarrow[\approx]{} \tau^*(\bar{\mathbb{C}} \oplus V)$ given by

$$(5.5.64) \qquad p - e + \lambda p + ia - \frac{\Phi(b,b)}{2} + b \mapsto (p + ia, \bar{\lambda} \oplus b)$$

an isomorphism of complex vector bundles over $T^{\#}(P_1)$. Let $\mathcal{J}$ be the corresponding almost-complex structure on $\Sigma_1^{\mathbb{C}}$.

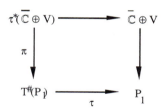

5.5.65. PROPOSITION. *The almost-complex structures* $\mathcal{J}^g$ and $\mathcal{J}$ *on* $\Sigma_1^{\mathbb{C}}$, *induced by the embedding* g_1 *and the vector bundle isomorphism* (5.5.64), *respectively, are homotopic.*

Proof. Since $\Sigma_1^{\mathbb{C}}$ is a real vector bundle over P_1 via the diagonal map

(5.5.66) $$\Sigma_1^{\mathbb{C}} \underset{\pi}{\longrightarrow} T^{\#}(P_1) \underset{\tau}{\longrightarrow} P_1$$

of (5.5.64), it suffices by Lemma 5.5.52 to show that $\mathcal{J}^g$ and $\mathcal{J}$ agree at the points $p - e \in \Sigma_1^{\mathbb{C}}$ of the zero-section of (5.5.66). We have

(5.5.67) $$T_{p-e}(\Sigma_1^{\mathbb{C}}) = \text{Ran } T_p(\nu) \oplus \text{Ran } T_0(i)$$

where

$$\nu : T^{\#}(P_1) \to \Sigma_1^{\mathbb{C}}, \quad p + i\xi \mapsto p - e + i\xi$$

is the zero-section map, with derivative

$$T_p(\nu)(x + i\xi) = x + i\xi$$

for all $x,\xi \in X_{1/2}(p)$, and

$$i : \bar{\mathbb{C}} \oplus V_{1/2}(p) \to \Sigma_1^{\mathbb{C}}, \quad (\bar{\lambda},b) \mapsto p - e + \lambda p - \frac{\Phi(b,b)}{2} + b$$

is the inclusion map of the fibre at $p - e \in \Sigma_1^{\mathbb{C}}$, with derivative

$$T_0(i)(\bar{\lambda},b) = \lambda p + b.$$

Since (5.5.67) is a complex direct sum by Lemma 5.5.63, we have

$$\mathcal{J}_{p-e} = \mathcal{J}^{\nu}_{p-e} \oplus \mathcal{J}^{i}_{p-e}$$

where $\mathcal{J}^{\nu}_{p-e}$ and $\mathcal{J}^{i}_{p-e}$ satisfy the commuting diagrams

$$\begin{array}{ccc} T_p(T^{\#}(P_1)) & \xrightarrow{T_p(v)} & \operatorname{Ran} T_p(v) \\ \Big\downarrow \mathcal{J}_p & & \Big\downarrow \mathcal{J}^{v}_{p-e} \\ T_p(T^{\#}(P_1)) & \xrightarrow[T_p(v)]{} & \operatorname{Ran} T_p(v) \end{array} \qquad \begin{array}{ccc} \bar{\mathbb{C}} \times V & \xrightarrow{T_0(i)} & \operatorname{Ran} T_0(i) \\ \Big\downarrow i & & \Big\downarrow \mathcal{J}^{i}_{p-e} \\ \bar{\mathbb{C}} \times V & \xrightarrow[T_0(i)]{} & \operatorname{Ran} T_0(i) \end{array}$$

Hence $\mathcal{J}^{v}_{p-e}(x + i\xi) = -\xi + ix$ and $\mathcal{J}^{i}_{p-e}(\lambda p + b) = -i\lambda p + ib$. Therefore

$$\mathcal{J}_{p-e}(\lambda p + x + i\xi + b) = -i\lambda p - \xi + ix + ib$$

which agrees with (5.5.62). Q.E.D.

5.5.68. THEOREM. *Let Π be an irreducible symmetric Siegel domain with extremal boundary Σ. Then the first analytic Hardy-Toeplitz index* $\operatorname{Ind}_1^{\Sigma}$ *over Σ has the topological expression*

$$\begin{array}{ccc} K_c^1(\Sigma_1) & \xrightarrow{\operatorname{Ind}_1^{\Sigma}} & \mathbb{Z} \\ \partial \Big\downarrow \approx & & \Big\downarrow \chi_{T^{\#}(P_1)} \\ K_c^0(\Sigma_1^{\mathbb{C}}) & \xrightarrow[\beta(\Sigma_1^{\mathbb{C}})]{\approx} & K_c^0(T^{\#}(P_1)) \end{array}$$

Here ∂ is the canonical isomorphism for $\Sigma_1^{\mathbb{C}} \approx \mathbb{R} \times \Sigma_1$, $\beta(\Sigma_1^{\mathbb{C}})$ is the Thom isomorphism (Theorem 5.1.15, *modified for K-theory with compact support) of the complex vector bundle $\Sigma_1^{\mathbb{C}}$ over $T^{\#}(P_1)$, and $\chi_{T^{\#}(P_1)}$ is the K-theoretic index character for $T^{\#}(P_1)$ endowed with the almost-complex structure* (5.5.51).

Proof. Let $g_1 : \Sigma_1 \to S_1$ denote the open embedding (5.5.17) induced by the Cayley transformation $g : \Pi \to \Omega$. Combining Theorem 5.5.28 with the

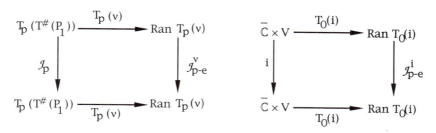

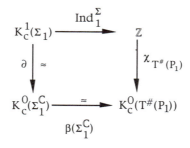

K-theoretic formula (5.4.79) for the first analytic Hardy-Toeplitz index Ind_1^S over S, we obtain

$$\mathrm{Ind}_1^{\Sigma}(F) = \chi_{S_1}((g_1)_! F)$$

for all $F \in K^1(\Sigma_1)$. Using the identifications

$$(5.5.69) \qquad \Sigma_1^{\mathbb{C}} \xrightarrow[\approx]{} \mathbb{R} \times \Sigma_1,$$

$$p - e + (s + it)p + ia - \frac{\Phi(b,b)}{2} + b \mapsto (s, p - e + itp + ia - \frac{\Phi(b,b)}{2} + b)$$

and

$$(5.5.70) \qquad S_1^{\mathbb{C}} \xrightarrow[\approx]{} \mathbb{R} \times S_1 \ , \ e^{2s}c \mapsto (s,c)$$

we see that the open embedding $g_1^{\mathbb{C}} : \Sigma_1^{\mathbb{C}} \to S_1^{\mathbb{C}}$ has the form $g_1^{\mathbb{C}}(s,z) = (s, g_1(z))$ for all $s \in \mathbb{R}$ and $z \in \Sigma_1$. Thus there is a commuting diagram

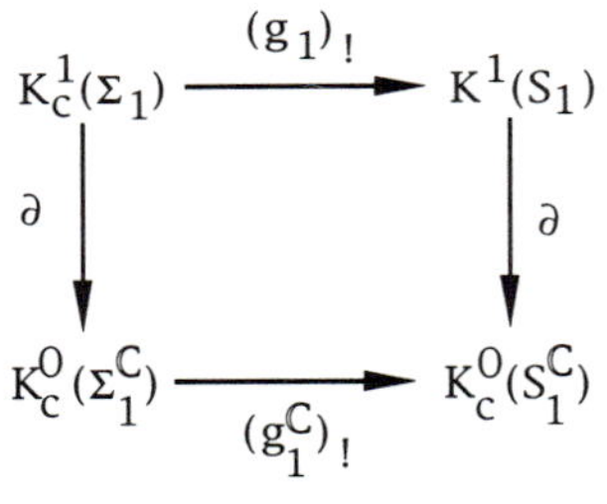

where ∂ denotes the natural isomorphism and $\Sigma_1^{\mathbb{C}}$ has the almost-complex structure $\mathcal{J}^g$. Under the identification (5.5.70), $S_1^{\mathbb{C}}$ becomes the "symplectic cone" over the contact manifold S_1 so that there is a commuting diagram

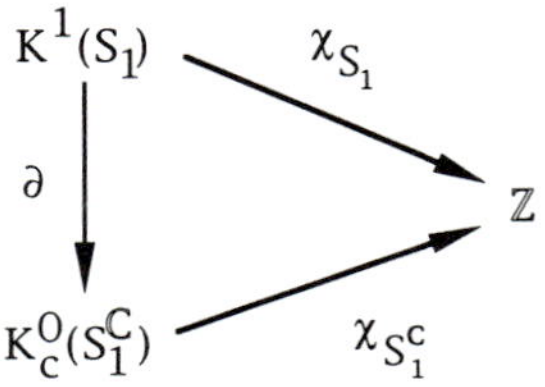

for the respective K-theoretic index characters. Now consider the complex embedding $\nu : T^{\#}(P_1) \to \Sigma_1^{\mathbb{C}}$ of the complex vector bundle $\pi : \Sigma_1^{\mathbb{C}} \to T^{\#}(P_1)$. Here $\Sigma_1^{\mathbb{C}}$ is endowed with the almost-complex structure $\mathcal{J}$. By [B5; Proposition 2.10.(ii)], there is a commuting diagram

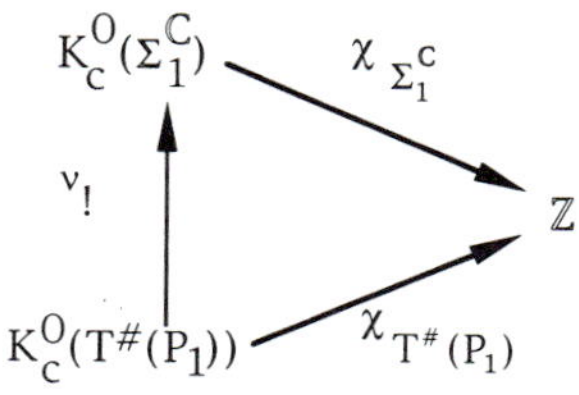

for the K-theoretic extension map $\nu_!$. Since the almost-complex structures $\mathcal{J}$ and $\mathcal{J}^g$ on $\Sigma_1^{\mathbb{C}}$ are homotopic by Proposition 5.5.65, they induce the same index character. Therefore we obtain for every $F \in K_c^1(\Sigma_1)$:

$$\mathrm{Ind}_1^{\Sigma}(F) = \chi_{S_1}((g_1)_!\, F) = \chi_{S_1^{\mathbb{C}}}\, \partial(g_1)_!\, F = \chi_{S_1^{\mathbb{C}}}\, (g_1^{\mathbb{C}})_!\, \partial F$$

$$= \chi_{(\Sigma_1^{\mathbb{C}}, \mathcal{J}^g)}\, \partial F = \chi_{(\Sigma_1^{\mathbb{C}}, \mathcal{J})}\, \partial F = \chi_{T^{\#}(P_1)}\, \nu_!^{-1}\, \partial F.$$

Now $\nu_!$ coincides with the Thom isomorphism of $\Sigma_1^{\mathbb{C}}$ [B5; §2.d]. Q.E.D.

5.6 Index Theory for Polycircular Domains

In this section we develop the index theory for Toeplitz operators over a polycircular domain Ω. We will restrict our attention to the particularly interesting example of "L-shaped domains", or rather their pseudoconvex hull

$$(5.6.1) \qquad \Omega = \{z \in \mathbb{B}^2 : |z_1|\, |z_2|^{\theta} < \frac{1}{e}\}$$

in $\mathbb{C}^2$. Here $\mathbb{B}^2$ is the bidisc and θ is irrational. The corresponding logarithmic domain is bounded by the horizontal and vertical faces $A_{\pm}$

and a line segment A_θ with slope $-\frac{1}{\theta}$ (cf. Section 1.4). Let $\mathcal{F}_\theta$ denote the Kronecker foliation of the 2-torus $\mathbb{T}^2$ associated with θ, and consider the corresponding foliation C*-algebra $C^*(\mathbb{T}^2, \mathcal{F}_\theta)$.

Now consider the Bergman-Toeplitz C*-algebra $\mathcal{T}(\Omega)$ on the Bergman space $H^2(\Omega)$. By Theorem 4.7.27 there is a C*-filtration

$$\mathcal{K}(H^2(\Omega)) = \mathcal{J}_1 \subset \mathcal{J}_1^{\text{sing}} \subset \mathcal{J}_2 \subset \mathcal{T}(\Omega) \tag{5.6.2}$$

with subquotients

$$\mathcal{T}(\Omega)/\mathcal{J}_2 \approx C(\mathbb{T}^2) \oplus C(\mathbb{T}^2), \tag{5.6.3}$$

$$\mathcal{J}_2/\mathcal{J}_1^{\text{sing}} \approx C^*(\mathbb{T}^2, \mathcal{F}_\theta), \tag{5.6.4}$$

$$\mathcal{J}_1^{\text{sing}}/\mathcal{K}(H^2(\Omega)) \approx (C(\mathbb{T}) \otimes \mathcal{K}) \oplus (\mathcal{K} \otimes C(\mathbb{T})). \tag{5.6.5}$$

As in Section 5.4, we thus obtain an analytic index mapping

$$\text{Ind}_1^{\text{sing}} : K^1(\mathbb{T}^2) \oplus K^1(\mathbb{T}^2) \to K_0(C^*(\mathbb{T}^2, \mathcal{F}_\theta)) \tag{5.6.6}$$

induced (via the K-theory exact sequence (cf. Theorem 5.3.8)) by the C*-extension

$$0 \to \mathcal{J}_2/\mathcal{J}_1^{\text{sing}} \to \mathcal{T}(\Omega)/\mathcal{J}_1^{\text{sing}} \to \mathcal{T}(\Omega)/\mathcal{J}_2 \to 0. \tag{5.6.7}$$

The unique trace tr_θ on $C^*(\mathbb{T}^2, \mathcal{F}_\theta)$ induces an injective homomorphism

$$\text{tr}_\theta : K_0(C^*(\mathbb{T}^2, \mathcal{F}_\theta)) \to \mathbb{R} \tag{5.6.8}$$

by which we may consider the index as a map

$$\text{tr}_\theta \circ \text{Ind}_1^{\text{sing}} : K^1(\mathbb{T}^2) \oplus K^1(\mathbb{T}^2) \to \mathbb{R}. \tag{5.6.9}$$

The occurrence of $\mathbb{R}$ as the co-domain of an index mapping reflects the non-type I character of $\mathcal{T}(\Omega)$ in the case where θ is irrational. It is our goal to express (5.6.9) in topological terms, using the facial geometry of $\partial\Omega$.

5.6.10. THEOREM. *Consider the odd Chern character*

(5.6.11) $$\mathrm{ch} : K^1(\mathbb{T}^2) \to H^1(\mathbb{T}^2, \mathbb{Z}) \approx \mathbb{Z}^2$$

(cf. (5.5.80)), *and define the dense embedding* $i_\theta : \mathbb{Z}^2 \to \mathbb{R}$ *by putting*

(5.6.12) $$i_\theta(m_1, m_2) := m_1\theta - m_2.$$

Then we have the index formula

(5.6.13) $$\mathrm{tr}_\theta(\mathrm{Ind}_1^{\mathrm{sing}}(f \oplus g)) = i_\theta \ \mathrm{ch}(fg^{-1})$$

for all $f,g \in K^1(\mathbb{T}^2)$.

In order to prove Theorem 5.6.10 we consider the groupoid $\mathcal{G}_\Omega(\mathbb{Z}^2)$ (cf. (4.7.9)) associated with the action

(5.6.14) $$(\alpha \ltimes \sigma)\varphi := \sigma(\alpha_\# \varphi)$$

of $\mathbb{Z}^2$ on the spectrum of the abelian C*-algebra $\mathcal{D}_\Omega(\mathbb{Z}^2)$ defined in (3.4.4). By Theorem 4.7.11, $\mathcal{T}(\Omega)$ is equivalent to the (spatial) groupoid C*-algebra

(5.6.15) $$\mathcal{T}(\Omega) \approx C^*_{0_A}(\mathcal{G}_\Omega(\mathbb{Z}^2))$$

(induced by the Dirac measure at $0_A \in \mathrm{Spec}\ \mathcal{D}_\Omega(\mathbb{Z}^2)$) since the domain (5.6.1) has no virtual faces. Using the notation of Proposition 3.4.27, we have a stratification

(5.6.16) $$X := \mathrm{Spec}_+ \mathcal{D}_\Omega(\mathbb{Z}^2) = X_0 \dot\cup X_1 \dot\cup X_2,$$

where

$$X_0 = \mathrm{Spec}_\Lambda\ \mathcal{D}_\Omega(\mathbb{Z}^2),$$

(5.6.17) $$X_1 = \mathrm{Spec}_{A_+}\ \mathcal{D}_\Omega(\mathbb{Z}^2) \dot\cup \mathrm{Spec}_{A_-}\ \mathcal{D}_\Omega(\mathbb{Z}^2) \dot\cup \mathrm{Spec}_{A_\theta}\ \mathcal{D}_\Omega(\mathbb{Z}^2),$$

$$X_2 = \mathrm{Spec}_p\ \mathcal{D}_\Omega(\mathbb{Z}^2) \dot\cup \mathrm{Spec}_q\ \mathcal{D}_\Omega(\mathbb{Z}^2)$$

and p and q are the extreme points of $\Lambda = \log |\Omega|$. The spaces X_k, $k = 0,1,2$, are invariant under the action (5.6.14) of $\mathbb{Z}^2$ and we have groupoid isomorphisms

$$\mathcal{G}|_{X_0} = \mathbb{Z}^2 \ltimes \mathbb{Z}_+^2|_{\mathbb{Z}_+^2} \cong \mathbb{Z}_+^2 \times \mathbb{Z}_+^2 \qquad \text{(trivial groupoid)}, \tag{5.6.18}$$

$$\mathcal{G}|_{X_2} \equiv \mathbb{Z}^2 \ltimes \partial_{ex}\Lambda \qquad \text{(trivial action)}. \tag{5.6.19}$$

For X_1, we write $X_1 = X_+ \dot\cup X_- \dot\cup X_\theta$ according to (5.6.17), and obtain in particular

$$\mathcal{G}|_{X_\theta} = \mathbb{Z}^2 \underset{\theta}{\ltimes} \mathbb{R} \tag{5.6.20}$$

for the translation action

$$\alpha \cdot x := x + i_\theta(\alpha) \tag{5.6.21}$$

of $\alpha \in \mathbb{Z}^2$ on $x \in \mathbb{R}$. The other faces $A_\pm$ are treated analogously. Via (5.6.21), the group $\mathbb{Z}^2$ acts also on $\overline{\mathbb{R}}$ leaving $\pm\infty$ invariant. Since $\mathbb{R} \subset \overline{\mathbb{R}}$ is an open invariant subset, it follows from [MR; Theorem 2.6] that there is a C*-exact sequence

$$0 \to C(\mathbb{R}) \underset{\theta}{\rtimes} \mathbb{Z}^2 \to C(\overline{\mathbb{R}}) \underset{\theta}{\rtimes} \mathbb{Z}^2 \xrightarrow{\mathcal{G}} C(\mathbb{T}^2) \oplus C(\mathbb{T}^2) \to 0 \tag{5.6.22}$$

for the corresponding crossed product C*-algebras. Here the quotient is the crossed product for the trivial action of $\mathbb{Z}^2$ on $\pm\infty$. On the other hand, the self-adjoint differential operator

$$D_\theta := i\left(\theta \frac{\partial}{\partial z_1} - \frac{\partial}{\partial z_2}\right) \tag{5.6.23}$$

on $\mathbb{T}^2$ is elliptic along the leaves of the foliation $\mathcal{F}_\theta$, identified with the translates of $\mathbb{R}(\theta,-1)/\mathbb{Z}^2$. By [DHK] this leads to another C*-exact sequence

$$0 \to C^*(\mathbb{T}^2, \mathcal{F}_\theta) \to \mathcal{S} \xrightarrow{\tilde{\mathcal{G}}} C(\mathbb{T}^2) \oplus C(\mathbb{T}^2) \to 0 \tag{5.6.24}$$

where $\mathcal{S}$ is the unital C*-algebra on $L^2(\mathbb{T}^2)$ generated by $\chi_\varepsilon(D_\theta)$ and all multiplication operators f, with $f \in C(\mathbb{T}^2)$. Here, for $\varepsilon > 0$, $\chi_\varepsilon: \mathbb{R} \to [0,1]$ is a smooth function interpolating the constant functions $1_{[\varepsilon,+\infty]}$ and $0_{(-\infty,-\varepsilon]}$. Moreover, $\tilde{\sigma}$ is determined by the conditions

$$\tilde{\sigma}(f) := f \oplus f, \ \ \tilde{\sigma}(\chi_\varepsilon(D_\theta)) := 1 \oplus 0. \tag{5.6.25}$$

5.6.26. PROPOSITION. *Let* θ *be irrational. Then the C*-extensions* (5.6.22) *and* (5.6.24) *are isomorphic. In particular,*

$$C^*(\mathbb{T}^2, \mathcal{F}_\theta) \approx C(\overline{\mathbb{R}}) \underset{\theta}{\rtimes} \mathbb{Z}^2 \tag{5.6.27}$$

(not just stably isomorphic [R4]*).*

Proof. Via the Fourier transform $\mathcal{F}: L^2(\mathbb{T}^2) \xrightarrow{\approx} L^2(\mathbb{Z}^2)$, $\mathcal{S}$ is realized as a C*-algebra $\hat{\mathcal{S}}$ on $L^2(\mathbb{Z}^2)$ generated by the translation operators

$$\mathrm{Ad}(\mathcal{F})(z^\alpha) = \tau_\alpha, \ \ (\tau_\alpha\varphi)(\beta) := \varphi(\beta - \alpha) \tag{5.6.28}$$

and the multiplication operator

$$\mathrm{Ad}(\mathcal{F})(\chi_\varepsilon(D_\theta)) = \chi_\varepsilon(\mathrm{Ad}(\mathcal{F})D_\theta) = \chi_\varepsilon \circ i_\theta. \tag{5.6.29}$$

The unital abelian subalgebra

$$\mathcal{D} := C^*(\chi_\varepsilon \circ (\tau_\alpha i_\theta) : \alpha \in \mathbb{Z}^2) \tag{5.6.30}$$

of $L^\infty(\mathbb{Z}^2)$ (realized as multiplication operators on $L^2(\mathbb{Z}^2)$) admits an action of $\mathbb{Z}^2$ since

$$\tau_\alpha(\chi_\varepsilon \circ \tau_\beta i_\theta) = \chi_\varepsilon \circ (\tau_{\alpha+\beta} i_\theta) \tag{5.6.31}$$

for all $\alpha,\beta \in \mathbb{Z}^2$. For every $\varphi \in C(\overline{\mathbb{R}})$ we have

$$\varphi \circ \tau_\alpha i_\theta = \tau_\alpha(\varphi \circ i_\theta) = (\tau_{i_\theta(\alpha)}\varphi) \circ i_\theta \tag{5.6.32}$$

and the functions $\tau_{i_\theta \alpha}\chi_\varepsilon$, $\alpha \in \mathbb{Z}^2$, separate the points of $\bar{\mathbb{R}}$ since $i_\theta(\mathbb{Z}^2)$ is dense in $\bar{\mathbb{R}}$. Applying the Stone-Weierstrass Theorem we obtain for the pullback

$$i_\theta^* \, C(\bar{\mathbb{R}}) = \mathcal{D}. \tag{5.6.33}$$

By (5.6.32) the mappings $i_\theta^* : C(\bar{\mathbb{R}}) \to \mathcal{D} \subset \hat{\mathcal{S}}$ and $\tau : \mathbb{Z}^2 \to \hat{\mathcal{S}}$ form a covariant representation for the action (5.6.21) of $\mathbb{Z}^2$ on $\bar{\mathbb{R}}$, and hence induce a C*-representation

$$\pi : C(\bar{\mathbb{R}}) \underset{\theta}{\rtimes} \mathbb{Z}^2 \to \hat{\mathcal{S}} \tag{5.6.34}$$

of the C*-crossed product which is onto by (5.6.33). Analogous to (5.6.30) consider the non-unital abelian C*-algebra

$$\mathcal{D}_0 := C^*(\varphi \circ (\tau_\alpha i_\theta) : \alpha \in \mathbb{Z}^2,\ \varphi \in C_0(\mathbb{R})) \tag{5.6.35}$$

and let $\hat{\mathcal{S}}_0$ be the C*-algebra generated by $\mathcal{D}$ and τ_β, $\beta \in \mathbb{Z}^2$. Since $\tau_{i_\theta(\alpha)}$ leaves $C_0(\mathbb{R})$ invariant (5.6.32) implies

$$i_\theta^* \, C_0(\mathbb{R}) = \mathcal{D}_0. \tag{5.6.36}$$

It follows that π induces a commuting diagram

$$\begin{array}{ccccccccc}
0 & \longrightarrow & C_0(\mathbb{R}) \underset{\theta}{\rtimes} \mathbb{Z}^2 & \longrightarrow & C(\bar{\mathbb{R}}) \underset{\theta}{\rtimes} \mathbb{Z}^2 & \xrightarrow{\ \sigma\ } & C(\mathbb{T}^2) \oplus C(\mathbb{T}^2) & \longrightarrow & 0 \\
 & & \Big\downarrow \pi_0 & & \Big\downarrow \pi & & \Big\downarrow \tilde{\pi} & & \\
0 & \longrightarrow & \hat{\mathcal{S}}_0 & \longrightarrow & \hat{\mathcal{S}} & \xrightarrow{\ \hat{\sigma}\ } & C^*(\mathbb{Z}^2) \oplus C^*(\mathbb{Z}^2) & \longrightarrow & 0 \\
 & & \Big\uparrow \mathrm{Ad}(\mathcal{F}) \approx & & \Big\uparrow \mathrm{Ad}(\mathcal{F}) \approx & & \Big\uparrow \mathrm{Ad}(\mathcal{F}) \approx & & \\
0 & \longrightarrow & C^*(\mathbb{T}^2, \mathcal{F}_\theta) & \longrightarrow & \mathcal{S} & \xrightarrow{\ \tilde{\sigma}\ } & C(\mathbb{T}^2) \oplus C(\mathbb{T}^2) & \longrightarrow & 0
\end{array}$$

where π_0 is an isomorphism since $C_0(\mathbb{R}) \rtimes_\theta \mathbb{Z}^2$ is simple by the ergodicity of (5.6.21) [R4]. The coordinate projections $p_i : \mathbb{T}^2 \to \mathbb{T}$ $(i = 1,2)$ satisfy

$$\sigma(\delta_{\varepsilon_i}) = p_i \oplus p_i = \tilde{\sigma}(p_i) = \tilde{\sigma}(\mathrm{Ad}(\mathcal{F}^*)\tau_{\varepsilon_i}) = \tilde{\sigma}(\mathrm{Ad}(\mathcal{F}^*)\pi\delta_{\varepsilon_i})$$

which implies $\tilde{\pi}(p_i \oplus p_i) = \mathrm{Ad}(\mathcal{F})(p_i \oplus p_i)$. Since $\chi_\varepsilon = 1$ at $+\infty$ we also have

$$\sigma(\chi_\varepsilon \cdot \delta_0) = 1 \oplus 0 = \tilde{\sigma}(\chi_\varepsilon(D_\theta)) = \tilde{\sigma}(\mathrm{Ad}(\mathcal{F}^*)(\chi_\varepsilon \circ i_\theta)) = \tilde{\sigma}(\mathrm{Ad}(\mathcal{F}^*)\pi(\chi_\varepsilon \cdot \delta_0))$$

which implies $\tilde{\pi}(1 \oplus 0) = \mathrm{Ad}(\mathcal{F})(1 \oplus 0)$. Since the C*-algebra $C(\mathbb{T}^2) \oplus C(\mathbb{T}^2)$ is generated by the functions $p_i \oplus p_i$ and $1 \oplus 0$ it follows that $\tilde{\pi} = \mathrm{Ad}(\mathcal{F})$. The 5-Lemma [ML] shows that π is an isomorphism. Q.E.D.

To complete the proof of Theorem 5.6.10 let $f,g \in K^1(\mathbb{T}^2)$. By [DHK], the index map

$$\widetilde{\mathrm{Ind}} : K^1(\mathbb{T}^2) \oplus K^1(\mathbb{T}^2) \to K_0(C^*(\mathbb{T}^2, \mathcal{F}_\theta)) \tag{5.6.37}$$

associated with the C*-extension (5.6.24) satisfies

$$\mathrm{tr}_\theta \ \widetilde{\mathrm{Ind}}(f \oplus 1) = i_\theta \ \mathrm{ch}(f). \tag{5.6.38}$$

Since $f \oplus g = (fg^{-1} \oplus 1)(g \oplus g)$ and (5.6.25) implies that $g \oplus g = \tilde{\sigma}(g)$, with the multiplication operator g being invertible on $L^2(\mathbb{T}^2)$, it follows from Proposition 5.6.26 that

$$\begin{aligned}\mathrm{tr}_\theta \ \mathrm{Ind}_1^{\mathrm{sing}}(f \oplus g) &= \mathrm{tr}_\theta \ \widetilde{\mathrm{Ind}}(f \oplus g) = \mathrm{tr}_\theta(\widetilde{\mathrm{Ind}}(fg^{-1} \oplus 1) + \widetilde{\mathrm{Ind}}(g \oplus g)) \\ &= \mathrm{tr}_\theta \ \widetilde{\mathrm{Ind}}(fg^{-1} \oplus 1) = i_\theta \ \mathrm{ch}(fg^{-1}).\end{aligned}$$

Q.E.D.

References

[APT] Akemann, C., Pedersen, G., Tomiyama, J.: Multipliers of C*-algebras. J. Funct. Anal. 13 (1973), 277-301.

[A1] Atiyah, M.: K-Theory, Benjamin, New York 1967.

[AS] Atiyah, M., Singer, I.: The index of elliptic operators III. Ann. Math. 87 (1968), 546-604.

[B1] Bauer, H.: Maß- und Wahrscheinlichkeitstheorie. De Gruyter 1990.

[BDT] Baum, P., Douglas, R., Taylor, M.: Cycles and relative cycles in analytic K-homology. J. Diff. Geom. 30 (1989) 3, 761-804.

[BBCZ] Bekollé, D., Berger, C., Coburn, L., Zhu, K.: BMO in the Bergman metric on bounded symmetric domains. J. Funct. Anal. 93 (1990), 310-350.

[BC] Berger, C., Coburn, L.: Wiener-Hopf operators on U_2. Int. Equ. Op. Th. 2 (1979), 139-173.

[BCK] Berger, C., Coburn, L., Korányi, A.: Opérateurs de Wiener-Hopf sur les sphères de Lie. C.R. Acad. Sci. Paris 290 (1980), 989-991.

[B2] Blackadar, B.: K-Theory of Operator Algebras. Springer, New York 1986.

[B3] Bochner, S.: Group invariance of Cauchy's formula in several variables. Ann. Math. 45 (1944), 686-707.

[BD] Bonsall, F., Duncan, J.: Complete Normed Algebras. Springer 1973.

[B4] Borel, A.: Sur la cohomologie des espaces fibrés principeaux et des espaces homogènes de groupes de Lie compacts. Ann. Math. 57 (1953), 165-197.

[BLU] Borthwick, D., Lesniewski, A., Upmeier, H.: Non-perturbative deformation quantization of Cartan domains. J. Funct. Anal. 113 (1993), 153-176.

[B5] Boutet de Monvel, L.: On the index of Toeplitz operators of several complex variables. Invent. Math. 50 (1979), 249-272.

[B6] Boutet de Monvel, L., Guillemin, V.: The Spectral Theory of Toeplitz Operators. Ann. Math. Studies 99 (1981).

[BS] Boutet de Monvel, L., Sjostrand, J.: Sur la singularité des noyaux de Bergman et de Szego, Astérisque 34-35 (1976), 123-164.

[BK] Braun, H., Koecher, M.: Jordan-Algebren. Springer, New York 1966.

[BKU] Braun, R., Kaup, W., Upmeier, H.: A holomorphic characterization of Jordan C*-algebras. Math. Z. 161 (1978), 277-290.

[B6] Bremermann, H.: On a generalized Dirichlet problem for plurisubharmonic functions and pseudo-convex domains. Characterization of Shilov boundaries. Trans. Amer. Math. Soc. 91 (1959), 246-276.

[BT] Bröcker, T., tom Dieck, T.: Representations of Compact Lie Groups. Springer 1985.

[BDF] Brown, L., Douglas, R., Fillmore, P.: Extensions of C*-algebras and K-homology. Ann. Math. 105 (1977), 265-324.

[CE] Choi, M.-D., Effros, E.: The completely positive lifting problem for C*-algebras. Ann. Math. 104 (1976), 585-609.

[C1] Coburn, L.: The C*-algebra generated by an isometry. I. Bull. Amer. Math. Soc. 73 (1967), 722-726, II, Trans. Amer. Math. Soc. 137 (1969), 211-217.

[C2] Coburn, L.: Singular integral operators and Toeplitz operators on odd spheres. Indiana Univ. Math. J. 23 (1973), 433-439.

[C3] Coburn, L.: Deformation estimates for the Berezin-Toeplitz quantization. Comm. Math. Phys. 149 (1992), 415-424.

[CW] Coifman, R., Weiss, G.: Analyse harmonique non-commutative sur certains espaces homogènes. Springer Lect. Notes Math. 242 (1971).

[C4] Connes, A.: A survey of foliations and operator algebras. Proc. Symp. Pure Math. 38.1 (1981), 521-628.

[CM] Curto, R., Muhly, P.: C*-algebras of multiplication operators on Bergman spaces. J. Funct. Anal. 64 (1985), 315-329.

[DG] Ding, H.-M., Gross, K.: Operator-valued Bessel functions on Jordan algebras. J. Reine Angew. Math. 435 (1993), 157-196.

[D1] Dixmier, J.: C*-Algebras. North-Holland, Amsterdam 1977.

[D2] Douglas, R.: Banach Algebra Techniques in Operator Theory. Academic Press, New York 1972.

[DH] Douglas, R., Howe, R.: On the C*-algebra of Toeplitz operators on the quarter-plane. Trans. Amer. Math. Soc. 158 (1971), 203-217.

[DHK] Douglas, R., Hurder, S., Kaminker, J.: Cyclic cocycles, renormalization and eta-invariants. Invent. Math. 103 (1991), 101-179.

[D3] Dynin, A.: Inversion problem for singular integral operators: C*-approach. Proc. Natl. Acad. Sci. USA 75 (1978), 4668-4670.

[D4] Dynin, A.: Multivariable Wiener-Hopf operators I. Int. Equ. Op. Th. 9 (1986), 537-556.

[E1] Eymard, P.: L'algèbre de Fourier d'un groupe localement compact. Bull. Soc. Math. France 92 (1964), 181-236.

[FK1] Faraut, J., Korányi, A.: Function spaces and reproducing kernels on bounded symmetric domains. J. Funct. Anal. 88 (1990), 64-89.

[FK2] Faraut, J., Korányi, A.: Analysis on Symmetric Cones. Oxford Univ. Press 1994.

[FK3] Folland, G.B., Kohn, J.J.: The Neumann Problem for the Cauchy-Riemann Complex. Ann. Math. Studies 75 (1972).

[FK4] Fornaess, J. Krantz, S.: Continuously varying peaking functions. Pac. J. Math. 83 (1979), 341-347.

[G1] Gindikin, S.: Analysis on homogeneous domains. Russ. Math. Surveys 19 (1964), 1-89.

[G2] Gindikin, S.: Invariant generalized functions in homogeneous domains. Funct. Anal. Appl. 9 (1975), 50-53.

[GK] Gohberg, I., Krein, M.: Systems of integral equations on a half-line with kernels depending on the difference of arguments. Amer. Math. Soc. Transl. 14 (1960), 217-287.

[G3] Guillemin, V.: Some micro-local aspects of analysis on compact symmetric spaces. Ann. Math. Studies 93 (1979), 79-111.

[G4] Guillemin, V.: Toeplitz operators in n-dimensions. Int. Equ. Op. Th. 7 (1984), 145-205.

[H1] Halmos, P.: A Hilbert Space Problem Book. Springer 1974.

[H2] Helgason, S.: Groups and Geometric Analysis. Academic Press, New York 1984.

[HLW] Hirschman, I., Liang, D., Wilson, E.: Szegö limit theorems for Toeplitz operators on compact homogeneous spaces. Trans. Amer. Math. Soc. 270 (1982), 351-376.

[H3] Hörmander, L.: An Introduction to Complex Analysis in Several Variables. Van Nostrand, 1966.

[H4] Hörmander, L.: The Analysis of Linear Partial Differential Operators. Springer 1984.

[H5] Hochschild, G.: The Structure of Lie Groups. Holden-Day 1965.

[H6] Hua, L.-K.: Harmonic Analysis of Functions of Several Complex Variables in the Classical Domains. Amer. Math. Soc., 1963.

[J1] Janas, J.: Toeplitz operators related to certain domains in $\mathbb{C}^n$. Studia Math. 54 (1975), 73-79.

[JK] Jewell, N., Krantz, S.: Toeplitz operators and related function algebras on certain pseudoconvex domains. Trans. Amer. Math. Soc. 252 (1979), 297-311.

[J2] Johnson, K.: On a ring of invariant polynomials on a hermitian symmetric space. J. Alg. 67 (1980), 72-80.

[K1] Karoubi, M.: K-Theory. Springer 1978.

[K2] Kasparov, G.: The operator K-functor and extensions of C*-algebras. Math. USSR Izv. 16 (1981), 513-572.

[K3] Kaup, W.: A Riemann mapping theorem for bounded symmetric domains in complex Banach spaces. Math. Z. 183 (1983), 503-529.

[KU] Kaup, W., Upmeier, H.: Jordan algebras and symmetric Siegel domains in Banach spaces. Math. Z. 157 (1977), 179-200.

[K4] Koecher, M.: An Elementary Approach to Bounded Symmetric Domains, Rice University, 1969.

[K5] Korányi, A.: The Poisson integral for generalized half-planes and bounded symmetric domains. Ann. Math. 82 (1965), 332-350.

[K6] Korányi, A.: The volume of symmetric domains, the Koecher gamma function , and an integral of Selberg. Stud. Sci. Math. Hungar. 17 (1982), 129-133.

[KS] Korányi, A., Stein, E.: H^2-spaces of generalized half-planes. Stud. Math. 44 (1972), 379-388.

[K6] Krantz, S.: Function Theory of Several Complex Variables. Wiley, New York, 1982.

[L1] Landstad, M.: Duality theory for covariant systems. Trans. Amer. Math. Soc. 248 (1979), 223-267.

[L2] Landstad, M.: Duality for dual C*-covariance algebras over compact groups. Preprint.

[LPRS] Landstad, M., Phillips, J., Raeburn, I., Sutherland, C.: Representations of crossed products by coactions and principal bundles. Trans. Amer. Math. Soc. 299 (1987), 747-784.

[L3] Lang, S.: Differential Manifolds. Addison-Wesley, 1972.

[L4] Lassalle, M.: L'espace de Hardy d'un domaine de Reinhardt generalisé. J. Funct. Anal. 60 (1985), 309-340.

[L45 Lassalle, M.: Algèbre de Jordan et ensemble de Wallach. Invent. Math. 89 (1987), 375-393.

[L6] Levine, D.: Systems of singular integral operators on spheres. Trans. Amer. Math. Soc. 144 (1967), 493-522.

[L7] Loos, O.: Symmetric Spaces, I, II. Benjamin 1969.

[L8] Loos, O.: Jordan Pairs. Springer Lect. Notes Math. 460 (1975).

[L9] Loos, O.: Bounded Symmetric Domains and Jordan Pairs. University of California, Irvine 1977.

[MR] Muhly, P., Renault, J.: C*-algebras of multivariable Wiener-Hopf operators. Trans. Amer. Math. Soc. 274 (1982), 1-44.

[N1] Nachbin, L.: Holomorphic Functions, Domains of Holomorphy and Local Properties. North Holland 1972.

[NT] Nakagami, Y., Takesaki, M.: Duality for Crossed Products of von Neumann Algebras. Springer Lect. Notes Math. 731 (1979).

[N2] Narasimhan, R.: Several Complex Variables. Univ. of Chicago, 1971.

[P1] Pedersen, G.: C*-Algebras and their Automorphism Groups. Academic Press, London 1979.

[P2] Pjateckij-Shapiro, I.: Automorphic Functions and the Geometry of the Classical Domains. Gordon-Breach, New York 1969.

[P3] Power, S.: Commutator ideals and pseudo-differential C*-algebras. Quart. J. Oxford 31 (1980), 467-489.

[R1] Raeburn, I.: On Toeplitz operators associated with strongly pseudo-convex domains. Studia Math. 63 (1979), 253-258.

[R2] Range, R.M.: Holomorphic Functions and Integral Representations in Several Complex Variables. Springer, 1986.

[R3] Renault, J.: A Groupoid Approach to C*-Algebras. Springer Lect. Notes Math. 793 (1980).

[R4] Rieffel, M.: Strong Morita equivalence of certain transformation group C*-algebras. Math. Ann. 222 (1976), 7-22.

[R5] Rosenberg, J.: Homological invariants of extensions of C*-algebras. Proc. Symp. Pure Math. 38.1 (1982), 35-75.

[R6] Royden, H.: Real Analysis. Macmillan 1963.

[R7] Rudin, W.: Function Theory on the Unit Ball of $\mathbb{C}^n$. Springer 1980.

[S1] Salinas, N.: Toeplitz operators and weighted Wiener-Hopf operators on pseudoconvex Reinhardt and tube domains. Trans. Amer. Math. Soc., to appear.

[SSU] Salinas, N., Sheu, A., Upmeier, H.: Toeplitz operators on pseudoconvex domains and foliation algebras. Ann. Math. 130 (1989), 531-565.

[S2] Schmid, W.: Die Randwerte holomorpher Funktionen auf hermitesch symmetrischen Räumen. Invent. Math. 9 (1969), 61-80.

[S3] Segal, I.: The complex wave representation of the free boson field. Adv. Math. Suppl. Stud. 3 (1978), 321-343.

[S4] Springer, T.: Jordan Algebras and Algebraic Groups. Springer 1973.

[S5] Stein, E.: Hardy spaces of homogeneous domains. Princeton 1982.

[S6] Stratila, S.: Modular Theory in Operator Algebras. Abacus Press, 1981.

[S7] Sugiura, M.: Fourier series of smooth functions on compact Lie groups. Osaka Math. J. 8 (1971), 33-47.

[T1] Takesaki, M.: Theory of Operator Algebras. Springer 1979.

[T2] Tits, J.: Tabellen zu den einfachen Liegruppen und ihren Darstellungen. Springer Lect. Notes Math. 40 (1967).

[T3] Topping, D.: An isomorphism invariant for spin factors. J. Math. Mech. 15 (1966), 1055-1064.

[U1] Upmeier, H.: Toeplitz operators on bounded symmetric domains. Trans. Amer. Math. Soc. 280 (1983), 221-237.

[U2] Upmeier, H.: Toeplitz C*-algebras on bounded symmetric domains. Ann. Math. 119 (1984), 549-576

[U3] Upmeier, H.: Jordan C*-Algebras and Symmetric Banach Manifolds. North-Holland, Amsterdam, 1985.

[U4] Upmeier, H.: Toeplitz operators on symmetric Siegel domains. Math. Ann. 271 (1985), 401-414.

[U5] Upmeier, H.: Jordan algebras and harmonic analysis on symmetric spaces. Amer. J. Math. 108 (1986), 1-25.

[U6] Upmeier, H.: An index theorem for multivariable Toeplitz operators. Int. Equ. Op. Th. 9 (1986), 355-386.

[U7] Upmeier, H.: Jordan Algebras in Analysis, Operator Theory and Quantum Mechanics. CBMS Lect. Notes 67, Amer. Math. Soc., 1987.

[U8] Upmeier, H.: Fredholm indices for Toeplitz operators on bounded symmetric domains. Amer. J. Math. 110 (1988), 811-832.

[U9] Upmeier, H.: Index theory for multivariable Wiener-Hopf operators. J. reine angew. Math. 384 (1988), 57-79.

[U10] Upmeier, H.: Toeplitz C*-algebras and non-commutative duality. J. Oper. Th. 26 (1991), 407-432.

[U11] Upmeier, H.: Quantization of discrete series representations. Preprint.

[V1] Vallin, J.-M.: C*-algèbres de Hopf et C*-algèbres de Kac. Proc. London Math. Soc. 50 (1985), 131-174.

[V2] Venugopalkrishna, U.: Fredholm operators associated with strongly pseudoconvex domains in $\mathbb{C}^n$. J. Funct. Anal. 9 (1972), 349-373.

[W1] Wassermann, A.: Algèbres d'opérateurs de Toeplitz sur les groupes unitaires. C.R. Acad. Sci. Paris 299 (1984), 871-874.

[W2] Wassermann, S.: A pathology in the ideal space of $L(H) \otimes L(H)$. Indiana Univ. Math. J. 27 (1978), 1011-1020.

[Y1] Yabuta, K.: A remark to a paper of Janas: Toeplitz operators related to certain domains in $\mathbb{C}^n$. Studia Math. 62 (1978), 73-74.

Index of Symbols and Notations

Titles previously published in the series

OPERATOR THEORY: ADVANCES AND APPLICATIONS

BIRKHÄUSER VERLAG

Edited by

I. Gohberg,

School of Mathematical Sciences, Tel-Aviv University, Ramat Aviv, Israel

71. **E.L. Basor, I. Gohberg** (Eds): Toeplitz Operators and Related Topics. The Harold Widom Anniversary Volume. Workshop on Toeplitz and Wiener-Hopf Operators, Santa Cruz, California, September 20–22, 1992, 1994, (ISBN 3-7643-5068-7)
72. **I. Gohberg, L.A. Sakhnovich** (Eds): Matrix and Operator Valued Functions. The Vladimir Petrovich Potapov Memorial Volume, 1994, (ISBN 3-7643-5091-1)
73. **A. Feintuch, I. Gohberg** (Eds): Nonselfadjoint Operators and Related Topics. Workshop on Operator Theory and Its Applications, Beersheva, February 24–28, 1994, (ISBN 3-7643-5097-0)
74. **R. Hagen, S. Roch, B. Silbermann**: Spectral Theory of Approximation Methods for Convolution Equations, 1994, (3-7643-5112-8)
75. **C.B. Huijsmans, M.A. Kaashoek, B. de Pagter** (Eds): Operator Theory in Function Spaces and Banach Lattices. The A.C. Zaanen Anniversary Volume, 1994, (ISBN 3-7643-5146-2)
76. **A.M. Krasnosel'skii**: Asymptotics of Nonlinearities and Operator Equations, 1995, (ISBN 3-7643-5175-6)
77. **J. Lindenstrauss, V.D. Milman** (Eds): Geometric Aspects of Functional Analysis Israel Seminar GAFA 1992-94, (ISBN 3-7643-5207-8)
78. **M. Demuth, B.-W. Schulze** (Eds): Partial Differential Operators and Mathematical Physics: International Conference in Holzhau (Germany), July 3-9, 1994, 1995, (ISBN 3-7643-5208-6)
79. **I. Gohberg, M.A. Kaashoek, F. van Schagen**: Partially Specified Matrices and Operators: Classification, Completion, Applications, 1995, (ISBN 3-7643-5259-0)
80. **I. Gohberg, H. Langer** (Eds): Operator Theory and Boundary Eigenvalue Problems International Workshop in Vienna, July 27-30, 1993, 1995, (ISBN 3-7643-5259-0)